GOETHE

IN THE HISTORY
OF SCIENCE

Studies in Modern German Literature

Peter D.G. Brown
General Editor

Vol. 29

PETER LANG
New York • Washington, D.C./Baltimore
Bern • Frankfurt am Main • Berlin • Vienna • Paris

GOETHE
IN THE HISTORY
OF SCIENCE

VOLUME I

BIBLIOGRAPHY, 1776-1949

EDITED BY
FREDERICK AMRINE

PETER LANG
New York • Washington, D.C./Baltimore
Bern • Frankfurt am Main • Berlin • Vienna • Paris

Library of Congress Cataloging-in-Publication Data

Amrine, Frederick.
Goethe in the history of science/ Frederick Amrine, editor.
p. cm. — (Studies in modern German literature; vol. 29-30)
Includes indexes.
Contents: v. 1. Bibliography, 1776-1949 — v. 2. Bibliography, 1950-1990.
1. Goethe, Johann Wolfgang von, 1749-1832—Bibliography. 2. Science—
History—Bibliography. I. Title. II. Series.
Z8350.A48   [Q125]   509'.2—dc20   95-20872
ISBN 0-8204-1076 (v. 1).
ISBN 0-8204-1077-2 (v. 2)

Die Deutsche Bibliothek-CIP-Einheitsaufnahme

Goethe in the history of science/ Frederick Amrine, ed. – New York;
Washington, D.C./Baltimore; Bern; Frankfurt am Main;
Berlin; Vienna; Paris: Lang.
Vol. 1. Bibliography, 1776-1949. - 1995
(Studies in modern German literature; Vol. 29)
ISBN 0-8204-1076-4
NE: GT
Vol. 2. Bibliography, 1950-1990. - 1995
(Studies in modern German literature; Vol. 30)
ISBN 0-8204-1077-2
NE: GT

Cover design by Nona Reuter.
Sketch on the front cover by Johann Wolfgang von Goethe, entitled,
"Metamorphoses of plants from seed to flower," Pen and ink, after 1790.

The paper in this book meets the guidelines for permanence and durability
of the Committee on Production Guidelines for Book Longevity
of the Council of Library Resources.

© 1996 Peter Lang Publishing, Inc., New York

Printed in the United States of America.

for my parents,

Caroline Williams Amrine
and
Frederick Muhleman Amrine,

with gratitude and love

TABLE OF CONTENTS

VOL. I: 1776-1949

ABBREVIATIONS
(aside from those in common usage)

Avanzi

Avanzi, G. and G. **Sichel**. *Bibliografia italiana su Goethe (1779-1965)*. Università di Genova, Facoltà di Lettere e Filosofia. Pubblicazioni dell' Instituto di Lingua e Letteratura Tedesca e di Filologia Germanica, 2. Firenze: Olschki, 1972. vii, 255 pp.

EdN

Elemente der Naturwissenschaft. Zeitschrift herausgegeben von der Naturwissenschaftlichen Sektion am Goetheanum, Dornach [No. 1964-7].

Goethe

The organ of the *Goethe-Gesellschaft* in its various guises: 1880-1913, *Goethe-Jahrbuch*; 1914-1935, *Jahrbuch der Goethe-Gesellschaft*; 1936-1937, *Goethe. Vierteljahresschrift der Goethe-Gesellschaft. Neue Folge des Jahrbuchs*; 1938-1944, *Goethe. Viermonatsschrift der Goethe-Gesellschaft. Neue Folge des Jahrbuchs*; 1947-1971, *Goethe. Neue Folge des Jahrbuchs der Goethe-Gesellschaft*; and 1972-, *Goethe-Jahrbuch* once again. The enumeration is even more confusing: new sequences were begun in 1914 and 1936 with the change in title, but the 1972 issue was published as Vol. 89 of a newly-established, single sequence beginning with 1 (1880). The publication did not appear in 1923, 1945, 1946, and 1948. Cf. the *Konkordanz* at the end of *Goethe* 89 (1972).

n.d.

undated entry

Zhitomirskaia

Zhitomirskaia, Z. B. *Iogann Vol'fgang Gete: Bibliograficheskii ukazatel' russkikh perevodov i kriticheskoi literatury na russkom iazyke 1780-1971*. Moskva: Izdatel'stvo 'Kniga', 1972. 616 pp.

INTRODUCTION

Goethe is a significant figure in the history of science. He sought to develop a rigorous and empirical approach to the study of qualities that represents an important complement to quantitative methods. His works were highly influential among contemporary scientists, and have called forth an unbroken research tradition, a "Goethean paradigm" persisting within and against other dominant paradigms, that continues to this day. I realize that many will find these claims surprising, and perhaps insupportable. Yet I believe they are supported by the evidence in the following pages, and I intend to argue them at length in the third volume of the project.

A bibliography such as this would have been unthinkable without the foundation provided by Günter Schmid's monumental descriptive bibliography of 1940 (No. 1940-12), yet it intends to be much more than a mere reworking and continuation of Schmid's. As these volumes are meant to provide the basis for the narrative history that is to follow, I thought it essential that the bibliography be arranged in chronological order, rather than by author or topic, so that the morphology of the historical development would be visible on the page. The indices at the end of volume II will enable readers to locate readily all the entries by a certain author, or pertaining to a particular subject.

I also thought it essential to include not only work on primary and secondary texts by and on Goethe himself, but also original scientific research in the spirit of Goethe's method. In many cases, it was difficult to decide whether to include particular items, and I am sure that the result is far from comprehensive, but I thought it important to make the attempt nevertheless. In general, the criterion for inclusion was that Goethe needed to be mentioned somewhere as a model, or the entry needed to be a substantial piece of research by a scientist whose other writings generally fit that criterion. A similar rationale led to the inclusion of scientific works dedicated to Goethe. On the other hand, Schmid's attempt to list every passing scholarly or scientific reference to Goethe had to be abandoned as impractical: such items were not included in this bibliography, but a full list of the omissions from Schmid's is appended for those who might want to consult those entries. The same applies to Schmid's inclusion of scientific works to which Goethe refers, but that do not deal with, and are unlikely to have been influenced by, Goethe. Entries in Richter's much less reliable and comprehensive bibliography on Goethe's chromatics (No. 1938-18) were accorded the same treatment.

Another important feature of the bibliography is the inclusion of descriptors at the end of each entry indicating the main topics covered. Descriptors are printed in capital letters, and preceded by a slash. For the most part, these indicate disciplines or sub-disciplines, such as "/CHROMATICS" and "/PHILOSOPHY: EPISTEMOLOGY," but treat-

xii

ments of individuals, places, institutions, exhibitions, Goethe's non-scientific works, his collections and apparatus have all been indexed separately as well. Editions and translations of Goethe's primary works have been noted and indexed by language. There is also a separate index of the aforementioned original research according to Goethe's methods organized by field and sub-field. Translations and reprints have been fully cross-referenced. In the case of entries that have gone through multiple editions, I have usually indicated only the first and the most recent I could find.

In order to ensure accuracy, I have tried to inspect every item included in the bibliography myself. Entries that could not be inspected are marked by asterisks, but readers should not assume they are impossible to find: in many cases, they were confirmed by more than one bibliographic source. The only exception was accorded to some entries covered by Schmid, who followed the same procedure. While I hope that my work will prove accurate, I realize that in a project of this magnitude a certain number of errors are inevitable, and can only hope that my readers will bring mistakes and omissions to my attention, so that they can be included in a revised and expanded edition at a later date. I will be especially grateful for offprints or references to new publications as they appear.

I would like to thank the University of Michigan for their generous support in the form of a Rackham Faculty Research Grant and the Lockwood Award, which were of invaluable help in bringing this project to completion. The staffs of the University of Michigan libraries and the Deutsches Literaturarchiv in Marbach, Germany gave me incalculable amounts of cheerful and thoroughly professional assistance. George Arlos and Margaret Bloomfield contributed many hours of searching; David Halsted, Richie Sakakibara, and Jindra Toman helped me with Polish, Japanese, and Czech respectively. Above all, however, I would like to thank Professor Dorothea Kuhn, who kindly made several items from her personal collection accessible to me and offered much-needed counsel and encouragement during my visit to Marbach.

Frederick Amrine
The University of Michigan

VOLUME I

BIBLIOGRAPHY, 1776-1949

1776-1 **Lavater**, Johann Caspar. *Physiognomische Fragmente zur Beförderung der Menschenkenntnis und Menschenliebe.* Leipzig/Winterthur: Weidmanns Erben und Reich, und Heinrich Steiner und Compagnie, 1776. 291 pp.
   Rpt. Nos. 1784-1, 1829-10 and 1908-15.
   Trans. into Dutch, No. 1781-1.
   Trans. into French, Nos. 1783-2 and 1806-7.
   Trans. into English, No. 1792-2.
   Eleven of these by Goethe.
   /EDITION/PHYSIOGNOMY

1781-1 *[**Lavater**, Johann Caspar.] *Over de physiognomie. Eerste-- Vierde deel.* Trans. J. W. van Haar. Amsterdam: Johannes Allart, 1781-1784.
   /TRANSLATION: DUTCH/PHYSIOGNOMY

1782-1 **Voigt**, Joh[ann]. Carl Wilhelm. *Mineralogische Beschreibung des Hochstifts Fuld und einiger merkwürdigen Gegenden am Rhein und Mayn.* Dessau/Leipzig: auf Kosten der Verlags-Kasse, 1783. 244 pp.
   Rpt. 1783.
   Written in collaboration with Goethe.
   /EDITION/RESEARCH: MINERALOGY

1783-1 [anon.] [**Tobler**, Georg Christoph?] "Fragment. Die Natur." *Pfälzisches Museum*, 1, No. 5 (1783/1784), 446ff.
   Rpt. No. 1833-13.
   Long thought to have been written by Goethe.
   /EDITION

1783-2 ***Lavater**, Jean Gaspard [Johann Caspar]. *Essai sur la Physiognomie, destiné à faire connoître l'homme et à le faire aimer. Seconde partie.* La Haye, 1783. viii, 404 pp.
   /TRANSLATION: FRENCH/RESEARCH: PHYSIOGNOMY

1784-1 **Lavater**, J[ohann]. C[aspar]. *Physiognomische Fragmente zur Beförderung der Menschenkenntniß und Menschenliebe.* Abbrev. edn. Ed. Johann Michael Armbruster. Vol. 2. Winterthur: Im Verlag Heinrich Steiners und Compagnie, 1784. 329 pp.
   Partial rpt. of No. 1776-1.
   /EDITION/PHYSIOGNOMY

1785-1 **Goethe**, Johann Wolfgang von and Christian Gottlob **Voigt**. "Erste Nachricht von dem Fortgang des neuen Bergbaues zu Ilmenau.

Mit einem Kupfer." Weimar: n.p., 1785. 16 pp.
/EDITION/RESEARCH: TECHNOLOGY

1786-1 **Schwabe**, Ernst. *D. Ernst Schwabe'ns Anweisung zu den Pflichten und Geschäften eines Stadt- oder Land-Physikus.* Pref. Gruner. Pt. I. Erfurt: Georg Adam Keyser, 1786. xii, 274 pp.
Dedicated to Goethe.
/RESEARCH: MEDICINE

1786-2 [**Voigt**, Johann Carl Wilhelm.] *J. C. W. Voigt's mineralogische Reise von Weimar über den Thüringer Wald, Meiningen, die Rhönberge, bis Bieber und Hanau im Herbst 1786.* Leipzig: Johann Gottfr. Müllersche Buchhandlung[, 1786]. 57 pp.
/RESEARCH: MINERALOGY

1787-1 **Goethe**, Johann Wolfgang von and Christian Gottlob **Voigt**. "Zweyte Nachricht von dem Fortgang des neuen Bergbaues zu Ilmenau." Weimar: n.p., 1787. 16 pp.
/EDITION/RESEARCH: TECHNOLOGY

1788-1 **Goethe**, Johann Wolfgang von and Christian Gottlob **Voigt**. "Dritte Nachricht von dem Fortgang des neuen Bergbaues zu Ilmenau." Weimar: n.p., 1788. 16 pp.
/EDITION/RESEARCH: TECHNOLOGY

1788-2 [**Goethe**, Johann Wolfgang von, and Christian Gottlob **Voigt**.] "Fortsetzung der Nachricht von dem Bergbaue bey Ilmenau in der Grafschaft Henneberg." *Bergmännisches Journal*, 2, No. 8 (1788), 675-92.
/EDITION/RESEARCH: TECHNOLOGY

1788-3 [**Goethe**, Johann Wolfgang von and Christian Gottlob **Voigt**.] "Fortsetzung der Nachricht von dem Bergbaue bey Ilmenau in der Grafschaft Henneberg." *Bergmännisches Journal*, 2, No. 9 (1788), 789-98.
/EDITION/RESEARCH: TECHNOLOGY

1789-1 [**Goethe**, J. W. von.] "Naturlehre. Antwort." *Der Teutsche Merkur*, No. 3, March 1789, pp. 252-6.
Continuation of No. 1789-2.
/EDITION

1789-2 [**Goethe**, J. W. von.] "Naturlehre. Neapel, den 10. Jan. 178-." *Der Teutsche Merkur*, No. 2, February 1789, pp. 126-31.

Cf. continuation, No. 1789-1.
/EDITION

1790-1 **Goethe**, J. W. von. *Versuch die Metamorphose der Pflanzen zu erklären*. Gotha: Carl Wilhelm Ettinger, 1790. vi + 86 pp.
Rpt. Nos. n.d.-13, n.d.-16 and No. 1984-35.
Rev. [anon.], *Hallische Gelehrte Zeitungen*, No. 57, 19 July 1790, 451-2.
Rev. [anon.], *Magazin für die Botanik*, 11 (1790), 164-71.
Rev. [anon.], *Göttingische Anzeigen von gelehrten Sachen*, No. 27, 14 February 1791, 269.
Rev. [anon.], *Gothaische gelehrte Zeitungen*, No. 31, 23 April 1791, 313-17.
Rev. [Giseke, Paul Dietrich?], *Beiträge von gelehrten Sachen zu der Hamburgischen Neuen Zeitung*, No. 4, 6 May 1791), [2].
Rev. [anon.], *Magazin für das Neueste aus der Physik und Naturgeschichte*, 7, No. 4 (1792), 177-90.
Rev. Bo[?] [Brandis, J. D.?], *Allgemeine deutsche Bibliothek*, 116, No. 2 (1794), 477-9.
Rev. [anon.], *Medicinisch-chirurgische Zeitung: Ergänzungsband*, 3, No. 60, 10 July 1798, 17-32; No. 61, 13 July 1798, 33-4.
Rev. [anon.], *Revision der Literatur in den drey letzten Quinquennien des achtzehnten Jahrhunderts in Ergänzungsblättern Zur Allgemeinen Literatur-Zeitung dieses Zeitraums*, 3, No. 66 (1803), cols. 521-5.
/EDITION

1791-1 **Goethe**, J. W. von. *Beyträge zur Optik. Erstes Stück*. Weimar: Im Verlag des Industrie-Comptoirs, 1791. 62 pp.
Cf. continuation, No. 1792-1.
Rpt. No. 1964-9.
Rev. [anon.], *Allgemeine Literatur-Zeitung*, No. 31, 28 January 1792, cols. 241-5.
Rev. [anon.], *Gothaische gelehrte Zeitungen*, No. 77, 26 September 1792, 713-18.
Rev. [anon.], *Magazin für das Neueste aus der Physik und Naturgeschichte*, 8, No. 1 (1792), 119-26.
Rev. Friedrich Gren [No. 1793-1].
/EDITION

1791-2 [**Goethe**, Johann Wolfgang von and Christian Gottlob **Voigt**.] "Fortsetzung der Nachricht von dem Bergbaue bey Ilmenau in der Grafschaft Henneberg." *Bergmännisches Journal*, 4, vol. 1, No. 5

(1791), 384-400.
/EDITION/RESEARCH: TECHNOLOGY

1791-3 [**Goethe**, Johann Wolfgang von and Christian Gottlob **Voigt**.]
"Fortsetzung der Nachricht von dem Bergbaue bey Ilmenau in der
Grafschaft Henneberg." *Bergmännisches Journal*, 4, vol. 1, No. 6
(1791), 483-502.
/EDITION/RESEARCH: TECHNOLOGY

1791-4 **Goethe**, Johann Wolfgang von and Christian Gottlob **Voigt**.
"Fünfte Nachricht von dem neuen Bergbau zu Ilmenau, wodurch der
Erfolg des am Sechsten Junius 1791 eröffneten Gewerkentages
bekannt gemacht wird." *Intelligenz-Blatt des Journals des Luxus und
der Moden*, 6 (1791), xcix-c.
/EDITION/RESEARCH: TECHNOLOGY

1791-5 **Goethe**, Johann Wolfgang von and Christian Gottlob **Voigt**.
"Fünfte Nachricht von dem neuen Bergbau zu Ilmenau. Wodurch der
Erfolg des am Sechsten Junius 1791 eröffneten Gewerkentages
bekannt gemacht wird." Weimar: n.p., 1791. 16 pp.
/EDITION/RESEARCH: TECHNOLOGY

1791-6 [**Goethe**, Johann Wolfgang von and Christian Gottlob **Voigt**.]
"Nachricht von dem Fortgange des Berg-Baues zu Ilmenau."
Intelligenz-Blatt des Journals des Luxus und der Moden, No. 4, April
1791. [8] pp.
/EDITION/RESEARCH: TECHNOLOGY

1791-7 **Goethe**, Johann Wolfgang von and Christian Gottlob **Voigt**.
"Vierte Nachricht von dem Fortgang des neuen Bergbaues zu
Ilmenau. Womit zugleich ein auf den Sechsten Junius 1791 zu
eröffnender Gewerkentag ausgeschrieben wird." Weimar: n.p.,
1791. 16 pp.
/EDITION/RESEARCH: TECHNOLOGY

1792-1 **Goethe**, J. W. von. *Beyträge zur Optik. Zweytes Stück*. Weimar:
im Verlag des Industrie-Comptoirs, 1792. 30 pp.
Continuation of No. 1791-1.
Rpt. No. 1964-9.
Rev. [anon.], *Allgemeine Literatur-Zeitung*, No. 316, 3 Decem-
ber 1792, cols. 457-8.
Rev. Friedrich Gren [No. 1793-1].
/EDITION/REVIEW

1792-2 **Lavater**, John Caspar. *Essays on Physiognomy, Designed to Promote the Knowledge and the Love of Mankind.* Trans. [from the French] Henry Hunter. London: John Murray, 1792. xii, 238 pp.
/TRANSLATION: ENGLISH/RESEARCH: PHYSIOGNOMY

1793-1 [**Gren**, Friedrich Albrecht Carl.] "Einige Bemerkungen über des Herrn von Göthe Beyträge zur Optik, vom Herausgeber." *Journal der Physik*, 7 (1793), 3-21.
Review of Nos. 1791-1 and 1792-1.
/REVIEW/CHROMATICS

1793-2 [**Goethe**, J. W. von.] "Von der Metamorphose der Pflanzen." In *Der Botaniker, oder compendiöse Bibliothek alles Wissenswürdigen aus dem Gebiete der Botanik.* Heft I. Sel. and ed. Georg Christoph Heim. Gotha/Halle: Johann Jacob Gebauer, 1793, pp. 15-28.
Rpt. No. 1799-3.
Rev. *Annalen der Botanik*, 8 (1794), 53-5.
/BOTANY/RESEARCH: BOTANY

1793-3 [**Goethe**, Johann Wolfgang von and Christian Gottlob **Voigt**.] "Fortgesetzte Nachrichten von dem Bergbau zu Ilmenau in der Grafschaft Henneberg." *Bergmännisches Journal*, 6, No. 4 (1791), 360-68.
/EDITION

1793-4 **Goethe**, Johann Wolfgang von and Christian Gottlob **Voigt**. "Sechste Nachricht von dem Bergbaue zu Ilmenau." Weimar: n.p., 1785. 11 pp.
/EDITION

1794-1 **Goethe**, Johann Wolfgang von and Christian Gottlob **Voigt**. "Siebente Nachricht von dem Bergbaue zu Ilmenau." Weimar: n.p., 1794. 16 pp.
/EDITION

1797-1 **Goethe**, Johann Wolfgang von and Christian Gottlob **Voigt**. "Nachdem die mit dem 10ten und 11ten Termin in Rest stehenden Beyträge zu dem Ilmenauer Bergbau. . ." Weimar: n.p., 1797. 1 p.
/EDITION

1797-2 **Göthe** [Goethe], J. W. von and C[hristian]. G[ottlob]. **Voigt**. "Publicandum." Weimar: n.p., 1797. 1 p.
/EDITION

1797-3 [**Voigt**, Johann Carl Wilhelm.] *Johann Carl Wilhelm Voigts, Herzogl. Sachsen-Weimarischen Bergraths und mehrerer Gelehrtengesellschaften Mitglieds. Erklärendes Verzeichniß seiner neuesten Cabinets von Gebirgsarten.* 3rd rev. edn. Weimar: Im Verlage des Industrie-Comptoirs, 1797. 46 pp.
/RESEARCH: GEOLOGY/RESEARCH: MINERALOGY

1798-1 **Link**, Henr. Frid. [Heinrich Friedrich]. *Philosophiae botanicae novae seu institutionum phytographicarum prodromus.* [Göttingen]: Jo. Christ. Dieterich, 1798. 192 pp.
/RESEARCH: BOTANY

1798-2 **Schelling**, F[riedrich]. W[ilhelm]. J[oseph von]. "Ueber den Ursprung des allgemeinen Organismus." In his *Von der Weltseele: eine Hypothese der höhern Physik zur Erklärung des allgemeinen Organismus.* Hamburg: bey Friedrich Perthes, 1798, pp. 177-305.
2nd. rev. edn. 1806; 3rd rev. edn. 1809.
Rpt. Nos. 1857-5, 1907-24 and 1911-31.
/BOTANY/MORPHOLOGY/OPTICS/RESEARCH: BIOLOGY

1799-1 [**Goethe**, J. W. von.] "Die Metamorphose der Pflanzen [poem]." *Archiv für die Botanik.* Ed. Johann Jacob Römer. Leipzig: Schäfersche Buchhandlung, 1799, pp. 34-6.
Rpt. of No. 1799-2.
/EDITION

1799-2 **Goethe**[, J. W. von.] "Die Metamorphose der Pflanzen [poem]." *Musen-Almanach für das Jahr 1799.* Ed. [Friedrich] Schiller. Tübingen: J. G. Cottaische Buchhandlung, 1799, pp. 17-23.
Rpt. No. 1799-1.
/EDITION

1799-3 [**Goethe**, J. W. von.] "Von der Metamorphose der Pflanzen." In *Deutsche Flora.* Sel. and ed. Georg Christoph Heim. Halle: Johann Jacob Gebauer, 1799, pp. 15-28.
Rpt. of No. 1793-2.
/EDITION

1799-4 **Schelling**, Friedrich Wilhelm Joseph [von]. *Einleitung zu seinem Entwurf eines Systems der Naturphilosophie. Oder: Ueber den Begriff der speculativen Physik und die innere Organisation eines Systems dieser Wissenschaft.* Jena/Leipzig: Christian Ernst Gabler, 1799. 83 pp.
Apparently with some collaboration on Goethe's part.

/NATURPHILOSOPHIE/RESEARCH: PHYSICS

1799-5 *[**Voigt**, Johann Carl Wilhelm.] *Kleine mineralogische Schriften.*
Pt. 1. Weimar: Gebr. Gädicke, 1799.
/RESEARCH: MINERALOGY

1800-1 **Göthe [Goethe]**, Johann Wolfgang von and Christian Gottlob **Voigt**. "Publicandum." Weimar: n.p., 1800. 1 p.
/EDITION

1800-2 **Lenz**, Johann Georg. *System der Mineralkörper, mit Benutzung der neuesten Entdeckungen.* Bamberg/Würzburg: Tobias Göbhard sel. Wittib, 1800. iv, xvi, 582 pp.
Dedicated to Goethe.
/RESEARCH: MINERALOGY

1800-3 **Stahl**, Conrad Diedrich Martin. *Grundriß der Combinationslehre nebst Anwendung derselben auf die Analysis.* Jena/Leipzig: Christian Ernst Gabler, 1800. xiv, 324 pp.
Dedicated to Goethe.
/RESEARCH: MATHEMATICS

1800-4 *[**Voigt**, Johann Carl Wilhelm.] *Kleine mineralogische Schriften.* Pt. 2. Weimar: Gebr. Gädicke, 1800.
/RESEARCH: MINERALOGY

1801-1 **Schelling**[, Friedrich Wilhelm Joseph von]. "Darstellung meines Systems der Philosophie." *Zeitschrift für spekulative Physik*, 2, No. 2 (1801), i-xiv; 1-127.
Rpt. Nos. 1859-7 and 1969-39.
/NATURPHILOSOPHIE/RESEARCH: MORPHOLOGY
/RESEARCH: CHROMATICS

1801-2 **Schelling**, Friedrich Wilhelm Joseph von. "Lasset uns den Göttern danken. . . ." *Zeitschrift für spekulative Philosophie*, 2, No. 2 (1801), 60.
/CHROMATICS/NEWTON, I

1801-3 **Steffens**, Henrik. *Beyträge zur innern Naturgeschichte der Erde.* Pt. I. Freyburg: Verlag der Crazischen Buchhandlung, 1801. 317 pp.
Dedicated to Goethe.
/RESEARCH: GEOLOGY

1803-1 **Graumüller**, J[ohann]. Chr[istian]. Fr[iedrich]. *Systematisches Verzeichniß wilder Pflanzen die in der Nähe und umliegenden Gegend von Jena wachsen nebst Bemerkung ihres Wohnorts, ihrer Blüthezeit, Fruchtreife und ihres Nutzens für angehende Aerzte, Apotheker, Technologen, Oekonomen, Gartenliebhaber etc.* Jena: in der akademischen Buchhandlung, 1803. xvi, lxii pp.

Dedicated to Goethe.
/RESEARCH: BOTANY

1803-2 **Himly**, Karl. "Einiges über die Polarität der Farbe." *Ophthalmologische Bibliothek*, 1, No. 2 (1803), 1-20.
/RESEARCH: CHROMATICS

1803-3 **Neuenhahn**, Carl Christian Adolph. *Handbuch der Gartenfreunde über alle bekannte Pflanzen der Welt*. Vol. I. 2nd rev. edn. Leipzig: Paul Gotthelf Kummer, 1803. xvi, 64 pp.
Dedicated to Goethe.
/RESEARCH: BOTANY

1803-4 **Voigt**, Friedrich Siegmund. *Handwörterbuch der botanischen Kunstsprache*. Jena: Wolfgang Stahl, 1803. xxviii, 269 pp.
/RESEARCH: BOTANY

1804-1 *[anon.] "Gelehrte Gesellschaften und Preise." *Intelligenzblatt der Jenaischen Allgemeinen Literatur-Zeitung*, No. 138, 1804, 1161.
Rpt. No. 1885-2.
Announcement of Goethe's election as President of the Naturforschende Gesellschaft zu Jena.
/INSTITUTIONS: NATURFORSCHENDE GESELLSCHAFT ZU JENA

1804-2 **Nordhof**, A[?]. W[?]. "Ueber einige prismatische Farbenerscheinungen ohne Prisma." *Magazin für den neuesten Zustand der Naturkunde*, 7 (1804), 52-60.
/RESEARCH: CHROMATICS

1805-1 [**Goethe**, J. W. von.] "Mineralogische Gesellschaft." *Intelligenzblatt der Jenaischen Allgemeinen Literatur-Zeitung vom Jahre 1805*, 2 (1805), cols. 325-6.
/EDITION/INSTITUTIONS: SOCIETÄT FÜR DIE GESAMTE MINERALOGIE

1805-2 **Humboldt**, A[lexander]. von and A[imé] G. **Bonpland**. *Geographie der Pflanzen in den Tropen-Ländern; ein Naturgemälde der Anden, gegründet auf Beobachtungen und Messungen, welche vom 10.ten Grade nördlicher bis zum 10.ten Grade südlicher Breite angestellt worden sind, in den Jahren 1799 bis 1803*. Paris: Langlois, 1805.
Trans. into French, No. 1805-3.
Dedicated to Goethe.

/RESEARCH: BOTANY

1805-3 **Humboldt**, Alexandre de [Alexander von] and Aimé [G.] **Bonpland**. *Géographie Des Plantes Équinoxiales. Tableau physique des Andes et Pays voisins: Dreßé d'après des Observations & Mesures prises Sur les Lieux depuis le 10e degré de latitude boréale jusqu'au 10e de latitude australe en 1799, 1800, 1801, 1802 et 1803.* Paris: Langlois, 1805.
> French trans. of No. 1805-2.
> Dedicated to Goethe.
> /RESEARCH: BOTANY

1806-1 **[Goethe, J. W. von.]** "An Freunde der Geognosie." *Intelligenzblatt der Jenaischen Allgem[einen] Literaturzeitung*, 3, No. 94, 6 October 1806, col. 773.
> Rpt. No. 1808-3.
> /EDITION/GOETHE'S COLLECTIONS

1806-2 **[Goethe, J. W. von.]** "[Review of] Ideen zu einer Physiognomik der Gewächse. . .[No. 1806-5]." *Jenaische Allgemeine Literatur-Zeitung*, 3, No. 62, 14 March 1806, cols. 489-92.
> Review of No. 1806-5.
> /EDITION/HUMBOLDT, A VON

1806-3 **[Goethe, J. W. von.]** "In Herrn *Cotta's Naturbeobacht-ungen* über die Bewegung und Function des Saftes in den Gewächsen. . ." *Intelligenzblatt der Jenaischen Allgem[einen]. Literaturzeitung*, 3, No. 97, 22 October 1806, col. 997 [799]/800.
> /EDITION/COTTA, H

1806-4 **[Goethe, J. W. von.]** "In Verbindung mit den berühmten Reisenden *v. Humboldt, v. Buch*, dem Mathematiker. . ." *Intelligenzblatt der Jenaischen Allgem[einen] Literaturzeitung*, 3, No. 57, 5 July 1806, col. 476.
> /EDITION/MECHEL, C VON

1806-5 **Humboldt**, Alexander von. "Ideen zu einer Physiognomik der Gewächse." Privately printed[, 1806]. 29 pp.
> Rpt. Nos. 1806-6, 1808-7 and 1826-7.
> "(Vorgelesen in der öffentlichen Sitzung der Königl. Preuß. Academie der Wissenschaften am 30. Januar 1806)."
> Dedicated to Goethe.
> Rev. Goethe [No. 1806-2].
> /RESEARCH: BOTANY

1806-6 **Humboldt**, Alexander von. "Ideen zu einer Physiognomik der Gewächse." Tübingen: J. G. Cotta'sche Buchhandlung, 1806. 28 pp.
  Rpt. of No. 1806-5.
  Dedicated to Goethe.
  /RESEARCH: BOTANY

1806-7 *****Lavater**, Gaspard [Johann Caspar]. *L'art de connaitre les hommes.* 10 vols. Paris, 1806-1809.
  Rpt. of No. 1776-1.
  Rpt. 1820.
  "Nouvelle édition, corigée et disposée dans un ordre plus méthodique, précédée d'une notice historique sur l'auteur; augmentée d'une exposition des recherches ou des opinions de la Chambre, de Porta, de Camper, de Gall, sur la physiognomie; d'une Histoire anatomique et physiologique de la face avec des figures colorées; et d'un très-grand nombre d'articles nouveaux sur les charactères des passions, des tempéramens et des maladies: par M. [Jacques-Louis] Moreau. . ."
  /TRANSLATION: FRENCH/PHYSIOGNOMY

1807-1 **Goethe**[, J. W. von], ed. *Sammlung zur Kenntniß der Gebirge von und um Karlsbad.* Karlsbad, 1807. 32 pp.
  Rpt. Nos. 1808-4 and 1817-3.
  Trans. into French, No. 1808-2.
  /EDITION/GOETHE'S COLLECTIONS/PLACES: KARLSBAD

1807-2 **Humboldt**, Al[exander]. de [von] and A[imé G.]. **Bonpland**. *Essai sur la géographie des plantes, accompagné d'un tableau physique des régions équinoxiales, Fondé sur des mesures exécutées, depuis le dixième degré de latitude boréale jusqu'au dixième degré de latitude australe, pendant les années 1799, 1800, 1801, 1802 et 1803.* Paris: Fr. Schoell/Tübingen: J. G. Cotta, 1807. 155 pp.
  French trans. of No. 1807-3.
  Dedicated to Goethe.
  /RESEARCH: BOTANY

1807-3 **Humboldt**, Alexander von. *Ideen zu einer Geographie der Pflanzen nebst einem Naturgemälde der Tropenländer, Auf Beobachtungen und Messungen gegründet, welche vom 10ten Grade nördlicher bis zum 10then Grade südlicher Breite, in den Jahren 1799, 1800, 1801 und 1803 angestellt worden sind, von Al. von Humboldt und A. Bonpland.* Tübingen: F. G. Cotta/Paris: F. Schoell, 1807. xii, 182 pp.

Trans. into French, No. 1807-2.
Dedicated to Goethe.
/RESEARCH: BOTANY

1807-4 **Link**, H[einrich]. F[riedrich]. *Grundlehren der Anatomie und Physiologie der Pflanzen*. Göttingen: bey Justus Friedrich Danckwerts, 1807.
/RESEARCH: BOTANY/RESEARCH: MORPHOLOGY

1807-5 **Oken**[, Lorenz]. "Über die Bedeutung der Schädelknochen. Ein Programm beim Antritt der Professur an der Gesammt-Universität zu Jena." Bamberg/ Würzburg: J. A. Göbhardt, 1807. 18 pp.
Rpt. Nos. 1817-12 and 1924-15.
/RESEARCH: OSTEOLOGY

1807-6 **Struve**, [Heinrich Christian Gottfried] von. "Mineralogische Bemerkungen über die Umgebungen Karlsbads." *Taschenbuch für die gesammte Mineralogie*, 1 (1807), 162-94.
Cf. continuation, No. 1808-11.
Written in collaboration with Goethe.
/RESEARCH: MINERALOGY

1808-1 **[anon.]** "Gelehrte Gesellschaften." *Intelligenzblatt der Jenaischen Allgemeinen Literatur-Zeitung*, 8 June 1808.
Rpt. No. 1885-1.
Announcement of Goethe's appointment as an "auswärtiger Mitglied."
/INSTITUTIONS: AKADEMIE DER WISSENSCHAFTEN ZU MÜNCHEN

1808-2 **Goet[h]e**[, J. W. von]. "Aperçu minéralogique des environs de Carlsbad." *Journal des mines, ou recueil de mémoires, sur l'explitation des Mines, et sur les Sciences et les Arts qui s'y rapportent*, 23 (1808).
French trans. of No. 1807-1.
/TRANSLATION: FRENCH

1808-3 **[Goethe**, J. W. von.] "Die Direction der mineralogischen Societät zu Jena. . ." *Efemeriden der Berg- und Hüttenkunde*, 4 [= *Annalen der Berg- und Hüttenkunde*, 7] (1808), 158-62/3.
Rpt. of No. 1806-1.
/EDITION/GOETHE'S COLLECTIONS

1808-4 **Goethe**[, J. W. von], ed. "Sammlung zur Kenntniß der Gebirge

von und um Karlsbad." *Taschenbuch für die gesammte Mineralogie, mit Hinsicht auf die neuesten Entdeckungen*, 2 (1808), 3-32.
   Rpt. of No. 1807-1.
   /EDITION/GOETHE'S COLLECTIONS

1808-5 **Goethe**[, J. W. von]. "*Weimar* den 25. Novbr. 1807. Sie haben die Gefälligkeit gehabt. . ." *Taschenbuch für die gesammte Mineralogie, mit Hinsicht auf die neuesten Entdeckungen*, 2 (1808), 389-98.
   /EDITION/GOETHE'S COLLECTIONS

1808-6 **Goethe**[, J. W. von]. *Zur Farbenlehre. Erster Band.* Tübingen: J. G. Cotta'sche Buchhandlung, 1808. xlviii, 352 pp.
   Cf. No. 1810-4.
   /EDITION

1808-7 **Humboldt**, Alexander von. "Ideen zu einer Physiognomik der Gewächse." In his *Ansichten der Natur, mit wissenschaftlichen Erläuterungen.* 2 vols. Stuttgart/Tübingen: J. G. Cotta'sche Buchhandlung, 1808, I, 157-278.
   Rpt. of No. 1806-5.
   Dedicated to Goethe.
   /RESEARCH: BOTANY

1808-8 **Kieser**[, Dietrich Georg (von)]. *Aphorismen aus der Physiologie der Pflanzen.* Göttingen: in Commission bei H. Dieterich, 1808. 150 pp.
   /RESEARCH: BOTANY

1808-9 **Leonhard**, Carl Caesar [von], ed. *Taschenbuch für die gesammte Mineralogie mit Hinsicht auf die neuesten Entdeckungen.* Zweiter Jahrgang. Frankfurt am Main: Johann Christian Hermann, 1808. viii, 406 pp.
   Dedicated to Goethe.
   /RESEARCH: MINERALOGY

1808-10 ***Oken**, Lorenz. "Über das Universum -- als Fortsetzung des Sinnessystems. Ein pythagoräisches Fragment." Jena, 1808.
   /NATURPHILOSOPHIE

1808-11 **Struve**, [Heinrich Christian Gottfried] von. "Mineralogische Bemerkungen über die Umgebungen Karlsbads." *Taschenbuch für die gesammte Mineralogie*, 2 (1808), 131-57.
   Continuation of No. 1807-6.

Written in collaboration with Goethe.
/RESEARCH: MINERALOGY

1808-12 **Voigt**, Friedrich Siegmund. "Von der Metamorphose der Pflanzen." In his *System der Botanik*. Jena: in der akademischen Buchhandlung, 1808, pp. 8-22.
Rpt. No. 1827-12.
/RESEARCH: BOTANY/RESEARCH: MORPHOLOGY

1809-1 **Göthe [Goethe]**, J. W. von. "Der Kammerberg bei Eger." *Taschenbuch für die gesammte Mineralogie, mit Hinsicht auf die neuesten Entdeckungen*, 3 (1809), 3-24.
/EDITION

1809-2 **Oken[, Lorenz]**. "Newton's erster Beweis für die verschiedene Brechbarkeit der Lichtstrahlen, wodurch die Verschiedenheit der Farben erzeugt werden soll." *Journal für die Chemie, Physik und Mineralogie*, 8 (1809), 269-76.
/RESEARCH: CHROMATICS/NEWTON, I

1809-3 **Oken[, Lorenz]**. "Ueber den Werth der Naturgeschichte besonders für die Bildung der Deutschen." Jena: Friedrich Frommann, 1809. 18 pp.
". . .bei Eröffnung seiner Vorlesungen über Zoologie. VI. Für die Herbstferien 1809."
/NATURPHILOSOPHIE/RESEARCH: ZOOLOGY

1810-1 [**Falk**, Johannes D.] "Erstes Sendschreiben über Goethes Farben-
lehre." *Morgenblatt für gebildete Stände*, 4, No. 226 (1810), 901-2.
First installment without name of author.
/CHROMATICS

1810-2 [**Falk**, Johannes D.] "Erstes Sendschreiben über Goethes Farbenlehre. (Beschluß)." *Morgenblatt für gebildete Stände*, 4, No. 227
(1810), 905-7.
/CHROMATICS

1810-3 [**Fries**, Jacob Friedrich.] "[Review of:] Zur Farbenlehre, von
Göthe. Erster Band. Nebst einem Hefte mit sechzehn Kupfertafeln
XLVIII u. 757 S. 8. Tübingen, in der J. G. Cotta'schen Buchhand-
lung. 1810. (15 fl.)." *Heidelberger Jahrbücher der Literatur: Vierte
Abteilung. Mathematik, Physik und Kameralwissenschaften*, 3, No. 7
(1810), 289-307.
Review of No. 1810-4.
Rpt. No. 1885-8.
/REVIEW/CHROMATICS

1810-4 **Goethe**, J. W. von. *Zur Farbenlehre*. 2 vols. Tübingen: J. G.
Cotta'sche Buchhandlung, 1810. xlviii, 654; xxviii, 757 pp.
Cf. No. 1808-6.
Rev. [anon.], *Neue Oberdeutsche allgemeine Literatur-Zeitung*,
2, No. 132, 5 July 1810, cols. 25-32. [Rpt. No. 1885-4].
Rev. [anon.], *Neue Leipziger Literaturzeitung*, 3, 102 (1810),
cols. 1629-32.
Rev. [No. 1810-3].
Rev. [No. 1810-6].
Rev. [anon.], *Göttingische gelehrte Anzeigen*, 22 June 1811,
977-90. [Rpt. No. 1885-3].
Rev. [No. 1811-3].
Rev. [No. 1811-6].
Rev. [No. 1812-6].
Rev. [No. 1813-4].
Rev. [No. 1813-6].
/EDITION

1810-5 **Kastner**, Carl Wilhelm Gottlob. "Von den Farben." In his
Grundriss der Experimentalphysik. 2 vols. Heidelberg: Mohr und
Zimmer, 1810, II, pp. 817-35.
Rpt. No. 1821-4.
/RESEACH: CHROMATICS/CHROMATICS

1810-6 **Klotz**, Mathias. "[Review of:] Zur Farbenlehre. Herausgegeben von Göthe. *Kritischer Anzeiger für Litteratur und Kunst [München]*, No. 30, 28 July 1810, 158-62; No. 31, 4 August 1810, 166-8; No. 32, 11 August 1810, 170-71; No. 33, 18 August 1810, 176-7.
Review of No. 1810-4.
/REVIEW/CHROMATICS

1810-7 **Klotz**, Mathias. *Erklärende Ankündigung einer Farbenlehre und des daraus entstandenen Farbensystems*. München: In Commission bei Jakob Giel, 1810.
/RESEARCH: CHROMATICS

1810-8 **Mollweide**[, Karl Brandan]. "Auszug aus einem Schreiben des Herrn Dr. Mollweide. -- Halle, am 5. Jun. 1810." *Monatliche Correspondenz zur Beförderung der Erd- und Himmelskunde*, 22 (1810), 91-3.
Review of No. 1810-4.
Rpt. No. 1885-16.
/REVIEW/CHROMATICS/NEWTON, I

1810-9 **Ritter**, J[ohann]. W[ilhelm]., ed. *Fragmente aus dem Nachlasse eines jungen Physikers. Ein Taschenbuch für Freunde der Natur.* Heidelberg: Mohr und Zimmer, 1810. 269 pp.
/RESEARCH: PHYSICS/RESEARCH: CHROMATICS

1810-10 **Runge**, Philipp Otto and Henrik **Steffens**. *Farben-Kugel oder Construction des Verhältnisses aller Mischungen der Farben zu einander, und ihrer vollständigen Affinität, mit angehängtem Versuch einer Ableitung der Harmonie in den Zusammenstellungen der Farben. Nebst einer Abhandlung über die Bedeutung der Farben in der Natur.* Hamburg: Friedrich Perthes, 1810. 60 pp.
Partial rpt., No. 1821-10.
The essay "Über die Bedeutung der Farben in der Natur" was written by Steffens.
/RESEARCH: CHROMATICS/FINE ARTS

1810-11 ***Wd[?]***., A[?]. "[Review of] Zur Farbenlehre, herausgegeben von Göthe. Im Verlag der Cottaischen Buchhandlung in Tübingen 1810. 2 Bde." *Heidelbergische Jahrbücher der Literatur für Philologie, Historie, schöne Literatur und Kunst*, 2, No. 16 (1810), 356-71.
Review of No. 1810-4.
Rpt. No. 1885-23.
/REVIEW/CHROMATICS

1811-1 **Fischer**, Ernst Gottfried. "Bericht über das 3. Quartal 1811." *Aus den Protokollen der philomatischen Gesellschaft Berlin*, 1 (1802-11), Blatt 108.
/CHROMATICS/NEWTON, I

1811-2 **Fischer [von Waldheim]**, Got[t]helf. "Observata quaedam de Osse epactali sive Goethiano Palmigradorum. Prodromo inservientia Craniologiae comparatae." [Moscow]: typis Nicolai Sergeidis Vsevolojsky, 1811. 6 pp.
/RESEARCH: OSTEOLOGY

1811-3 *[**Hassenfratz?**]. Traité des Couleurs, par M. Goethe. *Annales de Chimie*. Paris, 1811. lxxix, 199.
Rev. of No. 1810-4.
/REVIEW/CHROMATICS

1811-4 [**Malus**, Étienne Louis.] "[Review of:] Traité des couleurs; par M. Goethe (1810)." *Annales de Chimie*, 79 (1811), 199-219.
Review of No. 1810-4.
/REVIEW/CHROMATICS

1811-5 **Meinecke**, Joh[ann]. Ludw[ig]. Georg. *Über das Zahlenverhältniß in den Fructifications-Organen der Pflanzen, und Beyträge zur Pflanzen-Physiologie.* Neue Schriften der naturforschenden Gesellschaft zu Halle, 1. Halle: J. Ch. Hendels Verlag, 1811. 50 pp.
"Zwei Abhandlungen vorgelesen in der naturforschenden Gesellschaft zu Halle."
Cf. esp. "Ueber den Ursprung der Geschlechtsteile der Pflanzen," pp. 38-42.
/RESEARCH: BOTANY

1811-6 [**Mollweide**, Karl Brandan?]. "[Review of:] Tübingen, b. Cotta: Zur Farbenlehre, von v. Göthe. -- Erster Band. XLVIII und 654 S. Zweyter Band. XXVIII und 757 S. 1810. 8. Ein Heft mit XVI illuminirten Kupfertafeln und deren Erklärung." *Allgemeine Literatur-Zeitung* [Halle and Leipzig], 30 January 1811, cols. 233-47; 31 January 1811, cols. 249-51.
Review of No. 1810-4.
Rpt. No. 1885-17.
/REVIEW/CHROMATICS

1811-7 **Oken**, Lorenz. *Lehrbuch der Naturphilosophie.* Pt. III.3. Jena: Friedrich Frommann, 1811. xxiv, 374 pp.

/NATURPHILOSOPHIE/RESEARCH: OSTEOLOGY

1811-8 **Poselger**, Friedrich Theodor. "Der farbige Rand eines durch ein biconvexes Glas entstehenden Bildes untersucht mit Bezug auf Herrn von Göthe's Werk: Zur Farbenlehre." *Annalen der Physik*, 37, No. 2 (1811), 135-54.
Review of No. 1810-4.
Rpt. No. 1885-18.
/RESEARCH: CHROMATICS/CHROMATICS

1811-9 **Seebeck**, T[homas Johann]. "Von den Farben und dem Verhalten derselben gegen einander." *Journal für Chemie und Physik*, 1 (1811), 4-12.
Rev. [anon.], *Jenaer Allgemeine Literatur-Zeitung*, 9 (1812), 89-90.
/RESEARCH: CHROMATICS

1811-10 **Voigt**, Friedrich Siegmund. "Einige physiologisch-botanische Betrachtungen über die in gegenwärtiger Schrift enthaltenen Entdeckungen." In Louis-Claude Richard, *Analyse der Frucht und des Saamenkorns*. Ed. and trans. F[riedrich]. S[iegmund]. Voigt. Leipzig: Carl Heinrich Reclam, 1811, pp. 142-69.
/BOTANY/MORPHOLOGY

1812-1 **Benzenberg**, J[ohann]. F[riedrich]. "Goethes Farbenlehre." In his *Briefe geschrieben auf einer Reise durch die Schweiz im Jahr 1810*. Düsseldorf: J. H. C. Schreiner, 1812, pp. 501-13.
/CHROMATICS

1812-2 **Goethe**[, J. W. von]. *Zur Farbenlehre. Erster Band. Ersten Bandes erste Abteilung.* Vol. 20 of *Goethe's sämmtliche Schriften*. Wien: In Commission bey Geistinger, 1812. xl, 318 pp.
/EDITION

1812-3 **Goethe**[, J. W. von]. *Zur Farbenlehre. Erster Band. Ersten Bandes zweyte Abteilung.* Vol. 21 of *Goethe's sämmtliche Schriften*. Wien: In Commission bey Geistinger, 1812. 296 pp.
/EDITION

1812-4 **Goethe**[, J. W. von]. *Zur Farbenlehre. Zweyter Band. Zweyten Bandes erste Abteilung.* Vol. 22 of *Goethe's sämmtliche Schriften*. Wien: In Commission bey Geistinger, 1812. xx, 368 pp.
/EDITION

1812-5 **Goethe**[, J. W. von]. *Zur Farbenlehre. Zweyter Band. Zweyten Bandes zweyte Abteilung.* Vol. 23 of *Goethe's sämmtliche Schriften.* Wien: In Commission bey Geistinger, 1812. 333, viii pp.
/EDITION

1812-6 [**Malus**, Étienne Louis and Ludwig Wilhelm **Gilbert.**] "Bericht eines französischen Physikers über Herrn von Göthe's Werk: Zur Farbenlehre, 2 Bde. Tübingen 1810. 8." *Annalen der Physik*, 40 [NS 10], No. 1 (1812), 103-15.
Review of No. 1810-4.
Rpt. No. 1885-15.
/REVIEW/CHROMATICS

1812-7 **Pfaff**, C[hristoph]. H[einrich]. "Ueber das doppelte Grau, aus welchem das weiße Licht besteht, und die blos negative Wirksamkeit der schwarzen Bilder in optischen Versuchen. Ein Nachtrag zu dem Aufsatz über die farbigen Säume der Nebenbilder des Doppelspaths [No. 1812-8]." *Journal für Chemie und Physik*, 6, No. 2 (1812), 205-10.
/RESEARCH: CHROMATICS/CHROMATICS

1812-8 **Pfaff**, C[hristoph]. H[einrich]. "Ueber die farbigen Säume der Nebenbilder des Doppelspaths, mit besonderer Rücksicht auf Hrn. von Göthes Erklärung der Farbenentstehung durch Nebenbilder." *Journal für Chemie und Physik*, 6, No. 2 (1812), 177-204.
/RESEARCH: CHROMATICS/CHROMATICS

1812-9 *****Purkyne**, Jan. *De examine physiologico organi visus et systematis cutanei.* Breslau, 1812.
/RESEARCH: PHYSIOLOGY/RESEARCH: OPTICS

1812-10 **Schelver**, Franz Joseph. *Kritik der Lehre von den Geschlechtern der Pflanze.* Heidelberg: in Commission bei G. Braun, 1812. 86 pp.
Cf. continuation, No. 1814-5.
/RESEARCH: BOTANY

1812-11 *****Schultz**, Christoph Friedrich Ludwig. *Über die farbigen Ränder und die verkleinerten Bilder nach Goethe.* 1812.
/CHROMATICS

1812-12 **Sprengel**, Kurt. "Von der Entwickelung und Metamorphose der Theile." In his *Von dem Bau und der Natur der Gewächse.* Halle: K. A. Kümmel, 1812, pp. 487-93.
/RESEARCH: BOTANY

1813-1 **Göthe [Goethe**, J. W. von]. "Höhen der alten und neuen Welt bildlich verglichen von Göthe." *Allgemeine Geographische Ephemeriden*, 41 (1813), 3-8.
Rpt. No. 1910-5.
/EDITION

1813-2 **Pfaff**, Christoph Heinrich. *Ueber Newton's Farbentheorie, Herrn von Goethe's Farbenlehre und den chemischen Gegensatz der Farben. Ein Versuch in der experimentalen Optik.* Leipzig: Fr. Chr. Wilh. Vogel, 1813. xvi, 182 pp.
Rev. [anon.], *Göttingsche gelehrte Anzeigen unter der Aufsicht der königl. Gesellschaft der Wissenschaften*, 77, 15 May 1813, 761-7.
Rev. [anon.], *Heidelbergische Jb. Lit.*, 7, No. 1 (1814), 417-30.
Rev. [anon.], *Leipziger Literatur-Zeitung für das Jahr 1815*, No. 185, 1 August 1815, cols. 1473-80.
/CHROMATICS/RESEARCH: CHROMATICS/NEWTON, I

1813-3 ***Prévost**, P[ierre]. "Quelques remarques d'optique." *Bibliothèque Britannique (Sciences et Arts)*, 53 (1813), 18-36.
/RESEARCH: OPTICS

1813-4 **R[?], L[?] and K[arl]. J[oseph]. W[indischmann]**. "[Review of:] Tübingen, b. Cotta: Zur Farbenlehre von Goethe. . .(Von zwey Recensenten.)" *Ergänzungsblätter zur Jenaischen Allgemeinen Literatur-Zeitung*, 1 (1813), cols. 17-24; 25-32.
Review of No. 1810-4.
Rpt. Nos. 1953-12 and 1955-25.
/REVIEW/CHROMATICS

1813-5 **Seebeck[**, Thomas Johann]. "Einige neue Versuche und Beobachtungen über Spiegelung und Brechung des Lichtes." *Journal für Chemie und Physik*, 7 (1813), 259-98.
/RESEARCH: CHROMATICS

1813-6 **[Young**, Thomas]. "[Review of:] Zur Farbenlehre. On the Doctrine of Colours. By Goethe. 2 vol. 8 vo. Tubingen, 1810, pp. 1510; with 16 coloured plates in 4to." *The Quarterly Review*, 10 (1813/1814), 427-41.
Review of No. 1810-4.
/REVIEW/CHROMATICS

1814-1 **Fischer**, Nikolaus Wolfgang. *Ueber die Wirkung des Lichts auf*

das Hornsilber. Nürnberg: Johann Leonhard Schrag, 1814. viii, 66 pp.
/CHEMISTRY/CHROMATICS

1814-2 [**Goethe**, J. W. von]. "Jenaische Museen und Sternwarte." *Intelligenzblatt der Jenaischen Allgemeinen Literaturzeitung*, 11, No. 2 (1814), cols. 9-16.
/EDITION

1814-3 **Jäger**, Georg Friedrich [von]. *Über die Missbildungen der Gewächse: ein Beytrag zur Geschichte und Theorie der Missentwicklungen organischer Körper*. Stuttgart: Joh. Friedr. Steinkopf, 1814. xii, 320 pp.
/RESEARCH: BOTANY/RESEARCH: PATHOLOGY

1814-4 **Nees von Esenbeck**, C[hristian]. G[ottfried]. "Die Algen des süßen Wassers nach ihren Entwicklungsstufen dargestellt." Bamberg: C. F. Kunz, 1814. iv, 47 pp.
/RESEARCH: BOTANY

1814-5 ***Schelver**, Franz Joseph. *Erste Fortsetzung seiner Kritik der Lehre von den Pflanzengeschlechtern*. Carlsruhe, 1814.
Continuation of No. 1812-10.
/RESEARCH: BOTANY

1815-1 **Prévost**, Pierre. "Versuch, die verschiedene Brechbarkeit des farbigen Lichtes im Wasser unmittelbar sichtbar zu machen; in Beziehung auf Herrn von Göthe's Farbenlehre." *Annalen der Physik*, NS 19 (1815), 393-404.
"(Vorgel. in der physik. u. naturh. Ges. zu Genf d. 30. Juli 1812.) Frei zusammengezogen von Gilbert."
/OPTICS/RESEARCH: OPTICS/CHROMATICS/RESEARCH: CHROMATICS

1815-2 **Spix**, Joann Baptista [Johann Baptista]. *Cephalogenesis sive capitis ossei structura, formatio et significatio per omnes animalium classes, familias, genera ac aetates digesta, atque tabulis illustrata, legesque simul psychologiae, cranioscopiae ac physiognomiae inde derivatae*. Monachii [München]: typis Francisci Seraphici Hübschmannii, 1815. 72 pp.
/RESEARCH: OSTEOLOGY

1816-1 **Goethe**[, J. W.] von. "Über indische Stahlbereitung." *Neues Journal für Chemie und Physik*, 16, No. 1 (1816), 102-4.

/EDITION

1816-2 **Göthe** [Goethe, J. W. von]. *"Weimar*, im Dezember 1814. 'Auszug aus einem Briefe des Herrn Bergrath Voigt zu *Ilmenau'." Taschenbuch für die gesammte Mineralogie, mit Hinsicht auf die neuesten Entdeckungen*, 10 (1816), 300-301.
 /EDITION

1816-3 **Klotz**, Matthias. "Gründliche Farbenlehre." München: In Kommission bei der Lindauer'schen Buchhandlung, 1816. 28 pp.
 Rev. [Lorenz Oken?], *Isis oder Encyclopädische Zeitung von Oken*, No. 7, 1817, cols. 1001-4.
 /CHROMATICS/RESEARCH: CHROMATICS

1816-4 **Schopenhauer**, Arthur. *Ueber das Sehn und die Farben, eine Abhandlung*. Leipzig: Johann Friedrich Hartknoch, 1816. 88 pp.
 Rpt. Nos. 1891-14 and 1923-23.
 Trans. into Italian, No. 1959-34.
 Rev. [anon.], *Leipziger Literatur-Zeitung für das Jahr 1817*, No. 179, 14 July 1817, cols. 1425-8.
 /RESEARCH: CHROMATICS/CHROMATICS

1816-5 [**Schultz**, Christoph Ludwig Friedrich.] "Ueber physiologe Gesichts- und Farben-Erscheinungen." Jena, 1816. 37 pp.
 Rpt. of No. 1816-6.
 /RESEARCH: PHYSIOLOGY/RESEARCH: CHROMATICS

1816-6 **Schultz**, Christoph Ludwig Friedrich. "Ueber physiologe Gesichts- und Farben-Erscheinungen." *Journal für Chemie und Physik*, 16 (1816), 121-157.
 Rpt. Nos. 1816-5 and 1853-11.
 /RESEARCH: PHYSIOLOGY/RESEARCH: CHROMATICS

1816-7 **Varnhagen** von Ense, Karl August. "Bruchstücke aus Briefen und Denkblättern." *Schweizerisches Museum*, 1 (1816), 212-42.
 /VEIT, D/MEDICINE

1816-8 **Voigt**, Friedrich Siegmund. *Die Farben der organischen Körper*. Jena: in der Crökerschen Buchhandlung, 1816. xvi, 223 pp.
 /RESEARCH: BOTANY/RESEARCH: CHROMATICS

1817-1 **Cassel**, Franz Peter. *Lehrbuch der natürlichen Pflanzenordnung*. Frankfurt am Main: Andreäische Buchhandlung, 1817. viii, 403 pp.
 /RESEARCH: BOTANY

1817-2 **Goethe**[, J. W.] v[on]. "Glückliches Ereigniß. (Von Goethe: Zur Naturwissenschaft überhaupt, besonders zur Morphologie.)" *Morgenblatt für gebildete Stände*, 11, No. 216, 9 September 1817, 861-2; No. 217, 10 September 1817, 865-6.
/EDITION

1817-3 **Goethe**[, J. W. von]. *Sammlung zur Kenntniß der Gebirge von und um Carlsbad*. In Sartori, Franz. *Taschenbuch für Carlsbads Curgäste, wie auch für Liebhaber von dessen Naturschönheiten. Eine vollständige Beschreibung alles desjenigen, was Curbrauchende sowohl, als wißbegierige Reisende von diesem Heilorte und seinen Umgebungen in topographischer, pittoresker, naturhistorischer, geschichtlicher und medicinischer Hinsicht zu wissen wünschen*. Wien/Prag/Carlsbad: Carl Haas'sche Buchhandlung, 1817, pp. 199-219.
Rpt. of No. 1807-1.
/EDITION/GOETHE'S COLLECTIONS/PLACES: KARLSBAD

1817-4 **Goethe**[, J. W. von]. *Zur Morphologie. Erster Band*. Stuttgard[t] /Tübingen: J. G. Cotta'sche Buchhandlung, 1817. xxxii, 368 pp.
/EDITION

1817-5 **Goethe**[, J. W. von]. *Zur Naturwissenschaft überhaupt, besonders zur Morphologie. Erfahrung, Beobachtung, Folgerung, durch Lebensereignisse verbunden. Ersten Bandes, erstes Heft*. Stuttgard[t]/Tübingen: J. G. Cotta'sche Buchhandlung, 1817. xxxii, 96; 64 pp.
/EDITION

1817-6 **Goethe**[, J. W. von]. *Zur Naturwissenschaft überhaupt. Erster Band*. Stuttgard[t]/Tübingen: J. G. Cotta'sche Buchhandlung, 1817. 382 pp.
Rev. *Journal des Luxus und der Moden*, 32, October 1817.
Rev. [No. 1818-4].
Rev. [anon.], *Allgemeines Repertorium der neusten in- und ausländischen Literatur für 1820*, 3 (1820), 230.
Rev. [anon.], *Flora oder Botanische Zeitung*, 3 (1820), 717.
Rev. [anon.], *Allgemeine Medizinische Annalendes neunzehnten Jahrhunderts auf das Jahr 1821 oder: Kritische Annalen der Medizin als Wissenschaft und als Kunst vom dritten Jahrzehende des neunzehnten Jahrhunderts an*, 1 (1821), cols.

73-85.

Rev. [anon.], *Allgemeines Repertorium der neusten in- und ausländischen Literatur für 1821*, 4 (1821), 28-30.

Rev. [anon.], *Literarisches Conversations-Blatt*, No. 135, 13 June 1821, 537-9.

Rev. [No. 1821-3].

Rev. X[?], *Flora oder Botanische Zeitung*, 4, No. 14 (1821), 223.

Rev. [No. 1821-7].

Rev. [anon.], *Leipziger Literatur Zeitung für das Jahr 1822*, No. 128, 24 May 1822, cols. 1018-20.

Rev. [anon.], *Allgemeines Repertorium der neuesten in- und ausländischen Literatur für 1823*, 3 (1823), 15-16.

Rev. [No. 1823-9].

Rev. [anon.], *Mineralogisches Taschenbuch für das Jahr 1824*, Pt. I (1824), 164-9.

Rev. [No. 1824-10].

Rev. [No. 1824-14].

/EDITION

1817-7 **Hegel**, Georg Wilhelm Friedrich. *Encyklopädie der philosophischen Wissenschaften im Grundrisse. Zum Gebrauch seiner Vorlesungen.* Heidelberg: August Oßwald's Universitätsbuchhandlung, 1817. xvi, 288 pp.

Rpt. Nos. 1827-10, 1830-7, 1842-16, 1845-3, 1870-4, and 1929-16.

/CHROMATICS/NATURPHILOSOPHIE/NEWTON, I

1817-8 **Kopp**[, Johann Heinrich]. "von Goethe, Johann Wolfgang." In "Alphabetische Uebersicht der Autoren, Uebersetzer und Herausgeber in der Literatur der Mineralogie, sowie der andern mit den augeführten Schriften in Beziehung stehenden Gelehrten." In Leonard, C. C., J. H. Kopp and C. L. Gaertner. *Propaedeutik der Mineralogie.* Frankfurt am Main: in der Joh. Christ. Hermannschen Buchhandlung, 1817, pp. 278-309.

/MINERALOGY

1817-9 **Leonhard**, Carl Caesar [von], Johann Heinrich **Kopp** and Carl Ludwig **Gaertner**. *Einleitung und Vorbereitung zur Mineralogie. Als erster Theil der systematisch-tabellarischen Uebersicht und Charakteristik der Mineralkoerper.* Pt. I of *Propaedeutik der Mineralogie.* Frankfurt am Main: Joh. Christ. Hermannschen Buchhandlung, 1817. xii, 315 pp.

/RESEARCH: MINERALOGY

1817-10 **Nees von Esenbeck**, C[hristian]. G[ottfried]. *Das System der Pilze und Schwämme.* Würzburg: in der Stahelischen Buchhandlung, 1816. xxxvi, 329 pp.
/RESEARCH: BOTANY

1817-11 [**Oken**, Lorenz.] [Afterword to announcement of: Johannes Spix. *Cephalogenesis*, etc. Monachii 1815.] *Isis oder Encyclopädische Zeitung von Oken*, No. 2, 1817, cols. 157-9.
/RESEARCH: OSTEOLOGY/RECEPTION

1817-12 **Oken**, Lorenz. "Ueber die Bedeutung der Schädelknochen. Ein Programm beym Antritt der Professur an der Gesammt-Universität zu Jena." *Isis oder Encyclopädische Zeitung von Oken*, No. 8, 1817, cols. 1204-8.
Rpt. of No. 1807-5.
/RESEARCH: OSTEOLOGY

1817-13 **Voigt**, F[riedrich]. S[iegmund]. *Grundzüge einer Naturgeschichte als Geschichte der Entstehung und weiterer Ausbildung der Naturkörper.* Frankfurt a. M.: Heinrich Ludwig Brönner, 1817. xiv, 679 pp.
/RESEARCH: BIOLOGY/RESEARCH: MORPHOLOGY

1817-14 **Werneburg**, J. Friedrich Christian. "Merkwürdige Phänomene an und durch verschiedene Prismen. Zur richtigen Würdigung der Newton'schen und der Göthe'schen Farbenlehre." Nürnberg: Johann Leonhard Schrag, 1817. 39 pp.
Rev. Lorenz Oken[, No. 1818-10].
/CHROMATICS/NEWTON, I/RESEARCH: CHROMATICS

1818-1 **B[?]., G[?].** "Blumen-Farben." *Isis oder Encyclopädische Zeitung von Oken*, No. 3, 1818, cols. 468-71.
Cf. response by Oken, No. 1818-7.
/RESEARCH: BOTANY/RESEARCH: CHROMATICS

1818-2 **Bojanus**, L[udwig (von)]. "Versuch einer Deutung der Knochen im Kopfe der Fische." *Isis oder Encyclopädische Zeitung von Oken*, No. 3, 1818, cols. 498-510.
Cf. response by Oken, No. 1818-6.
/RESEARCH: OSTEOLOGY/OKEN, L

1818-3 **Carus**, Carl Gustav. *Lehrbuch der Zootomie. Mit stäter Hinsicht auf Physiologie ausgearbeitet.* Leipzig: Gerhard Fischer der Jüngere,

1818. xxxii, 702 pp.
Rpt. No. 1834-2.
/RESEARCH: BIOLOGY

1818-4 **F[?]**, [?]. "Von der Metamorphose der Botanik." *Isis oder Encyclopädische Zeitung von Oken*, No. 6, 1818, cols. 991-1008.
Review of No. 1817-6.
Cols. 996ff. on Goethe.
/REVIEW/BOTANY/MORPHOLOGY/THEOPHRASTUS

1818-5 **Nees von Esenbeck**[, Christian Gottfried]. "Über die bartmündigen Enzianarten (Gentianae fauce barbata)." *Nova Acta Physico Medica Academiae Caesareae Leopoldino-Carolinae Naturae Curiosorum / Verhandlungen der Leopoldinisch-Carolinischen Academie der Naturforscher*, 1 (1818), 141-79.
/RESEARCH: BOTANY/RESEARCH: MORPHOLOGY

1818-6 **[Oken, Lorenz.]** "Diese Apostrophe ist sehr gelegen. . ." *Isis oder Encyclopädische Zeitung von Oken*, No. 3, 1818, cols. 510-12.
Response to No. 1818-2.
In table of contents: "Oken wie er zur Bedeutung der Schädelknochen gekommen."
/RESEARCH: OSTEOLOGY/BOJANUS, L

1818-7 **[Oken, Lorenz.]** "Man kann diesen Bemerkungen. . ." *Isis oder Encyclopädische Zeitung von Oken*, No. 3, 1818, cols. 471-449 [473].
Response to No. 1818-1.
/RESEARCH: BOTANY/RESEARCH: CHROMATICS

1818-8 **[Oken, Lorenz.]** "Okens Mineralsystem." *Isis oder Encyclopädische Zeitung von Oken*, No. 6, 1818, cols. 959-73.
/RESEARCH: MINERALOGY/RESEARCH: GE-OLOGY/NATURPHILOSOPHIE

1818-9 **Oken**[, Lorenz.] "Quappe (Thalassema)." *Isis oder Encyclopädische Zeitung von Oken*, No. 5, 1818, cols. 878-9.
/RESEARCH: ZOOLOGY/RESEARCH: ANATOMY

1818-10 **Oken**, Lorenz. [Review of Werneburg, J. Friedrich Christian. "Merkwürdige Phänomene an und durch verschiedene Prismen. Zur richtigen Würdigung der Newton'schen und der Göthe'schen Farbenlehre." Nürnberg: Johann Leonhard Schrag, 1817. 39 pp.] *Isis oder Encyclopädische Zeitung von Oken*, No. 3, 1818, cols. 433-46.
Review of No. 1817-14.

Rpt. No. 1922-30.
/REVIEW/CHROMATICS/RESEARCH: CHROMA-
TICS/NEWTON, I

1818-11 **Sprengel**, Kurt. "Fortschritte in der Lehre von dem Bau und der Natur der Pflanzen. I. Lehre von der Entwickelung und Metamorphose." In *Kurt Sprengels Geschichte der Botanik*. Rev. edn. 2 pts. Altenburt/Leipzig: F. A. Brockhaus, 1818, Pt. I, 301-5.
/BOTANY

1819-1 **Bojanus**[, Ludwig (von)]. "Weiterer Beytrag zur Deutung der Schädel-Knochen. Ein Schreiben an den herausgeber der Isis von Bojanus. 2. Juli 1819." *Isis oder Encyclopädische Zeitung von Oken*, No. 8, 1819, cols. 1360-68.
/RESEARCH: OSTEOLOGY

1819-2 **Candolle**, Augustin Pyramus de. *Théorie élémentaire de la botanique ou exposition des principes de la classification naturelle et de l'art de décrire et d'étudier les végétaux*. 2nd rev. and exp. edn. Paris: Deterville, 1819. viii, 566 pp.
/RESEARCH: BOTANY

1819-3 **Falk**, Johannes. "Von den göttlichen Urbildern und deren Bezug auf die Metamorphose der Pflanzen." In Pt. II of *Johannes Falk's auserlesene Werke*. *(Alt und neu.)* 3 pts. Leipzig: F. A. Brockhaus, 1819, pp. 267-74.
/BOTANY/MORPHOLOGY/NATURPHILOSOPHIE

1819-4 **Falk**, Johannes. "Von der Verwandtschaft des innern und äußern Lichts. Göthischer Platonismus." In Pt. II of *Johannes Falk's auserlesene Werke*. *(Alt und neu.)* 3 pts. Leipzig: F. A. Brockhaus, 1819, pp. 275-84.
/CHROMATICS/EPISTEMOLOGY/NATURPHILOSOPHIE

1819-5 **Ficinus**[, Heinrich]. "Farbe, (Colores.)" In Pierer, Johann Friedrich. *Medizinisches Realwörterbuch zum Handgebrauch practischer Aerzte und Wundärzte un zu belehrender Nachweisung für gebildete Personen aller Stände*. Leipzig: Brockhaus, 1819, pp. 19-39.
/CHROMATICS/RESEARCH: CHROMATICS/NEWTON, I

1819-6 **Fischer**, Ernst Gottfried. "Ueber die sogenannten zufälligen Farben, die Hr. v. Göthe recht schicklich physiologische nennt." In his *Lehrbuch der mechanischen Naturlehre. Zweiter Theil, welcher die*

Lehre von der Elektricität, von der magnetischen Kraft und von dem Lichte enthält. 2nd rev. and exp. edn. Berlin/Leipzig: C. G. Nauck's Buchhandlung, 1819, §§ 28-30, pp. 313-16.
> Rpt. No. 1826-4.
> Not in 1st edn. of 1801.
> /RESEARCH: CHROMATICS/CHROMATICS

1819-7 **Hjertman**, Christ[?]. Rudolphus [Rudolph]. "Examen theoriae celeberrimi a Goethe de coloribus physiologicis." Diss. Aböens. Aboae: Typis Frenckellianis, 1819. 10 pp.
> /CHROMATICS

1819-8 **O[ken**, Lorenz]. "Bein-Philosophie; umgerissen von O[ken]." *Isis oder Encyclopädische Zeitung von Oken*, No. 9, 1819, cols. 1528-48.
> /RESEARCH: OSTEOLOGY/NATURPHILOSOPHIE

1819-9 **[Oken**, Lorenz.] "Mineral-System von 1819." *Isis oder Encyclopädische Zeitung von Oken*, No. 1, 1819, cols. 47-54.
> /RESEARCH: MINERALOGY/RESEARCH: GEOLOGY/NATURPHILOSOPHIE

1819-10 **[Oken**, Lorenz.] "Okens Pflanzensystem." *Isis oder Encyclopädische Zeitung von Oken*, No. 3, 1819, cols. 445-74.
> /RESEARCH: BOTANY/NATURPHILOSOPHIE

1819-11 **[Oken**, Lorenz.] [Review of Purkinje (Purkyne), Johann (Jan). *Beiträge zur Kenntniß des Sehens in subjectiver Hinsicht.* Prag: In Commission bei Johann Gottfried Calve, 1819. 176 pp.] *Isis oder Encyclopädische Zeitung von Oken*, No. 8, 1819, col. 1369.
> Rev. of No. 1819-12.
> /REVIEW/RESEARCH: CHROMATICS/CHROMATICS/NATURPHILOSOPHIE

1819-12 **Purkinje [Purkyne]**, Johann [Jan]. *Beiträge zur Kenntniß des Sehens in subjectiver Hinsicht.* Prag: In Commission bei Johann Gottfried Calve, 1819. 176 pp.
> Rpt. Nos. 1823-10, 1825-9 and 1948-27.
> Rev. Lorenz Oken [No. 1819-11].
> /RESEARCH: SENSORY PHYSIOLOGY/RESEARCH: CHROMATICS

1819-13 **Wilbrand**, Johann Bernhard. "Polares Verhalten in den Functionen des vegetabilischen Lebens." In his *Das Gesetz des*

polaren Verhaltens in der Natur dargestellt in den magnetischen, elec-trischen und chemischen Naturerscheinungen; in dem Verhalten der unorganischen Natur zur organischen Schöpfung; in den Erscheinungen des Pflanzen- und Thierlebens; in dem Verhalten unsers Weltkörpers zu dem umgebenden Planetensystem zur Begründung einer wissenschaftlichen Physiologie. Giessen: C. G. Müller, 1819, pp. 154-225.
/NATURPHILOSOPHIE

1819-14 **Wilbrand**, Johann Bernhard. "Verhalten des Lichts im Far-benspektrum." In his *Das Gesetz des polaren Verhaltens in der Natur dargestellt in den magnetischen, electrischen und chemischen Naturerscheinungen; in dem Verhalten der unorganischen Natur zur organischen Schöpfung; in den Erscheinungen des Pflanzen- und Thierlebens; in dem Verhalten unsers Weltkörpers zu dem umgebenden Planetensystem zur Begründung einer wissenschaftlichen Physiologie.* Giessen: C. G. Müller, 1819, pp. 296-320.
/CHROMATICS/RESEARCH: CHROMATICS /NATUR-PHILOSOPHIE

1820-1 [**Goethe**, J. W. von.] "Ein paar Worte aus Goethes Morphologie." *Morgenblatt für gebildete Stände*, 14, 4 May 1820, 430-31.
/EDITION

1820-2 **Goethe**[, J. W. von]. *Zur Naturwissenschaft überhaupt, besonders zur Morphologie. Erfahrung, Beobachtung, Folgerung, durch Lebensereignisse verbunden. Ersten Bandes, zweytes Heft.* Stuttgard[t]/Tübingen: J. G. Cotta'sche Buchhandlung, 1820. [97-256; 25-96] pp.
/EDITION

1820-3 **Goethe**[, J. W. von]. *Zur Naturwissenschaft überhaupt, besonders zur Morphologie. Erfahrung, Beobachtung, Folgerung, durch Lebensereignisse verbunden. Ersten Bandes drittes Heft.* Stuttgard[t]/Tübingen: J. G. Cotta'sche Buchhandlung, 1820. [257-304; 97-240] pp.
/EDITION

1820-4 **Nees von Esenbeck**, C[hristian] G[ottfried]. *Handbuch der Botanik.* 2 vols. Nürnberg: Johann Leonhard Schrag, 1820-1821. xxx, 725 pp.; vi, 691 pp.
Dedicated to Goethe.
/RESEARCH: BOTANY/RESEARCH: MORPHOLOGY

1820-5 *****Weber**, M[oritz]. I[gnaz]. *Grundlinien der Osteologie und Syndesmologie des Menschen: Zu den Vorlesungen entworfen.* Bonn: Weber, 1820. viii, 242 pp.
Rev. Lorenz Oken, *Isis oder Encyclopädische Zeitung von Oken*, No. 5, 1824, cols. 554-5.
/RESEARCH: OSTEOLOGY/OKEN, L

1821-1 **Bojanus**[, Ludwig (von)]. "Abermals ein Wort zur Deutung der Kopfknochen. (Ein Schreiben an den Herausgeber der Isis, von Bojanus, Wilna, im Juli 1821)." *Isis oder Encyclopädische Zeitung von Oken*, No. 12, 1821, cols. 1145-67.
/RESEARCH: OSTEOLOGY

1821-2 **Burdach**, Karl Friedrich. *Nachträge zur Morphologie des Kopfs. Berichte von der Königlichen anatomischen Anstalt zu Königsberg*, 4 (1821), 8-63.
/RESEARCH: OSTEOLOGY

1821-3 **Ch[oulant**, Ludwig?]. "[Review of:] Zur Naturwissenschaft überhaupt . . . Ersten Bandes drittes Heft." *Allgemeine Medizinische*

Annalen des neunzehnten Jahrhunderts auf das Jahr 1821, No. 5
(1821), cols. 668-70.
Review of No. 1817-6.
/REVIEW

1821-4 **Kastner**, Carl Wilhelm. "Von den Farben." In his *Grundriss der Experimentalphysik*. 2 vols. 2nd rev. and exp. edn. Heidelberg: Mohr und Winter, 1821, pp. 457-508.
/RESEARCH: CHROMATICS/CHROMATICS

1821-5 **Keferstein**, Christian, ed. *Teutschland, geognostisch-geologisch dargestellt, mit Charten und Durchschnittszeichnungen erläutert. Eine Zeitschrift in freien Heften*. Vol. I. Weimar: Verlag des Landes-Industrie-Comptoirs, 1821. xiv, 156 pp.
Dedicated to Goethe.
/RESEARCH: GEOLOGY

1821-6 **[Nees von Esenbeck**, Christian Gottfried.] "Fliegendes Blättchen." *Flora oder Botanische Zeitung*, 4, No. 2 (1821), 633.
/RESEARCH: BOTANY/RESEARCH: MORPHOLOGY

1821-7 **Nees von Esenbeck**, Christian Gottfried. "Ueber Henschels Schrift von der Sexualität der Pflanzen. Breslau 1820. Aus Briefen." *Flora oder Botanische Zeitung*, 4 (1821), 1-44.
Review of No. 1817-6.
/HENSCHEL, G/RESEARCH: BOTANY/BOTANY/REVIEW

1821-8 **Runge**, [Friedl.] Ferdinand. "Beurtheilungen der Leistungen von 1. Göthe. §. 55." In his *Neueste Phytochemische Entdeckungen zur Begründung einer wissenschaftlichen Phytochemie*. Berlin: G. Reimer, 1821, pp. 87-9.
/BOTANY/MORPHOLOGY

1821-9 **Schütz**, Wilhelm von. *Zur intellectuellen und substantiellen Morphologie, mit Rücksicht auf die Schöpfung und das Entstehen der Erde*. 3 Hefte. Leipzig: Brockhaus, 1821-1823.
/RESEARCH: MORPHOLOGY/RESEARCH: CHROMATICS

1821-10 **Steffens**, Henrik. "Ueber die Bedeutung der Farben in der Natur." In his *Schriften von Henrich Steffens. Alt und Neu*. 2 vols. Breslau: Verlag von Josef Max, 1821, 5-35.
Partial rpt. of No. 1810-10.
/RESEARCH: CHROMATICS/FINE ARTS

1821-11 **Voigt**, F[riedrich]. S[iegmund]. "Vorläufige Nachricht von den Pflanzen der Melville-Insel, einer von Captain Perry im vorigen Sommer bei der Nordpol-Expedition entdeckten Insel." *Flora oder Botanische Zeitung*, 4 (1821), 201-3.
/RESEARCH: BIOLOGY/RESEARCH: MORPHOLOGY

1821-12 **Wilbrand**[, Johann Bernhard] and [Ferdinand] **Ritgen**. *Gemälde der organischen Natur in ihrer Verbreitung auf der Erde*. Giessen: C. G. Müller, 1821. 128 pp.
Accompanied by four separate plates.
Dedicated to Goethe.
/RESEARCH: GEOGRAPHY/RESEARCH: BIOLOGY

1822-1 **Arendt**, Eduardus [Eduard]. "De capitis ossei Esocis Lucii structura singulari." Diss. Regensburg. Regiomontani [Regensburg]: Typis academicis Hartungianis, 1822. 26 pp.
/RESEARCH: OSTEOLOGY

1822-2 **A[rni]m**[, Achim von]. "[Review of:] *Aus meinem Leben. Von Göthe. II. Abth. V. Th. Auch ich in der Champagne*. Stuttgart. Cotta'sche Buchh. 1822. . ." *Morgenblatt für gebildete Stände [Literatur-Blatt]*, No. 196, 16 August 1822, pp. 261-4.
/GENERAL INTRODUCTION/CHROMATICS

1822-3 **Bronn**, Henr. Georg. [Heinrich Georg]. *De formis plantarum leguminosarum primitivis et derivatis*. [Heidelberg]: Caroli Groos, 1822. 140 pp.
/RESEARCH: BOTANY

1822-4 **[Goethe**, J. W. von.] "Betrachtungen." *Morgenblatt für gebildete Stände*, 16, 21 August 1822, 797-8.
/EDITION

1822-5 **[Goethe**, J. W. von.] "Erlauchter Gegner aller Vulkanität!. . ." In *Wunsch für Herrn Direktor Lenz, zu Seinem Jubiläum den 25ten October 1822*. Jena: Karl Wilhelm Theodor Joch, 1822, p. 5.
/EDITION

1822-6 ***Goethe**, J. W. von. "Morphologie (Auszüge)." *Morgenblatt für gebildete Stände*, 1, No. 4 (1822).
/EDITION

1822-7 **Goethe**[, J. W. von]. *Zur Naturwissenschaft überhaupt, besonders zur Morphologie. Erfahrung, Beobachtung, Folgerung, durch*

Lebensereignisse verbunden. Ersten Bandes viertes Heft.
Stuttgard[t]/Tübingen: J. G. Cotta'sche Buchhandlung, 1822. [305-
68; 241-384] pp.
/EDITION

1822-8 **Heinroth**, Joh[ann]. Christian August. *Lehrbuch der
Anthropologie. Zum Behuf academischer Vorträge, und zum Privat-
studium. Nebst einem Anhange erläuternder und beweisführender
Aufsätze.* Leipzig: Friedr. Christ. Wilh. Vogel, 1822.
/ R E S E A R C H : A N T H R O P O L O G Y / M E T H -
OD/NATURPHILOSOPHIE

1822-9 **Henning**, Leopold von. *Einleitung zu öffentlichen Vorlesungen
über Göthe's Farbenlehre gehalten an der Königl. Universität zu Berlin.* Berlin: Duncker und Humblot, 1822. xii, 49 pp.
/CHROMATICS

1822-10 **Saint-Hilaire**, Geoffroy Étienne de. "Considérations générales
sur la vertèbre." *Mémoires du Muséum d'Histoire Naturelle*, 9
(1822), 89-119.
/RESEARCH: OSTEOLOGY

1822-11 **Schelver**, Franz Joseph. *Lebens- und Formengeschichte der
Pflanzenwelt: Handbuch seiner Vorlesungen über die physiologische
Botanik für seine Zuhörer und gebildete Naturfreunde.* Vol. I.
Heidelberg: Joseph Engelmann, 1822. xii, 269 pp.
Dedicated to Goethe.
/RESEARCH: BOTANY

1822-12 **Schultes**, Joseph August. "Ueber botanische Gärten in Sachsen
und Preußen." *Flora oder botanische Zeitung*, 5, Vol. 1 (1822), 129-
60.
"Vorgelesen in der am 10. November zu Regensburg gehaltenen
Sitzung der k. botanischen Gesellschaft von J. A. Schultes, M.
D. k. baier. Hofrathe und Professor."
/BOTANY

1823-1 **[Goethe**, J. W. von.] "Aelteres, beynahe Veraltetes." *Morgenblatt für gebildete Stände*, No. 230, 25 September 1823, 919.
/EDITION

1823-2 **Göthe [Goethe**, J. W. von]. "Ein Gelegenheits-Gedicht von
Göthe." *Mosella, eine Monatsschrift*, 3 (1823), 281-367 [376].
/EDITION

1823-3 [**Goethe**, J. W. von.] "Eins und Alles." *Morgenblatt für gebildete Stände*, No. 229, 24 September 1823, 913.
/EDITION

1823-4 **Goethe**[, J. W. von]. *Zur Naturwissenschaft überhaupt, besonders zur Morphologie. Erfahrung, Beobachtung, Folgerung, durch Lebensereignisse verbunden. Zweyten Bandes erstes Heft.* Stuttgard[t]/Tübingen: J. G. Cotta'sche Buchhandlung, 1823. 64; 124 pp.
/EDITION

1823-5 **Loder**, Justus [Christian von]. *Osteologia. Syndesmologia. Myologia.* Vol. I of his *Elementa Anatomiae Humani Corporis.* [Moscow/Riga/Dorpat]: C. Joh. [Gottfried] Hartmann/[Leipzig]: Hirschfeld, 1823. xii, 572 pp.
Dedicated to Goethe.
/RESEARCH: ANATOMY

1823-6 **Meyer**, Ernst [H. F.]. "Erwiederung." In *Zur Morphologie. Von Goethe*, 2, No. 1, 1823, 31-45.
Repsonse to Goethe's essay "Probleme" in the same vol.
/MORPHOLOGY

1823-7 **Meyer**, Nikolaus. "An Goethe. Zur Feier seines Geburtstages- und Genesungsfestes am 28sten August 1823. -- Mit einigen Flaschen des ältesten Weines aus der Rose des Rathskellers zu Bremen, gelagert 1624." Minden: Georg Wilhelm Eßmann[, 1823]. 7 pp.
/MEYER, N/MEDICINE

1823-8 **Naumann**, Moritz Ernst Adolph. *Ueber die Grenzen zwischen Philosophie und Naturwissenschaften.* Leipzig: Adolph Wienbrack, 1823. x, 265 pp.
Dedicated to Goethe.
/NATURPHILOSOPHIE/RESEARCH: PHILOSOPHY

1823-9 [**Nees von Esenbeck**, Christian Gottfried, Johann Jacob **Noegge- rath**, and ?.] "[Review of:] Stuttgart u. Tübingen, b. Cotta: Zur Naturwissenschaft überhaupt, [etc.]. Ersten Bandes 1-4 Heft. [Etc.] (Von drey Recensenten.)" *Jenaische Allgemeine Literatur-Zeitung*, No. 101, 1823, cols. 321-8; No. 102, 1823, cols. 329-36; No. 103, 1823, cols. 337-44; No. 104, 1823, cols. 345-52; No. 105, 1823, cols. 353-60; No. 106, 1823, cols. 361-8; No. 107, 1823, cols. 369- 76; No. 108, 1823, cols. 377-83.

Review of No. 1817-6.
/REVIEW

1823-10 **Purkinje [Purkyne]**, Johann [Jan]. *Beobachtungen und Versuche zur Physiologie der Sinne. Erstes Bändchen. Beiträge zur Kenntniss des Sehens in subjectiver Hinsicht.* 2nd edn. Prag: In Commission bei Gottfried Calve, 1819. 176 pp.
Rpt. of No. 1819-12.
New title only; otherwise unrevised.
/RESEARCH: SENSORY PHYSIOLOGY/RESEARCH: CHROMATICS

1823-11 **Schultz [Schultzenstein]**, Carl Heinrich. "Goethes Darstellung." In his *Das Leben des Individuums.* Part I of *Die Natur der lebendigen Pflanze. Erweiterung und Bereicherung der Entdeckungen des Kreislaufs im Zusammenhange mit dem ganzen Pflanzenleben nach einer neuen Methode dargestellt.* Berlin: G. Reimer, 1823, § 125, pp. 287-9.
/RESEARCH: BOTANY/RESEARCH: MORPHOLOGY

1823-12 **Schultz [Schultzenstein]**, Carl Heinrich. "Metamorphosenlehre." In his *Das Leben des Individuums.* Part I of *Die Natur der lebendigen Pflanze. Erweiterung und Bereicherung der Entdeckungen des Kreislaufs im Zusammenhange mit dem ganzen Pflanzenleben nach einer neuen Methode dargestellt.* Berlin: G. Reimer, 1823, §§ 121-6, pp. 287-9.
/BOTANY/MORPHOLOGY

1823-13 **[Schultz**, Christoph Ludwig Friedrich.] "Die subjectiven Höfe." In Goethe, J. W. von. *Zur Naturwissenschaft überhaupt*, 2, No. 1 (1823), pp. 20-38.
Rpt. No. 1853-10.
/RESEARCH: CHROMATICS/CHROMATICS

1823-14 **[Schultz**, Christoph Ludwig Friedrich.] "Ueber physiologe [sic] Farbenerscheinungen, insbesondere das phosphorische Augenlicht, als Quelle derselben, betreffend." In Goethe, J. W. von. *Zur Naturwissenschaft überhaupt*, 2, No. 1 (1823), pp. 20-38.
/RESEARCH: CHROMATICS

1823-15 **Voigt**, Friedr[ich]. Siegmund. *System der Natur und ihre Geschichte.* Jena: August Schmid, 1823. xii, 866 pp.
/OSTEOLOGY/RESEARCH: OSTEOLOGY

1824-1 [anon.] "Pyrotechnische Versuche mit niederrheinischem Basalt, nebst Folgerungen." In *Das Gebirge in Rheinland-Westphalen nach mineralogischem und chemischem Bezuge*. Ed. Jakob Nöggerath. Bonn: Eduard Weber, 1824, III, 150-73.
/RESEARCH: GEOLOGY

1824-2 **Ebermaier**, Carolus Henricus [Carl Heinrich]. *Dissertatio inauguralis sistens plantarum papilionacearum monographiam medicam*. Diss. Berlin. Berolini [Berlin]: Formis Bruschckianis, 1824. 108 pp.
/RESEARCH: BOTANY

1824-3 [**Goethe**, J. W. von.] "On the Geognostical Phaenomena at the Temple of Serapis." *The Edinburgh Philosophical Journal*, 11, No. 21 (1824), 91-9.
/TRANSLATION: ENGLISH

1824-4 **Goethe**[, J. W. von]. *Zur Naturwissenschaft überhaupt, besonders zur Morphologie. Erfahrung, Beobachtung, Folgerung, durch Lebensereignisse verbunden. Zweyten Bandes zweytes Heft.* Stuttgard[t]/Tübingen: J. G. Cotta'sche Buchhandlung, 1824. [65-160; 125-220] pp.
/EDITION

1824-5 **Göthe** [**Goethe**, J. W.] v[on]. "Die Wandwolke; eine neue Hauptform der Wolke beobachtet und beschrieben von dem Großh. S. W. Minister v. Göthe." *Archiv für die gesammte Naturlehre*, 3, No. 4 (1824), 385-500.
/EDITION

1824-6 **Goethe**[, J. W. von]. "Zur vergleichenden Osteologie." *Verhandlungen der Kaiserlichen Leopoldinisch-Carolinschen Akademie der Naturforscher*, 12.1 (1824), 323-32.
"Mit Zusaetzen und Bemerkungen von Dr. Ed. D'Alton."
Rev. [No. 1825-8].
/EDITION

1824-7 **Hoppe**, Ernst Friedrich. *Versuch einer ganz neuen Theorie der Entstehung sämmtlicher Farben nebst einer nähern Erläuterung des Sehens und den dazu nöthigen Eigenschaften des Lichts für Liebhaber der Naturkunde.* Breslau: Joh. Friedr. Korn d. ält., 1824. xvi, 230 pp.
/RESEARCH: CHROMATICS

1824-8 **Link**, Heinrich Friedrich. *Elementa philosophiae botanicae.*
Berolini [Berlin]: Haude & Spener, 1824. 486 pp.
/RESEARCH: BOTANY

1824-9 **Nöggerath**, Jakob. "Beilage vom Herausgeber [to: Becher, J. P.
"Ueber die Entdeckung von Kunst-Produkten in der Braunkohlen-
Formation auf dem hohen Westerwalde und in Böhmen."]." In *Das
Gebirge in Rheinland-Westphalen nach mineralogischem und
chemischem Bezuge.* Ed. Jakob Nöggerath. Bonn: Eduard Weber,
1824, III, 181-4.
/GEOLOGY/MINERALOGY

1824-10 **[Paulus(, ?)]**. "Les't! Les't!" *Der Eil-Bote [Coblenz]*, No. 197,
9 December 1824, 896.
Review of No. 1817-6.
/REVIEW

1824-11 ***Purkyne**, J[ohann]. E[vangelista]. "Versuche über die
Schwingungen des Wassers auf gestrichenen horizontalen
Glasscheiben." *Übersicht d. Arb. im Jahre 1824 (25). Schl. Probl. 3
Bull. 3. St.*, March 1824, p. 249.
/RESEARCH: HYDROLOGY/CHLADNI, E

1824-12 **Saint-Hilaire**, Geoffroy Étienne de. "Composition de la tête
osseuse de l'homme et des animaux." *Annales des sciences
naturelles*, 3 (1824), 173-92; 245-99.
Cf. No. 1824-13.
/RESEARCH: OSTEOLOGY

1824-13 **Saint-Hilaire**, Geoffroy Étienne de. "Composition de la tête
osseuse de l'homme et des animaux, trouvée semblable en nombre,
connexions et application usuelle de ses parties." *Annales des
sciences naturelles: Aslas des tomes 1, 2, 3*, 3 (1824), 43-5.
Cf. No. 1822-12.
/RESEARCH: OSTEOLOGY

1824-14 **[Straus(, ?)]**. "Remarque sur l'ostéologie comparée." *Bulletin
des sciences naturelles et de géologie*, No. 2, February 1826, 240.
Review of No. 1817-6.
/REVIEW/COMPARATIVE ANATOMY/RECEPTION

1824-15 **Weber**, M[oritz]. I[gnaz]. *Handbuch der vergleichenden
Osteologie. Anatomie, physiologisch, philosophisch und
geschichtlich-kritisch bearbeitet.* Bonn: Eduard Weber, 1824. xvi,

293 pp.
/RESEARCH: OSTEOLOGY

1825-1 **Hoff**[, Karl Ernst Adolf] v[on]. *Bemerkungen über Karlsbad.*
Archiv für die gesammte Naturlehre, 6 (1825), 103-44; 221-4.
Rpt. of No. 1825-2.
/RESEARCH: GEOLOGY

1825-2 **Hoff**, K[arl]. E[rnst]. A[dolf]. von. *Geognostische Bemerkungen*
über Karlsbad. Gotha: bey Justus Perthes, 1825. iv, 99 pp.
Rpt. No. 1825-1.
/RESEARCH: GEOLOGY

1825-3 **Müller**[, Christian Heinrich]. "Darstellung der Gegenstände, die
in den Sitzungen der Naturwissenschaftlichen Section im Jahre 1825
zur Sprache gebracht wurden." In *Uebersicht der Arbeiten und*
Veränderungen der schlesischen Gesellschaft für vaterländische
Cultur im Jahre 1825. Breslau: Graß, Barth und Comp., 1826, pp.
21-41.
/CHEMISTRY/RESEARCH: CHEMISTRY

1825-4 **Müller**[, Christian Heinrich]. "Dr. Müller's Bemerkung über
angeblich durch Wirkung des Blitzes entstandene verkohlte
Holzspähnekugeln." *Archiv für die gesammte Naturlehre*, 6 (1825),
479.
/CHEMISTRY/RESEARCH: CHEMISTRY

1825-5 **Müller**[, Christian Heinrich]. In "Siebentes Bülletin der naturwissenschaftlichen Section der schlesischen Gesellschaft für
vaterländische Cultur im Jahre 1825." *Außerordentliche Beilage zu*
No. 135. der Neuen Breslauer Zeitung, 27 August 1825, 23-6.
/CHEMISTRY/RESEARCH: CHEMISTRY

1825-6 **Nasse**, Friedrich. "Ueber das Physiologische in der Färbung der
Menschenracen." *Zeitschrift für die Anthropologie*, No. 2 (1825),
270-90.
/CHROMATICS/RESEARCH: CHROMATICS

1825-7 **Nasse**, Friedrich et al., eds. *Zeitschrift für die Anthropologie*,
Nos. 1 and 2, 1825. 192 pp.; 192 pp.
Dedicated to Goethe.
/RESEARCH: ANTHROPOLOGY

1825-8 **[Oken**, Lorenz?]. "[Review of:] Zur vergleichenden Osteologie v.

Goethe, mit Zusätzen und Bemerkungen von Dalton." *Isis von Oken*, No. 2, 1825, col. 203.
>Review of No. 1824-6.
>/REVIEW/OSTEOLOGY/COMPARATIVE ANATOMY/RECEPTION

1825-9 **Purkinje [Purkyne]**, Johann [Jan]. *Neue Beiträge zur Kenntniß des Sehens in subjectiver Hinsicht.* Vol. 2 of *Beobachtungen und Versuche zur Physiologie der Sinne.* Zweites Bändchen. Berlin: G. Reimer, 1825. viii, 192 pp.
>Rpt. of No. 1819-12.
>Dedicated to Goethe.
>/RESEARCH: SENSORY PHYSIOLOGY/RESEARCH: CHROMATICS

1825-10 *****Purkyne**, J[ohann]. E[vangelista]. "Über die Fortpflanzung der Klangfiguren in der Luft." *Beilage der Breslauer Zeitung*, No. 42, 14 March 1825, 2nd bulletin.
>/RESEARCH: ACOUSTICS/CHLADNI, E

1825-11 **Sternberg**, Graf Kaspar von. "Versuch einer geognostisch-botanischen Darstellung der Flora der Vorwelt." Viertes Heft. Regensburg: Christoph Ernst Brenck's Wittwe[, 1825]. xlii, 48 pp.
>Trans. into French, No. 1826-12.
>/RESEARCH: BOTANY

1826-1 **[anon.]** [Untitled.] *Flora oder botanische Zeitung*, 9 (1826), 448.
>/BOTANY/MORPHOLOGY

1826-2 **Carus**, C[arl]. G[ustav]. "Von dem Unterschiede zwischen descriptiver, geschichtlicher, vergleichender und philosophischer Anatomie, von der Entwickelung dieser einzelnen Methoden in verschiedenen Zeitaltern, und von der zweckmäßigsten Aufeinanderfolge im Studium dieser verschiedenen Methoden." *Litterarische Annalen der gesammten Heilkunde*, 4 (1826), 1-30.
>/RESEARCH: OSTEOLOGY

1826-3 **C[otta**, Heinrich von]. "Beytrag zur Untersuchung über die Entstehung des Kammerbühls bey Eger." *Isis oder Encyclopädische Zeitung von Oken*, 20, 1826, cols. 324-9.
>In "Versammlung der deutschen Naturforscher und Aerzte zu Dresden, vom 18ten bis 23ten September 1826."
>/RESEARCH: GEOLOGY/GEOLOGY

1826-4 **Fischer**, Ernst Gottfried. "Über die sogenannten zufälligen Farben, die Hr. v. Göthe recht schicklich physiologische nennt." In his *Lehrbuch der mechanischen Naturlehre. Zweiter Theil, welcher die Lehre von der Elektricität, von der magnetischen Kraft und von dem Lichte enthält.* 3rd rev. and exp. edn. Berlin/Leipzig: C. G. Nauck's Buchhandlung, 1819, §§ 28-30, pp. 331-4.
> Rpt. of No. 1819-6.
> Not in 1st edn. of 1801.
> /RESEARCH: CHROMATICS/CHROMATICS

1826-5 **Gmelin**, F[erdinand]. G[ottlob]. "Beiträge zur Kenntniss der Metamorphose der Gewächse, vornehmlich in Hinsicht ihrer innern und äussern Bedingungen." *Naturwissenschaftliche Abhandlungen*, 1, No. 1 (1826), 73-132.
> Continuation No. 1827-8.
> /BOTANY/MORPHOLOGY

1826-6 **[Goethe**, J. W. von.] "Göthe's Ideen über die Natur." In *Göthe's Philosophie. Eine vollständige, systematisch geordnete Zusammenstellung seiner Ideen über Leben, Liebe, Ehe, Freundschaft, Erziehung, Religion, Moral, Politik, Literatur, Kunst und Natur; aus seinen sämmtlichen poetischen und wissenschaftlichen Werken.* Ed. Friedrich Karl Julius Schütz. 7 vols. Hamburg: Verlag von Friedrich Hermann Nestler, 1826, pp. 233-306.
> /EDITION: SELECTIONS/NATURPHILOSOPHIE

1826-7 **Humboldt**, Alexander von. "Ideen zu einer Physiognomik der Gewächse." In his *Ansichten der Natur, mit wissenschaftlichen Erläuterungen.* 2 vols. 2nd rev. and exp. edn. Stuttgart/Tübingen: J. G. Cotta'sche Buchhandlung, 1826, II, 1-125.
> Rpt. of No. 1806-5.
> Dedicated to Goethe.
> /RESEARCH: BOTANY

1826-8 **Keferstein**[, Christian]. "Verzeichniß der Mineraliensammlungen in Teutschland." *Zeitung für Geognosie, Geologie und innere Naturgeschichte der Erde*, 1826, pp. 107-39.
> Goethe, p. 123.
> /GOETHE'S COLLECTIONS

1826-9 **Müller**, Johannes. *Ueber die phantastischen Gesichtserscheinungen. Eine physiologische Untersuchung mit einer physiologischen Urkunde des Aristoteles über den Traum.* Coblenz: Jacob Hölscher, 1826. x, 117 pp.

Rpt. No. 1927-41.
/RESEARCH: CHROMATICS/RESEARCH: PHYSIOLOGY

1826-10 **Müller**, Johannes. *Zur vergleichenden Physiologie des Gesichtsinnes des Menschen und der Thiere nebst einem Versuch über die Bewegungen der Augen und über den menschlichen Blick.* Leipzig: C. Cnobloch, 1826. xxxii, 462 pp.
Cf. esp. "Fragmente zur Farbenlehre, insbesondere zur Goetheschen Farbenlehre," pp. 391-434."
/RESEARCH: CHROMATICS/RESEARCH: SENSORY PHYSIOLOGY/NATURPHILOSOPHIE

1826-11 *****Oken**, Lorenz. "Die farbigen Schatten, ihr Entstehen und Gesetz von Heinrich Zschokke. (Rezension.)" *Isis oder Encyclopädische Zeitung von Oken*, No. 8, 1826, cols. 775-6.
Rpt. No. 1922-29.
"Vorlesung, gehalten in der Naturforschenden Gesellschaft zu Aarau 1826. Bei Sauerländer."
/REVIEW/ZSCHOKKE, H/RESEARCH: CHROMATICS/CHROMATICS

1826-12 **Sternberg**, Comte Gaspard [Graf Kaspar von]. *Essai d'un exposé géognostico-botanique de la flore du monde primitif.* Trans. Comte de Bray. quatrième cahier. Ratisbonne: veuve de Christophe Ernest Brenck, 1826. 53, xli pp.
French trans. of No. 1825-11.
/RESEARCH: BOTANY

1826-13 **Zschokke**, [J.] Heinrich [D.]. *Die farbigen Schatten, ihr Entstehen und Gesetz.* Aarau: Heinrich Remigius Sauerlaender[, 1826]. 61 pp.
/RESEARCH: CHROMATICS

1827-1 **B[randes**, Heinrich Wilhelm]. "Farbe." In *Johann Samuel Traugott Gehler's Physikalisches Wörterbuch.* Revised by Brandes et al. Leipzig: E. B. Schwickert, 1827, IV, 39-131.
/CHROMATICS/NEWTON, I

1827-2 **Candolle**, Aug[ustin].-Pyr[amus]. de. "Conclusions et Considérations générales sur la Structure des fleurs." In his *Organographie végétale, ou description raisonée des organes des plantes, pour servir de suite et de développement à la théorie élémentaire de la botanique, et d'introduction à la physiologie végétale et à la description des familles.* Vol. I of his *Cours de Botanique.* Paris: Deterville, 1827,

pp. 547-58.
Trans. into German, No. 1828-5.
/RESEARCH: BOTANY

1827-3 **Candolle**, Aug[ustin].-Pyr[amus]. de. "De la Symétrie végétale."
In his *Organographie végétale, ou description raisonée des organes
des plantes, pour servir de suite et de développement à la théorie
élémentaire de la botanique, et d'introduction à la physiologie
végétale et à la description des familles.* Vol. I of his *Cours de
Botanique.* Paris: Deterville, 1827, pp. 236-44.
Trans. into German, No. 1828-6.
Rev. No. 1829-16.
/RESEARCH: BOTANY

1827-4 **Carus**, Carl Gustav. "Tagebuch einer Reise nach Genua.
Manuskript für Freunde. Vom Professor Dr. C. G. Carus. Erstes
Fragment. Weimar -- Gotha." *Dresdner Morgen-Zeitung*, No. 57, 9
April 1827, cols. 449-56.
"Bericht über den Besuch bei Goethe, 21. Juli 1821."
/CARUS, C

1827-5 **Carus**, C[arl]. G[ustav]. "Von der Skeletbildung im Allgemeinen
und insbesondere von der nothwendigen Unterscheidung eines
Hautskelets. Eingeweideskelets und eines eigentlichen oder Nerven-
skelets." *Isis von Oken*, 20, No. 2 (1827), cols. 185-99.
/RESEARCH: OSTEOLOGY

1827-6 **Cramer**, Ludwig Wilhelm. *Geognostische Fragmente von
Dillenburg und der umliegenden Gegend.* Giessen: in Commission
bei Georg Friedrich Heyer, 1827. 118 pp.
Dedicated to Goethe.
/RESEARCH: GEOLOGY

1827-7 **Ficinus**[, Heinrich]. "Die entoptische Erscheinung objectiv und
im Kleinen dargestellt." *Archiv für die gesammte Naturlehre*, 10
(1827), 257-60.
/RESEARCH: CHROMATICS/SEEBECK, T

1827-8 **Gmelin**, Ferdinand Gottlob. "Beiträge zur Kenntniss der
Metamorphose der Gewächse, vornehmlich in Hinsicht ihrer innern
und äussern Bedingungen." *Naturwissenschaftliche Abhandlungen*, 1,
No. 2 (1827), 271-306.
Continuation of No. 1826-5.
/BOTANY/MORPHOLOGY

1827-9 **Göthe [Goethe**, J. W. von]. "Beschreibung der karlsbader müllerischen Steinsammlung. Zur Kenntniß der böhmischen Gebirge." Karlsbad: Johanna Franieck & Sohn[, 1827]. 32 pp.
/EDITION

1827-10 **Hegel**, Georg Wilhelm Friedrich. *Encyclopädie der philosophischen Wissenschaften im Grundrisse. Zum Gebrauch seiner Vorlesungen.* 2nd edn. Heidelberg: Druck und Verlag von August Oßwald, 1827. xlii, 544 pp.
Rpt. of No. 1817-7.
/CHROMATICS/NATURPHILOSOPHIE/NEWTON, I

1827-11 **[Meyer**, Ernst H. F.] "Der Pflanzenfreund aus der Ferne, mit dem Bilde einer Einsiedeley." In *Ueber Kunst und Alterthum* [ed. Goethe], 6, No. 1 (1827), 112-13.
/RESEARCH: BOTANY

1827-12 **Voigt**, F[riedrich]. S[iegmund]., ed. *Lehrbuch der Botanik.* 2nd rev. edn. Jena: August Schmid, 1827. x, 485 pp.
Rpt. of No. 1808-12.
/RESEARCH: BOTANY/RESEARCH: MORPHOLOGY

1828-1 *[anon.] "Randglossen zur Farbenlehre von Goethe. Die physiologischen Farben. *Wegweiser Künste und Wissenschaften*, No. 37, 7 May 1828, 145-6. (Beil. z. Dresdner Abend-Ztg.)
/CHROMATICS

1828-2 **[anon.]** "Ein Urteil Alexander von Humboldts über Goethe als Naturforscher." *Berliner Conversations-Blatt*, 2 (1828), 513-14. (5 July, Heft 130).
/GENERAL INTRODUCTION

1828-3 **Agardh**, Carl Adolf. *Essai de réduire la physiologie végétale à des principes fondamentaux.* Lund: C. F. Berling, [1828]. 56 pp.
/RESEARCH: BOTANY/RESEARCH: MORPHOLOGY
/BOTANY/MORPHOLOGY

1828-4 **Busse**, Friedr[ich]. Gottlieb v[on]. *Metaphysische Anfangsgründe der Naturwissenschaft von Immanuel Kant in ihren Gründen widerlegt.* Dresden/Leipzig: in der Arnoldischen Buchhandlung, 1828. xv, 166 pp.
Dedicated to Goethe.
/KANT, I/NATURPHILOSOPHIE

1828-5 **Candolle**, August[in]. Pyramus de. "Allgemeine Schlüsse und Betrachtungen über den Bau der Blumen." In *August Pyramus De Candolle's Organographie der Gewächse oder kritische Beschreibung der Pflanzen-Organe. Eine Fortsetzung und Entwicklung der Anfangsgründe der Botanik und Einleitung zur Pflanzen-Physiologie und der Beschreibung der Familien.* Vol. I of his *A. P. De Candolle's Vorlesungen über die Botanik.* Trans. and notes Carl Friedrich Meisner. Stuttgart/Tübingen: J. G. Cotta'sche Buchhandlung, 1828, pp. 482-91.
German trans. of No. 1827-2.
/RESEARCH: BOTANY

1828-6 **Candolle**, August[in]. Pyramus de. "Von der vegetabilischen Symmetrie." In *August Pyramus De Candolle's Organographie der Gewächse oder kritische Beschreibung der Pflanzen-Organe. Eine Fortsetzung und Entwicklung der Anfangsgründe der Botanik und Einleitung zur Pflanzen-Physiologie und der Beschreibung der Familien.* Vol. I of his *A. P. De Candolle's Vorlesungen über die Botanik.* Trans. and notes Carl Friedrich Meisner. Stuttgart/Tübingen: J. G. Cotta'sche Buchhandlung, 1828, pp. 206-13.
German trans. of No. 1827-3.
/RESEARCH: BOTANY

1828-7 **Carus**, Karl Gustav. *Grundzüge der vergleichenden Anatomie und Physiologie.* Allgemeine Taschenbibliothek der Naturwissenschaften, 4. 4 vols. Dresden: P. G. Hilschersche Buchhandlung, 1828.
/RESEARCH: ANATOMY/RESEARCH: PHYSIOLOGY
/RESEARCH: OSTEOLOGY

1828-8 **Carus**, Carl Gustav. *Von den Ur-Theilen des Knochen- und Schalen-Gerüstes.* Leipzig: Gerh. Fleischer, 1828. xvi, 186 pp., 12 plates
Rev. Lorenz Oken, *Isis oder Encyclopädische Zeitung von Oken*, 22, No. 5 (1829), cols. 552-4.
/RESEARCH: OSTEOLOGY/OKEN, L

1828-9 **Cruse**, Guilelmus [Wilhelm]. "De Asparagi officinalis L. germinatione." Diss. Regensburg. Regiomonti [Regensburg]: typis academicis Hartungianis, 1828. viii, 34 pp.
/RESEARCH: BOTANY

1828-10 **Ficinus**[, Heinrich]. *Optik oder Versuch eines folgerechten Umrisses der gesammten Lehre vom Licht, wie sie dem gegenwärtigen*

Stande unsrer physiologischen und physikalischen Kentnisse angemessen ist. Dresden: P. G. Hilschersche Buchhandlung, 1828. 185, iv pp.
  Rpt. No. 1841-5.
  /RESEARCH: OPTICS/RESEARCH: CHROMATICS

1828-11 **H[enning**, Leopold]. v[on]. "Randglossen zur Farbenlehre von Göthe." *Wegweiser im Gebiete der Künste und Wissenschaften [Abend-Zeitung auf das Jahr 1828]*, 37, 7 May 1828, 145-6.
  /CHROMATICS

1828-12 **Humboldt**, Alexander von. "Ein Urtheil Alexander von Humboldt's über Göthe als Naturforscher." *Berliner Conversations-Blatt für Poesie, Literatur und Kritik*, No. 130, 5 July 1828, 513-4.
  /RECEPTION/BOTANY/GEOLOGY/CHROMATICS

1828-13 **Keferstein**, Christian. "Joh. Wolfg. v. Göthe." In "Chronologische Uebersicht der Geburts- und Sterbejahre derjenigen Naturforscher, welche auf die Ausbildung der Mineralogie eingewirkt haben." *Zeitung für Geognosie, Geologie und Naturgeschichte des Innern der Erde*, 7 (1828), 57.
  /MINERALOGY

1828-14 **Reichenbach**, Heinrich Gottl. Ludwig. *Botanik für Damen, Künstler und Freunde der Pflanzenwelt überhaupt, enthaltend eine Darstellung des Pflanzenreiches in seiner Metamorphose, eine Anleitung zum Studium der Wissenschaft, und zum Anlegen von Herbarien. Ein Versuch.* Leipzig: Carl Cnobloch, 1828.
  /RESEARCH: BOTANY

1828-15 **Schultz [Schultzenstein]**, Carl Heinrich. *Die Fortpflanzung und Ernährung der Pflanzen im Zusammenhange mit dem ganzen Pflanzenleben und mit Rücksicht auf die Culturgesetze nach einer natürlichen Methode dargestellt.* Part II of *Die Natur der lebendigen Pflanzen. Erweiterung und Bereicherung der Entdeckungen der Cyklose im Zusammenhange mit dem ganzen Pflanzenleben nach einer neuen Methode dargestellt.* Stuttgart/Tübingen: J. G. Cotta'sche Buchhandlung, 1828. xvi, 624 pp.
  /RESEARCH: BOTANY/RESEARCH: MORPHOLOGY

1828-16 **Sternberg**, Graf Kaspar von. *Anthericum comosum. Eine neue Pflanzen-Species. Monatsschrift der Gesellschaft des vaterländischen Museums in Böhmen*, 2 (1828), 336-9.
  /RESEARCH: BOTANY

1828-17 **Weber**, M[oritz]. I[gnaz]. "Ueber die Zwischenkieferknochen des Menschen und über die Entstehung des gespaltenen Gaumens (Wolfsrachen)." In *Notizen aus dem Gebiete de Natur- und Heilkunde*. Ed. Ludwig Friedrich v. Froriep. Erfurt: Lossius, 1828, vol. 19, cols. 281-5.
/RESEARCH: OSTEOLOGY

1829-1 **A[?]**. "Bemerkung über das Colorit in Bezug auf Goethe's Farbenlehre." *Morgenblatt für gebildete Stände*, 23, Kunstblatt No. 5, 15 January 1829, 20; No. 6, 19 January 1829, 23-4.
/CHROMATICS/RESEARCH: CHROMATICS

1829-2 **Agardh**, Carl Adolf. "Öfversigt af vextmetamorfosen." In *Lärobok i Botanik*. Malmö: N. H. Thomsons Boktryckeri, 1829-1830, pp. 389-416.
In Swedish.
Trans. into German, No. 1831-1.
/RESEARCH: BOTANY/RESEARCH: MORPHOLOGY

1829-3 **Candolle**, A[ugustin]. P[yramus]. de. "[Review of:] Essai sur la métamorphose des plantes; par [J]. W. de Goethe." *Bibliotheque Universelle, des sciences, belles-lettres et arts*, 14, No. 60 (1829), 262-3.
Review of No. 1829-8.
/REVIEW/BOTANY/MORPHOLOGY/RECEPTION

1829-4 **[Carus**, Carl Gustav.] "Versammlung der Flora, am 28. August 1829." *Mittheilungen aus dem Gebiete der Flora und Pomona*, No. 15 (1829), 57-60; No. 16 (1829), 61-4.
/BOTANY/MORPHOLOGY

1829-5 **C[otta**, Heinrich von]. "Beytrag zur Untersuchung über die Entstehung des Kammerbühls bey Eger." *Monatschrift der Gesellschaft des vaterländischen Museums in Böhmen*, 3 (1829), 321-9.
In "Versammlung der deutschen Naturforscher und Aerzte zu Dresden, vom 18ten bis 23ten September 1826."
/RESEARCH: GEOLOGY/GEOLOGY

1829-6 **Falkenstein**, Karl. "Ueber Speciesbildung im Allgemeinen, und über den Einfluß des Lichtes und der Nahrung auf den Organismus der Pflanzenwelt." *Mittheilungen aus dem Gebiete der Flora und Pomona*, No. 19 (1829), 74-6; No. 20 (1829), 77.
/BOTANY/MORPHOLOGY

1829-7 **Gingins-Lassaraz**, Frédéric de. "Précis historique et avant-propos du traducteur." In J. W. de Goethe. *Essai sur la métamorphose des plantes.* Trans. Frédéric de Gingins-Lassaraz. Genève: J. Barbezat et Cie., 1829, pp. v-xiv.
/RESEARCH: BOTANY/RESEARCH: MORPHOLOGY

1829-8 **Goethe**, J. W. de [von]. *Essai sur la métamorphose des plantes.* Trans. Frédéric de Gingins-Lassaraz. Genève: J. Barbezat et Cie., 1829. 87 pp.
Rev. [anon.], *Botanische Literatur-Blätter zur periodischen Darstellung der Fortschritte der Pflanzenkunde.* . ., 2 (1829), 348.
Rev. [No. 1829-3].
Rev. [No. 1829-9].
/TRANSLATION: FRENCH

1829-9 **Juss**, A[ntoine Laurent? Adrien?]. de. "[Review of:] Essai sur la métamorphose des plantes; [etc.]." *Bulletin des Sciences Naturelles et de Géologie*, No. 6, June 1829, 422-3.
Review of No. 1829-8.
/REVIEW/BOTANY/MORPHOLOGY/RECEPTION

1829-10 ***Lavaters** Physiognomik.* 4 vols. Wien: Sollinger, 1829.
Rpt. of No. 1776-1.
"Vervollständigte neue Auflage der verkürzt herausgegebenen physiognomischen Fragmente."
/EDITION/PHYSIOGNOMY

1829-11 **Martius**, Carl Fr. Ph. von. "Ueber die Architectonik der Blumen, um die Möglichkeit einer stenographischen Darstellung der Character der Pflanzenfamilien daraus zu entwickeln (½ St.)." *Isis von Oken*, 22 (1829), cols. 333-41.
"Versammlung der Naturforscher und Aerzte zu Berlin, im September 1828."
/RESEARCH: BOTANY/RESEARCH: MORPHOLOGY

1829-12 **Muncke**, G[eorg]. W[ilhelm]. "Subjective Farben." In his *Handbuch der Naturlehre. Erster Theil, welcher die Experimentalphysik enthält.* Heidelberg: Universitäts-Buchhandlung von C. F. Winter, 1829, pp. 641-4.
/RESEARCH: CHROMATICS/CHROMATICS

1829-13 **Oken**[, Lorenz]. "Ueber das Zahlengesetz in den Wirbeln des Menschen (½ St.)." *Isis oder Encyclopädische Zeitung von Oken*, 22, Nos. 3/4 (1829), cols. 306-12.

"Versammlung der Naturforscher und Aerzte zu Berlin, im September 1828."
/RESEARCH: OSTEOLOGY

1829-14 **Purkinje [Purkyne]**, Johann [Jan]. "Über die bisherigen Versuche in der Systematik der Farben." *Drittes Bülletin der naturwissenschaftlichen Section der schlesischen Gesellschaft für vaterländische Cultur im Jahre 1829 [Außerordentliche Beilage zu No. 140. der Breslauer Zeitung]*, 18 June 1829, 12-13.
/CHROMATICS/RESEARCH: CHROMATICS

1829-15 **Roux**, Jakob. *Entdeckungen auf dem Gebiete der physikalischen Farbenlehre.* Pt. III of his *Die Farben.* 3 Hefte. Heidelberg: Universitäts-Buchhandlung von C. F. Winter, 1829. x, 101 pp.
/RESEARCH: CHROMATICS

1829-16 **V[oigt].**, F[riedrich]. S[iegmund]. "[Review of:] Organographie végetale, ou déscription raisonée des organes des plantes, [etc.] Par Mr. Aug. Pyr. Decandolle. Tome I. et II. Paris 1827." *Hermes oder Kritisches Jahrbuch der Literatur*, 32 (1829), 154-64.
Rev. of No. 1827-4.
/CANDOLLE, A DE

1830-1 **Brück**, A[nton]. T[heobald]. "Trinius hielt am 29. Dec. 1828 eine Vorlesung. . ." *Isis von Oken*, 23 (1830), cols. 123-5.
/MORPHOLOGY

1830-2 **Cruse**, Wilhelm. "Ueber den Blüthenbau der Gramineen." *Linnaea. Ein Journal für die Botanik in ihrem ganzen Umfange*, 5 (1830), 299-335.
/RESEARCH: BOTANY

1830-3 **Frank**[, ?]. "Den 17ten Februar [1830] hielt Hr. Dr. Phil. Frank einen Vortrag über die Berührungs-Punkte in der Göthischen Farbenlehre und der Wellentheorie." *Erstes bis Viertes Bülletin der naturwissenschaftlichen Section der schlesischen Gesellschaft für vaterländische Cultur im Jahre 1830 [Außerordentliche Beilage zu No. 115. der Breslauer Zeitung]*, 18 May 1830, p. 2.
Cf. No. 1831-4.
/CHROMATICS/RESEARCH: CHROMATICS

1830-4 **Goethe**[, J. W. von]. "Die ersten Erzeugnisse der Stottenheimer Saline begleitet von einem dichterischen Dialog zwischen den Gnomen, der Geognosie und der Technik." *Musenalmanach auf das Jahr 1830*. Ed. Amadeus Wendt. Leipzig: Weidmannische Buchhandlung G. Reimer, 1830, pp. 1-8.
/EDITION

1830-5 **Goethe**[, J. W. von]. "Principes de Philosophie Zoologique. Discutés en Mars 1830 au sein de l'académie royale des sciences par Geoffroy de Saint-Hillaire. Ouvrage analysé par J. W. Goethe. *Revue medicale française et étrangère*, 4 (1830), 445-57.
/TRANSLATION: FRENCH

1830-6 **Goethe**[, J. W. von]. "Principes de Philosophie Zoologique. Discutés en Mars 1830 au sein de l'académie royale des sciences par Mr. Geoffroy de Saint-Hillaire. Paris, 1830." *Jahrbücher für wissenschaftliche Kritik*, 2, No. 52, September 1830, cols. 413-16; No. 53, September 1830, cols. 417-24.
Trans. into French, Nos. 1830-5 and (partial) 1831-7.
/EDITION

1830-7 **Hegel**, Georg Wilhelm Friedrich. *Encyclopädie der philosophischen Wissenschaften im Grundrisse. Zum Gebrauch seiner Vorlesungen*. 3rd edn. Heidelberg: Druck und Verlag von August Oßwald, 1830. xlii, 544 pp.
Rpt. of No. 1817-7.

Cf. esp. "Dritte Abteilung: Organische Physik."
/CHROMATICS/NATURPHILOSOPHIE/NEWTON, I

1830-8 **Hueck**, Alexander. *Das Sehen seinem äußern Processe nach entwickelt.* Göttingen: in Commission der Dieterichschen Buchhandlung, 1830. 146 pp.
/RESEARCH: SENSORY PHYSIOLOGY/RESEARCH: CHROMATICS

1830-9 **Schopenhauer**, Arthur. *Commentatio undecima, exponens theoriam colorum physiologicam, eandemque primariam.* Vol. 3 of Radius, Justus. *Scriptores ophthalmologici minores.* [Leipzig]: Leop[old Voss]., 1830, pp. 1-58.
Rpt. No. 1891-13.
/RESEARCH: CHROMATICS/CHROMATICS

1830-10 **Vogel**, Carl. *Versuch einer neuen Darstellung der practischen Heilmittellehre.* Berlin: Ferdinand Dümmler, 1830. xx, 439 pp.
Dedicated to Goethe.
/RESEARCH: PHARMACOLOGY

1830-11 **Weber**, Ernst Heinrich. "Entwickelung der Oberkieferbeine." In his *Beschreibung des Knochensystems, des Muskelsystems und der Haut.* Vol. 2 of *Handbuch der Anatomie des Menschen.* 4th rev. and exp. edn. Braunschweig: Verlag der Schulbuchhandlung, 1830, pp. 94-5.
/RESEARCH: OSTEOLOGY/OSTEOLOGY

1831-1 **Agardh**, C[arl]. A[dolf]. "Uebersicht der Gewächsmetamorphose." In his *Lehrbuch der Botanik: Erste Abtheilung: Organographie.* Kopenhagen: Verlag der Gyldendalschen Buchhandlung, 1831, pp. 388-415.
German trans. of No. 1829-2.
/RESEARCH: BOTANY/RESEARCH: MORPHOLOGY

1831-2 **[B***(?).]** "Goethe scienziato [Goethe the Scientist]." *Biblioteca italiana*, 16, No. 64 (1831), 247-51.
In Italian.
/GENERAL INTRODUCTION

1831-3 **Carus**, Carl Gustav. *Neun Briefe über Landschaftsmalerei, geschrieben in den Jahren 1815-1824. Zuvor ein Brief von Goethe als Einleitung.* Leipzig: Verlag von Gerhard Fleischer: In Commission bei Adolf Frohberger, 1831. 208 pp.

Rpt. Nos. 1835-2 and 1927-10.
/RESEARCH: FINE ARTS

1831-4 **Frank**[, ?]. "Herr Dr. Ph. Frank wies die Berührungspunkte in der Göthischen Farbenlehre und der Wellentheorie nach. . ." In *Uebersicht der Arbeiten und Veränderungen der schlesischen Gesellschaft für vaterländische Kultur im Jahre 1830. Zur Kenntnißnahme für sämmtliche einheimische und auswärtige wirkliche Herren Mitglieder der genannten Gesellschaft.* Breslau: Graß, Barth und Comp., 1831, p. 34.
   Cf. No. 1830-3.
   /CHROMATICS/RESEARCH: CHROMATICS

1831-5 **Goethe**, J. W. von/Goethe, J. W. de. *Versuch über die Metamorphose der Pflanzen/Essai sur la métamorphose des plantes.* Trans. with historical notes by Frédéric Soret. Stuttgart: in der Cotta'schen Buchhandlung/J. G. Cotta, Libraire, 1831. 239 pp.
   Rev. [anon.], *Litteratur-Bericht zur Linnaea*, 1831, pp. 43-4.
   Rev. [No. 1831-10].
   Rev. [No. 1831-12].
   Rev. [No. 1832-3].
   /EDITION/TRANSLATION: FRENCH

1831-6 **Göthe** [Goethe, J. W. von]. "Mitteilungen aus der Pflanzenwelt." *Verhandlungen der Kaiserlichen Leopoldinisch-Carolinischen Akademie der Naturforscher*, 15.2 (1831), 363-84.
   Rev. [anon.], *Litteratur-Bericht zur Linnaea für das Jahr 1833*, pp. 172-4.
   Rev. [No. 1833-12].
   /EDITION

1831-7 **Goethe**[, J. W. von]. "Réflexions de Goethe sur les débats scientifiques de mars 1830 dans le sein de l'Académie des Sciences, publiées à Berlin dans les Annales de critique scientifique." *Annales des sciences naturelles*, 22 (1831), 179-88.
   French trans. (partial) of No. 1830-6.
   /TRANSLATION: FRENCH

1831-8 **Goethe**[, J. W. von]. "Über den Zwischenkiefer des Menschen und der Thiere, von Goethe. Jena, 1786." *Verhandlungen der Kaiserlichen Leopoldinisch-Carolinischen Akademie der Naturforscher*, 15, Pt. 1 (1831), 1-48.
   Rev. [anon.], *Isis. Encyclopädische Zeitschrift, vorzüglich für Naturgeschichte, vergleichende Anatomie und Physiologie, von*

Oken, 26, No. 7 (1833), col. 594.
/EDITION

1831-9 **Lövy**, Hermann. "Goethes Farbenlehre, im Gegentheil eine zu wenig beachtete Ergänzung der Theorie der Polarität." In his *Ueber Polarität*. Diss. Prag. Prag: M. J. Landau, 1831, pp. 47-54.
/CHROMATICS

1831-10 **Saint-Hilaire**, [Étienne] Geoffroy [de]. "[Review of:] Essai sur la métamorphose des plantes, par J. W. de Goethe; traduit en français par Frédéric Sore[t], et suivi de notes historiques. Stuttgart, 1831; G. Cotta. In-8o. (Note lue . . .à l'Académie des Sciences les 5 juillet 1831.)" *Revue encyclopédique: Politique, Religion, Philosophie, Sciences, Économie politique, Industrie, Littérature et Beaux-Arts*, 51 (1831), 523-6.
　　　Rpt. No. 1831-12.
　　　Review of No. 1831-5.
　　　/REVIEW/BOTANY/MORPHOLOGY/RECEPTION

1831-11 **Saint-Hilaire**, Étienne Geoffroy [de]. "Sur les Écrits de Goethe lui donnant des droits au titre de savant naturaliste." *Annales des sciences naturelles*, 22 (1831), 188-93.
　　　/GENERAL INTRODUCTION

1831-12 **Saint-Hilaire**, [Étienne] Geoffroy [de]. "Sur un nouvel ouvrage de Goëthe, traitant des analogies et de la métamorphoses des parties végétales; communiqué à l'Académie des Sciences le 25 juillet 1831." *Journal complémentaire des sciences médicales*, 40 (1831), 279-82.
　　　Rpt. of No. 1831-10.
　　　Review of No. 1831-5.
　　　/REVIEW/BOTANY/MORPHOLOGY/RECEPTION

1831-13 **Schmidt**, Jos[eph]. Herm[ann]. *Ueber Anwendung der Morphologie auf die vergleichende Krankheitslehre*. Vol. 2 of *Zwölf Bücher über Morphologie überhaupt und vergleichende Noso-Morphologie insbesondere*. Berlin: Verlag von Th. Chr. Fr. Enslin, 1831. 178 pp.
　　　Cf. vol. 1, No. 1831-14.
　　　/RESEARCH: PATHOLOGY

1831-14 **Schmidt**, Jos[eph]. Herm[ann]. *Versuch die Metamorphose der Thiere zu erklären, mit vergleichenden Hinblicken auf die Pflanzen-Entwickelung*. Vol. 1 of *Zwölf Bücher über Morphologie überhaupt und vergleichende Noso-Morphologie insbesondere*. Berlin: Verlag

von Th. Chr. Fr. Enslin, 1831. 150 pp.
Cf. vol. 2, No. 1831-13.
/RESEARCH: ZOOLOGY/RESEARCH: BOTANY

1831-15 **Seifensand**, Karl August. *Ueber die Sinnesempfindung. Ein Versuch in der vergleichenden Physiologie der Sinnesorgane.* Crefeld: C. M. Schüller, 1831. 159 pp.
Dedicated to Goethe.
/RESEARCH: SENSORY PHYSIOLOGY

1832-1 [anon.] "Erinnerungsfeier an Göthe als Naturforscher, gehalten den 22. April 1832 zu Freiberg." *Literarisches Notizen-Blatt*, 5 May 1832, 37-9.
/RECEPTION

1832-2 **Candolle**, Aug[ustin].-Pyr[amus]. de. "Des Dégénérescences ou Métamorphoses." In *Physiologie végétale, ou exposition des forces et des fonctions vitales des végétaux, pour servir de suite à la botanique géographique et agricole.* 3 vols. Paris: Béchet jeune, libraire de la Faculté de Médecine, 1832, II, 771-7.
Trans. into French, No. 1835-1.
/RESEARCH: BOTANY/RESEARCH: MORPHOLOGY

1832-3 **Carus**[, Carl Gustav]. "[Review of:] J. W. von Goethe, Versuch über die Metamorphose der Pflanzen, übersetzt von Friedr. Soret, [etc]." *Jahrbücher für wissenschaftliche Kritik*, No. 1-3 (1832), cols. 1-23.
Review of No. 1831-5.
/REVIEW/BOTANY/MORPHOLOGY/RECEPTION

1832-4 **Engelmann**, Georg[e]. "Deantholysi prodromus. Dissertatio inauguralis phytomorphologica." Francofurti ad Moenum: H. L. Broenner, 1832. 68 pp.
/RESEARCH: BOTANY

1832-5 **Falk**, Johannes. "Goethe's Ansicht der Natur." In his *Goethe aus näherem persönlichem Umgange dargestellt. Ein nachgelassenes Werk.* Leipzig: F. A. Brockhaus, 1832, pp. 26-49.
/GENERAL INTRODUCTION

1832-6 **Falk**, Johannes. "Goethe's wissenschaftliche Ansichten." In his *Goethe aus näherem persönlichem Umgange dargestellt. Ein nachgelassenes Werk.* Leipzig: F. A. Brockhaus, 1832, pp. 50-84.
Rpt. 2nd edn. 1836.

/GENERAL INTRODUCTION

1832-7 **Goethe**[, J. W. von]. "David Knoll'sche Sammlung von Sprudel-Steine, roh oder geschliffen, angezeigt und eingeführt von Goethe." Prag: Gottlieb Haase Söhne, 1832. 8 pp.
/EDITION

1832-8 **Goethe**[, J. W. von]. "Dernières pages de Goethe. Expliquant a l'Allemagne les sujets de philosophie naturelle controversés au sein de l'Académie des Sciences de Paris." *Revue encyclopédique*, No. 53, March 1832, 563-73; No. 54, April 1832, 54-68.
Rpt. Nos. 1832-10 and 1832-11.
/TRANSLATION: FRENCH

1832-9 **Goethe**[, J. W. von]. "Joseph Müller'sche jetzt David Knoll'sche Sammlung zur Kenntniss der Gebirge von und um Karlsbad, angezeigt und erläutert von Goethe." Prag: Gottlieb Haase Söhne, 1832. viii pp.
/EDITION

1832-10 **Goethe**[, J. W. von]. "Les Naturalistes français, ou méditations de Goethe sur la marche et le caract[è]re philosophique des sciences naturelles a Paris." *Collection portative d'oeuvres choisies de la littérature française*. 3e série. Vol. 55. Stuttgart: chez la rédaction de la collection, 1832, 129-254.
Rpt. of No. 1832-8.
/TRANSLATION: FRENCH

1832-11 **Goethe**[, J. W. von]. "Les Naturalistes français, ou méditations de Goethe sur la marche et le caractère philosophique des sciences naturelles a Paris." *Paris, ou le livre des cent-et-un*, 5 (1832), 145-58.
Rpt. of No. 1832-8.
/TRANSLATION: FRENCH

1832-12 **Goethe**[, J. W. von]. "Principes de Philosophie Zoologique. Discutés en Mars 1830. au sein de l'académie royale des sciences par Mr. Geoffroy de Saint-Hilaire." *Jahrbücher für wissenschaftliche Kritik*, No. 51, March 1832, cols. 401-8; No. 52, March 1832, cols. 409-16; No. 53, March 1832, cols. 417-22.
/EDITION

1832-13 **Martens**[, Georg von]. "(Zur Morphologie der Algen.)" *Flora oder allgemeine botanische Zeitung*, 15 (1832), 123-7.

/RESEARCH: BOTANY

1832-14 **Meyer**, Ernst [H. Fr.]. "Die Metamorphose der Pflanze und ihre Widersacher. Kritische Blätter." *Linnea*, 7 (1832), 401-60.
/BOTANY/MORPHOLOGY/RECEPTION

1832-15 **Soret**, Frédéric. "Notice sur Goethe." *Bibliothèque Universelle des Sciences, Belles-Lettres et Arts, rédigé à Genève*
/GENERAL INTRODUCTION

1833-1 **Bischoff**, Gottlieb Wilhelm. "Metamorphose (Metamorphosis -- Métamorphose)." In his *Handbuch der botanischen Terminologie und Systemkunde. Erster Band, die Einleitung, die allgemeinen und die besonderen für die phenerogamischen Pflanzen gebräuchlichen Kunstausdrücke enthaltend.* Nürnberg: Verlag von Johann Leonhard Schrag, 1833, I, 15-16.
Cf. vols. II and III, 1842 and 1844.
/RESEARCH: BOTANY

1833-2 **Cotta**, Heinrich [von]. "Der Kammerbühl nach wiederholten Untersuchungen auf's neue beschrieben." Dresden: Gärtner'sche Buchdruckerei, 1833. 19 pp.
/RESEARCH: GEOLOGY

1833-3 **[Goethe**, J. W. von.] *Geschichte der Farbenlehre. Erster Theil. Von den Griechen und Römern bis auf Newton.* Vol. 13 [53] of *Goethe's nachgelassene Werke.* Stuttgart/Tübingen: J. G. Cotta'sche Buchhandlung, 1833. vi, 271 pp.
/EDITION

1833-4 **[Goethe**, J. W. von.] *Geschichte der Farbenlehre. Zweyter Theil. Von Newton bis auf unsere Zeit.* Vol. 14 [54] of *Goethe's nachgelassene Werke.* Stuttgart/Tübingen: J. G. Cotta'sche Buchhandlung, 1833. viii, 320 pp.
/EDITION

1833-5 **[Goethe**, J. W. von.] *Mineralogie und Geologie.* Vol. 11 [51] of *Goethe's nachgelassene Werke.* Stuttgart/Tübingen: J. G. Cotta'sche Buchhandlung, 1833. vi, 290 pp.
/EDITION

1833-6 **[Goethe**, J. W. von.] *Nachträge zur Farbenlehre [etc].* Vol. 15 [55] of *Goethe's nachgelassene Werke.* Stuttgart/ Tübingen: J. G. Cotta'sche Buchhandlung, 1833. vi, 330 pp.

/EDITION

1833-7 [**Goethe**, J. W. von.] *Zur Farbenlehre. Didaktischer Theil.* Vol. 12 [52] of *Goethe's nachgelassene Werke.* Stuttgart/Tübingen: J. G. Cotta'sche Buchhandlung, 1833. xxiv, 374 pp.
/EDITION

1833-8 [**Goethe**, J. W. von.] *Zur Naturwissenschaft im Allgemeinen.* Vol. 10 [50] of *Goethe's nachgelassene Werke.* Stuttgart/Tübingen: J. G. Cotta'sche Buchhandlung, 1833. vi, 253 pp.
/EDITION

1833-9 **Miquel**, Frederici Antonii Guilielmi [Friedrich Anton Wilhelm]. *Commentatio de organorum in vegetabilibus ortu et metamorphosi.* Lugduni Batavorum: S. et J. Luchtmans, 1833. 101 pp.
"in certamine literario civium Academiarum Belgicarum die VIII mensis februarii A. MDCCCXXXIII, ex sententia ordinis disciplinarum mathematicarum et physicarum in Academia Lugduno-Batava praemio ornata."
RESEARCH: BOTANY/RESEARCH: MORPHOLOGY/BOTANY/MORPHOLOGY

1833-10 *****Müller**, Johannes. *Handbuch der Physiologie des Menschen.* 2 vols. Koblenz, 1833.
/RESEARCH: SENSORY PHYSIOLOGY/CHROMATICS

1833-11 **Oken**[, Lorenz]. *Allgemeine Naturgeschichte für alle Stände.* 13 [15] vols. Stuttgart: Carl Hoffmann, 1833-1843.
Rev. [Hermann] Burmeister, *Hallische Jahrbücher für deutsche Wissenschaft und Kunst*, 1 (1838), cols. 1167-8; 1173-6; 1204-8; 1211-16.
/RESEARCH: VARIOUS/NATURPHILOSOPHIE

1833-12 **rrr**[?]. "[Review of:] Mitteilungen aus der Pflanzenwelt, von Göthe. Mit 2 Steindrucktafeln." *Literaturberichte zur Flora oder allgemeinen Botanischen Zeitung*, 3, No. 15 (1833), 227-9.
Review of No. 1831-6.
/REVIEW/BOTANY/MORPHOLOGY/RECEPTION

1833-13 [**Tobler**, Georg Christoph?] [**Goethe**, J. W. von] "Die Natur. Aphoristisch." In vol. 10 of his *Nachgelassene Werke.* Vol. 15 of his *Werke. Vollständige Ausgabe letzter Hand.* Stuttgart/Tübingen: J. G. Cotta'sche Buchhandlung, 1833, pp. 3-7.
Rpt. of No. 1783-1.

Rpt. 1833.
/EDITION

1833-14 **Wilbrand**, Johann Bernhard. *Allgemeine Physiologie insbesondere vergleichende Physiologie der Pflanzen und der Thiere.* Heidelberg/Leipzig: Neue akademische Buchhandlung von Karl Groos/Wien: Karl Gerold, 1833. xii, 452 pp.
/RESEARCH: MORPHOLOGY/RESEARCH: BIOLOGY

1834-1 [**anon.**] "Göthe's Witterungs-Deutung." *Archiv für Chemie und Meteorologie*, 8 (1834), 320-24.
/METEOROLOGY/ZELTER, K

1834-2 **Carus**, Carl Gustav. *Lehrbuch der vergleichenden Zootomie. Mit stäter Hinsicht auf Physiologie ausgearbeitet.* 2nd rev. and exp. edn. Leipzig: Gerhard Fischer der Jüngere, 1834. xxxii, 414 pp.
Rpt. of No. 1818-3.
/RESEARCH: BIOLOGY

1834-3 **Göschel**, Carl Friedrich. "Göthe und Schiller, oder die Metamorphose der Pflanzen und die Kantische Philosophie." In his *Unterhaltungen zur Schilderung Göthescher Dicht- und Denkweise.* 3 vols. Schleusingen: Glaser, 1834, II, pp. 24-31.
Rpt. No. 1852-4.
/SCHILLER, F/KANT, I/PHILOSOPHY/BOTANY /MOR-PHOLOGY

1834-4 **Göschel**, Carl Friedrich. "Göthe und Stilling." In his *Unterhaltungen zur Schilderung Göthescher Dicht- und Denkweise.* 3 vols. Schleusingen: Glaser, 1834, II, 2-8.
Rpt. 2nd edn. 1852.
/STILLING [JUNG], H

1834-5 **Göschel**, Carl Friedrich. "Zur Gottes-, Geistes- und Natur-Philosophie. Zur Einleitung in die Farbenlehre." In his *Unterhaltungen zur Schilderung Göthescher Dicht- und Denkweise.* 3 vols. Schleusingen: Glaser, 1834, II, 133-234.
Rpt. No. 1852-5.
/CHROMATICS/RESEARCH: CHROMATICS /NATUR-PHILOSOPHIE

1834-6 **K[lotzsch**, Friedrich?]. "Materialien zu einem Verzeichniss der jetzt lebenden botanischen Schriftsteller, so wie derer, die im letzten Decennium, bis Ende 1833, verstorben sind." *Linnaea*, 9 (1834),

707-36
/BOTANY

1834-7 **Moser**, Ludwig. "Ueber Göthes Leistungen in der Farbenlehre." *Historische und literärische Abhandlungen der königlichen Deutschen Gesellschaft zu Königsberg*, 3 (1834), 111-40.
/CHROMATICS

1834-8 **Müller**[, Johannes]. "Vergleichung des Schädels der Cyclostomen mit dem Rückgrath derselben und mit dem Schädel der Embryonen der höheren Thiere." In his *Osteologie und Myologie*. Pt. I of *Vergleichende Anatomie der Myxinoiden, der Cyclostomen mit durchbohrtem Gaumen*. Abhandlungen der Königlichen Akademie der Wissenschaften zu Berlin. Aus dem Jahre 1834. Berlin: in Commission bei F. Dümmler, 1836, pp. 185-97.
/RESEARCH: OSTEOLOGY

1835-1 **Candolle**, Augustin Pyramus de. "Von den Ausartungen der Organe (dégénérescences) oder den Metamorphosen." In his *Pflanzen-Physiologie, oder Darstellung der Lebenskräfte und Lebensverrichtungen der Gewächse. Eine Fortsetzung der Pflanzen-Organographie, und eine Einleitung zur Pflanzen-Geographie und ökonomische Botanik*. Trans. and notes Johannes Röper. A. P. De Candolle's Vorlesungen über die Botanik, Pt. 3, vol. 2. Stuttgart and Tübingen: J. G. Cotta'sche Buchhandlung, 1835, pp. 484-93.
French trans. of No. 1832-2.
/RESEARCH: BOTANY/RESEARCH: MORPHOLOGY

1835-2 **Carus**, Carl Gustav. *Neun Briefe über Landschaftsmalerei, geschrieben in den Jahren 1815-1824. Zuvor ein Brief von Goethe als Einleitung*. 2nd exp. edn. Leipzig: Verlag von Gerhard Fleischer: In Commission bei Adolf Frohberger, 1831. 276 pp.
Rpt. of No. 1831-3.
/FINE ARTS

1835-3 **Pfizer**, Gustav. "Goethes Farbenlehre." In his *Gedichte, neue Sammlung*. Stuttgart: Neff, 1835, pp. 124-8.
Revised and abbreviated version of No. 1835-4.
/CHROMATICS/METEOROLOGY

1835-4 **Pfizer**, Gustav. "Goethes Farbenlehre." *Deutscher Musenalmanach für das Jahr 1835*, 6 (1835), 33-8.
Cf. No. 1835-3.
A poem.

/CHROMATICS/METEOROLOGY

1835-5 **Saint-Hilaire**, [Étienne] Geoffroy [de]. "Extrait d'un mémoire, par M. Geoffroy Saint-Hilaire, ayant pour titre: Analyse des travaux de Goëthe en histoire naturelle, et Considérations sur le caractère de leur portée scientifique." *Comptes Rendus hebdomadaires des Séances de l'Académie des Sciences*, 2, No. 55 (1836), 555-7.
Cf. continuation, No. 1836-6.
"Séance du lundi 6 juin 1836."
/GENERAL INTRODUCTION

1835-6 **Saint-Hilaire**, [Étienne] Geoffroy [de]. "Suite et fin du mémoire, lu en partie le 6 juin dernier, intitulé: Analyse des travaux de Goëthe en histoire naturelle, et Considérations sur le caractère de leur portée scientifique." *Comptes Rendus hebdomadaires des Séances de l'Académie des Sciences*, 2, No. 55 (1836), 563-5.
Continuation of No. 1835-5.
"Séance du lundi 13 juin 1836."
/GENERAL INTRODUCTION

1835-7 **Voigt**, F[riedrich]. S[iegmund]. *Allgemeine Zoologie, Specielle Zoologie. -- Säugethiere.* Vol. 1 of *Lehrbuch der Zoologie.* Naturgeschichte der drei Reiche, 7. Stuttgart: E. Schweizerbart's Verlagshandlung, 1835. 502 pp.
/RESEARCH: ZOOLOGY

1836-1 **[anon.]** "Stimmen der Zeit über Goethe." *Außerordentliche Beilage zur Allgemeinen Zeitung*, No. 142/3, 30 March 1836, 565-7; No. 144/5, 31 March 1836, 573-5; No. 146/7, 1 April 1836, 581-3; No. 148/9, 2 April 1836, 591-2; No. 150/51, 3 April 1836, 597-9; No. 152, 4 April 1836, 606-8.
/GENERAL INTRODUCTION/RECEPTION/OKEN, L

1836-2 "**Briefwechsel** zwischen Göthe und D. Chr. Fr. L. Schultz, Geh. Ober-Reg. R." *Rheinisches Museum für Philologie*, 4 (1836), 309-54.
Rpt. No. 1836-3.
/EDITION/SCHULTZ, C/OPTICS

1836-3 "**Briefwechsel** zwischen Göthe und Schultz. Aus dem Rheinischen Museum für Philologie." Bonn: Eduard Weber, 1836. 2, 46 pp.
Rpt. of No. 1836-2.
/EDITION/SCHULTZ, C/OPTICS

1836-4 **Cesati**, Vicenzo. "Le teoriche più recenti dei botanici del Nord in

fatto di fisica vegetabile, esposte compendiosamente in una serie di discorsi [The Most Recent Theories from the North with Regard to Vegetable Nature, Expounded Compendiously in a Series of Discourses]." *Biblioteca Italiana o sia Giornale di Letteratura, Scienze ed Arti compilato a vari letterati*, 84 (1836), 92-9.
  In Italian.
  /BOTANY

1836-5 **Eckermann**, Johann Peter. *Gespräche mit Goethe in den letzten Jahren seines Lebens. 1823-1832.* 2 pts. Leipzig: F. A. Brockhaus, 1836. xiv, 386; 360 pp.
  Rpt. No. 1948-4.
  Trans. into English, No. 1984-32.
  /EDITION

1836-6 **Geist[**, Johann Jacob]. "Ueber Pflanzen-Monstrositäten." *Neue Blumen-Zeitung*, 9, 3 May 1836, cols. 132-4 [129-36].
  /RESEARCH: BOTANY/RESEARCH: PATHOLOGY

1836-7 *[**Goethe**, J. W. von.] [Extracts from Goethe's *Farbenlehre* in English.] *Western Messenger [Louisville]*, 1 (1836), 824-7.
  /TRANSLATION: ENGLISH

1836-8 **Martins**, Charles. "Analyse des travaux de Goethe en histoire naturelle." *Le Temps, Journal des progrès*, 7, No. 2416, 30 May 1836, cols. 37550-37560.
  /GENERAL INTRODUCTION

1836-9 **Mohl**, Hugo [von]. "Beobachtungen über die Umwandlungen von Antheren in Carpelle." Diss. Tübingen. Tübingen: Gustav Bähr, 1836. 37 pp.
  Trans. into French, No. 1837-11.
  Rpt. Nos. 1836-10 and 1845-8.
  /RESEARCH: BOTANY/RESEARCH: MORPHOLOGY

1836-10 **Mohl**, Hugo [von]. "Beobachtungen über die Umwandlungen von Antheren in Carpelle." *Flora oder allgemeine botanische Zeitung*, 19, Nos. 33-5 (1836), 513-26; 529-73; 545-58.
  Rpt. of No. 1836-9.
  /RESEARCH: BOTANY/RESEARCH: MORPHOLOGY

1836-11 **Oken[**, Lorenz]. "Wegen Goethe." *Außerordentliche Beilage zur Allgemeinen Zeitung*, No. 282/283, 20 June 1836, p. 1128.
  /OSTEOLOGY/RESEARCH: OSTEOLOGY

1837-1 **Feuchtersleben**, Ernst Freih[err]. v[on]. "Göthe's naturwissen-
schaftliche Ansichten." In his *Beiträge zur Literatur, Kunst- und
Lebens-Theorie*. Wien: J. G. Ritter von Mösle's We. und
Braumüller, 1837, pp. 99-140.
  Rpt. No. 1977-17.
  /GENERAL INTRODUCTION

1837-2 **[Goethe**, J. W. von.] *Oeuvres d'histoire naturelle de Goethe,
comprenant divers mémoires d'anatomie comparée, trois de botanique
et deux de géologie, Atlas contenant deux planches d'anatomie comparée, trois de botanique et deux de géologie, accompagnées d'une
explication raisonée et d'une esquisse d'organographie végétale.*
Trans. and comm. Ch. Fr. Martins. Paris/Genève: Abraham Cherbulicz et Compagnie, 1837. 35 pp.
  Cf. Nos. 1837-3 and 1837-15.
  Rev. F.-J. Pictet, *Bibliothèque universelle des Genève*, NS 15
    (1838), 338-50.
  Rev. L. Aimé Martin, *Journal des débats*, 5 April 1839, cols.
    10-14.
  /TRANSLATION: FRENCH

1837-3 **Goethe**[, J. W. von]. *Oeuvres d'histoire naturelle de Goethe,
comprenant divers mémoires d'anatomie comparée, de botanique et
de géologie.* Trans. and comm. Chr. Fr. Martins. Paris/Genève:
Ab[raham]. Cherbuliez et Ce., 1837. viii, 468 pp.
  Later rpt. without atlas, n.d.
  Cf. Nos. 1837-2 and 1837-15.
  Rev. [anon.], *Annales des Sciences Naturelles*, 2nd series, vol.
    10, 1838, 379-82.
  /TRANSLATION: FRENCH

1837-4 **Goethe**[, J. W. von]. *Pflanzen und Gebirgsarten von Marienbad,
gesammelt und beschrieben von Seiner königlichen Hoheit dem Prinzen Friedrich, Mitregenten von Sachsen, (1834 und 1835) und von Sr.
Excellenz J. W. von Göthe, grossherzoglich-sächsisch-weimar'schem
wirklichem geheimen Rathe und Staatsminister, (1821, 1822, 1823)
ergänzt, und mit einem Anhange über die andern naturhistorischen
Verhältnisse des Curortes herausgegeben von Dr. C. J. Heidler.*
Prag: Bei Kronberger und Weber, 1837. x, 203 pp.
  /EDITION/RESEARCH: BOTANY/RESEARCH: GEOLOGY

1837-5 **Griesbach**, August. "Ueber die heutige Bedeutung der Goetheschen Pflanzenmetamorphose." Manuscript, 1837. 16 pp.

Cf. also S 1724.
/BOTANY

1837-6 **Heidler [von Heilborn]**, Carl Joseph. "Gang- und Gebirgs-Arten von Marienbad, gesammelt und beschrieben von Sr. Excellenz dem grossherzogl. sächs. weimar'schen wirklichen geheimen Rathe und Staatsminister J. W. von Göthe." In his *Pflanzen und Gebirgsarten von Marienbad, gesammelt und beschrieben von Seiner königlichen Hoheit dem Prinzen Friedrich, Mitregenten von Sachsen, (1834 und 1835) und von Sr. Excellenz J. W. von Göthe.* Prag: 1837, pp. 55-65.
/GOETHE'S COLLECTIONS

1837-7 **Kieser**, D[ietrich]. G[eorg von]. [In: Bericht der 4. allgemeinen Sitzung."] *Amtlicher Bericht über die Versammlung deutscher Natur-forscher und Ärzte zu Jena im September 1836.* Weimar: Verlag von Bernhard Friedrich Voigt, 1837, pp. 95-6.
/OKEN, L/OSTEOLOGY/RESEARCH: OSTEOLOGY

1837-8 **Laube**, Heinrich. "Goethe mündlich über Gall." In his *Neue Reisenovellen.* 2 vols. Mannheim: Verlag von Heinrich Hoff, 1837, pp. 158-60.
/GALL, F/PHRENOLOGY

1837-9 **Lichtenstein**, Heinrich M. E. [In: Bericht der 4. allgemeinen Sitzung." *Amtlicher Bericht über die Versammlung deutscher Natur-forscher und Ärzte zu Jena im September 1836.* Weimar: Verlag von Bernhard Friedrich Voigt, 1837, p. 96.
/OKEN, L/OSTEOLOGY/RESEARCH: OSTEOLOGY

1837-10 **Link**, Heinrich Friedrich. *Grundlehren der Kräuterkunde. Erster Theil.* 2nd edn. Berlin: Haude und Spenersche Buchhandlung, 1837. xii, 501 pp.
/BOTANY/RESEARCH: BOTANY

1837-11 **Mohl**, Hugo [von]. "Sur la métamorphose des anthères en car-pelles." *Annales des sciences naturelles*, 8 (1837), 50-75. French trans. of No. 1836-9.
/RESEARCH: BOTANY/RESEARCH: MORPHOLOGY

1837-12 **Reichenbach**, Heinr[ich]. Gottl[ieb]. Ludwig. "Versuch einer Fortbildung von Göthe's Metamorphose zu einer Beschauung des Pflanzenreichs in seiner Totalität." In his *Handbuch des natürlichen Pflanzensystems nach allen seinen Classen, Ordnungen und Familien, nebst naturgemäßer Gruppirung der Gattungen, oder Stamm und*

63

Verzweigung des Gewächsreiches, enthaltend eine vollständige Charakteristik und Ausführung der natürlichen Verwandtschaften der Pflanzen in ihrer Richtung aus der Metamorphose und geographischen Verbreitung, wie die fortgebildete Zeit deren Anschauung fordert. Dresden/Leipzig: in der Arnoldischen Buchhandlung, 1837, pp. 19-96.
  Cf. rev. edn. No. 1850-4.
  /RESEARCH: MORPHOLOGY/RESEARCH: BOTA-NY/BOTANY /MORPHOLOGY

1837-13 **Saint-Hilaire**, Auguste de. "Deuxième mémoire sur les Résédacées; corrigé et augmenté." Montpellier: Jean Martel, 1837. 42 pp.
  /RESEARCH: BOTANY

1837-14 ***Schouw**, Joakim Frederik. *Natur-Skildringer.* Kjobenhavn: Gyldendal, 1837.
  Trans. into German, No. 1840-11.
  In Danish.
  /RESEARCH: BOTANY/RESEARCH: MORPHOLOGY

1837-15 **Turpin**, Jean François. "Equisse d'organographie végétale, fondée sur le principe d'unité de composition organique et d'évolution rayonnante ou centrifuge, pour servir à prouver l'identité des organes appendiculaires des végétaux et d'histoire naturelle de Goethe." In *Oeuvres d'histoire naturelle de Goethe, comprenant divers mémoires d'anatomie comparée, trois de botanique et deux de géologie. Atlas.* Trans. and comm. Ch. Fr. Martins. Paris/Genève: Abraham Cherbulicz et Compagnie, 1837, cols. 5-70.
  Cf. Nos. 1837-2 and 1837-3.
  /RESEARCH: BOTANY/RESEARCH: MORPHOLOGY /BOTANY /MORPHOLOGY

1837-16 **Whewell**, William. "Discovery of the Law of Dispersion by Refraction." In his *History of the inductive sciences, from the earliest to the present times.* 3 vols. London: John W. Parker/Cambridge: J. and J. J. Deighton, 1837, II, 349-61.
  Rpt. No. 1847-11.
  Trans. into German, No. 1840-12.
  /OPTICS/CHROMATICS/NEWTON, I/HISTORY OF SCIENCE

1837-17 **Whewell**, William. "Vegetable morphology. Göthe. De Candolle." In his *History of the inductive sciences, from the earliest*

to the present times. 3 vols. London: John W. Parker/Cambridge: J. and J. J. Deighton, 1837, III, 433-41.
>Rpt. No. 1847-13.
>Trans. into German, No. 1841-17.
>/BOTANY/CANDOLLE, A DE/HISTORY OF SCIENCE

1838-1 **Carus**, Carl Gustav. *System der Physiologie umfassend das Allgemeine der Physiologie, die physiologische Geschichte der Menschheit, die des Menschen und die der einzelnen organischen Systeme im Menschen, für Naturforscher und Aerzte bearbeitet.* 3 pts. Dresden/Leipzig: Verlag von Gerhard Fischer, 1838-40.
>Rpt. No. 1847-1.
>/RESEARCH: PHYSIOLOGY

1838-2 **Dove**, H[einrich]. W[ilelm]. "Die neuere Farbenlehre mit andern chromatischen Theorien verglichen." In *Zu der öffentlichen Prüfung des Königlichen Friedrich-Wilhelms-Gymnasiums, welche am Freitag und Sonnabend, den 28. und 29. September d. J. veranstaltet werden soll, ladet ehrerbietigst ein der Direktor Spilleke.* Berlin: A. W. Hayn, 1838, [3]-52.
>Rpt. No. 1853-6.
>/CHROMATICS/HISTORY OF SCIENCE

1838-3 **Fuhlrott**, Johann Carl. "Das Pflanzenreich und seine Metamorphose." In *Programm zu der am 9. und 10. April 1838 in der Real- und Gewerbeschule zu Elberfeld zu veranstaltenden öffentlichen Prüfung und Redeübung.* Elberfeld: Sam. Lucas, 1838, pp. 1-31.
>/RESEARCH: BOTANY/RESEARCH: MORPHOLOGY

1838-4 **Littré**, Émile. "Oeuvres d'histoire naturelle de Goethe." *Revue des deux mondes*, 14 (1838), 94-110.
>/GENERAL INTRODUCTION

1838-5 **Martius**, Karl Fr. Ph. von. "Die Metamorphose der Pflanzen. Vier Vorlesungen, gehalten vor einem häuslichen Kreise von Freunden." In his *Reden und Vorträge über Gegenstände aus dem Gebiete der Naturforschung.* Stuttgart and Tübingen: Verlag der J. G. Cotta'schen Buchhandlung, 1838, pp. 109-222.
>Trans. into Danish, No. 1840-5.
>/RESEARCH: BOTANY/RESEARCH: MORPHOLOGY

1838-6 **Menge**, A[?]. "Farbenlehre (Chromatik)." In his *Physik.* Graudenz: C. G. Röthesche Buchhandlung/Berlin: Enslinsche Buchhandlung, 1838, pp. 326-48.

/RESEARCH: CHROMATICS/CHROMATICS

1838-7 **Michelet**, Carl Ludwig. "Zugeständnisse der neuesten Physik in Bezug auf Goethes Farbenlehre." *Hallische Jahrbücher für deutsche Wissenschaft und Kunst*, 1, No. 305 (1838), cols. 2433-7; No. 306 (1838), cols. 2441-8; No. 307 (1838), cols. 2455-6.
/CHROMATICS/RESEARCH: CHROMATICS

1838-8 **Saint-Hilaire**, Auguste de. "Rapport sur la Traduction de la partie botanique des oeuvres de Goethe, publiée par M. Martins." *Comptes rendus hebdomadaires des séances de l'Académie des Sciences*, 7 (1838), 434-40.
/BOTANY

1838-9 **Saint-Hilaire**, Geoffroy Isidore. "Documents biographiques et philosophiques, recueillis sous le point de vue des théories de l'unité de composition organique; ou précis des principes de la nouvelle école, dont Linné, dans ses Prolepsis, Buffon et Goethe, sont les illustres chefs." In his *Fragments biographiques, précédés d'études sur la vie, les ouvrages et les doctrines de Buffon*. Paris: F. D. Pillot, 1838, pp. 267-328.
/SAINT-HILAIRE, G DE/RECEPTION

1838-10 **Saint-Hilaire**, Geoffroy Isidore. "Rapport a l'Académie des Sciences sur les oeuvres d'histoire naturelle de Goëthe." In his *Fragmens biographiques, précédés d'études sur la vie, les ouvrages et les doctrines de Buffon*. Paris: F. D. Pillot, 1838, pp. 103-31.
   Rpt. of No. 1838-11.
   /SAINT-HILAIRE, G DE/RECEPTION

1838-11 **Saint-Hilaire**, Geoffroy Isidore. "Rapport verbal sur les Oeuvres d'histoire naturelle de Goethe, traduites par M. le docteur Marins. (Partie zoologique et anatomique.)" *Comptes rendus des séances de l'Académie des Sciences*, No. 55 (1838), 320-31.
   Rpt. Nos. 1838-10 and 1841-15.
   /SAINT-HILAIRE, G DE/RECEPTION

1838-12 **Saint-Hilaire**, Geoffroy Isidore. "Sur les travaux zoologiques et anatomiques de Goethe." In his *Essais de zoologie générale, ou mémoires et notices sur la zoologie générale, l'anthropologie et l'histoire de la science*. Paris: de Roret, 1841, pp. 153-74.
   /SAINT-HILAIRE, G DE/RECEPTION

1839-1 **Darlington**, William. "An Essay on the Development and

Modifications of the External Organs of Plants. Compiled chiefly from the writings of J. Wolfgang von Goethe, for a public lecture to the class of the Chester County Cabinet of Natural Science, March 1, 1839." West Chester, Penn[sylvania], 1839. 38 pp.
   /BOTANY

1840-1 **Dietrich**, Friedrich Gottlieb. *Neuer Nachtrag zum vollständigen Lexicon der Gärtnerei und Botanik oder alphabetische Beschreibung vom Bau, Wartung und Nutzen aller in- und ausländischen, ökonomischen, officinellen und zur Zierde dienenden Gewächse.* Vol. 10 [30]. Ulm: Verlag der Ebner'schen Buchhandlung, 1840. xiii, 750 pp.
/RESEARCH: BOTANY

1840-2 [**Goethe**, J. W. von.] "Blatt und Wurzel." In "Drei Briefe Goethe's an den Großherzog Carl August." *Der Gesellschafter oder Blätter für Geist und Herz*, 24 (1840), 897-8.
= WA IV 39, 143-5.
/EDITION

1840-3 [**Goethe**, J. W. von.] *Goethe's Theory of Colours.* Trans. and notes Charles Lock Eastlake. London: John Murray, 1840. xlviii, 423 pp.
Rpt. Nos. 1967-17, 1970-17, 1971-13 and 1975-18.
Rev. anon., *The Athenaeum: Journal of literature, science, and the fine arts*, No. 683, 28 November 1840, 941-2.
Rev. anon., *Syn otechestva*, cp. 6, 1, No. 10 (1841), pt. 1, 321-6 [In Russian; Zhitomirskaia 2687].
Rev. David Brewster [No. 1841-1].
/TRANSLATION: ENGLISH

1840-4 **Leuckart**, Friedr[ich]. Sigism[und]. *Untersuchungen über das Zwischenkieferbein des Menschen in seiner normalen und abnormen Metamorphose. Ein Beitrag zur Entwickelungs-Geschichte des Menschen nebst Betrachtungen über das Zwischenkieferbein der Thiere.* Stuttgart: E. Schweizerbart's Verlagshandlung, 1840. viii, 116 pp.
/RESEARCH: OSTEOLOGY

1840-5 *****Martius**, Karl Fr. Ph. von. *Planternes Metamorphose, Fire Forelaesninger.* Ed. and intro. S[alomon] Drejer. Kopenhagen, 1840. 80 pp.
Danish trans. of No. 1838-5.
/RESEARCH: BOTANY/RESEARCH: MORPHOLOGY

1840-6 **Müller**, Johannes. *Handbuch der Physiologie des Menschen für Vorlesungen.* 2 vols. Coblenz: Verlag von J. Hölscher, 1840. vi, 780 pp.
/RESEARCH: CHROMATICS/CHROMATICS

1840-7 **Raumer**, Karl von. "Göthe als Naturforscher." In his *Kreuzzüge.*

Erster Theil. Stuttgart: Verlag von S. G. Liesching, 1840, pp. 70-92.
/GENERAL INTRODUCTION

1840-8 **Runge**, Philipp Otto. "Farbenkugel oder Construction des Verhältnisses aller Mischungen der Farben zu einander und ihrer vollständigen Affinität; mit angehängtem Versuch einer Ableitung der Harmonie in den Zusammenstellungen der Farben." In *Hinterlassene Schriften: Erster Theil.* Hamburg: Verlag von Friedrich Perthes, 1840, pp. 112-28.
    Rpt. No. 1965-30.
    Cf. Pt. II, No. 1841-14.
    "Herausgegeben von dessen ältestem Bruder."
    /RESEARCH: CHROMATICS/FINE ARTS

1840-9 **Runge**, Philipp Otto. "Farbenlehre. 1806-1810." In *Hinterlassene Schriften: Erster Theil.* Hamburg: Verlag von Friedrich Perthes, 1840, pp. 84-170.
    Rpt. No. 1965-30.
    Cf. continuation, No. 1841-14.
    "Herausgegeben von dessen ältestem Bruder."
    /RESEARCH: CHROMATICS/FINE ARTS

1840-10 **Saint-Hilaire**, Auguste de. *Leçons de botanique comprenant principalement la morphologie végétale, la terminologie, la botanique comparée, l'examen de la valeur des caractères dans les diverses familles naturelles.* Paris: P.-J. Loss, 1840. viii, 930 pp.
    /RESEARCH: BOTANY/BOTANY

1840-11 **Schouw**, J[oakim]. F[rederik]. "Die Verwandlung der Pflanzentheile." In his *Naturschilderungen: Eine Reihe allgemein faßlicher Vorlesungen.* Kiel: Universitäts-Buchhandlung, 1840, pp. 40-44.
    German trans. of No. 1837-14.
    /RESEARCH: BOTANY/RESEARCH: MORPHOLOGY

1840-12 **Whewell**, William. "Dispersion des Lichtes durch Refraktion." *Geschichte der induktiven Wissenschaften, der Astronomie, Physik, Mechanik, Chemie, Geologie, etc. von der frühesten bis zu unserer Zeit.* Trans. J. J. v. Littrow. Stuttgart: Hoffmann'sche Verlags-Buchhandlung, 1841, pp. 370-80.
    German trans. of No. 1837-16.
    /OPTICS/CHROMATICS/NEWTON, I

1840-13 **Zunck**, Hermann Leopold. *Die natürlichen Pflanzensysteme geschichtlich entwickelt.* Leipzig: Hinrichssche Buchhandlung, 1840.

vi, 208 pp.
"Eine von der philosophischen Fakultät zu Leipzig gekrönte Preisschrift."
/RESEARCH: BOTANY

1841-1 [**Brewster**, David.] "[Review of:] *Goethe's Theory of Colours* [etc.; cf. No. 1840-3]." *The Edinburgh Review, or Critical Journal*, 72 (1841), 99-131.
/CHROMATICS/EASTLAKE, C/REVIEW

1841-2 **Carus**, Carl Gustav. *Grundzüge einer neuen und wissenschaftlich begründeten Cranioscopie (Schädellehre)*. Stuttgart: Verlag der Balz'schen Buchhandlung, 1841. viii, 87 pp.
Rpt. No. 1926-4.
/RESEARCH: OSTEOLOGY

1841-3 **Carus**, Carl Gustav. "Brief über Goethes Meteorologie." In his *Zwölf Briefe über das Erdleben*. Stuttgart: P. Balz'sche Buchhandlung, 1841, pp. 226-46.
Rpt. Nos. 1926-6 and 1986-24.
/METEOROLOGY

1841-4 **Clemens**, Aloys. "Goethe als Naturforscher. Eine Skizze." Frankfurt am Main: Verlag von Karl Küchler, 1841. viii, 30 pp.
Cf. No. 1853-5.
/GENERAL INTRODUCTION

1841-5 **Ficinus**, Heinrich, ed. *Optik oder Umriß der sogenannten folgerechten Lehre vom Licht*. 2nd edn. Quedlinburg und Leipzig: Ernst'sche Buchhandlung, 1841. iv, 135 [133] pp.
Rpt. of No. 1828-10.
/RESEARCH: OPTICS/RESEARCH: CHROMATICS

1841-6 **Goethe**[, J. W. von]. *Nachträge zu Goethe's sämmtlichen Werken*. Coll. and ed. Eduard Boas. Leipzig: Verlag von L. H. Bösenberg, 1841. v, 256 pp.
Contains various scientific entries.
/EDITION

1841-7 **Jaeger [Jäger]**, G[eorg]. F[riedrich von]. "De monstrosa folii Phoenicis dactyliferae conformatione, a Geotheo olim observata et figura picta illustrata, nec non de ramo eiusdem arboris intra spadicem contento." *Novorum Actorum Academiae Caesareae Leopoldino-Carolinae Naturae Curiosorum [Verhandlungen der*

*Kaiserlichen Leopoldinisch-Carolinischen Akademie der Natur-
forscher]*, 18 (1841), pp. 289-94.
/RESEARCH: BOTANY/RESEARCH: PATHOLOGY

1841-8 [**Martins**, Charles.] "Végétal." In *Encyclopédie nouvelle ou Dic-
tionnaire philosophique, scientifique, littéraire et industriel.* Ed. P.
Leroux and J. Reynaud. Paris: Librairie de Charles Gosselin, 1841,
VIII, 615-33.
/RESEARCH: BOTANY/RESEARCH: MORPHOLOGY

1841-9 **Martius**[, Karl Fr. Ph.] v[on]. "v. Martius über de Candolle."
Beilage zur Allgemeinen Zeitung [Augsburg], Nos. 348-51, 13-16
December 1841, 2777-8; 2785-6; 2793-4; 2801-3.
Rpt. No. 1842-18.
/BOTANY/CANDOLLE, A DE

1841-10 **Martius**, C[Karl]. F[r]. Ph. von. "Über die Entwickelung der
Botanik seit dem Bestehen der k. b. botanischen Gesellschaft zu
Regensburg, ein Vortrag, gehalten in der Sitzung der Gesellschaft am
15. April 1840." In *Denkschrift zur Feier des fünfzigjährigen Be-
standes der k. b. botanischen Gesellschaft zu Regensburg.*
Denkschriften der königlich-bayerischen botanischen Gesellschaft zu
Regensburg, 3. Regensburg: Julius Heinrich Demmler (vormals
Brenck), 1841, pp. 1-29.
/BOTANY/RECEPTION

1841-11 **Moquin-Tandon**, Alfred. "Des transformations des organes les
uns dans les autres ou des métamorphoses." In his *Éléments de
tératologie végétale ou histoire abrégée des anomalies de
l'organisation dans les végétaux.* Paris: P.-J. Loss, 1841, pp. 194-
200.
Trans. into German, No. 1842-19.
/BOTANY/MORPHOLOGY/RECEPTION

1841-12 **Riemer**, Friedrich Wilhelm. "Farbenlehre." In his *Mitteilungen
über Goethe. Aus mündlichen und schriftlichen, gedruckten und
ungedruckten Quellen.* 2 vols. Berlin: Verlag von Duncker und
Humblot, 1841, pp. 563-5.
Rpt. No. 1921-20.
/CHROMATICS

1841-13 **Riemer**, Friedrich Wilhelm. "IV. Naturforscher." In his *Mitteilungen über Goethe. Aus mündlichen und schriftlichen, gedruckten
und ungedruckten Quellen.* 2 vols. Berlin: Verlag von Duncker und

Humblot, 1841, pp. 679-86.
/EDITION/INFLUENCES

1841-14 **Runge**, Philipp Otto. *Hinterlassene Schriften: Zweyter Theil.*
Hamburg: Verlag von Friedrich Perthes, 1840. 554 pp.
Rpt. No. 1965-30.
Continuation of No. 1840-9.
"Herausgegeben von dessen ältestem Bruder."
/RESEARCH: CHROMATICS/FINE ARTS

1841-15 **Saint-Hilaire**, Geoffroy Isidore. "I. Considérations historiques
sur la zoologie. II. Additions aux considérations historiques sur la
zoologie." In his *Essais de zoologie générale, ou mémoires et notices
sur la zoologie générale, l'anthropologie et l'histoire de la science.*
Paris: de Roret, 1841, pp. 3-50; 51-97.
Rpt. of No. 1838-11.
/SAINT-HILAIRE, G DE/RECEPTION

1841-16 **Whewell**, William. "Fortgang der animalischen Morphologie."
In his *Geschichte der induktiven Wissenschaften, der Astronomie,
Physik, Mechanik, Chemie, Geologie, etc. von der frühesten bis zu
unserer Zeit.* Trans. J. J. v. Littrow. Stuttgart: Hoffmann'sche
Verlags-Buchhandlung, 1841, III, 511-29.
/ZOOLOGY/MORPHOLOGY/RECEPTION

1841-17 **Whewell**, William. "Vegatabilische Morphologie. Göthe und
Decandole." In his *Geschichte der induktiven Wissenschaften, der
Astronomie, Physik, Mechanik, Chemie, Geologie, etc. von der
frühesten bis zu unserer Zeit.* Trans. J. J. v. Littrow. Stuttgart:
Hoffmann'sche Verlags-Buchhandlung, 1841, III, 502-10.
German trans. of No. 1837-17.
/BOTANY/RECEPTION

1842-1 [anon.] "Goethe als Naturforscher." *Der Gesellschafter oder
Blätter für Geist und Herz*, 26 (1842), p. 152.
/GENERAL INTRODUCTION

1842-2 [anon.] "Goethe als Naturforscher." *Minerva. Ein Journal historischen und politischen Inhalts*, 3 (1846), 432-47.
/GENERAL INTRODUCTION

1842-3 **Agassiz**, Louis. "Erwiderung auf Dr. Karl Schimpers Angriffe."
Allgemeine Zeitung: Außerordentliche Beilage, No. 295, 22 October
1842, pp. 2-4.

/PALEONTOLOGY/GEOLOGY

1842-4 **Bavais**, Louis. "Examen organographique des Nectaires." In *Annales des sciences naturelles*. 2nd series, vol. 18. Paris: Fortin, Masson & Cie., 1842, pp. 152-84.
Trans. into German, No. 1843-3.
/RESEARCH: BOTANY

1842-5 **Blainville**, H[enri Marie Ducrotay]. de. "Goethe." In *Histoire des sciences de l'organisation et de leurs progrès, comme base de la philosophie.* Ed. F. L. M. Maupied. 3 vols. Paris/Lyon: Librairie classique de Perisse frères, 1845, III, 483-94.
/GENERAL INTRODUCTION

1842-6 **Buttel**, C[?]. D. von. "Zwei noch ungedruckte Briefe von Goethe, dessen Farbenlehre und die Insel Helgoland betreffend." *Der Freihafen*, 5, No. 4 (1842), 1-20.
/CHROMATICS

1842-7 **Frankl**, Ludwig August. "Graf Kaspar August und Goethe." *Sonntags-Blätter für heimatliche Interessen [Wien]*, No. 40, 2 October 1842, 705-8.
Rpt. No. 1886-3.
/STERNBERG, K VON/BOTANY/PALEONTOLOGY

1842-8 **Goethe**[, J. W. von]. *Goethe's nachgelassene Werke.* Vol. 18. Stuttgart/Tübingen: J. G. Cotta'sche Buchhandlung, 1842. viii, 320 pp.
Contains numerous scientific essays.
/EDITION

1842-9 **Goethe**[, J. W. von]. *Goethe's nachgelassene Werke.* Vol. 19. Stuttgart/Tübingen: J. G. Cotta'sche Buchhandlung, 1842. x, 308 pp.
Contains numerous scientific essays.
/EDITION

1842-10 **Goethe**[, J. W. von]. *Goethe's nachgelassene Werke.* Vol. 20. Stuttgart/Tübingen: J. G. Cotta'sche Buchhandlung, 1842. x, 332 pp.
Contains numerous scientific essays.
/EDITION

1842-11 **[Goethe**, J. W. von.] *Jana Wolfganga z Göthe pokus o pretvore rostlin [Goethe's Essay on the Metamorphosis of Plants].* Trans. J. Rod. Cejka. *Wlastimil. Prjtel oswety a zabawy*, 1842, pp. 152-75;

256-72.
/TRANSLATION: CZECH

1842-12 [**Goethe**, J. W. von.] *Saggio sulla metamorfosi delle piante.*
Trans. Pietro Robiati. Milano: Pirotta, 1842. xii, 112 pp.
/TRANSLATION: ITALIAN

1842-13 **Goethe**[, J. W. von]. "Sechzehn Tafeln zu Goethe's Farbenlehre
und Siebenundzwanzig Tafeln zu Goethe's sämmtlichen Werken zu
allen erschienen Ausgaben." Stuttgart/Tübingen: J. G. Cotta'scher
Verlag, 1842. 24 pp.
/EDITION

1842-14 **Hamburger**, Emanuel. "Symbolae quaedam ad doctrinam de
plantarum metamorphosi." Diss. Vratislava. Vratislaviae
[Vratislava]: Leopoldi [Leopold] Freund, 1842. 49 pp.
/BOTANY/MORPHOLOGY/HISTORY OF SCIENCE

1842-15 **Hegel**, Georg Wilhelm Friedrich. "Die Physik." In his *Vorlesungen über die Naturphilsophie als der Encyclopädie der
philosophischen Wissenschaften im Grundrisse.*" Vol. 7.1 of *Georg
Wilhelm Friedrich Hegel's Werke.* Ed. Carl Ludwig Michelet. Berlin: Verlag von Duncker und Humblot, 1842, pp. 127-422.
2nd edn. 1847.
/RESEARCH: OPTICS/RESEARCH: CHRO-
MATICS/OPTICS/CHROMATICS/NATURPHILOSOPHIE

1842-16 **Hegel**, Georg Wilhelm Friedrich. "Der vegetabilische
Organismus." In his *Vorlesungen über die Naturphilsophie als der
Encyclopädie der philosophischen Wissenschaften im Grundrisse.*"
Vol. 7.1 of *Georg Wilhelm Friedrich Hegel's Werke.* Ed. Carl Lud-
wig Michelet. Berlin: Verlag von Duncker und Humblot, 1842, pp.
470-549.
Rpt. of No. 1817-7.
2nd edn. 1847.
/BOTANY/RESEARCH: BOTANY/NATURPHILOSOPHIE

1842-17 **Mappes**, J[ohann]. M[ichael]. "Ueber Goethe als Naturforscher;
zugleich Jahresbericht." In his *Festreden gehalten im naturge-
schichtlichen Museum zu Frankfurt am Main.* Frankfurt am Main:
Johann David Sauerländer, 1842, pp. 143-51.
"Vorgetragen am 6. Mai 1832."
/GENERAL INTRODUCTION

1842-18 **Martius**, [Karl Fr. Ph.] von. "Gedächtnisrede auf A. P. de Candolle." *Flora oder allgemeine botanische Zeitung*, 25 (1842), 1-47.
> Rpt. of No. 1841-9.
> "Gehalten in der ausserordentl. Sitzung der k. b. botan. Gesellschaft am 28. November 1841."
> /BOTANY/CANDOLLE, A DE

1842-19 **Moquin-Tandon**, Alfred. "Von den Umbildungen der Organe in einander oder von den Umwandlungen." In his *Pflanzen-Teratologie. Lehre von dem regelwidrigen Wachsen und Bilden der Pflanzen.* Trans. and annotated by Johann Conrad Schauer. Berlin: Haude und Spenersche Buchhandlung, 1842, pp. 179-86.
> Trans. into German of No. 1841-11.
> /BOTANY/MORPHOLOGY/RECEPTION

1842-20 **Robiati**, Pietro. "Cenno preliminare del traduttore [Translator's Preface]." In *Saggio sulla Metamorfosi delle piante di G. W. Goethe.* Trans. Pietro Robiati. Milano: Tipografia e Libreria Pirotta e C., 1842, pp. xi-xii.
> In Italian.
> /BOTANY/MORPHOLOGY

1843-1 **[anon.]** "Goethe and Swedenborg." *The Dial: A Magazine for Literature, Philosophy, and Religion*, 3, No. 11 (1943), 416.
> /CHROMATICS/SWEDENBORG, E

1843-2 **[anon.]** "Schelling und Göthe." *Die Grenzboten. Eine deutsche Revue*, 2, No. 20 (1843), 533-5.
> /SCHELLING, F VON

1843-3 **Bavais**, Louis. "Organographische Untersuchung der Nectarien [excerpt]." Trans. and abbrev. A. Schnizlein. *Flora oder allgemeine botanische Zeitung*, NS 1 (1843), 265-77.
> German trans. of No. 1842-4.
> /RESEARCH: BOTANY

1843-4 **Bernhardi**[, Johann Jacob]. "Ueber die Metamorphose der Pflanzen." *Flora oder allgemeine botanische Zeitung*, NS 1 (1843), 37-51; 53-67.
> /BOTANY

1843-5 **Carus**, C[arl]. G[ustav]. "Göthe's Verhältniß zur Natur und Naturwissenschaft." In his *Göthe. Zu dessen näherem Verständniß.*

Leipzig: August Weichardt, 1843. x, 188 pp.
Rpt. Nos. 1927-9, 1931-10, 1933-13, 1949-23 and 1977-13.
"Beigegeben ist eine Reihe bisher ungedruckter Briefe Göthe's
an den Herausgeber."
/GENERAL INTRODUCTION

1843-6 **Danzel**, Wilhelm. "Ueber Goethe's Spinozismus. Ein Beitrag zur
tiefern Würdigung des Dichters und Forschers." Hamburg: bei
Johann August Meißner, 1843. iv, 138 pp.
2nd edn. 1850.
/SPINOZA, B/PHILOSOPHY

1843-7 **Grüner**, Joseph Sebastian. "Goethes Briefwechsel und Gespräche
mit Grüner." *Wiener Zeitschrift für Kunst, Literatur, Theater und
Mode*, No. 3 (1843), 1033-5; 1041-3; 1049-51; 1057-60; 1065-8;
1073-6; 1081-4; 1089-92; 1097-1100; 1105-7; 1113-5; 1121-3; 1129-
32; 1137-9; 1145-8; 1153-7.
Cf. also No. 1853-3.
/GRÜNER, J/MINERALOGY

1843-8 **Link**, H[einrich]. F[riedrich]. "Gestalt der Pflanze im
Allgemeinen. Verhältnissmässige Entwickelung der Theile.
Metamorphose und Prolepsis." In *Vorlesungen über die Kräuter-
kunde für Freunde der Wissenschaft, der Natur, und der Gärten*. Vol.
I.1. Berlin: Verlag von C. G. Lüderitz, 1843, pp. 28-39.
/RESEARCH: BOTANY

1843-9 **Link**, H[einrich]. F[riedrich]. "Morphologie der Pflanzen.
Terminologie." In *Vorlesungen über die Kräuterkunde für Freunde
der Wissenschaft, der Natur, und der Gärten*. Vol. I.1. Berlin: Verlag von C. G. Lüderitz, 1843, pp. 167-84.
/RESEARCH: BOTANY

1843-10 **Schultz**, C[arl] H[einrich]. "Göthes Metamorphosenlehre." In
his *Die Anaphytose oder Verjüngung der Pflanzen. Ein Schlüssel zur
Erklärung des Wachsens, Blühens und Fruchttragens, mit praktischen
Rücksichten auf die Kultur der Pflanzen*. Berlin: Verlag von August
Hirschwald, 1843, pp. 12-14.
/BOTANY/MORPHOLOGY

1843-11 **Wilde**, Emil. "Die Einwürfe Goethe's gegen die Newtonsche
Theorie." In *Von Newton bis Euler*. Pt. 2 of his *Geschichte der
Optik, vom Ursprunge dieser Wissenschaft bis auf die gegenwärtige
Zeit*. Berlin: Rücker und Püchler, 1843, pp. 153-217.

/CHROMATICS/OPTICS/NEWTON, I

1843-12 **Wilde**, Emil. "Die Farben-Terminologie Goethe's." In *Von Newton bis Euler*. Pt. 2 of his *Geschichte der Optik, vom Ursprunge dieser Wissenschaft bis auf die gegenwärtige Zeit*. Berlin: Rücker und Püchler, 1843, pp. 218-25.
/CHROMATICS

1844-1 **Carus**, Carl Gustav. "Vom gegenwärtigen Stande der wissenschaftlich begründeten Cranioscopie. Ein öffentlicher Vortrag gehalten am 3. Februar 1844 zu Leipzig." Nürnberg: Verlag von Theodor Cramer, 1844. 59 pp.
/RESEARCH: OSTEOLOGY

1844-2 **Rosenkranz**, Karl. "Apologie der Göthe'schen Farbenlehre." In his *Georg Wilhelm Friedrich Hegel's Leben*. Berlin: Verlag von Duncker und Humblot, 1844, pp. 339-40.
/CHROMATICS

1844-3 **Schleiden**, M[atthias]. J[acob]. "Botanische Notizen. 4) Zur Geschichte der Metamorphose." In his *Beiträge zur Botanik: Gesammelte Aufsätze*. Vol. I. Leipzig: Verlag von Wilh. Engelmann, 1844, p. 9.
/BOTANY/RECEPTION

1844-4 **Schleiden**, M[atthias]. J[acob]. "Einige Blicke auf die Entwicklungsgeschichte des vegetabilischen Organismus bei den Phanerogamen." In his *Beiträge zur Botanik: Gesammelte Aufsätze*. Vol. I. Leipzig: Verlag von Wilh. Engelmann, 1844, pp. 86-120.
/RESEARCH: BOTANY

1845-1 ***Gilette**[, ?]. "Goethe." In *Dictionnaire des sciences naturelles, par plusieurs professeurs du Jardin du Roi*, 61 (1845), p. 155.
/GENERAL INTRODUCTION

1845-2 ***[Goethe**, J. W. von.] "Priroda [Nature]." Trans. Iskander [A. Herzen]. *Otech. Zapiski*, cp. 6, 39, No. 2 (1845), 116-18.
Rpt. No. 1954-11.
[Zhitomirskaia 2189]
/TRANSLATION: RUSSIAN

1845-3 **Hegel**, Georg Wilhelm Friedrich. *Encyclopädie der philosophischen Wissenschaften im Grundrisse. Zum Gebrauch seiner Vorlesungen*. 4th edn. Berlin: Verlag von Duncker und Humblot, 1845.

xxxii, 528 pp.
Rpt. of No. 1817-7.
/CHROMATICS/NATURPHILOSOPHIE/NEWTON, I

1845-4 **Humboldt**, Alexander von. *Kosmos. Entwurf einer physischen Weltbeschreibung.* 5 vols. Stuttgart/Tübingen: J. G. Cotta'scher Verlag, 1845-1862.
Trans. into Danish, Dutch, English, French, Hungarian, Italian, Polish, Russian, Spanish, and Swedish [see S 1781].
/RESEARCH: GEOGRAPHY

1845-5 **Kirschleger**, Frédéric. "Essai historique de la tératologie végétale." Diss. Strasbourg. Strasbourg: G. Silbermann, 1845. 71 pp.
/RESEARCH: MORPHOLOGY/RESEARCH: PATHOLOGY

1845-6 ***Link**, H[einrich]. F[riedrich]. *Vorlesungen über die Kräuterkunde für Freunde der Wissenschaft, der Natur, und der Gärten.* Vol. I.2. Berlin: Verlag von C. G. Lüderitz, 1845.
/RESEARCH: BOTANY

1845-7 **Martins**, Ch[arles]. "La métamorphose des plantes de Goethe et la loi de symétrie d'Aug. Pyr. De Candolle." *La Revue Indépendante*, 16 (1845), 38-60.
/BOTANY/MORPHOLOGY/RECEPTION

1845-8 **Mohl**, Hugo von. "Beobachtungen über die Umwandlung von Antheren in Carpelle." In his *Vermischte Schriften*. Tübingen: Ludwig Freidrich Fues, 1845, pp. 28-44.
Rpt. of No. 1836-9.
/RESEARCH: BOTANY/RESEARCH: MORPHOLOGY

1846-1 **Düntzer**, Heinrich. "Göthes Gutachten über die Unterdrückung von Oken's Isis." *Kölnische Zeitung*, No. 259, 16 September; No. 260, 17 September 1846.
Rpt. No. 1849-3.
/OKEN, L/[OKEN'S] *ISIS*

1846-2 **Goethe**[, J. W. von]. "Das Medizinische." In his *Ephemerides. Was man treibt, Heut dies und morgen das. 1770.* In *Briefe und Aufsätze von Goethe aus den Jahren 1766 bis 1786.* Ed. A Schöll. Weimar: Druck und Verlag des Landes-Industrie-Comptoirs, 1846, pp. 75-8.
/EDITION

1846-3 **Goethe**[, J. W. von]. "Naturlehre." In his *Ephemerides. Was man treibt, Heut dies und morgen das. 1770.* In *Briefe und Aufsätze von Goethe aus den Jahren 1766 bis 1786.* Ed. A Schöll. Weimar: Druck und Verlag des Landes-Industrie-Comptoirs, 1846, pp. 78-81.
/EDITION

1846-4 **Goethe**[, J. W. von]. "Naturhistorisches." In *Nachträge zu Goethe's sämmtlichen Werken.* Pt. 2. Coll. and ed. Eduard Boas. Leipzig: Verlags-Magazin, 1846, pp. 250-56.
/EDITION

1846-5 **Mercklin**, Carl Eugen v[on]. *Zur Entwicklungsgeschichte der Blattgestalten.* Jena: Carl Hochhausen, 1846.
/RESEARCH: BOTANY/RESEARCH: MORPHOLOGY

1846-6 **Wigand**, Albert. "Göthe." In his *Kritik und Geschichte von der Metamorphose der Pflanze.* Leipzig: in Commission bei Wilhelm Engelmann, 1846, pp. 41-50.
/BOTANY/MORPHOLOGY

1847-1 **Carus**, Carl Gustav. *System der Physiologie.* 3 pts. 2nd rev. and exp. edn. Leipzig: F. A. Brockhaus, 1847-9.
Rpt. of No. 1838-1.
/RESEARCH: PHYSIOLOGY

1847-2 **Clemens**, Aloys. "Goethes Farbenlehre, zum 28. August in einer Skizze dargestellt." *Morgenblatt für gebildete Leser,* 41, No. 209, 1 September 1847, 833-4; No. 210, 2 September 1847, 838-9; No. 211, 3 September 1847, 841-2; No. 212 4 September 1847, 846-7; No. 213, 6 September 1847, 849-50.
/CHROMATICS

1847-3 **Clemens**, A[loys]. "Ueber Goethes Naturbetrachtung." *Morgenblatt für gebildete Leser,* 41, No. 34, 9 February 1847, 138-40.
/GENERAL INTRODUCTION/PHILOSOPHY

1847-4 **Oken**[, Lorenz]. "Professor Oken, über die Schädelwirbel. Gegen Hegel und Göthe." *Isis von Oken,* No. 7, 1847, cols. 557-60.
/RESEARCH: OSTEOLOGY/HEGEL, G

1847-5 **[Oken**, Lorenz.] "[Review of:] St. Hilaire, Isidore G[eoffroy]. *Vie, Travaux et Doctrine scientifique d'Etienne Geoffroy St. Hilaire.* Paris: Bertrand/Strasbourg: Levrault, 1847." *Isis von Oken,* No. 11,

1847, cols. 877-[8].
    /RESEARCH: OSTEOLOGY/SAINT-HILAIRE, G DE/SAINT-
    HILAIRE, I DE

1847-6 **Rosenkranz**, Karl. "Göthe und die Naturwissenschaft." In his
Göthe und seine Werke. Königsberg: Verlag von Gebrüder
Bornträger, 1847, pp. 51-65.
    Rpt. No. 1856-7.
    /GENERAL INTRODUCTION

1847-7 **Schimper**, Karl. "Göthe in der Naturwissenschaft." In his
Gedichte von Karl Schimper. 1840-1846. Mannheim: Verlag von
Heinrich Hoff, 1847, pp. 302-4; 342-5.
    Rpt. No. 1850-5.
    /RECEPTION

1847-8 **Schultz Schultzenstein**, Carl Heinr[ich]. *Neues System der Mor-*
phologie der Pflanzen nach den organischen Bildungsgesetzen als
Grundlage eines wissenschaftlichen Studiums der Botanik besonders
auf Universitäten und Schulen. Berlin: Verlag von August
Hirschwald, 1847. xxiv, 246 pp.
    /RESEARCH: MORPHOLOGY/RESEARCH: BOTANY

1847-9 **Viehoff**, Heinrich. "Die Metamorphose der Pflanzen." In his
Periode der classischen Kunstpoesie 1783-1805. Pt. 2 of *Goethe's*
Gedichte erläutert und auf ihre Veranlassungen, Quellen und Vor-
bilder zurückgeführt, nebst Variantensammlung und Nachlese.
Düsseldorf: Verlag der Bötticher'schen Buchhandlung, 1847, pp. 372-
83.
    /WORKS: LYRICS

1847-10 **Vischer**, Friedrich Theodor. "Die Farbe." In *Die Lehre von*
dem Naturschönen. Pt. II.1 of his *Aesthetik oder Wissenschaft des*
Schönen. Zum Gebrauche für Vorlesungen. Reutlingen/Leipzig: Carl
Mäcken's Verlag, 1847, 37-55.
    /RESEARCH: CHROMATICS/AESTHETICS

1847-11 **Whewell**, William. "Discovery of the Law of Dispersion by
Refraction." In his *History of the Inductive Sciences, from the Ear-*
liest to the Present Time. Rev. edn. 3 vols. London: John W.
Parker, 1847, II, 382-95.
    Rpt. of No. 1837-16.
    /OPTICS/CHROMATICS/NEWTON, I/HISTORY OF
    SCIENCE

1847-12 **Whewell**, William. "Progress of Animal Morphology." In his *History of the Inductive Sciences, from the Earliest to the Present Time*. Rev. edn. 3 vols. London: John W. Parker, 1847, III, 487-98.
/ZOOLOGY/MORPHOLOGY/RECEPTION

1847-13 **Whewell**, William. "Vegetable Morphology. Göthe. De Candolle." In his *History of the Inductive Sciences, from the Earliest to the Present Time*. Rev. edn. 3 vols. London: John W. Parker, 1847, III, 475-86.
Cf. No. 1837-17.
/BOTANY/CANDOLLE, A DE/HISTORY OF SCIENCE

1848-1 ***Carus**, Carl Gustav. "Frommsein und Pietismus. Fragment eines vor ungefähr 30 Jahren an einen Freund nach L. . . . . . geschriebenen Briefes." In his *Mnemosyne, Blätter aus Gedenk- und Tagebüchern*, 1848.
Rpt. No. 1922-7.
/NATURPHILOSOPHIE

1848-2 **[Clemens**, Aloys.] "Goethe's geognostische Ansichten." *Morgenblatt für gebildete Leser*, 42, No. 206 (1848), 822-4.
Rpt. No. 1857-1.
/GEOLOGY

1848-3 **[Goethe**, J. W. von.] "Extracts from the translation of Goethe's theory of colours." In Eastlake, Charles Lock. *Contributions to the literature of the fine arts*. London: John Murray, 1848, pp. 288-324.
Rpt. (partial) No. 1870-2.
/TRANSLATION: ENGLISH

1848-4 **Owen**, Richard. *On the Archetype and Homologies of the Vertebrate Skeleton*. London: John van Voorst, 1848. viii, 203 pp.
/RESEARCH: OSTEOLOGY/RESEARCH: COMPARATIVE ANATOMY

1848-5 **Schleiden**, M[atthias]. J[acob]. "Die Morphologie der Pflanzen." In his *Die Pflanze und ihr Leben. Populäre Vorträge*. Leipzig: Verlag von Wilhelm Engelmann, 1848, pp. 75-100.
Cf. exp. edns., Nos. 1850-6, 1852-11 and 1855-4.
Trans. into English, No. 1848-6.
/RESEARCH: BOTANY/RESEARCH: MORPHOLOGY

1848-6 *Schleiden, M[atthias]. J[acob]. *The Plant: A Biography. In a series of popular lectures.* Tr. Arthur Henfrey. London, 1848. English trans. of No. 1848-5.
/RESEARCH: BOTANY/RESEARCH: MORPHOLOGY

1849-1 **Berthold**, Arnold Adolph. "Am 28. August des J. 100 nach der Geburt Goethe's in einem Kreise Göttingischer Verehrer und Verehrinnen dieses grossen Genius über seine Anatome comparata." Göttingen: Vandenhoeck u. Ruprecht, 1849. 32 pp.
/ZOOLOGY/COMPARATIVE ANATOMY

1849-2 **Carus**, Carl Gustav. "Göthe und seine Bedeutung für diese und die künftige Zeit. Eine Festrede gehalten zu Dresden am 28. August 1849." Dresden: in Commission bei H. M. Gottschalck, 1849. 16 pp.
    Rpt. Nos. 1938-3, 1943-2 and 1957-3.
/GENERAL INTRODUCTION

1849-3 **Düntzer**, Heinrich. "Göthes Gutachten über die Unterdrückung von Oken's Isis." In his *Zu Goethe's Jubelfeier. Studien zu Goethe's Werken.* Elberfeld/Iserlohn: Julius Bädeker, 1849, pp. 345-89.
    Rpt. of No. 1846-1.
/OKEN, L/[OKEN'S] *ISIS*

1849-4 **Gutrauer**, Gottschalk Eduard. "Aus Goethes Archive. Zum 25. August 1849." *Deutsche Vierteljahrs Schrift*, 3.2 (1849), 366-74.
/JUNGIUS, J/BOTANY

1849-5 **Gutrauer**, Gottschalk Eduard. *Joachim Jungius und sein Zeitalter. Nebst Goethe's Fragmenten über Jungius.* Stuttgart/Tübingen: J. G. Cotta'scher Verlag, 1850. xii, 383 pp.
/EDITION/JUNGIUS, J

1849-6 **Humboldt**, Alexander von. "Ideen zu einer Physiognomik der Gewächse." In his *Ansichten der Natur, mit wissenschaftlichen Erläuterungen.* 2 vols. 3rd rev. and exp. edn. Stuttgart/Tübingen: J. G. Cotta'scher Verlag, 1849, II, 1-248.
    Trans. into Dutch, English, French, and Russian [see S 1782].
/RESEARCH: BOTANY/BOTANY

1849-7 **Müglich**, J[?]. K. A. G. "Göthe's Farbenlehre." In his *Die Hegel-Weisheit und ihre Früchte. Oder: Arnold Ruge mit seinen Genossen in den hallischen Jahrbüchern und in der Pauluskirche zu Frankfurt und anderswo. Briefe an den Pastor Fix.* Regensburg:

Verlag von G. Joseph Manz, 1849, pp. 371-2.
/CHROMATICS

1849-8 **Schuchardt**, Christian. *Goethes Sammlungen. 3. Teil: Mineralogische und andere naturwissenschaftliche Sammlungen: Mit einer Vorrede der Gebrüder von Goethe.* Jena: Friedrich Frommann, 1849. xii, 297 pp.
/GOETHE'S COLLECTIONS

1850-1 [**Goethe**, J. W. von.] "Leben und Verdienste des Doctor Joachim Jungius Rektors zu Hamburg. Von Goethe. Aus Goethes nachgelassenen Schriften." In *Joachim Jungius und sein Zeitalter. Nebst Goethe's Fragmenten über Jungius.* Stuttgart/Tübingen: J. G. Cotta'scher Verlag, 1850, pp. 183-209.
= WA II 7, 105ff.
/EDITION/JUNGIUS, J

1850-2 **Guhrauer**, G[ottschalk]. E[duard]. *Joachim Jungius und sein Zeitalter: Nebst Goethe's Fragmenten über Jungius.* Stuttgart und Tübingen: J. G. Cotta'scher Verlag, 1850. xii, 383 pp.
/JUNGIUS, J/EDITION/MORPHOLOGY

1850-3 **Reichenbach**, Heinrich Gottlieb Ludwig. "Blick in die Geschichte der botanischen Systematik." In *Handbuch des natürlichen Pflanzensystems nach allen seinen Classen, [etc.] in ihrer Richtung aus der Metamorphose und geognostischen [!] Verbreitung, wie die fortgebildete Zeit deren Anschauung fordert.* 2nd edn. Leipzig: Arnoldische Buchhandlung, 1850, pp. 1-18.
/RESEARCH: MORPHOLOGY/RESEARCH: BOTANY
/BOTANY/MORPHOLOGY/HISTORY OF SCIENCE

1850-4 **Reichenbach**, H[einrich]. G[ottlieb Ludwig]. "Versuch einer Fortbildung von Göthe's Metamorphose zu einer Beschauung des Pflanzenreichs in seiner Totalität." In *Handbuch des natürlichen Pflanzensystems nach allen seinen Classen, [etc.] in ihrer Richtung aus der Metamorphose und geognostischen [!] Verbreitung, wie die fortgebildete Zeit deren Anschauung fordert.* 2nd edn. Leipzig: Arnoldische Buchhandlung, 1850, pp. 19-96.
Rev. edn. of No. 1837-12.
/RESEARCH: BOTANY/RESEARCH: MORPHOLOGY
/BOTANY /MORPHOLOGY

1850-5 **Schimper**, Karl. "Göthe in der Naturwissenschaft." In his *Gedichte von Karl Schimper. 1840-1846.* 2nd edn. Stuttgart: Verlag von Franz Köhler, 1850, pp. 302-4; 342-5.
Rpt. of No. 1847-7.
/RECEPTION

1850-6 **Schleiden**, M[atthias]. J[acob]. "Die Morphologie der Pflanzen." In his *Die Pflanze und ihr Leben. Populäre Vorträge.* 2nd exp. edn. Leipzig: Verlag von Wilhelm Engelmann, 1850, pp. 77-102.
Exp. edn. of No. 1848-5.
/RESEARCH: MORPHOLOGY/RESEARCH: BOTANY

1851-1 **Martin**, Charles. *De la tératologie végétale, de ses rapports avec la tératologie animale. Thèse présentée a la Faculté de Médecine de Montpellier.* Montpellier: Jean Martel aîné, imprimeur de la Faculté de Médecine, 1851. 72 pp.
/RESEARCH: PATHOLOGY/RESEARCH: BOTANY

1851-2 **Schopenhauer**, Arthur. "Zur Farbenlehre." In his *Parerga und Paralipomena.* Berlin: Druck und Verlag von A. W. Hayn, 1851, §§ 103-107, pp. 143-67.
Rpt. Nos. 1862-17 and 1891-15.
3rd edn. 1874.
/CHROMATICS/RESEARCH: CHROMATICS

1852-1 *[anon.]. "Goethe as a Man of Science." *Eclectic Magazine,* 27 (1852), 460-75.
/GENERAL INTRODUCTION

1852-2 **Brücke**, Ernst von. "Über die Farben, welche trübe Medien im auffallenden und durchfallenden Lichte zeigen." *Sitzungsberichte der Mathematisch-Naturwissenschaftlichen Classe der Kaiserlichen Akademie der Wissenschaften,* 9 (1852), 530-49.
/CHROMATICS

1852-3 **Feuchtersleben**, Ernst Freiherr von. "Goethe's naturwissenschaftliche Ansichten." In his *Sämtliche Werke. Mit Ausschluß der rein medizinischen.* Ed. Friedrich Hebbel. 6 vols. Wien: Verlag von Karl Gerold und Sohn, 1852, V, 83-116.
/GENERAL INTRODUCTION

1852-4 **Göschel**, Carl Friedrich. "Göthe und Schiller, oder die Metamorphose der Pflanzen und die Kantische Philosophie." In his *Unterhaltungen zur Schilderung Göthescher Dicht- und Denkweise. Ein Denkmal.* 3 vols. 2nd edn. Leipzig: Dyk'sche Buchhandlung, 1852, II, pp. 24-31.
Rpt. of No. 1834-3.
/SCHILLER, F/KANT, I/PHILOSOPHY/BOTANY/MORPHOLOGY

1852-5 **Göschel**, Carl Friedrich. "Zur Gottes-, Geistes- und Naturphilosophie." In his *Unterhaltungen zur Schilderung Göthescher Dicht- und Denkweise. Ein Denkmal.* 2 vols. 2nd edn. Leipzig: Dyk'sche Buchhandlung, 1852, pp. 24-31.
Rpt. of No. 1834-5.

/CHROMATICS/RESEARCH: CHROMATICS /NATUR-
PHILOSOPHIE

1852-6 **Goethe**[, J. W. von]. "Beschreibung der karlsbader Müllerischen
Steinsammlung. Zur Kenntniss der böhmischen Gebirge." Carlsbad:
Gebrüder Franieck, 1852. 31 pp.
/EDITION

1852-7 **Goethe**[, J. W. von]. "David Knoll'sche Sammlung von Sprudel-
Steinen, roh oder geschliffen." Carlsbad: Gebrüder Franieck, 1852.
8 pp.
/EDITION

1852-8 [**Goethe**, J. W. von.] "Naturbetrachtung und Naturwissenschaft."
In *Goethe in Briefen und Gesprächen. Sammlung der brieflichen und
mündlichen Bemerkungen und Betrachtungen Goethe's über Welt und
Menschen, Wissenschaft, Literatur und Kunst. Supplement zu den
Werken des Dichters.* Berlin: Verlag der Vereins-Buchhandlung,
1852, pp. 77-102.
/EDITION: SELECTIONS

1852-9 [**Lewes**, George Henry.] "Goethe as a man of science." *The
Westminster Review*, NS 2 (1852), 479-506.
Cf. No. 1855-2.
/BIOLOGY/GENERAL INTRODUCTION

1852-10 **P[lanchon]**, J[ules]. É[mile]. "Pavonia (Goethea) strictiflora."
In *Flore des serres et des jardins de l'Europe, ou descriptions et figures des plantes les plus rares et les plus méritantes nouvellement
introduites sur le continent ou en Angleterre.* Ed. C. L. Blume, Louis
van Houtte, and J. E. Planchon. Vol 8. Gand: n.p., 1852-1853, pp.
175-6.
/BOTANY/HISTORY OF SCIENCE/ZOOLOGY/GEOLOGY

1852-11 **Schleiden**, M[atthias]. J[acob]. "Die Morphologie der Pflanzen." In his *Die Pflanze und ihr Leben. Populäre Vorträge.* 3rd
exp. edn. Leipzig: Verlag von Wilhelm Engelmann, 1852, pp. 81-
106.
Exp. edn. of No. 1848-5.
/RESEARCH: MORPHOLOGY/RESEARCH: BOTANY

1852-12 **Unger**, Franz. "Die Pflanze als beblaetterte Achse." In his
Botanische Briefe. Wien: Verlag von Carl Gerold & Sohn, 1852, pp.
69-74.

/RESEARCH: BOTANY/RESEARCH: MORPHOLOGY/BO-
TANY/MORPHOLOGY

1852-13 **Welcker**, Hermann. "Goethe." In his "Ueber Irradiation und
einige andere Erscheinungen des Sehens." Diss. Universität Gießen.
Giessen: J. Ricker'sche Buchhandlung, §§23-5, pp. 62-4.
/CHROMATICS/RESEARCH: CHROMATICS

1853-1 **[anon.]** "Goethe und der Scharfrichter Huß zu Eger." *Die
Grenzboten. Zeitschrift für Politik und Literatur*, 12 (1853), 241-5.
Rpt. No. 1901-7.
/FREYTAG, G/MINERALOGY

1853-2 **Bechstein**, Ludwig. *Natur und Poesie. Berggeschichte aus
Carlsbad.* In *Eine Nacht im Spessartwalde. Natur und Poesie. Der
Pakt mit dem Bösen. Drei Novellen.* Vol. 4 of his *Hainsterne.
Berg-, Wald- und Wander-Geschichten.* Halle: C. E. Pfeiffer, 1853,
pp. 77-182.
/DIETRICH, F/BOTANY

1853-3 **Briefwechsel** *und mündlicher Verkehr zwischen Goethe und dem
Rathe Grüner.* Leipzig: Verlag von Gustav Mayer, 1853. viii, 248
pp.
Cf. No. 1843-7.
/EDITION/GRÜNER, J/MINERALOGY

1853-4 **Briefwechsel** *zwischen Goethe und Staatsrath Schultz.* Ed. Hein-
rich Düntzer. Leipzig: Dyk'sche Buchhandlung, 1853. x, 410 pp.
Cf. Nos. 1853-10 and 1853-11.
/RESEARCH: CHROMATICS/SCHULTZ, C

1853-5 **Clemens**, Aloys. "Goethe der Dichter und Goethe der Natur-
forscher. Bruchstück aus der zweiten vermehrten und verbesserte
Auflage der Schrift 'Goethe als Naturforscher'." *Frankfurter Konver-
sationsblatt. Belletristische Beilage zur Postzeitung*, No. 204, 27
August 1853, 814-15; No. 205, 29 August 1853, 818-19; No. 206, 30
August 1853, 822-3.
Rpt. of No. 1841-4.
/GENERAL INTRODUCTION/LITERATURE

1853-6 **Dove**, H[einrich]. W[ilhelm]. "Die neuere Farbenlehre mit andern
chromatischen Theorieen verglichen." In his *Darstellung der Farbenlehre und optische Studien.* Berlin: Verlag von G. W. F. Müller,
1853, pp. 1-158.

Rpt. of No. 1838-2.
/CHROMATICS/HISTORY OF SCIENCE

1853-7 [**Goethe**, J. W. von.] "Natural philosophy." In *Goethe's opinions on the world, mankind, literature, science, and art.* Trans. Otto Wenckstern. London: John W. Parker and Son, 1853, pp. 60-68.
/TRANSLATION: ENGLISH

1853-8 **Helmholtz**, Hermann von. "Ueber Goethe's naturwissenschaftliche Arbeiten." *Allgemeine Monatsschrift für Literaturwissenschaft und Literatur*, 1853, 383-98.
> Rpt. Nos. 1865-4, 1873-1, 1876-4, 1884-8, 1889-6, 1896-9, 1899-16, 1903-16, 1904-19, 1905-17, 1917-24, 1926-15, 1966-14, 1971-21 and 1977-26.
> Trans. into French, No. 1870-5.
> Trans. into Italian, No. 1900-7.
> Trans. into English, No. 1971-20.
> "Vortrag Königsberg 1853."
/GENERAL INTRODUCTION

1853-9 **Schmidt**, Oscar. *Göthe's Verhältniß zu den organischen Naturwissenschaften.* Berlin: Verlag von Wilhelm Hertz (Besser'sche Buchhandlung), 1853. 24 pp.
> "Vortrag gehalten im wissenschaftlichen Verein zu Berlin."
/BIOLOGY/MORPHOLOGY/RECEPTION

1853-10 [**Schultz**, Christoph Friedrich Ludwig.] "Die subjektiven Höfe." In *Briefwechsel zwischen Goethe und Staatsrath Schultz.* Ed. Heinrich Düntzer. Leipzig: Dyk'sche Buchhandlung, 1853, pp. 398-400.
> Rpt. of No. 1823-13.
/RESEARCH: CHROMATICS/CHROMATICS

1853-11 **Schultz**, Christoph Friedrich Ludwig. "Über physiologe Gesichts- und Farbenerscheinungen." In *Briefwechsel zwischen Goethe und Staatsrath Schultz.* Ed. Heinrich Düntzer. Leipzig: Dyk'sche Buchhandlung, 1853, pp. 391-8.
> Rpt. of No. 1816-6.
> Rpt. 2nd edn. 1856.
/RESEARCH: CHROMATICS

1854-1 [**anon.**]. "Die Metamorphose der Pflanze." In *Unterhaltungen am häuslichen Herd.* Ed. Karl Gutzkow. Leipzig: F. A. Brockhaus, 1854, vol. 2, pp. 814-15.
/BOTANY/MORPHOLOGY

1854-2 **Düntzer**, Heinrich. "Ein Prioritätsstreit zwischen Oken und Goethe." *Morgenblatt für gebildete Leser*, No. 35, 27 August; No. 36, 3 September; No. 37, 10 September 1854, 829-34; 841-7; 876-80.
/OKEN, L/MORPHOLOGY/RESEARCH: MORPHOLOGY

1854-3 **Saint-Hilaire**, Isidore Geoffroy. "Définitions diverses de l'espèce organique et résumé des vues émises sur les rapports des êtres actuels avec ceux des temps antérieurs." *Histoire naturelle générale des règnes organiques, principalement étudiée chez l'homme et les animaux.* 3 vols. Paris: librairie de Victor Masson, 1854, II, 365-446.
/RESEARCH: MORPHOLOGY/RESEARCH: BIOLOGY
/MORPHOLOGY/BIOLOGY/RECEPTION

1854-4 **Saint-Hilaire**, Isidore Geoffroy. "Histoire naturelle générale des règnes organiques. Introduction historique." In his *Histoire naturelle générale des règnes organiques, principalement étudiée chez l'homme et les animaux.* 3 vols. Paris: librairie de Victor Masson, 1854, I, 1-164.
/RESEARCH: MORPHOLOGY/RESEARCH: COMPARA-
TIVE ANATOMY/MORPHOLOGY/COMPARATIVE ANA-
TOMY/RECEPTION

1854-5 **Saint-Hilaire**, Isidore Geoffroy. "Notion générale du type." In his *Histoire naturelle générale des règnes organiques, principalement étudiée chez l'homme et les animaux.* 3 vols. Paris: librairie de Victor Masson, 1854, II, 303-6.
/RESEARCH: MORPHOLOGY/RESEARCH: COMPARA-
TIVE ANATOMY/MORPHOLOGY/COMPARATIVE ANA-
TOMY

1854-6 **Saint-Hilaire**, Isidore Geoffroy. "Des trois écoles principales en histoire naturelle, et de leurs vues sur la méthode." In his *Histoire naturelle générale des règnes organiques, principalement étudiée chez l'homme et les animaux.* 3 vols. Paris: librairie de Victor Masson, 1854, I, 281-336.
/RESEARCH: MORPHOLOGY/RESEARCH: COMPARA-
TIVE ANATOMY/MORPHOLOGY/COMPARATIVE ANA-
TOMY/RECEPTION

1854-7 **Schopenhauer**, Arthur. "§14. Einige Zugaben zu Göthes Lehre von der Entstehung der physischen Farben." In his *Ueber das Sehn und die Farben: Eine Abhandlung.* 2nd rev. and exp. edn. Leipzig:

Verlag von Johann Friedrich Hartknoch, 1854, pp. 77-86.
Rpt. No. 1870-11.
Not in the 1st edn.
/RESEARCH: CHROMATICS/CHROMATICS

1854-8 **Winckler**, Emil. "Joh. Wolfgang von Göthe." In his *Geschichte der Botanik*. Frankfurt a. M.: Literarische Anstalt (J. Rütten), 1854, pp. 389-91.
/BOTANY

1855-1 **Frauenstädt**, Julius. "Goethes Farbenlehre, verteidigt durch Arthur Schopenhauer." *Blätter für literarische Unterhaltung*, 2 (1855), 674-9.
/CHROMATICS/SCHOPENHAUER, A/RESEARCH: CHROMATICS

1855-2 **Lewes**, G[eorge]. H[enry]. "The poet as a man of science." In his *The life and works of Goethe: with sketches of his age and contemporaries from published and unpublished sources*. 2 vols. London: David Nutt, 1855, II, 113-60.
Rpt. Nos. 1858-10, 1864-3 and 1873-2.
Trans. into German, No. 1857-4.
Cf. No. 1852-9.
/GENERAL INTRODUCTION

1855-3 **P[reller].**, L[udwig]. "Goethes letzter Aufenthalt in Ilmenau, nach einer Mittheilung des Herrn Berginspektor Mahr zu Kammerberg bei Ilmenau." *Weimarer Sonntags-Blatt*, No. 29, 15 July 1855, 123-4.
/MAHR, J/MINERALOGY

1855-4 **Schleiden**, M[atthias]. J[acob]. "Die Morphologie der Pflanzen." In his *Die Pflanze und ihr Leben. Populäre Vorträge.* 4th exp. edn. Leipzig: Verlag von Wilhelm Engelmann, 1855, pp. 63-89.
Exp. edn. of No. 1848-5.
Trans. into French, No. 1859-9.
5th rev. edn. 1855 (pagination unchanged; (1828]).
/RESEARCH: MORPHOLOGY/RESEARCH: BOTANY

1855-5 **Stiehler**, August Wilhelm. "Goethe in seinem Verhältniß zum Neptunismus und Vulkanismus." *Deutsches Museum: Zeitschrift für Literatur, Kunst und öffentliches Leben*, 5, No. 30 (1855), 124-37.
/GEOLOGY

1856-1 **[anon.]** "Goethe, Schopenhauer und Newton." *Frankfurter*

Museum. Süddeutsche Wochenschrift für Kunst, Literatur und öffentliches Leben, 2, No. 8, 23 February 1856, 64.
/CHROMATICS/SCHOPENAUER, A/NEWTON, I

1856-2 **Briefe** *des Großherzogs Carl August und Göthes an Döbereiner.* Ed. Oskar Schade. Weimar: Hermann Böhlau, 1856. 147 pp.
/DÖBEREINER, J/CARL AUGUST [GROSSHERZOG VON WEIMAR] /CHEMISTRY

1856-3 **Briefwechsel** *zwischen Goethe und Staatsrath Schultz.* Ed. Heinrich Düntzer. Leipzig: Dyk'sche Buchhandlung, 1853. x, 410, 55 pp.
    Rpt. of No. 1853-4.
    Cf. Nos. 1856-8 and 1956-9.
    /RESEARCH: CHROMATICS/SCHULTZ, C

1856-4 **Clemens**, Aloys. "Goethes Metamorphose der Pflanzen. Bruchstück aus der Schrift 'Goethe als Naturforscher' gezeichnet." *Frankfurter Konversationsblatt. Belletristische Beilage zur Postzeitung*, No. 206, 28 August - No. 209, 31 August 1856, 822-3; 826-7; 830-31; 834-5.
    /BOTANY/MORPHOLOGY

1856-5 **Reichenbach**, [Heinrich Gottl.] Ludwig. "Freunde und Kenner der Natur. I. König Friedrich August. II. Wolfgang Goethe. Zwei Vorträge." Dresden: Verlagsbuchhandlung von Rudolf Kuntze, 1856.
    Rpt. of No. 1856-6.
    /GENERAL INTRODUCTION

1856-6 **Reichenbach**, [Heinrich Gottl.] Ludwig. "Göthe als Naturforscher." *Allgemeine deutsche Naturhistorische Zeitung*, NS 2 (1856), 281-92.
    Rpt. No. 1856-5.
    /GENERAL INTRODUCTION

1856-7 **Rosenkranz**, Karl. "Göthe und die Naturwissenschaft." In his *Göthe und seine Werke.* 2nd rev. and exp. edn. Königsberg: Verlag von Gebrüder Bornträger, 1856, pp. 44-57.
    Rpt. of No. 1847-6.
    /GENERAL INTRODUCTION

1856-8 **[Schultz**, Christoph Friedrich Ludwig.] "Die subjektiven Höfe." In *Briefwechsel zwischen Goethe und Staatsrath Schultz.* Ed. Heinrich Düntzer. Leipzig: Dyk'sche Buchhandlung, 1856, pp. 398-400.

/RESEARCH: CHROMATICS

1856-9 [**Schultz**, Christoph Friedrich Ludwig.] "Über physiologe Gesichts- und Farbenerscheinungen (II)." In *Briefwechsel zwischen Goethe und Staatsrat Schultz*. Ed. Heinrich Düntzer. Leipzig: Dyk'sche Buchhandlung, 1856, pp. 391-8.
  /RESEARCH: CHROMATICS

1857-1 **Clemens**, Aloys. "Goethe's geognostische Ansichten." *Frankfurter Konversationsblatt*, Nos. 205-8 (1857), 818-19; 822-4; 826-7; 830-31.
  Rpt. of No. 1848-2.
  /GEOLOGY

1857-2 [**Goethe**, J. W. von.] "Nachricht von dem ilmenauischen Bergwesen, aufgesetzt im Mai 1781 von Goethe." In Diezmann, August. *Goethe und die lustige Zeit in Weimar. Mit einem Plane vom damaligen Weimar und mit einer bisher ungedruckten Abhandlung von Goethe*. Leipzig: Verlag von Ernst Keil, 1857, pp. 278-96.
  = WA II 13, 341-54
  /EDITION

1857-3 **Grävell**, F[riedrich]. *Göthe im Recht gegen Newton*. Berlin: Verlag von F. A. Herbig, 1857. 191 pp.
  Rpt. No. 1922-20.
  Rev. [anon]., *Kgl. privil. Berlinische Ztg. (Voss. Ztg.)*, 1860, 12 Februar (Nr. 37), 1. Beilage.
  Rev. Gustav von Quintus Icilius, *Kritische Zeitschrift für Chemie, Physik und Mathematik*, 1858, pp. 108-14; 206-26.
  /CHROMATICS/NEWTON, I

1857-4 **Lewes**, G[eorge]. H[enry]. "Goethe als Naturforscher." In his *Goethe's Leben und Schriften*. Trans. Julius Frese. 2 vols. Berlin: Verlag von Franz Duncker, 1857, II, 100-137.
  Rpt. Nos. 1858-9, 1882-17, 1885-13 and 1903-20.
  German trans. of No. 1855-2.
  /GENERAL INTRODUCTION

1857-5 **Schelling**, F[riedrich]. W[ilhelm]. J[oseph]. "Ueber den Ursprung des allgemeinen Organismus." In his *Von der Weltseele: eine Hypothese der höhern Physik zur Erklärung des allgemeinen Organismus*. Vol. I.2 of his *Sämmtliche Werke*. Stuttgart/Augsburg: J. G. Cotta'scher Verlag, 1857, pp. 345-83.
  Rpt. of No. 1798-2.

/BOTANY/MORPHOLOGY/OPTICS/RESEARCH: BIOLOGY

1857-6 **Visiani**, Roberto de. "Di alcune piante storiche del giardino di Padova [On Some Historic Plants in the [Botanical] Garden at Padua]." *Nuovi Saggi della Imperiale Regia Academia di Scienze, Lettere ed Arti in Padova*, 7 (1857), 222-28.
In Italian.
/BOTANY/INSTITUTIONS: ORTO BOTANICO, PADOVA

1858-1 **Aderholdt**, August. *Über Goethes Farbenlehre. Ein Vortrag gehalten in der mathematischen Gesellschaft zu Jena. Nebst einem Anhang: Grävell's Bemühungen zur Rechtfertigung Göthe's*. Weimar: Hermann Böhlau, 1858. 72 pp.
/CHROMATICS/NEWTON, I/GRÄVELL, F

1858-2 **[anon.]** "Christian Gottfried Daniel Nees v. Esenbeck." *Illustrirte Zeitung*, 29 May 1858, 345-7.
/NEES VON ESENBECK, C/BOTANY /NATUR-PHILOSOPHIE

1858-3 **[anon.]** "Farbenlehre." *Erste Beilage zur Königl. privilegirten Berlinischen Zeitung*, No. 71, 25 March 1858, 4-5.
/CHROMATICS/WOLFF, T/GRÄVELL, F

1858-4 **Düntzer**, Heinrich. "Goethes Tonlehre." *Morgenblatt für gebildete Leser*, 52, No. 22, 30 May 1858, 517-21; No. 23, 6 June 1858, 535-9.
/MUSICOLOGY

1858-5 **Faivre**, Ernest. "Goethe naturaliste: Deuxième partie: Botanique --Anatomie comparée." *Revue contemporaine*, NS 7, (1858), 326-43.
Rpt. No. 1862-7.
/BOTANY/COMPARATIVE ANATOMY

1858-6 **Faivre**, Ernest. "Goethe naturaliste: Première partie: La vie et les relations scientifiques de Goethe." *Revue contemporaine*, NS 7, (1858), 837-56.
Rpt. No. 1862-7.
/GENERAL INTRODUCTION

1858-7 **Faivre**, Ernest. "Goethe naturaliste: Troisième partie: Géologie -- Minéralogie -- Optique." *Revue contemporaine*, NS 7, (1858), 681-98.
Rpt. No. 1862-7.

/GEOLOGY/CHROMATICS/MINERALOGY

1858-8 **Grävell**, F[riedrich]. "Charakteristik der Newton'schen Far-
bentheorie." Berlin: Herbig, 1858. 32 pp.
"Vortrag in der Berliner polytechnischen Gesellschaft am 25.
März 1858."
/NEWTON, I/CHROMATICS

1858-9 **Lewes**, G[eorge]. H[enry]. "Goethe als Naturforscher." In his
Goethe's Leben und Schriften. Trans. Julius Frese. 2nd edn. 2 vols.
Berlin: Verlag von Franz Duncker (W. Besser's Verlagshandlung),
1858, pp. 150-208.
Rpt. of No. 1857-4.
/GENERAL INTRODUCTION

1858-10 **Lewes**, G[eorge]. H[enry]. "The poet as a man of science." In
his *The life and works of Goethe: with sketches of his age and contemporaries from published and unpublished sources*. 2 vols. 2nd
rev. edn. Leipzig: F. A. Brockhaus, 1858, II, 98-139.
Rpt. of No. 1855-2.
/GENERAL INTRODUCTION

1858-11 **Oppel**, J[ohann]. J[oseph]. "Ueber den wahren Grund der
Schwierigkeit, mittelst Farbenspindeln etc. ein reines Weiss zusam-
menzusetzen." *Jahres-Bericht des physikalischen Vereins zu
Frankfurt am Main für das Rechnungsjahr 1858-1859*, pp. 57-63.
/CHROMATICS/NEWTON, I

1859-1 **Faivre**, Ernest. "Goethe naturaliste. Cinquième partie. Vues de
Goethe sur la méthode et l'unité de composition." *Revue con-
temporaine*, NS 8 (1859), 263-78.
Rpt. No. 1862-7.
/GENERAL INTRODUCTION

1859-2 **Faivre**, Ernest. "Goethe naturaliste. Quatrième partie. La
science dans les poésies, les romans et les oeuvres artistiques de
Goethe." *Revue contemporaine*, NS 8 (1859), 39-68.
Rpt. No. 1862-7.
/WORKS: VARIOUS

1859-3 **Faivre**, Ernest. "Goethe naturaliste: Siexième partie: Études de
Goethe sur la métamorphose." *Revue contemporaine*, NS 9 (1859),
464-80.
Rpt. No. 1862-7.

/MORPHOLOGY

1859-4 **Grävell**, F[riedrich]. *Ueber Licht und Farben. Mit besonderer Beziehung auf die Farbenlehren Newton's und Goethe's.* Berlin: Gustav Hempel, 1859. xiv, 206 pp.
Rev. [anon.], *Königl. privil. Berlinische Zeitung (Vossische Zeitung)*, No. 37, 12 February 1860.
/RESEARCH: CHROMATICS/CHROMATICS/NEWTON, I

1859-5 **Huxley**, Thomas H[enry]. "On the Theory of the Vertebrate Skull." *Proceedings of the Royal Society of London*, 9 (1859), 381-457.
/OSTEOLOGY/MORPHOLOGY/OKEN, L

1859-6 **Neumann**, Rudolph. "Professor Ernst Meyer und seine Beziehungen zu Göthe." *Botanische Zeitung*, 17 (1859), 112-16.
/MEYER, E/BOTANY

1859-7 **Schelling**[, Friedrich Wilhelm Joseph von]. "Darstellung meines Systems der Philosophie." In his *Sämmtliche Werke 1800-1802*. Vol. I.4 of his *Sämmtliche Werke*. Stuttgart/ Augsburg: J. G. Cotta'scher Verlag, 1859, pp. 105-212.
Rpt. of No. 1801-1.
/NATURPHILOSOPHIE/RESEARCH: MORPHOLOGY /RESEARCH: CHROMATICS

1859-8 **Schleiden**, M[atthias]. J[acob]. "Geschichte der Botanik in Jena." *Album des pädagogischen Seminars an der Universität Jena, II.* Leipzig: Verlag von Wilhelm Engelmann, 1859. 45 pp.
/BOTANY/BATSCH, A/VOIGT, F/INSTITUTIONS: BOTANISCHER GARTEN, JENA

1859-9 **Schleiden**, [Matthias]. J[acob]. "La morphologie des plantes." In his *La plante et sa vie: Leçons populaires de botanique à l'usage des gens du monde.* Trans. M. Scheidweiler. Paris: Schulz & Thuillié /Bruxelles: Aug. Schnée, 1859, pp. 61-84.
French trans. of No. 1855-4 (5th edn.).
/RESEARCH: MORPHOLOGY/RESEARCH: BOTANY

1860-1 **[anon.]** "Goethe und die Metamorphose der Pflanzen." *Frankfurter Konversationsblatt*, No. 23, 27 January 1860, 91-2. /BOTANY/MORPHOLOGY

1860-2 **Clemens**, Aloys. "Neueste Actenstücke über Goethe's Farbenlehre." *Frankfurter Konversationsblatt*, No. 240, 10 October 1860, 958-9; No. 241, 11 October 1860, 962-3; No. 242, 12 October 1860, 966-7; No. 243, 13 October 1860, 970-71; No. 245, 16 October 1860, 978-9. /CHROMATICS/GRÄVELL, F/GOETHE, W VON

1860-3 **Foglar**, Ludwig. "Die Goethe-Palme zu Padua." *Unterhaltungen am häuslichen Herd*, NS 5, No. 23 (1860), 353-5. /BOTANY/INSTITUTIONS: ORTO BOTANICO, PADOVA

1860-4 **Graevell**, Friedrich. *Die zu sühnende Schuld gegen Goethe*. Berlin: Verlag von Gustav Hempel, 1860. 61 pp. /CHROMATICS/NEWTON, I

1861-1 **Aderholdt**, August. "Goethe's Farbenlehre." *Unterhaltungen am häuslichen Herd*, 3. Folge, 1 (1861), 508-11. /CHROMATICS

1861-2 **Bähr**, Johann Karl. "Die Farben." In his *Der dynamische Kreis. Die natürliche Reihenfolge der Elemente und zusammengesetzten Körper als Resultat der Beobachtung ihrer dynamischen Wirksamkeit.* Dresden: Verlag von Woldemar Türk, 1861, pp. 228-46. /CHROMATICS/RESEARCH: CHROMATICS

1861-3 **Carus**, Carl Gustav. "Die Urpflanze. Begriff der Spirale. Metamorphose der Pflanze." In his *Natur und Idee oder das Werdende und sein Gesetz. Eine philosophische Grundlage für die specielle Naturwissenschaft.* Wien: Wilhelm Braumüller, 1861, pp. 233-45. Rpt. (partial) No. 1926-5. /BOTANY/MORPHOLOGY/RESEARCH: BOTANY /RESEARCH: MORPHOLOGY

1861-4 **Foglar**, L[udwig]. "Die Goethe-Palme in Padua. (Zur Erinnerung an den Todestag Goethe's, 22. März.)" *Bonplandia. Zeitschrift für die gesammte Botanik*, 9 (15 April 1861), 85. Partial rpt. of No. 1861-5. /BOTANY/INSTITUTIONS: ORTO BOTANICO, PADOVA

1861-5 **Foglar**, L[udwig]. "Die Goethe-Palme in Padua. Zur Erinnerung

an den Todestag Goethe's, 22. März." *Illustrirte Zeitung*, 36 (1861), 200.
> Partial rpt. No. 1861-4.
> /BOTANY/INSTITUTIONS: ORTO BOTANICO, PADOVA

1861-6 **[Goethe. J. W. von.]** *Goethe's Sämmtliche Werke in Sechs Bänden.* Amerikanische Stereotypausgabe. Vol. 6. Philadelphia: Verlag von F. W. Thomas, 1861. 580 pp.
> Devoted entirely to the scientific writings.
> /EDITION

1861-7 **[Goethe, J. W. von.]** "'Und so wird jeder, der den Reiz kennt. . . .'" In *Verzeichniß von Goethes Handschriften, Zeichnungen und Radierungen, Drucke seiner Werke. . ., welche im Concertsaale des Königlichen Schauspielhauses von 19ten Mai 1861 an ausgestellt sind.* Berlin: E. H. Schroeder, 1861, p. 23.
> Rpt. 1861.
> First publication of a large segment of Goethe's essay "Über den Granit."
> /EDITION

1861-8 **Meding**, Karl Heinrich. "Goethe als Naturforscher in Beziehung zur Gegenwart." Dresden: In Commission bei Adler und Dietze, 1861. 46 pp.
> /RECEPTION/CHROMATICS/DARWIN, C

1861-9 **St[?]**. "Goethe und Sömmerring." *Neues Frankfurter Museum. Beilage der "Zeit"*, 1, No. 187, 8 November 1861, 1485-7.
> /SÖMMERING, S VON

1861-10 **Virchow**, Rudolf. *Göthe als Naturforscher und in besonderer Beziehung auf Schiller. Eine Rede nebst Erläuterungen.* Berlin: Verlag von August Hirschwald, 1861. vi, 127 pp.
> Rpt. Nos. 1932-346, 1962-36 and 1971-58.
> Trans. into Russian, No. 1862-18.
> /GENERAL INTRODUCTION/LAVATER, J/ALBERTUS MAGNUS/KIELMEYER, K/CUVIER, G

1862-1 **Aderholdt[, August]**. "über die Goethe'sche Farbenlehre." *Sitzungs-Berichte der naturwissenschaftlichen Gesellschaft Isis zu Dresden*, No. 10-12, 1862, pp. 265-9.
> "Sitzung am 27. November 1862."
> /CHROMATICS

1862-2 **Biedermann**, Woldemar Freiherr von. "Goethe's Beziehungen zum sächsischen Erzgebirge und zu Erzgebirgern." *Wissenschaftliche Beilage der Leipziger Zeitung*, (1862), 273-5; 277-9; 281-2; 285-6; 289-90; 293-5; 387-9; 391-4; 395-8; 399-400; 404-5.
> Rpt. exp. edn. No. 1862-3.
> /GEOLOGY/PLACES: SACHSEN

1862-3 **Biedermann**, Woldemar Freiherr von. "Goethe's Beziehungen zum sächsischen Erzgebirge und zu Erzgebirgern." Leipzig: B. G. Teubner, 1862. 72 pp.
> Rpt. exp. edn. of No. 1862-2.
> Rpt. rev. and exp. edn. No. 1877-1.
> /GEOLOGY/PLACES: SACHSEN

1862-4 **Candolle**, Augustin Pyramus and Alphonse de **Candolle**. *Mémoires et souvenirs de Augustin-Pyramus de Candolle*. Genève: Joël Cherbuliez, 1862. xvi, 599 pp.
> /RESEARCH: BOTANY/RESEARCH: MORPHOLOGY
> /CANDOLLE, A DE

1862-5 ***Clemens**, Aloys. "Goethes geognostischer Triumph." *Frankfurter Konversationsblatt*, Nos. 205 and 207, 1862.
> /GEOLOGY

1862-6 **Cohn**, Ferdinand. "Goethe und die Metamorphose der Pflanzen." *Deutsches Museum. Zeitschrift für Literatur, Kunst und öffentliches Leben*, 12, No. 4 (1862), 128-41.
> /BOTANY

1862-7 **Faivre**, Ernest. *Oeuvres scientifiques de Goethe analysées et appréciées*. Paris: Librairie de L. Hachette et Cie., 1862. 444 pp.
> Rpt. of Nos. 1858-5, 1858-6, 1858-7, 1959-1, 1959-2 and 1959-3.
> Cf. No. 1862-8.
> Rev. Grandeau, *Le Temps*, 8 October 1862.
> Rev. David Brewster [No. 1863-2].
> Rev. Eugène Fournier [No. 1163-4].
> /GENERAL INTRODUCTION

1862-8 **Faivre**, Ernest. "La Science dans les écrits litteraires et esthétiques de Goethe." In his *Oeuvres scientifiques de Goethe*. Paris: Librairie de L. Hachette, 1862, pp. 301-50.
> /GENERAL INTRODUCTION

1862-9 **Hantzsch**, Rudolf. "Goethe's Farbenlehre und die Farbenlehre der heutigen Physik." Dresden: Verlag von Woldemar Türk, 1862. xii, 142 pp.
/CHROMATICS/RESEARCH: CHROMATICS /SCHOPEN-HAUER, A

1862-10 **Hantzsch**[, Rudolf]. "Ueber die der Göthe'schen Farbenlehre bisher zu Theil gewordene Kritik." *Sitzungs-Berichte der Naturwissenschaftlichen Gesellschaft Isis zu Dresden*, No. 10-12, 1862, 244-56.
/CHROMATICS

1862-11 ***Hemerdinger**, M[?]. "Goethe naturaliste." *La Critique français*, 15 February 1862.
/GENERAL INTRODUCTION

1862-12 **L[?]**, W. "De Candolles Memoiren. -- Stellung desselben zur Wissenschaft. -- Goethes Pflanzenmetamorphose und de Candolles Auffassung der Botanik." *Morgenblatt für gebildete Leser*, 56 (1862), 93-5.
/CANDOLLE, A DE/BOTANY/RESEARCH: BOTANY

1862-13 **Lindner**, [Ernst] O[tto]. "Arthur Schopenhauer. Von ihm. Ueber ihn. IV." *Erste Beilage zur Königl. privilegirte Berlinische Zeitung*, No. 121, 25 May 1862, 1-4.
/SCHOPENHAUER, A/RESEARCH: CHROMA-TICS/CHROMATICS/EASTLAKE, C/SEEBECK, T

1862-14 **Martins**, Charles. "De l'unité organique dans les animaux et les végétaux." *Revue des deux mondes*, 32 (1862), 868-92.
/RESEARCH: BIOLOGY/RESEARCH: COMPARATIVE ANATOMY

1862-15 **Masters**, Maxwell T. "Vegetable morphology: its history and present condition." *The British and Foreign Medico-Chirurgical Review or Quarterly Journal of Practical Medicine and Surgery*, 29 (1862), 202-18.
Rpt. No. 1862-16.
/BOTANY/MORPHOLOGY/HISTORY OF SCIENCE

1862-16 **Masters**, Maxwell T. "Vegetable morphology: its history and present condition." (From the British and Foreign Medico-Chirurgical Review for January, 1862.) 19 pp.
Rpt. of No. 1862-15.

/BOTANY/MORPHOLOGY/HISTORY OF SCIENCE

1862-17 **Schopenhauer**, Arthur. "Zur Farbenlehre." In his *Parerga und Paralipomena: kleine philosophische Schriften.* 2nd rev. and exp. edn. Berlin: Druck und Verlag von A. W. Hayn, 1862, pp. 190-214.
Rpt. of No. 1851-2.
/CHROMATICS/RESEARCH: CHROMATICS

1862-18 *****Virchow**, Rudolf. *Gete kak estestvoispytatel' i ossobennoe otnoshenie ego k Shilleru. Rech' s poiasneniiami [Goethe as a Naturalist, and especially his Relationship to Schiller. Lecture with annotations].* Trans. A. Virenius. S.-Peterburg, 1862.
Russian trans. of No. 1861-10.
/GENERAL INTRODUCTION/LAVATER, J/ALBERTUS MAGNUS
/KIELMEYER, K/CUVIER, G

1863-1 **Bähr**, Joh[ann]. Karl. *Vorträge über Newtons und Goethes Farbenlehre.* Dresden: Türk, 1863. 161 pp.
Held in the Künstler-Verein, Dresden.
/CHROMATICS/NEWTON, I

1863-2 [**Brewster**, David.] Review of: Faivre, Ernest. *Oeuvres Scientifiques de Goethe, Analysées et Apprecieés.* Paris: Librairie de L. Hachette et Cie., 1862. *The North British Review*, 38 (1863), 107-33.
Rev. of No. 1862-7.
/REVIEW/GENERAL INTRODUCTION

1863-3 **Carus**, C[arl]. G[ustav]. *Goethe, dessen Bedeutung für unsere und die kommende Zeit.* Wien: Wilhelm Braumüller k. k. Hofbuchhändler, 1863. 132 pp.
"Hiebei fünfzehn kurze, früher gänzlich unbekannte und ungedruckte Parabeln Goethe's."
/GENERAL INTRODUCTION/EDITION

1863-4 **Fournier**, Eugène. Review of: Faivre, Ernest. *Oeuvres scientifiques de Goethe, analysées et appréciées.* Paris: Librairie de L. Hachette et Cie., 1862. *Revue de l'instruction publique de la littérature et des sciences en France et dans les pays étrangers*, 23, No. 11 (1863), 165-7.
Rev. of No. 1862-7.
/REVIEW/GENERAL INTRODUCTION

1863-5 **Goethe**, J. W. von. "Essay on the Metamorphosis of Plants."

The Journal of Botany, British and Foreign, 1 (1863), 327-45; 360-74.
> Rpt. No. 1974-14.
> "Translated by Emily M. Cox; with Explanatory Notes by Maxwell T. Masters."
> /TRANSLATION: ENGLISH

1863-6 **Neumann**, Carl. *Vortrag über die wesentlichsten Irrthümer in Göthe's Farbenlehre, gehalten in der naturwissenschaftlichen Gesellschaft "Isis" in Dresden.* Dresden: Druck und Verlag von Ernst und Portèger, 1863. 52 pp.
> Cf. précis, No. 1863-7.
> /CHROMATICS

1863-7 **Neumann**, Carl. [Vortrag über die wesentlichsten Irrthümer in Göthe's Farbenlehre.] *Sitzungs-Berichte der naturwissenschaftlichen Gesellschaft Isis zu Dresden*, 1863, pp. 105-7.
> Précis of No. 1863-6.
> /CHROMATICS

1863-8 **Poggendorff**, J[ohann]. C[hristian]. "Goethe, Johann Wolfgang von." In his *Biographisch-Literarisches Handwörterbuch zur Geschichte des exacten Wissenschaften enthaltend Nachweisungen über Lebensverhältnisse und Leistungen von Mathematikern, Astronomen, Physikern, Chemikern, Mineralogen, Geologen usw. aller Völker und Zeiten gesammelt.* Leipzig: Verlag von Johann Ambrosius Barth, 1863, I, cols. 922-3.
> /GENERAL INTRODUCTION

1864-1 **Huxley**, Thomas H[enry]. "The Theory of the Vertebrate Skull." In his *Lectures on the Elements of Comparative Anatomy: On the Classification Animals and on the Vertebrate Skull.* London: John Churchill and Sons, 1864. xi, 303 pp.
> /OSTEOLOGY/RESEARCH: OSTEOLOGY/OKEN, L/SAINT-HILAIRE, G DE/CUVIER, G

1864-2 **Jäger**, Georg [Fr.] v[on]. *Ueber die Wirkungen des Arseniks auf Pflanzen im Zusammenhange mit Physiologie, Landwirtschaft und Medicinalpolizei.* Stuttgart: E. Schweizerbart'sche Verlagsbuchhandlung, 1864. viii, 115 pp.
> /RESEARCH: BOTANY

1864-3 **Lewes**, George Henry. "The poet as a man of science." In his *The life of Goethe.* 2nd edn. London: Smith, Elder, and Co., 1864,

pp. 326-64.
Rpt. of No. 1855-2.
/GENERAL INTRODUCTION

1864-4 **Schleiden**, Mathias Jacob. "Die Morphologie der Pflanzen." In his *Die Pflanze und ihr Leben. Populäre Vorträge.* 6th rev. edn. Leipzig: Verlag von Wilhelm Engelmann, 1864, pp. 81-107.
/RESEARCH: BOTANY/RESEARCH: MORPHOLOGY

1864-5 **Springer**, Robert. "Die naturwissenschaftlichen Anschauungen in Goethe's poetischen Werken." *Deutsche Jahrbücher für Politik und Literatur*, 11 (1864), 71-89.
/WORKS: VARIOUS

1865-1 **Caro**, E[dmond]. "La philosophie de Goethe. I. Histoire de son esprit. -- Goethe et Spinoza." *Revue des deux mondes*, 35 (1865), 846-80.
Rpt. Nos. 1866-3 and 1880-3.
Cf. continuation, No. 1866-3.
/PHILOSOPHY/SPINOZA, B/METHOD

1865-2 **Caro**, E[dmond]. "La philosophie de Goethe. II. Ses travaux scientifiques. -- Goethe et Geoffroy Saint-Hilaire. III. Ses conceptions sur la nature, sur Dieu et la destinée humaine. -- Éclectisme et panthéisme." *Revue des deux mondes*, 35 (1865), 147-87; 301-38.
Rpt. Nos. 1866-3 and 1880-3.
Continuation of No. 1866-3.
/SAINT-HILAIRE, G DE/GENERAL INTRODUCTION
/ZOOLOGY/PHILOSOPHY/METHOD

1865-3 *****Goethe**[, J. W. von]. "Poem on the Clouds." Free trans. John Eliot Howard. [n.p.]: privately printed, 1865. [2] pp.
/TRANSLATION: ENGLISH

1865-4 **Helmholtz**, Hermann [von]. "Über Goethe's naturwissen-schaftliche Arbeiten." In his *Populäre wissenschaftliche Vorträge: Erstes Heft*. Braunschweig: Friedrich Vieweg und Sohn, 1865, pp. 31-53.
Rpt. of No. 1853-8.
"Vortrag gehalten im Frühling 1853 in der deutschen Gesellschaft zu Königsberg."
/GENERAL INTRODUCTION

1865-5 **Kirschleger**, Frédéric. "Goethe naturaliste et spécialement

botaniste." Strasbourg: Imprimerie Christophe, 1865. 25 pp.
"Société littéraire de Strasbourg. . .Lecture publique faite le 21
décembre 1864 à la Préfecture du Bas-Rhin"
/BOTANY/MORPHOLOGY/GENERAL INTRODUCTION

1865-6 **Kirschleger**, Frédéric. "La métamorphose des plantes de
Goethe." Strasbourg: Imprimerie Christophe, 1865. 18 pp.
/BOTANY/MORPHOLOGY

1865-7 **Weber**, Max Maria Freiherr von. "Göthe und die Dampfma-
schine. Aphorisme." *Zeitung des Vereins Deutscher Eisenbahn-
Verwaltungen*, No. 7, 18 February 1965, 83-5.
Rpt. Nos. 1868-12, 1882-24 and 1907-28.
/TECHNOLOGY

1865-8 **Wretschko**, Matthias. "Über Metamorphose der Pflanzen."
*Schriften des Vereines zur Verbreitung naturwissenschaftlicher
Kenntnisse in Wien [= Populäre Vorträge aus allen Fächern der
Naturwissenschaft]*, 6 (1865/1866), 349-72.
/ B O T A N Y / M O R P H O L O G Y / R E S E A R C H :
BOTANY/RESEARCH: MORPHOLOGY

1866-1 **Bratranek**, F[ranz]. Th[omas]. Bratranek. "Einleitung." In
*Briefwechsel zwischen Goethe und Kaspar Graf von Sternberg. (1820-
1832.)*. Ed. and intro. F[ranz]. Th[omas]. Bratranek. Wien: Wilhelm Braumüller k. k. Hof- und Universitätsbuchhändler, 1866, pp.
1-61.
/STERNBERG, K VON/BOTANY/PALEONTOLOGY

1866-2 **Briefwechsel** *zwischen Goethe und Kaspar Graf von Sternberg.
(1820-1832.)*. Ed. and intro. F[ranz]. Th[omas]. Bratranek. Wien:
Wilhelm Braumüller k. k. Hof- und Universitätsbuchhändler, 1866.
viii, 309 pp.
See No. 1866-1.
/STERNBERG, K VON/BOTANY/PALEONTOLOGY

1866-3 **Caro**, E[dmond]. *La philosophie de Goethe*. Paris: librairie de L.
Hachette et Cie., 1866. viii, 430 pp.
Rpt. of Nos. 1865-1 and 1865-2.
Trans. into Spanish, No. n.d.-4.
/PHILOSOPHY/METHOD/SAINT-HILAIRE, G DE/EDITION:
SELECTIONS

1866-4 **Haeckel**, Ernst. *Allgemeine Anatomie der Organismen*. Vol. I of

his *Generelle Morphologie der Organismen. Allgemeine Grundzüge der organischen Formen-Wissenschaft, mechanisch begründet durch die von Charles Darwin reformirte Descendenz-Theorie.* Berlin: Georg Reimer, 1866. xxxii, 574 pp.
/RESEARCH: BIOLOGY/DARWIN, C

1866-5 **Haeckel**, Ernst. *Allgemeine Anatomie der Organismen.* Vol. I of his *Generelle Morphologie der Organismen. Allgemeine Grundzüge der organischen Formen-Wissenschaft, mechanisch begründet durch die von Charles Darwin reformirte Descendenz-Theorie.* Berlin: Georg Reimer, 1866. xxxii, 574 pp.
/RESEARCH: BIOLOGY/DARWIN, C

1866-6 **Quetelet**, Adolphe. "Jean-Wolfgang Goethe." In his *Sciences mathématiques et physiques chez les Belges, au commencement du XIXe siècle.* Bruxelles: H. Thiry-van Buggenhoudt, 1866, 656-68.
/QUETELET, A/ASTRONOMY

1866-7 **Springer**, Robert. "Goethes Verdienste um die Naturwissenschaften." *Deutsches Museum,* 16 (1866), 289-304.
Rpt. No. 1885-20.
/RECEPTION/GENERAL INTRODUCTION

1867-1 **[Goedeke**, Karl.] Introduction to: *Goethes Werke.* Vol. 32. Stuttgart: Verlag der J. G. Cotta'schen Buchhandlung, 1867, pp. vii-xiv.
Rpt. No. 1895-3.
/MORPHOLOGY/BIOLOGY

1867-2 **Kirchhoff**, Alfred. "Die Idee der Pflanzen-Metamorphose bei Wolff und bei Göthe." In *Zweiter Jahresbericht über die Luisenstädtische Gewerbeschule in Berlin.* Berlin: A. W. Schade, 1867, pp. [3-4] and 1-33.
Rpt. No. 1867-3.
/BOTANY/MORPHOLOGY/WOLFF, T

1867-3 **Kirchhoff**, Alfred. "Die Idee der Pflanzen-Metamorphose bei Wolff und bei Göthe." Berlin: Verlag von Rudolf Gaertner, 1867. iv, 35 pp.
Rpt. of No. 1867-2.
/BOTANY/MORPHOLOGY/WOLFF, T

1867-4 **[Kirschleger**, Frédéric?]. "La pomme de terre épigée, c'est-à-dire au-dessus de terre." *Annales de l'Association philomatique vogéso-*

rhénane, NS 2, no. 8 (1867), 61.
/BOTANY

1867-5 **Runge**, F[riedlieb]. F[erdinand]. "Mein Besuch bei Goethe im Jahre 1819." In his *Hauswirtschaftliche Briefe*. Drittes Dutzend. Oranienburg: Friedr. Schulze's Buchhandlung, 1867, pp. 153-66. Rpt. No. 1911-29.
/CHEMISTRY

1868-1 **[anon.]** "Voltaire und Goethe als Naturforscher." *Philosophische Monatshefte*, 1 (1868), 150-58.
/VOLTAIRE, F/DU BOIS-REYMOND, E

1868-2 **Düntzer**, Heinrich. "Goethe's Tonlehre und Christian Heinrich Schlosser." In his *Aus Goethe's Freundeskreis. Darstellungen aus dem Leben des Dichters*. Braunschweig: Druck und Verlag von Friedrich Vieweg und Sohn, 1868, pp. 523-50.
/MUSIC THEORY/SCHLOSSER, C

1868-3 **Düntzer**, Heinrich. "Oken." In his *Aus Goethe's Freundeskreis. Darstellungen aus dem Leben des Dichters*. Braunschweig: Druck und Verlag von Friedrich Vieweg und Sohn, 1868, pp. 417-66.
/OKEN, L/MORPHOLOGY/RESEARCH: MORPHOLOGY

1868-4 **[Goethe, J. W. von.]** "Pis'mo Gëte kantsleru Miulleru 24 maia 1828 [Kanzler von Müller's Letter of 24 May 1828]." Trans. A[?]. Strugovshchikov. *Vsemirnyi trud*, cp. 6, 1868, 100-101.
[Zhitomirskaia 2194]
/TRANSLATION: RUSSIAN

1868-5 **[Goethe, J. W. von.]** ["Principes de philosophie zoologique. . .]" Trans. A[?]. Strugovshchikov. *Vsemirnyi trud*, cp. 6, No. 2, November 1868, 207-14.
[Zhitomirskaia 2188]
/TRANSLATION: RUSSIAN

1868-6 **[Goethe, J. W. von.]** "Priroda [Nature]." Trans. A[?]. Strugovshchikov. *Vsemirnyi trud*, cp. 6, 1868, 97-9.
[Zhitomirskaia 2190]
/TRANSLATION: RUSSIAN

1868-7 **Haeckel**, Ernst. *Natürliche Schöpfungsgeschichte. Gemeinverständliche wissenschaftliche Vorträge über die Entwicklungslehre im Allgemeinen und diejenige von Darwin, Goethe und Lamarck im Be-*

sonderen, über die Anwendung derselben auf den Ursprung des Menschen und andere damit zusammenhängende Grundfragen der Naturwissenschaft. Berlin: Verlag von Georg Reimer, 1868. xvi, 568, viii pp.
  Rpt. No. 1870-3.
  See esp. 4th lecture, "Entwicklungstheorie von Goethe und Oken," pp. 59-79.
  /RESEARCH: BIOLOGY/BIOLOGY: EVOLUTION /DARWIN, C/OKEN, L/LAMARCK, J DE

1868-8 **Hofmeister**, Wilhelm. "Metamorphose." In his *Allgemeine Morphologie der Gewächse.* Vol. I.2 of his *Handbuch der Physiologischen Botanik.* Leipzig: Verlag von Wilhelm Engelmann, 1868, pp. 554-5.
  /RESEARCH: MORPHOLOGY

1868-9 **Rosenkranz**, Karl. "Aus Véra's Commentar zu Hegel's Naturphilosophie: die Theorie der Farbe." In his *Hegel's Naturphilosophie und die Bearbeitung derselben durch den Italienischen Philosophen A. Véra.* Berlin: Nicolaische Verlagsbuchhandlung, 1868, pp. 46-106.
  /HEGEL, G/CHROMATICS/RESEARCH: CHROMATICS/SCHOPENHAUER, A

1868-10 **Schleiden**, Matthias Jakob. "Goethe als Naturforscher." *Westermann's Jahrbuch der Illustrirten Deutschen Monatshefte,* 23 [NF 7], March 1868, 614-25.
  /GENERAL INTRODUCTION/BOTANY

1868-11 **Stricker**, Wilhelm. "Ueber Goethe's Beziehungen zu Quetelet." *Mittheilungen an die Mitglieder des Vereins für Geschichte und Alterthumskunde in Frankfurt a. M.,* 3 (1868), 248-53.
  /QUETELET, A/ASTRONOMY

1868-12 **Weber**, Max Maria Freiherr von. "Göthe und die Dampfmaschine. Aphorisme." In his *Aus der Welt der Arbeit.* Berlin: Verlag von R. Lesser, [1868], pp. 97-108.
  Rpt. of No. 1865-7.
  /TECHNOLOGY

1869-1 **Boulay**, Abbé [Jean Nicolas]. *Goethe et la science de la nature.* Strasbourg: E.-P. Le Roux, 1869. 119 pp.
  /GENERAL INTRODUCTION

1869-2 **Carus**, Carl Gustav. "Erinnerung von C. G. Carus an Carl

Friedrich Philipp von Martius." *Leopoldina: Amtliches Organ der Kaiserlichen Leopoldino-Carolinischen Deutschen Akademie der Naturforscher*, 6, No. 12 (February 1869), 103-11.
/BOTANY/MORPHOLOGY/MARTIUS, K [VON]

1869-3 **Huxley**, T[homas]. H. "Nature: Aphorisms by Goethe." [Trans. T. H. Huxley.] *Nature: A Weekly illustrated journal of science*, 1 (1869/1870), 9-11.
Rpt. No. 1932-165.
/TRANSLATION: ENGLISH

1869-4 **Küntzer [Künzer]**, Eduard. "Göthes Stellung zu den Naturwissenschaften." *Jahresbericht des Königlichen Gymnasiums zu Marienwerder*. Marienwerder: Friedr. Aug. Harich, 1869, pp. 11-48.
/GENERAL INTRODUCTION

1869-5 **Pisko**, Franz Josef. "Die Farbenlehre Göthe's." In his *Licht und Farbe*. 2nd exp. edn. München: Verlag von R. Oldenbourg, 1876, pp. 513-25.
Rpt. No. 1876-9.
/CHROMATICS/OPTICS

1870-1 **Czermak**, Johann. "Über Schopenhauers Theorie der Farbe. Ein Beitrag zur Geschichte der Farbenlehre." *Sitzungsberichte der Mathematisch-Naturwissenschaftlichen Classe der Kaiserlichen Akademie der Wissenschaften*, 62, No. 2 (1870), 393-411.
/CHROMATICS/SCHOPENHAUER, A/RESEARCH: CHROMATICS /NEWTON, I

1870-2 **Eastlake**, Charles Lock. "Extracts from the translation of Goethe's theory of colours." In his *Contributions to the literature of the fine arts*. 2nd edn. London: John Murray, 1870, pp. 292-328.
  Rpt. of No. 1848-3.
  /TRANSLATION: ENGLISH

1870-3 **Haeckel**, Ernst. "Entwicklungstheorie von Goethe und Oken." In his *Natürliche Schöpfungsgeschichte. Gemeinverständliche wissenschaftliche Vorträge über die Entwicklungslehre im Allgemeinen und diejenige von Darwin, Goethe und Lamarck im Besonderen, über die Anwendung derselben auf den Ursprung des Menschen und andere damit zusammenhängende Grundfragen der Naturwissenschaft.* 2nd rev. and exp. edn. Berlin: Verlag von Georg Reimer, 1870, pp. 65-88.
  Rpt. of No. 1868-7.
  5th rev. and exp. edn., 1874; title changed to "Entwicklungstheorie nach Goethe und Oken" in 6th rev. edn., 1875.
  Trans. into English by E. R. Lancaster, London, 1876.
  Trans. into French by Ch. Letourneau, Paris, 1874.
  Trans into English, No. 1890-9.
  /RESEARCH: BIOLOGY/BIOLOGY: EVOLUTION /DARWIN, C/OKEN, L/LAMARCK, J DE

1870-4 **Hegel**[, Georg Wilhelm Friedrich]. *Encyclopädie der philosophischen Wissenschaften.* Ed. J. H. v. Kirchmann. Philosophische Bibliothek, 30. Berlin: Verlag von L. Heimann, 1870.
  Rpt. of No. 1817-7.
  /CHROMATICS/NATURPHILOSOPHIE/NEWTON, I

1870-5 **Helmholtz**, H[ermann von]. "Goethe naturaliste." Trans. L. Koch. *Revue des cours scientifiques de la France et de l'étranger*, 7 (1870), 18-25.
  French trans. of No. 1853-8.
  /GENERAL INTRODUCTION

1870-6 **Hirzel**, Ludwig. "Goethe und Heinrich Zschokke." *Die Grenzboten. Zeitschrift für Politik und Literatur*, 29, No. 1 (1870),

33-4.
/ZSCHOKKE, H/CHROMATICS

1870-7 **Hoh**, Theodor. "Göthe als Naturforscher." In *Neunter Bericht der naturforschenden Gesellschaft zu Bamberg. Für die Jahre 1869- 70.* Bamberg: J. M. Reindl, 1870, 1-20.
/GENERAL INTRODUCTION

1870-8 **Leclerc**, François. "Goethe et le livre de la métamorphose des plantes." *Mémoires de la Société d'Emulation du Doubs*, Series 4, 6 (1870/1871), 155-82.
Rpt. No. 1870-9.
/BOTANY/MORPHOLOGY

1870-9 **Leclerc**, François. "Goethe et le livre de la métamorphose des plantes." 28 pp.
Rpt. of No. 1870-8.
"Extrait des Mémoires de la Société d'Emulation du Doubs. Séance du 9 juillet 1870."
/BOTANY/MORPHOLOGY

1870-10 *****Löwenberg**, Julius. "Alexander von Humboldt im Verkehr mit Goethe." *National-Zeitung*, No. 285, 23 June 1870.
/HUMB0LDT, A VON

1870-11 **Schopenhauer**, Arthur. "Einige Zugaben zu Göthes Lehre von der Entstehung der physischen Farben." In his *Ueber das Sehn und die Farben. Eine Abhandlung.* 3rd rev. and exp. edn. Ed. Julius Frauenstädt. Leipzig: F. A. Brockhaus, 1870, pp. 80-93.
Rpt. of No. 1854-7.
/CHROMATICS/RESEARCH: CHROMATICS

1871-1 **Schmidt**, Oscar. "War Goethe ein Darwinianer?" Graz: Leuschner & Lubensky, 1871. 32 pp.
/BIOLOGY: EVOLUTION/DARWIN, C

1872-1 **Boehmer**, Heinrich. "Goethe und Herder über Sehen und Farben." In his *Geschichte der Entwickelung der naturwissenschaftlichen Weltanschauung in Deutschland.* Gotha: Rud[olf]. Besser, 1872, pp. 102-5.
/CHROMATICS/HERDER, J

1872-2 **Gegenbaur**, Carl. "Einleitung." In his *Untersuchungen zur vergleichenden Anatomie der Wirbelthiere.* Leipzig: Verlag von Wil-

helm Engelmann, 1872, pp. 1-9.
/RESEARCH: OSTEOLOGY/RESEARCH: COMPARATIVE
ANATOMY/OKEN, L

1872-3 **Strauß**, David Friedrich. "Goethe als Vorgänger Darwin's." In
his *Der alte und der neue Glaube. Ein Bekenntniß*. Leipzig: Verlag
von S. Hirzel, 1872, pp. 177-81.
  Rpt. Nos. 1873-6 and 1877-14.
  /BIOLOGY: EVOLUTION/DARWIN, C

1873-1 *****Helmholtz**, Hermann [von]. "Scientific researches of Goethe."
In his *Popular Scientific Lectures*. Trans. Atkinson. London, 1873,
I, 33ff.
  English trans. of No. 1853-8.
  /GENERAL INTRODUCTION

1873-2 **Lewes**, G[eorge]. H[enry]. "Goethe als Naturforscher." In his
Goethes Leben und Werke. Trans. Julius. Frese. 8th edn. 2 vols.
Berlin: Dunker, 1873, II, 146-96.
  English trans. of No. 1855-2.
  /GENERAL INTRODUCTION

1873-3 **Schmidt**, Oscar. ""Die Naturphilosophie. Goethe. Prädestinirte
Umbildung nach Richard Owen. Lamarck." In his *Descendenzlehre
und Darwinismus*. Internationale Wissenschaftliche Bibliothek, 2.
Leipzig: F. A. Brockhaus, 1873, pp. 94-114.
  2nd rev. edn., 1884.
  Trans. into French, Paris, 1876.
  /BIOLOGY/NATURPHILOSOPHIE/OWEN, R/LAMARCK, J
  DE

1873-4 **Schopenhauer**, Arthur. "Einige Zugaben zu Göthe's Lehre von
der Entstehung der physischen Farben." In his *Ueber das Sehn und
die Farben. Eine Abhandlung*. Vol. 1 of his *Sämmtliche Werke*. Ed.
Julius Frauenstädt. Leipzig: F. A. Brockhaus, 1873. xvi, 93 pp.
  Rpt. 4th edn. 1908.
  Cf. esp. "Einige Zugaben zu Göthes Lehre," pp. 80-93.
  /RESEARCH: CHROMATICS/CHROMATICS

1873-5 **Schopenhauer**, Arthur. "Theoria colorum physilogica, eademque
primaria, auctore Arthurio Schopenhauero Berolinensi." In his *Ueber
das Sehn und die Farben. Eine Abhandlung*. Vol. 1 of his
Sämmtliche Werke. Ed. Julius Frauenstädt. Leipzig: F. A. Brockhaus, 1873. 58 pp.

/RESEARCH: CHROMATICS/CHROMATICS

1873-6 Strauß, David Friedrich. "Goethe als Vorgänger Darwin's." In his *Der alte und der neue Glaube. Ein Bekenntniß*. 4th edn. Leipzig: Verlag von S. Hirzel, 1873, pp. 181-5.
Rpt. of No. 1872-3.
Rpt. 8th edn. 1875.
/BIOLOGY: EVOLUTION/DARWIN, C

1874-1 Bratranek, Franz Thomas. "Goethe's naturwissenschaftliche Bedeutung." In *Goethe's naturwissenschaftliche Correspondenz, 1812-1832*. 2 vols. Ed. F[ranz]. Th[omas]. Bratranek. 2 vols. Neue Mittheilungen aus Johann Wolfgang von Goethes handschriftlichem Nachlasse, 1 and 2. Leipzig: F. A. Brockhaus, 1874, I, xxxiii-lxxxix.
/GENERAL INTRODUCTION/HISTORY OF SCIENCE

1874-2 C[?], A[?]. "Lamarck e Goethe i precursori di Darwin, Haeckel il suo apostolo [Lamarck and Goethe, the Precursors of Darwin; His Apostle Haeckel]." *Il Convegno*, 2, 4 (1874), fasc. 4, 322-37.
In Italian.
/BIOLOGY: EVOLUTION/LAMARCK, J DE/DARWIN, C/HAECKEL, E

1874-3 Dove, Alfred. "Goethe unter den Naturforschern." *Im neuen Reich. Wochenschrift für das Leben des deutschen Volkes in Staat, Wissenschaft und Kunst*, 4 (1874), 821-8.
Rpt. No. 1898-5.
/RECEPTION/GENERAL INTRODUCTION

1874-4 Goedeke, Karl. "Farbenlehre." In *Goethes Leben und Schriften*. Stuttgart: Verlag der J. G. Cotta'schen Buchhandlung, 1874, pp. 466-86.
Rpt. 2nd edn. 1877.
/CHROMATICS

1874-5 Goedeke, Karl. "Naturwissenschaftliche Studien." In *Goethes Leben und Schriften*. Stuttgart: Verlag der J. G. Cotta'schen Buchhandlung, 1874, pp. 278-90.
Rpt. 2nd edn. 1877.
/GENERAL INTRODUCTION

1874-6 Goethe's *naturwissenschaftliche Correspondenz, 1812-1832*. 2 vols. Ed. F[ranz]. Th[omas]. Bratranek. 2 vols. Neue Mittheilungen

aus Johann Wolfgang von Goethes handschriftlichem Nachlasse, 1 and 2. Leipzig: F. A. Brockhaus, 1874. lxxxix, 400; 424 pp.
Cf. No. 1874-1.
Rev. J[ulius]. Löwenberg, *Sonntags-Beilage No 45. zur Voss-ischen Zeitung [Berlin]*, 1874, 4.
/EDITION

1874-7 **Leyser**, J[acob?]. "Göthe als Botaniker." In *XXX-XXXII. Jahresbericht der Pollichia, eines naturwissenschaftlichen Vereins der Rheinpfalz*. Dürkheim a/H: Buchdruckerei von J. Rheinberger, 1874, pp. 4-14.
"Vortrag, gehalten auf der Wanderversammlung der Pollichia zu Frankenthal."
/BOTANY

1874-8 **Leyser**, J[acob?]. "Über Göthe's Farbentheorie." In *XXX-XXXII. Jahresbericht der Pollichia, eines naturwissenschaftlichen Vereins der Rheinpfalz*. Dürkheim a/H: Buchdruckerei von J. Rheinberger, 1874, pp. vi-vii.
/CHROMATICS

1874-9 **Plüss**, N[?]. "Die Begründung der Farbenlehre durch Newton und ihre Bekämpfung durch Göthe." In his *Einladungsschrift zur Promotionsfeier des Pädagogiums*. Basel: Carl Schultze's Universitaetsbuchdruckerei, 1874, pp. 3-30.
/CHROMATICS/NEWTON, I

1874-10 **Reitlinger**, Edmund. "Doctor Faust und die Naturwissenschaft. (1866.) Ins Innere der Natur. (1874.)" In his *Freie Blicke. Populär wissenschaftliche Aufsätze von Edmund Reitlinger*. Berlin: A. Hofmann & Co., 1877, pp. 296-307; 326-46.
3rd edn. 1877.
/GENERAL INTRODUCTION/WORKS: FAUST

1874-11 **Vetter**[, Benjamin]. "Geschichte und gegenwärtiger Stand der Schädelwirbeltheorie." *Sitzungs-Berichte der naturwissenschaftlichen Gesellschaft Isis in Dresden*, 1874, pp. 22-31.
/RESEARCH: OSTEOLOGY/OKEN, L/HISTORY OF SCIENCE

1875-1 **Gizycki**, Georg von. "Versuch über die philosophischen Consequenzen der Goethe-Lamarck-Darwin'schen Evolutionstheorie." Diss. Berlin. Berlin: Carl Lindow, 1875. 66 pp.
/BIOLOGY: EVOLUTION/DARWIN, C/LAMARCK, J DE

1875-2 **Jastrowitz**, M[?]. "Historische Notiz über Aphasie." *Berliner Klinische Wochenschrift: Organ für practische Aerzte*, 12 (1875), 323. Rpt. No. 1895-5.
/MEDICINE/PSYCHOLOGY

1875-3 **Lewes**, Henry George. "Der Dichter als Naturforscher." In his *Goethe's Leben*. Trans. by J. von Sydow. *Supplementband* to *Goethe's Werke*. Berlin: G. Grote'sche Verlagsbuchhandlung, 1875, pp. 241-77.
/GENERAL INTRODUCTION

1875-4 **Leyser**, J[acob?]. "Goethe als Osteologe." In *XXX-XXXII. Jahresbericht der Pollichia, eines naturwissenschaftlichen Vereins der Rheinpfalz*. Dürkheim a/H: Buchdruckerei von J. Rheinberger, 1874, pp. 33-45.
"Vortrag, gehalten auf der Wanderversammlung der Pollichia zu Frankenthal."
/OSTEOLOGY

1875-5 **Sachs**, Julius. "Die Morphologie unter dem Einfluß der Metamorphosenlehre und der Spiraltheorie. 1790-1850." In his *Geschichte der Botanik vom 16. Jahrhundert bis 1860*. Geschichte der Wissenschaften in Deutschland: Neuere Zeit, 15. München: R. Oldenbourg, 1875, pp. 166-95.
". . .herausgegeben durch die historische Commission bei der Königl. Academie der Wissenschaften"
/BOTANY

1875-6 **Stromeyer**, Georg Friedrich Louis. "Carus und Goethe, oder: Der neue Empedokles." In his *Erinnerungen eines deutschen Arztes. Erster Band. Leben und Lernen*. Hannover: Carl Rümpler, 1875, pp. 230-36.
/CARUS, C/GENERAL INTRODUCTION

1875-7 **Volkelt**, Johannes. "Häckel und Goethe." *Deutsche Zeitung [Morgenblatt]*, No. 1348, 2 October 1875, 1-2; No. 1859, 13 October 1875, 1-2.
/HAECKEL, E/BIOLOGY: EVOLUTION

1876-1 **[anon.]** "Goethe's Briefwechsel mit den Humboldts." *Die Wage. Wochenblatt für Politik und Literatur*, 1876, 81-5; 97-104; 120-28; 137-44; 151-8.
/EDITION/HUMBOLDT, A VON/HUMBOLDT, W VON

1876-2 **Callenberg**, A[?]. "Goethes Beziehungen zur Geologie." *Die Gegenwart: Wochenschrift für Literatur, Kunst und öffentliches Leben*, 10 [1876], 104-6; 134-6.
/GEOLOGY

1876-3 **Goethe's** *Briefwechsel mit den Gebrüdern von Humboldt (1795-1832)*. Ed. and intro. F[ranz]. Th[omas]. Bratranek. Neue Mittheilungen aus Johann Wolfgang von Goethes handschriftlichem Nachlasse, 3. Leipzig: F. A. Brockhaus, 1876. xlix, 443 pp.
Rev. No. 1899-7.
/EDITION/HUMBOLDT, A VON/HUMBOLDT, W VON

1876-4 **Helmholtz**, Hermann [von]. "Über Goethe's naturwissenschaftliche Arbeiten." In his *Populäre wissenschaftliche Vorträge*. 2nd rev. edn. Braunschweig: Verlag von Friedrich Vieweg und Sohn, 1876, pp. 31-53.
Rpt. of No. 1853-8.
/GENERAL INTRODUCTION

1876-5 **Henning**, Rudolf. "Neue mitteilungen aus Johann Wolfgang von Goethes handschriftlichem nachlasse. Goethes briefwechsel mit den Gebrüdern von Humboldt (1795-1832)." *Anzeiger für deutsches Alterthum und deutsche Literatur*, 2 (1876), 115-34.
/EDITION/HUMBOLDT, A VON/HUMBOLDT, W VON

1876-6 **Kalischer**, Salomon. "Goethe als Entdecker der Eiszeit." *Die Wage. Wochenschrift für Politik und Literatur*, 1876, pp. 220-24.
/GEOLOGY

1876-7 **Kalischer**, Salomon. "Goethe und Darwin." *Die Wage. Wochenschrift für Politik und Literatur*, 1876, pp. 166-76; 179-92.
/BIOLOGY: EVOLUTION/DARWIN, C

1876-8 **Loeper**, Gustav von. "Goethe's chemisch-alchemische Studien." In *Goethes Werke: Nach den vorzüglichsten Quellen revidirte Ausgabe*. Vol. 21.2. *Dichtung und Wahrheit*. Intro. and notes G. von Loeper. Berlin: Gustav Hempel[, 1876], pp. 348-54.
/CHEMISTRY/ALCHEMY

1876-9 **Pisko**, Franz Josef. "Die Farbenlehre Göthe's." In his *Licht und Farbe. Eine gemeinfaßliche Darstellung der Optik*. 2nd exp. edn. München: R. Oldenbourg, 1876, pp. 513-25.
Rpt. of 1869-5.

/CHROMATICS/OPTICS

1876-10 **Zacharias**, Otto. "Ist Goethe als ein Vorläufer Darwins zu betrachten?" *Die Gegenwart. Wochenschrift für Literatur, Kunst und öffentliches Leben*, 9 (1876), 110-11.
/DARWIN, C/BIOLOGY: EVOLUTION/VOIGT, F

1877-1 **Biedermann**, Woldemar Freiherr von. *Goethe und die sächsische Erzgebürge. Nebst Ueberblick der gesteinkundigen und bergmännischen Thätigkeit Goethe's.* Stuttgart: Verlag der J. G. Cotta'-schen Buchhandlung, 1877. 305 pp.
Rpt. rev. and exp. edn. of No. 1862-3.
Contains first publications of several short essays by Goethe.
/GEOLOGY/EDITION/PLACES: SACHSEN

1877-2 **Cattie**, J[?]. Th. "Göthe ein Gegner der Descendenztheorie. Eine Streitschrift gegen Ernst Haeckel." Utrecht: Verlag von J. L. Beijers, 1877. 31 pp.
/BIOLOGY: EVOLUTION/HAECKEL, E/DARWIN, C

1877-3 **Genast**, Wilhelm. "Karl August und Goethe als Quellenforscher." *Preußische Jahrbücher*, 39 (1877), 516-33.
/MINERALOGY/GEOLOGY

1877-4 **Goethe**[, J. W. von]. *Zur Meteorologie. -- Zur Naturwissenschaft im Allgemeinen. -- Naturwissenschaftliche Einzelheiten.* Vol. 34 of *Goethe's Werke. Nach den vorzüglichsten Quellen revidirte Ausgabe.* Ed. and intro. S. Kalischer. Berlin: Gustav Hempel[, 1877]. xvi, 296 pp.
/EDITION

1877-5 **Goethe**[, J. W. von]. *Zur Morphologie. -- Zur Mineralogie und Geologie.* Vol. 33 of *Goethe's Werke. Nach den vorzüglichsten Quellen revidirte Ausgabe.* Ed. and intro. S. Kalischer. Berlin: Gustav Hempel[, 1877]. clxxxiv, 567 pp.
/EDITION

1877-6 **Grimm**, Herman. "Studium der Naturwissenschaften. Die Natürliche Tochter. Die Wahlverwandtschaften." In his *Goethe: Vorlesungen gehalten an der Kgl. Universität zu Berlin.* 2 vols. Berlin: Verlag von Wilhelm Hertz, 1877, II, 204-43.
/GENERAL INTRODUCTION

1877-7 **Hlawacek**, Eduard. "Goethe in Karlsbad." Karlsbad: Verlag von

Hans Feller, 1877. 95 pp.
  Rpt. No. 1883-10.
  /GEOLOGY/MINERALOGY/PLACES: KARLSBAD

1877-8 **Kossmann**, Robby. "War Göthe ein Mitbegründer der Descendenztheorie?" *Verhandlungen des Naturhistorisch-medicinischen Vereins zu Heidelberg*, NF 1 (1877), 152-64.
  Rpt. 2nd exp. edn. 1877-9.
  /BIOLOGY: EVOLUTION/DARWIN, C

1877-9 **Kossmann**, Robby. "War Göthe ein Mitbegründer der Descendenztheorie? Eine Warnung vor E. Häckel's Citaten." 2nd exp. edn. Heidelberg: Carl Winter's Universitätsbuchhandlung, 1877. 32 pp.
  Rpt. of No. 1875-8.
  /BIOLOGY: EVOLUTION/DARWIN, C

1877-10 **Leyser**, J[acob?]. "Goethe kein Vorläufer Darwins. Wider Haeckel." *Jahresbericht der Pollichia, eines naturwissenschaftlichen Vereins der Rheinpfalz*, 1877, pp. 89-103.
  "Vortrag, gehalten auf der XI. Wanderversammlung der Pollichia zu Pirmasens den 20. April 1876."
  /BIOLOGY: EVOLUTION

1877-11 **Sch[?].**, Th[?]. "Die Räthseleidechse oder der Urvogel. (*Archaeopteryx lithographica* Herm. v. Meyer; *A. macrura* Rich. Owen; *Griphosaurus* Andr. Wagner.)" *Das Museum. Literarisch-belletristisches Unterhaltungsblatt der Neuen Frankfurter Presse*, No. 262, 8 November 1877, cols. [6-8].
  /RECEPTION

1877-12 ***Schmied**, Georg. "Goethe als Beobachter insektenfressender Pflanzen." *Egerer Zeitung*, No. 91 and 92, 1877.
  /BOTANY

1877-13 ***Stepniewski**, Tymoteusz. "Goethe, znaczenie jego prac na polu biologii i filozofii [The Significance of Goethe's Work in the Fields of Biology and Philosophy]." Warszawa, 1877. 48 pp.
  In Polish.
  /BIOLOGY

1877-14 **Strauß**, David Friedrich. "Goethe als Vorgänger Darwin's." In his *Der alte und der neue Glaube. Ein Bekenntniß*. 9th edn. Vol. 6 of his *Gesammelte Schriften*. Bonn: Verlag von Emil Strauß, 1877, pp. 119-22.

Rpt. of No. 1872-3.
/BIOLOGY: EVOLUTION/DARWIN, C

1877-15 **Uhde**, Hermann. "Goethe, Seelus und der Kanzler v. Müller."
Allgemeine Zeitung, No. 120, 30 April 1877, 1822-3.
/SEELUS, ? VON/BOTANY

1878-1 **[anon.]** "Goethe's Naturbetrachtung." *Die Wage. Wochenblatt
für Politik und Literatur*, 1878, 17-22.
Cf. No. 1878-8.
/GENERAL INTRODUCTION

1878-2 **Biedermann**, Woldemar Freiherr von. "Goethe und die
Fikentscher." Dresden: Druck von B. G. Teubner, 1878. 12 pp.
Rpt. No. 1879-2.
/FIKENTSCHER, F/CHEMISTRY

1878-3 **Classen**, August. "Entwurf einer Psychologie der Licht- und Far-
benempfindung." Sammlung physiologischer Abhandlungen, Zweite
Reihe, 2. Jena: Verlag von Gustav Fischer, 1878.
/RESEARCH: CHROMATICS

1878-4 **Fitger**, Artur. "Faust' Schatten an Charles Darwin." *Kosmos.
Zeitschrift für einheitliche Weltanschauung auf Grund der Entwick-
lungslehre in Verbindung mit Charles Darwin und Ernst Haeckel*, 2,
No. 4 (1878/1879), 335-8.
A poem.
/BIOLOGY: EVOLUTION/DARWIN, C/HAECKEL, E

1878-5 **Goedeke**, Karl. "Zu Goethes Gleichnissen." *Archiv für Literaturgeschichte*, 7 (1878), 93-4.
/ASTRONOMY/WORKS: LYRICS

1878-6 **Goethe**[, J. W. von]. *Beiträge zur Optik. -- Versuch, die Elemente
der Farbenlehre zu entdecken. -- Zur Farbenlehre: Didaktischer und
Polemischer Theil.* Vol. 35 of *Goethe's Werke. Nach den
vorzüglichsten Quellen revidirte Ausgabe.* Ed. and intro. S. Kalischer. Berlin: Gustav Hempel[, 1878]. lxiv, 616 pp.
/EDITION

1878-7 **[Goethe**, J. W. von.] *La metamorfosi delle piante [Die Metamorphose der Pflanzen].* Trans. Anselmo Guerrieri Gonzaga. *Rassegna
settimanale [Firenze]*, 1, No. 15 (1878), 274ff.
/TRANSLATION: ITALIAN

1878-8 [**Goethe**, J. W. von.] "Ueber den Granit." In [anon]. "Goethe's Naturbetrachtung." *Die Wage. Wochenblatt für Politik und Literatur*, 1878, pp. 19-22.
Cf. No. 1878-1.
/EDITION

1879-1 **Biedermann**, Woldemar Freiherr von. "Zu Goethe und das sächsische Erzgebirge." In his *Goethe-Forschungen*. Frankfurt a/M: Literarische Anstalt Rütten & Loening, 1879, pp. 454-5.
/GEOLOGY/PLACES: SACHSEN

1879-2 **Biedermann**, Woldemar Freiherr von. "Goethe und die Fikentscher." In his *Goethe-Forschungen*. Frankfurt a/M: Literarische Anstalt Rütten & Loening, 1879, pp. 295-312.
Rpt. of No. 1878-2.
/FIKENTSCHER, F/CHEMISTRY

1879-3 **Brück**, A[nton]. T[heobald]. "Goethe. Eine biologische Studie." *Die Gegenwart. Wochenschrift für Literatur, Kunst und öffentliches Leben*, 15 (1979), 8-10.
/BIOLOGY

1879-4 **Foerster**, Wilhelm. "Zur Geschichte einer astronomischen Episode in Wilhelm Meisters Wanderjahren." *Westermann's illustrirte deutsche Monats-Hefte*, 46 (1879), 330-36.
= *Jahrbuch der Illustrirten Deutschen Monatshefte*, Folge 4, vol. 2.
/ASTRONOMY/WORKS: WILHELM MEISTERS WANDER-JAHRE

1879-5 **Goethe**[, J. W. von]. *Geschichte der Farbenlehre. -- Die entoptischen Farben. -- Nachträge zur Farbenlehre.* Vol. 36 of *Goethe's Werke. Nach den vorzüglichsten Quellen revidirte Ausgabe.* Ed. and intro. S. Kalischer. Berlin: Gustav Hempel[, 1879]. XIX, 764 pp.
/EDITION

1879-6 **Kalischer**, Salomon. "Zur Geschichte einer astronomischen Episode in Wilhelm Meister's Wanderjahren." *Westermann's illustrirte deutsche Monats:Hefte*, 47 (1879/1880), 130-31.
/ASTRONOMY/WORKS: WILHELM MEISTERS WANDER-JAHRE

1879-7 **Laube**, Gustav C. "Goethe als Naturforscher in Böhmen." *Mit-

theilungen des Vereins für Geschichte der Deutschen in Böhmen, 18 (1879), 16-37.
/GEOLOGY/PLACES: BÖHMEN

1879-8 **Laube*, Gustav C. "Goethe als Naturforscher in Eger." *Prager Tageblatt*, Nos. 154 and 155, 5 and 6 June 1879.
/GEOLOGY/PLACES: BÖHMEN

1879-9 **Stinde**, Julius. "Goethe als Naturforscher." *Die Gegenwart: Wochenschrift für Literatur, Kunst und öffentliches Leben*, 15 (1879), 198-9.
/GENERAL INTRODUCTION

1879-10 **Wouvermans**, Alwin von. *Farbenlehre. Für die praktische Anwendung in den verschiedenen Gewerben und in der Kunstindustrie.* Wien/Pest/Leipzig: A. Hartleben's Verlag, 1879. xiv [vi], 160 pp.
/CHROMATICS/RESEARCH: CHROMATICS

1880-1 *[anon.] "Goethe als Naturforscher." *Hamburger Nachrichten*, No. 205, 28 August 1880.
/GENERAL INTRODUCTION

1880-2 *[anon.] "Goethe's Farbenlehre." *Popular Science Review*, NS June 1880.
/CHROMATICS

1880-3 **Caro**, E[dmond]. *La philosophie de Goethe.* 2nd edn. Paris: librairie Hachette et Cie., 1880. vi, 398 pp.
Rpt. of Nos. 1865-1 and 1865-2.
/PHILOSOPHY/GENERAL INTRODUCTION/SPINOZA, B/METHOD/SAINT-HILAIRE, G DE

1880-4 **Dreher**, Eugen. "Goethe's Bedeutung als Naturforscher." *Die Natur. Zeitung zur Verbreitung naturwissenschaftlicher Kenntniß und Naturanschauung für Leser aller Stände*, 29 [NS 6] (1880), 516-19.
Rpt. No. 1903-4.
Cf. Kalischer's response, No. 1880-7.
/GENERAL INTRODUCTION

1880-5 [**Düntzer**, Heinrich?]. "Herr Alexander Ecker über Oken und Goethe." *Im neuen Reich. Wochenschrift für das Leben des deutschen Staat, Wissenschaft und Kunst*, 10 (1880), 537-46.
Cf. reply, No. 1880-6.
/ECKER, A/OKEN, L/OSTEOLOGY

1880-6 **Ecker**, Alexander. "Erwiderung." *Im neuen Reich. Wochenschrift für das Leben des deutschen Staat, Wissenschaft und Kunst*, 10 (1880), 767-8.
Reply to No. 1880-5.
/DÜNTZER, H/OKEN, L/OSTEOLOGY

1880-7 **Kalischer**, S[alomon]. "Bemerkungen zu Herrn Dr. Dreher's Vortrag 'Goethe's Bedeutung als Naturforscher'." *Die Natur. Zeitung zur Verbreitung naturwissenschaftlicher Kenntniß und Naturanschauung für Leser aller Stände*, 29 [NS 6] (1880), 606-7.
Response to No. 1880-4.
/GENERAL INTRODUCTION

1880-8 **Kalischer**, Salomon. "Noch einmal 'Goethe als Geologe'. Mit Bezug auf den gleichnamigen Aufsatz des Herrn Prof. Franz Toula in Wien." *Die Natur: Zeitung zur Verbreitung naturwissenschaftlicher Kenntniß und Naturanschauung für Leser aller Stände*, NF 6 (1880),

654-5.
Cf. No. 1880-11.
/GEOLOGY

1880-9 *Kerner von Marilaun, Anton. "Goethe und Darwin." *Neue Freie Presse [Abendblatt]*, No. 1441, 29 April 1880.
Rpt. No. 1908-14.
/BIOLOGY: EVOLUTION/DARWIN, C

1880-10 Laube, Gustav C. "Goethe als Naturforscher in Böhmen." *Mittheilungen des Vereins für Geschichte der Deutschen in Böhmen*, 18 (1880), 16-37.
/PLACES: BÖHMEN/GEOLOGY

1880-11 Toula, Franz. "Goethe als Geologe." *Die Natur: Zeitung zur Verbreitung naturwissenschaftlicher Kenntniß und Naturanschauung für Leser aller Stände*, NF 6 (1880), 581-2; 587-90.
Cf. response, No. 1880-8.
/GEOLOGY

1880-12 Tyndall, John. "Goethe's Farbenlehre." *The Fortnightly Review*, NS 27 (1880), 471-90.
Rpt. No. 1892-19.
Trans. into French, No. 1880-13.
Trans. into German, Nos. 1881-6 and 1895-18.
/CHROMATICS

1880-13 Tyndall, J[ohn]. "Theorie des couleurs de Goethe." *La Revue Scientifique de la France et de l'Étranger*, 9, No. 25 (1880), 1198-1205.
Rpt. No. 1880-14.
French trans. of No. 1880-12.
/CHROMATICS

1880-14 Tyndall, John. "Une théorie des couleurs de Goethe." *Annales d'Oculistique*, 84 (1880), 192-202.
Rpt. of No. 1880-13.
/CHROMATICS

1880-15 wa[?]. "Goethe und Göttling." *Die Grenzboten. Zeitschrift für Politik, Literatur und Kunst*, 39, No. 3 (1880), 110-17.
/GÖTTLING, J/CHEMISTRY/PHARMACOLOGY

1881-1 *[anon.] "Ueber Goethe." *Schlesische Zeitung*, No. 614, 24

December 1881.
/STERNBERG, K VON/BOTANY/PALEONTOLOGY

1881-2 **Cohn**, Ferdinand. "Goethe als Botaniker." *Deutsche Rundschau*, 28 (1881), 26-56.
　　Rpt. Nos. 1882-4 and 1896-4.
　　Trans. into Russian, No. 1902-15.
　　/BOTANY

1881-3 **Geiger**, Ludwig. "Zwei Briefe Soret's an Goethe." *Goethe*, 2 (1881), 365-8.
　　/SORET, F/MINERALOGY

1881-4 **Lambel**, H[?]. *Goethe-Reliquien aus Böhmen. Mittheilungen des Vereins für Geschichte der Deutschen in Böhmen*, 19 (1881), 161-83.
　　/EDITION/GEOLOGY/PLACES: BÖHMEN

1881-5 **Lambel**, H[?]. "Goethe's Verzeichnisse der dem Stifte Tepl und dem Prager Museum übermachten Mineralien." In his *Goethe-Reliquien aus Böhmen. Mittheilungen des Vereins für Geschichte der Deutschen in Böhmen*, 19 (1881), 161-83; 168-78.
　　/GOETHE'S COLLECTIONS/MINERALOGY/INSTITU-
　　TIONS: STIFT TEPL/INSTITUTIONS: ROYAL
　　BOHEMIAN MUSEUM, PRAGUE

1881-6 **[Tyndall**, John.] "Goethe's Farbenlehre." *Sonntags-Beilage zur Vossischen Zeitung*, No. 3, 16 January 1881, cols. 7-9; No. 4, 23 January 1881, cols. 8-11; No. 5, 30 January 1881, cols. 9-10.
　　German trans. of No. 1880-12.
　　Signed: "R. B."
　　/CHROMATICS

1882-1 **Brahm**, Otto. "Eine Episode in Goethes Wahlverwandtschaften." *Zeitschrift für deutsches Altertum und deutsche Literatur*, NF 14 (1882), 194-7.
　　/GEOLOGY/WORKS: DIE WAHLVERWANDTSCHAFTEN

1882-2 **Brauns**, David. "Herr Brauns über: die Niveauschwankungen an der Küste der Umgegend von Neapel." *Bericht über die Sitzungen der Naturforschenden Gesellschaft zu Halle*, 1882, pp. 48-51.
　　/GEOLOGY

1882-3 **Cohn**, Ferdinand. "Botanische Probleme." In his *Die Pflanze. Vorträge aus dem Gebiete der Botanik*. Breslau: J. U. Kern's Verlag

(Max Müller), 1882, pp. 1-21.
/RESEARCH: BOTANY

1882-4 **Cohn**, Ferdinand. "Goethe als Botaniker." In his *Die Pflanze.*
Vorträge aus dem Gebiete der Botanik. Breslau: J. U. Kern's Verlag
(Max Müller), 1882, pp. 23-64.
Rpt. of No. 1881-2.
Rpt. 2nd exp. edn. No. 1896-4.
/BOTANY

1882-5 **Draheim**, H[?]. "Goethe's Gebirgsreisen." *Westermann's
Illustrierte Deutsche Monatshefte*, 52 (1882), 479-85.
/GEOLOGY

1882-6 **Du Bois-Reymond**, E[mil]. "Goethe." *Revue scientifique de la
France et de l'étranger: Revue des cours scientifiques (3e série)*, 4,
No. 20 (1882/1883), 769-76.
French trans. of No. 1882-7.
/GENERAL INTRODUCTION

1882-7 **Du Bois-Reymond**, Emil. "Goethe und kein Ende." Berlin:
Buchdruckerei der Koenigl. Akademie der Wissenschaften (G. Vogt),
1882. 27 pp.
Rpt. Nos. 1883-4, 1886-1 and 1979-18.
Trans. into French, No. 1882-6.
Cf. Responses, Nos. 1882-8, 1882-15, 1882-20, 1883-2, 1883-12
and 1883-18.
"Rede bei Antritt des Rectorats der Koenigl. Friedrich-
Wilhelms-Universität zu Berlin am 15. October 1882."
/GENERAL INTRODUCTION

1882-8 *****Finkel**, Ludwig. "Contra Goethe." *Gazeta Lwoska*, 21 Novem-
ber 1882.
Report on Du Bois-Reymond's "Rektoratsrede" [No. 1882-7].
Cf. response, No. 1882-15.
/DU BOIS-REYMOND, E/GENERAL INTRODUCTION

1882-9 [**Goethe**, J. W. von.] "Ein Goethe'sches Aktenstück." Ed.
L[udwig]. G[eiger]. *Goethe*, 3 (1882), 317-18.
/EDITION

1882-10 [**Goethe**, Johann Wolfgang von.] *Goethes naturwissenschaftliche
Schriften.* Vol. 1. Ed and intro. Rudolf Steiner. Vol. 33 of *Goethes
Werke.* Vol. 114 of *Deutsche National-Literatur: Historisch kritische*

Ausgabe. Ed. Joseph Kürschner. Berlin/Stuttgart: Verlag von W.
Spemann[, 1882]. lxxxiv, 472 pp.
  Rpt. Nos. 1890-5, 1897-6, 1897-7, 1921-9, 1947-11, 1949-172,
    1975-17 and 1982-46.
  Cf. Nos. 1882-21, -22 and -23.
  /EDITION

1882-11 **Haeckel**, E[rnst]. "Darwin, Goethe et Lamarck." *La Revue
scientifique de la France et de l'étranger: Revue des courses scientifiques (3e série)*, 30 (1882/1883), 705-16.
  French trans. of No. 1882-13.
  /BIOLOGY: EVOLUTION/DARWIN, C/LAMARCK, J DE

1882-12 **Haeckel**, Ernst. "Die Naturanschauung von Darwin, Goethe und
Lamark." *Deutsche Rundschau*, 9 (1882), 69-92.
  Rpt. of No. 1882-14.
  /BIOLOGY: EVOLUTION/DARWIN, C/LAMARCK, J DE

1882-13 **Haeckel**, Ernst. "Die Naturanschauung von Darwin, Goethe und
Lamarck." Jena: Verlag von Gustav Fischer, 1882. vii, 64 pp.
  Rpt. of No. 1882-14.
  "Vortrag in der ersten öffentlichen Sitzung der
    fünfundfünfzigsten Versammlung Deutscher Naturforscher
    und Aerzte zu Eisenach am 18. September 1882."
  /BIOLOGY: EVOLUTION/DARWIN, C/LAMARCK, J DE

1882-14 **Haeckel**, Ernst. "Ueber die Naturanschauung von Darwin,
Göthe und Lamarck." *Tageblatt der 55. Versammlung Deutscher
Naturforscher und Aerzte in Eisenach vom 18. bis 22. September
1882*, No. 6, October 1882, pp. 81-91.
  Rpt. No. 1882-12, 1882-13 and 1902-13.
  Trans. into French, No. 1882-11.
  Trans. into Swedish, No. 1902-12.
  "Vortrag. . .Gehalten in der ersten allgemeinen Versammlung
    am 18. September."
  /BIOLOGY: EVOLUTION/DARWIN, C/LAMARCK, J DE

1882-15 ***Kawczynski**, Maxim[?]. *Gazeta Lwoska*, 29 November 1882;
30 November 1882.
  Response to No. 1882-8.
  /DU BOIS-REYMOND, E/FINKEL, L/GENERAL INTRO-
    DUCTION

1882-16 **Lange**, Ernst[E]. "Ueber Goethe's Farbenlehre vom Stand-

punkte der Wissenschaftstheorie und Aesthetik." Diss. Göttingen 1882. 36 pp.
/CHROMATICS/METHOD/AESTHETICS/NEWTON, I

1882-17 **Lewes**, George Henry. "Der Dichter als Naturforscher." In his *Goethes Leben und Werke*. 2 vols. Berlin: Verlag von J. Jolowicz, 1882, II, 680-744.
Rpt. of No. 1857-4.
/GENERAL INTRODUCTION

1882-18 **Rollett**, Alexander. "Aus dem Zeitalter der Phrenologie mit besonderer Beziehung auf Göthes Verkehr mit dem Phrenologen Gall." *Deutsche Revue über das gesamte nationale Leben der Gegenwart*, 7 (1882), 360-80.
/GALL, F/PHRENOLOGY

1882-19 **Schasler**, Max. "Goethe im Lichte der Empirie." *Beilage zur Allgemeinen Zeitung*, No. 349, 15 December 1882, pp. 5145-6.
/CHROMATICS/DU BOIS-REYMOND, E

1882-20 ***Schiff**, Emil. "Goethe und kein Ende." *Neue Freie Presse [Wien]*, No. 6548 (1882).
Report on No. 1882-7.
/DU BOIS-REYMOND, E/GENERAL INTRODUCTION

1882-21 **Schröer**, Karl Julius. "Vorwort." In [**Goethe**, Johann Wolfgang von]. *Goethes naturwissenschaftliche Schriften*. Vol. 1. Ed and intro. Rudolf Steiner. Vol. 33 of *Goethes Werke*. Vol. 114 of *Deutsche National-Literatur: Historisch kritische Ausgabe*. Ed. Joseph Kürschner. Berlin/Stuttgart: Verlag von W. Spemann[, 1882], i-xiv.
/GENERAL INTRODUCTION/METHOD/NATUR-PHILOSOPHIE

1882-22 **Steiner**, Rudolf. "Die Entstehung der Metamorphosenlehre." In [**Goethe**, Johann Wolfgang von]. *Goethes naturwissenschaftliche Schriften*. Vol. 1. Ed and intro. Rudolf Steiner. Vol. 33 of *Goethes Werke*. Vol. 114 of *Deutsche National-Literatur: Historisch kritische Ausgabe*. Ed. Joseph Kürschner. Berlin/Stuttgart: Verlag von W. Spemann[, 1882], xx-xxxv; lii-lxxvii.
Rpt. Nos. 1890-5, 1897-6, 1897-7, 1921-9, 1947-11, 1949-172, 1975-17 and 1982-46.
Trans. into Dutch, No. 1981-97.
/MORPHOLOGY/BIOLOGY

1882-23 **Steiner**, Rudolf. "Die Entstehung von Goethes Gedanken über die Bildung der Tiere." In [**Goethe**, Johann Wolfgang von]. *Goethes naturwissenschaftliche Schriften*. Vol. 1. Ed and intro. Rudolf Steiner. Vol. 33 of *Goethes Werke*. Vol. 114 of *Deutsche National-Literatur: Historisch kritische Ausgabe*. Ed. Joseph Kürschner. Berlin/Stuttgart: Verlag von W. Spemann[, 1882], xxxiv-lii.
Rpt. No. 1921-25.
/ZOOLOGY/COMPARATIVE ANATOMY

1882-24 **Weber**, Max Maria Freiherr von. "Göthe und die Dampfmaschine. Aphorisme." In his *Vom rollenden Flügelrade*. Intro. Max Jahns. Berlin: A. Hofmann & Comp., 1882, pp. 1-9.
Rpt. of No. 1865-7.
/TECHNOLOGY

1882-25 **Weis**, L[?]. "Goethe und Swedenborg." *Goethe*, 3 (1882), 349-51.
/SWEDENBORG, E/NATURPHILOSOPHIE

1883-1 **Albrecht**, Paul. "Sur les 4 os intermaxillaires, le bec-de-lièvre et la valeur morphologique des dents incisives supérieures de l'homme." Bruxelles: librairie médicale de A. Manceaux, 1883. 27 pp.
/RESEARCH: OSTEOLOGY/OSTEOLOGY

1883-2 **Berger**, Alfred Freiherr von. "Goethe's Faust und die Grenzen des Naturerkennens. Wider 'Goethe und kein Ende' von Emil du Bois-Reymond." Wien: Druck und Verlag von Carl Gerold's Sohn, 1883. 40 pp.
Response to No. 1882-7.
/DU BOIS-REYMOND, E/WORKS: FAUST

1883-3 **Classen**, A[ugust]. "Goethe und die Koryphäen der heutigen Naturwissenschaft." *Die Grenzboten. Zeitschrift für Politik, Literatur und Kunst*, 42 (1883), 619-34.
/RECEPTION

1883-4 **Du Bois-Reymond**, Emil. "Goethe und kein Ende." Leipzig: Verlag von Veit & Comp., 1883. 43 pp.
Rpt. of No. 1882-7.
"Rede bei Antritt des Rectorats der Koenigl. Friedrich-Wilhelms- Universität zu Berlin am 15. October 1882."
/GENERAL INTRODUCTION

1883-5 [**Goethe**, J. W. von.] "Notizen zur Mineralogie und Geologie." Ed. G[?]. Weisstein. *Goethe*, 4 (1883), 347-8.
/EDITION

1883-6 **Hahn**, L[?]. "Göthe (Johann-Wolfgang)." In *Dictionnaire encyclopédique des sciences médicales*. Paris: G. Masson, 1883, IX, 738-44.
/MEDICINE

1883-7 **Harpf**, Adolf. "Goethe's Erkenntnisprinzip." *Philosophische Monatshefte*, 19 (1883), 1-39..
/NATURPHILOSOPHIE/EPISTEMOLOGY

1883-8 **Hellmann**, Gustav. "Goethe, Johann Wolfgang von." In his *Repertorium der deutschen Meteorologie. Leistungen der Deutschen in Schriften, Erfindungen und Beobachtungen auf dem Gebiete der Meteorologie und des Erdmagnetismus von den ältesten Zeiten bis zum Schlusse des Jahres 1881.* Leipzig: Verlag von Wilhelm Engelmann, 1883, col. 156.
/METEOROLOGY

1883-9 **Hellmann**, Gustav. "Umriss einer Geschichte der meteorologischen Beobachtungen in Deutschland. Sachsen--Weimar--Eisenach, 1822ff." In his *Repertorium der deutschen Meteorologie. Leistungen der Deutschen in Schriften, Erfindungen und Beobachtungen auf dem Gebiete der Meteorologie und des Erdmagnetismus von den ältesten Zeiten bis zum Schlusse des Jahres 1881.* Leipzig: Verlag von Wilhelm Engelmann, 1883, col. 919-923/4.
/METEOROLOGY

1883-10 **Hlawacek**, Eduard and Viktor **Ruß**. *Goethe in Karlsbad.* 2nd rev. and exp. edn. Karlsbad/Leipzig/Wien: Verlag von Hans Feller, 1883. vii, 121 pp.
Rpt. of No. 1877-7.
/GEOLOGY/MINERALOGY/PLACES: KARLSBAD

1883-11 **Kalischer**, Salomon. "Bemerkungen zu obiger Mitteilung von A. König." *Verhandlungen der physikalischen Gesellschaft in Berlin*, 2 (1883), 74.
Rpt. No. 1883-13.
Cf. No. 1883-14.
/COLORBLINDNESS/KÖNIG, A

1883-12 **Kalischer**, Salomon. "Goethe als Naturforscher und Herr Du

Bois-Reymond als sein Kritiker. Eine Antikritik von Dr. S. Kalischer." Berlin: Verlag von Gustav Hempel, 1883. 90 pp.
Cf. No. 1882-7.
/GENERAL INTRODUCTION/DU BOIS-REYMOND, E

1883-13 **Kalischer**, Salomon. "Hr. Kalischer bemerkte hierzu . . ." *Centralblatt für praktische Augenheilkunde*, 17 (1883), 497-8.
Rpt. of No. 1883-11.
/CHROMATICS: COLORBLINDNESS/KÖNIG, A

1883-14 **König**, Arthur. "Ueber Goethes Bezeichnung der von ihm beobachteten Fälle von Farbenblindheit als 'Akyanoblepsie'." *Centralblatt für praktische Augenheilkunde*, 7 (1883), 497.
Rpt. No. 1884-9.
/COLORBLINDNESS

1883-15 **Köstlin**, Otto. "Goethe und sein Verhältniß zu den Naturwissenschaften." *Beilage zur Allgemeinen Zeitung*, No. 221, 10 August 1883, 3241-2; No. 222, 11 August 1883, 3258-60; No. 223, 12 August 1883, 3274-6.
/GENERAL INTRODUCTION

1883-16 **Schasler**, Max. *Die Farben in ihrer Beziehung zu einander und zum Auge.* Pt. 1 of *Die Farbenwelt. Ein neuer Versuch zur Erklärung der Entstehung und der Natur der Farben, nebst einer praktischen Anleitung zur Auffindung gesetzmäßiger harmonischer Farbenverbindungen.* Sammlung gemeinverständlicher wissenschaftlicher Vorträge, 18th Series, No. 409/410. Berlin: Verlag von Carl Habel, 1883. 102 pp.
/RESEARCH: CHROMATICS/CHROMATICS

1883-17 **Schasler**, Max. "Das Gesetz der Farbenharmonie in seiner Anwendung auf das kunstindustrielle Gebiet." Pt. 2 of *Die Farbenwelt. Ein neuer Versuch zur Erklärung der Entstehung und der Natur der Farben, nebst einer praktischen Anleitung zur Auffindung gesetzmäßiger harmonischer Farbenverbindungen."* Sammlung gemeinverständlicher wissenschaftlicher Vorträge, 18th Series, No. 415. Berlin: Verlag von Carl Habel, 1883. 48 pp.
/RESEARCH: CHROMATICS/CHROMATICS

1883-18 **Schasler**, Max. "Goethe als Naturforscher und Herr Dubois-Reymond." *Die Gegenwart: Wochenschrift für Literatur, Kunst und öffentliches Leben [Berlin]*, 23 (1883), 7-10.
Response to No. 1882-7.

/DU BOIS-REYMOND, E/GENERAL INTRODUCTION

1883-19 **Schasler**, Max. "Die Harmonie der Farben und der Töne." *Die Grenzboten. Zeitschrift für Politik, Literatur und Kunst*, 42 (1883), 251-66.
/CHROMATICS/NEWTON, I/DUBOIS-REYMOND, E

1883-20 *****Vogt**, Carl. "Goethes geologische Studien in Karlsbad und bei Franzensbad." *Fremdenblatt für die böhmischen Kurorte*, Nos. 10 and 11, 8 and 15 June 1883.
Rpt. No. 1883-21.
/GEOLOGY/PLACES: BÖHMEN

1883-21 **Vogt**, Carl. "Goethes geologische Studien in Karlsbad und bei Franzensbad." *Nord und Süd. Eine deutsche Monatsschrift*, 25 (1883), 319-36.
Rpt. of No. 1883-20.
/GEOLOGY/PLACES: BÖHMEN

1883-22 **Weisstein**, Gotthilf. "Notizen zur Mineralogie und Geologie." *Goethe*, 4 (1883), 347-8.
/GEOLOGY/MINERALOGY

1884-1 **Ascherson**, P[aul]. "Forskal über die Metamorphose der Pflanze." *Berichte der Deutschen Botanischen Gesellschaft*, 2 (1884), 293-7.
/FORSKAL, P/BOTANY/LINNAEUS [LINNÉ], C

1884-2 **"Briefwechsel** zwischen Goethe und Ernst Meyer." Ed. Ludwig Geiger. Intro. Carl Jessen. *Goethe*, 5 (1884), 134-76.
/MEYER, E/BOTANY

1884-3 **Classen**, A[ugust]. "Goethes naturwissenschaftliche Schriften." *Die Grenzboten. Zeitschrift für Politik, Literatur und Kunst*, 43 (1884), 544-52.
/GENERAL INTRODUCTION

1884-4 **Goebel**, K[arl von]. "Die Metamorphosenlehre." In his "Vergleichende Entwicklungsgeschichte der Pflanzenorgane." In *Handbuch der Botanik*. Ed. A. Schenk. Vol. I.1 of *Encyclopaedie der Naturwissenschaften*. Ed. W. Förster et. al. Breslau: Verlag von Eduard Trewendt, 1884, 103-14.
/RESEARCH: MORPHOLOGY/RESEARCH: BOTANY

1884-5 [**Goethe**, Johann Wolfgang von.] *Goethes naturwissenschaftliche Schriften*. Vol. 2. Ed and intro. Rudolf Steiner. Vol. 34 of *Goethes Werke*. Vol. 115 of *Deutsche National-Literatur: Historisch kritische Ausgabe*. Ed. Joseph Kürschner. Stuttgart/Berlin/Leipzig: Union Deutsche Verlagsgesellschaft[, 1884]. lxxiv, 403 pp.
    Rpt. Nos. 1921-10, 1947-11, 1949-172, 1975-26, 1982-64 and 1984-96.
    Cf. Nos. 1882-10, 1884-6, -11, -12, -13 and -14.
    /EDITION

1884-6 [**Goethe**, Johann Wolfgang von.] *Goethes naturwissenschaftliche Schriften*. Vol. 3. Ed and intro. Rudolf Steiner. Vol. 35 of *Goethes Werke*. Vol. 116 of *Deutsche National-Literatur: Historisch kritische Ausgabe*. Ed. Joseph Kürschner. Stuttgart/Berlin/Leipzig: Union Deutsche Verlagsgesellschaft[, 1884]. xxxii, 540 pp.
    Rpt. Nos. 1921-11, 1947-11, 1949-172, 1975-16 and 1982-45.
    Cf. Nos. 1882-10, 1884-5 and 1884-15.
    /EDITION

1884-7 **Heller**, August. "Johann Wolfgang von Goethe." In *Von Descartes bis Robert Mayer*. Vol. 2 of *Geschichte der Physik von Aristoteles bis auf die neueste Zeit*. 2 vols. Stuttgart: Verlag von Ferdinand Enke, 1884, pp. 670-74.
    /CHROMATICS

1884-8 **Helmholtz**, Hermann von. "Über Goethe's naturwissenschaftliche Arbeiten." In his *Vorträge und Reden*. 2 vols. Braunschweig: Friedrich Vieweg und Sohn, 1884, pp. 1-24.
    Rpt. of No. 1853-8.
    "Vortrag gehalten im Frühling 1853 in der deutschen Gesellschaft zu Königsberg."
    /GENERAL INTRODUCTION

1884-9 **König**, Arthur. "Ueber Goethes Bezeichnung der von ihm beobachteten Fälle von Farbenblindheit als 'Akyanoblepsie'." *Verhandlungen der physikalischen Gesellschaft in Berlin*, 2 (1884), 72-3.
    Rpt. of No. 1883-14.
    /COLORBLINDNESS

1884-10 **Perrier**, Edmond. "Goethe: Idées de Goethe sur l'unité des types organiques. -- La métamorphose des plantes; structure des végétaux; le végétal idéal. -- Travaux d'anatomie comparée; recherche du type idéal du squelette. -- Transformisme de Goethe. -- Kielmeyer." In his *La philosophie zoologique avant Darwin*. Bibliothèque scientifique

internationale, 45. Paris: Ancienne Librairie Germer Ballière et Cie., 1884, pp. 142-8.
> 2nd edn. 1886; 3rd edn. 1896.
> /BIOLOGY/MORPHOLOGY/KIELMEYER, K

1884-11 **Steiner**, Rudolf. "Goethe und die Mathematik." In [Goethe, Johann Wolfgang von]. *Goethes naturwissenschaftliche Schriften.* Vol. 2. Ed and intro. Rudolf Steiner. Vol. 34 of *Goethes Werke.* Vol. 115 of *Deutsche National-Literatur: Historisch kritische Ausgabe.* Ed. Joseph Kürschner. Stuttgart/Berlin/Leipzig: Union Deutsche Verlagsgesellschaft[, 1884], lxvii-lxix.
> Rpt. Nos. 1921-10, 1947-11, 1949-172, 1975-26, 1982-64 and 1984-96.
> /MATHEMATICS

1884-12 **Steiner**, Rudolf. "Das geologische Grundprinzip Goethes." In [Goethe, Johann Wolfgang von]. *Goethes naturwissenschaftliche Schriften.* Vol. 2. Ed and intro. Rudolf Steiner. Vol. 34 of *Goethes Werke.* Vol. 115 of *Deutsche National-Literatur: Historisch kritische Ausgabe.* Ed. Joseph Kürschner. Stuttgart/Berlin/Leipzig: Union Deutsche Verlagsgesellschaft[, 1884], lix-lxxiii.
> Rpt. Nos. 1921-10, 1947-11, 1949-172, 1975-26, 1982-64 and 1984-96.
> /GEOLOGY

1884-13 **Steiner**, Rudolf. "Die meteorologischen Vorstellungen Goethes." In [Goethe, Johann Wolfgang von]. *Goethes naturwissenschaftliche Schriften.* Vol. 2. Ed and intro. Rudolf Steiner. Vol. 34 of *Goethes Werke.* Vol. 115 of *Deutsche National-Literatur: Historisch kritische Ausgabe.* Ed. Joseph Kürschner. Stuttgart/Berlin/Leipzig: Union Deutsche Verlagsgesellschaft[, 1884], lxxiii-lxxiv.
> Rpt. Nos. 1921-10, 1947-11, 1949-172, 1975-26, 1982-64 and 1984-96.
> /METEOROLOGY

1884-14 **Steiner**, Rudolf. "Über die Anordnung der naturwissenschaftlichen Schriften Goethes." In [Goethe, Johann Wolfgang von]. *Goethes naturwissenschaftliche Schriften.* Vol. 2. Ed and intro. Rudolf Steiner. Vol. 34 of *Goethes Werke.* Vol. 115 of *Deutsche National-Literatur: Historisch kritische Ausgabe.* Ed. Joseph Kürschner. Stuttgart/ Berlin/Leipzig: Union Deutsche Verlagsgesellschaft[, 1884], vii-ix.
> Rpt. Nos. 1921-10, 1947-11, 1949-172, 1975-26, 1982-64 and

1984-96.
/EDITIONS

1884-15 **Steiner**, Rudolf. "Vorrede." In [Goethe, Johann Wolfgang von]. *Goethes naturwissenschaftliche Schriften*. Vol. 3. Ed and intro. Rudolf Steiner. Vol. 35 of *Goethes Werke*. Vol. 116 of *Deutsche National-Literatur: Historisch kritische Ausgabe*. Ed. Joseph Kürschner. Stuttgart/Berlin /Leipzig: Union Deutsche Verlagsgesellschaft[, 1884], i-iv.
    Rpt. Nos. 1921-11, 1947-11, 1949-172, 1975-16 and 1982-45.
    /PHILOSOPHY/METHOD

1885-1 **[anon.]** "Gelehrte Gesellschaften." In *Goethe im Urtheile seiner Zeitgenossen. Zeitungskritiken, Berichte, Notizen, Goethe und seine Werke betreffend, aus den Jahren 1802-1812*. Ed. Julius W. Braun. Berlin: Verlag von Friedrich Luckhardt, 1885, p. 167.
    Rpt. of No. 1808-1.
    Announcement of Goethe's appointment as an "auswärtiger Mitglied."
    /INSTITUTIONS: AKADEMIE DER WISSENSCHAFTEN ZU MÜNCHEN

1885-2 ***[anon.]** "Gelehrte Gesellschaften und Preise." In *Goethe im Urtheile seiner Zeitgenossen. Zeitungskritiken, Berichte, Notizen, Goethe und seine Werke betreffend, aus den Jahren 1802-1812*. Ed. Julius W. Braun. Berlin: Verlag von Friedrich Luckhardt, 1885, p. 91.
    Rpt. of No. 1804-1.
    Announcement of Goethe's election as President of the Naturforschende Gesellschaft zu Jena.
    /INSTITUTIONS: NATURFORSCHENDE GESELLSCHAFT ZU JENA

1885-3 **[anon.]** "[Review of:] Bey Cotta: Zur Farbenlehre, von Goethe. Erster Band 654 S.; Zweyter Band 757 S. in Octav, nebst einem Heft Kupfertafeln mit deren Erklärung. 16 Kupfert. 12 S. Text in Quart. 1810." In *Goethe im Urtheile seiner Zeitgenossen. Zeitungskritiken, Berichte, Notizen, Goethe und seine Werke betreffend, aus den Jahren 1802-1812*. Ed. Julius W. Braun. Berlin: Verlag von Friedrich Luckhardt, 1885, pp. 278-9.
    Review of No. 1810-4.
    /REVIEW

1885-4 **[anon.]** "[Review of:] Zur Farbenlehre von Göthe. Cotta,

Tübingen. 1810. 2 Bde. 95 Bogen." In *Goethe im Urtheile seiner Zeitgenossen. Zeitungskritiken, Berichte, Notizen, Goethe und seine Werke betreffend, aus den Jahren 1802-1812.* Ed. Julius W. Braun. Berlin: Verlag von Friedrich Luckhardt, 1885, pp. 246-51.
Rpt. of No. 1810-4.
/REVIEW/RECEPTION

1885-5 **Bride**, T[?]. H. Mc. "Vegetable morphology a century ago -- Goethe." *Science*, 6 (1885), 130-31.
/BOTANY/MORPHOLOGY

1885-6 **Celakovsky**, Ladislav. "Linné's Anteil an der Lehre von der Metamorphose der Pflanze." *Botanische Jahrbücher für Systematik, Pflanzengeschichte und Pflanzengeographie*, 6 (1885), 146-86.
/BOTANY/MORPHOLOGY/LINNAEUS [LINNÉ], C

1885-7 **Fischer**, Kuno. "Der Goethe-Seebeck'sche Briefwechsel." *Beilage zur Allgemeinen Zeitung*, No. 189, 10 July 1885, 2777-9.
/SEEBECK, T/CHROMATICS

1885-8 [**Fries**, Jacob Friedrich.] "[Review of:] Zur Farbenlehre, von Göthe. Erster Band. Nebst einem Hefte mit sechzehn Kupfertafeln XLVIII u. 757 S. 8. Tübingen, in der J. G. Cotta'schen Buchhandlung. 1810. (15 fl.)." *Heidelberger Jahrbücher der Literatur: Vierte Abteilung. Mathematik, Physik und Kameralwissenschaften*, 3, No. 7 (1810), 288[9?]-307.
Rpt. of No. 1810-3.
/REVIEW

1885-9 [**Goethe**, J. W. von.] *Principii di Filosofia zoologica e anatomia comparata.* Trans. Michele Lessona. Biblioteca scientifica, 5. Roma: Perino, 1885. 94 pp.
/TRANSLATION: ITALIAN

1885-10 *****Harpf**, Adolf. "Goethe und die Organik." *Tagespost [Graz]*, No. 178, 7 July 1885.
/BIOLOGY

1885-11 **Harpf**, Adolf. "Schopenhauer und Goethe. Ein Beitrag zur Entwicklungsgeschichte der Schopenhauer'schen Philosophie." *Philosophische Monatshefte*, 21 (1885), 449-79.
/SCHOPENHAUER, A/CHROMATICS

1885-12 **K[?].**, M[?]. "Die Metamorphose der Pflanzen." *Deutsche*

Zeitung [Morgen-Ausgabe], No. 4840 (26 June 1885), 1-3.
/BOTANY/MORPHOLOGY

1885-13 **Lewes**, G[eorge]. H[enry]. "Der Dichter als Naturforscher." In
his *Goethes Leben und Werke*. Trans. Paul Lippert. 2 vols.
Berlin: Druck und Verlag der Bibliographischen Anstalt[, 1885], 150-214.
Rpt. of No. 1857-4.
/GENERAL INTRODUCTION

1885-14 [**Lindenau**, Bernhard August von.] "Versuch einer geschichtlichen Darstellung der Fortschritte der Sternkunde im verflos-
senen Decennio." In *Goethe im Urtheile seiner Zeitgenossen.*
Zeitungskritiken, Berichte, Notizen, Goethe und seine Werke betref-
fend, aus den Jahren 1802-1812. Ed. Julius W. Braun. Berlin: Verlag von Friedrich Luckhardt, 1885, pp. 278-9.
/RECEPTION/ASTRONOMY

1885-15 [**Malus**, Étienne Louis.] "Bericht eines französischen Physikers
über Herrn von Goethes Werk: Zur Farbenlehre. 2 Bde. Tübingen
1810. 8." In *Goethe im Urtheile seiner Zeitgenossen.*
Zeitungskritiken, Berichte, Notizen, Goethe und seine Werke betref-
fend, aus den Jahren 1802-1812. Ed. Julius W. Braun. Berlin: Verlag von Friedrich Luckhardt, 1885, pp. 283-5.
Rpt. of No. 1812-6.
/REVIEW/CHROMATICS

1885-16 [**Mollweide**, Karl Brandan.] "Auszug aus einem Schreiben des
Herrn Dr. Mollweide." In *Goethe im Urtheile seiner Zeitgenossen.*
Zeitungskritiken, Berichte, Notizen, Goethe und seine Werke betref-
fend, aus den Jahren 1802-1812. Ed. Julius W. Braun. Berlin: Ver-
lag von Friedrich Luckhardt, 1885, pp. 251-2.
Rpt. of No. 1810-8.
/CHROMATICS/NEWTON, I/REVIEW

1885-17 [**Mollweide**, Karl Brandan.] "[Review of:] Tübingen, b. Cotta.
Zur Farbenlehre, von v. Göthe. -- Erster Band. XLVIII und 654 S.
Zweyter Band. XXVIII und 757 S. 1810. 8. Ein Heft mit XVI illu-
minirten Kupfertafeln und deren Erklärung." In *Goethe im Urtheile*
seiner Zeitgenossen. Zeitungskritiken, Berichte, Notizen, Goethe und
seine Werke betreffend, aus den Jahren 1802-1812. Ed. Julius W.
Braun. Berlin: Verlag von Friedrich Luckhardt, 1885, pp. 273-6.
Rpt. of No. 1811-6.
/REVIEW/CHROMATICS

1885-18 **Poselger**, Friedrich Theodor. "Der farbige Rand eines durch bi-convexes Glas entstehenden Bildes untersucht mit Bezug auf Herrn Göthes Werk: Zur Farbenlehre." In *Goethe im Urtheile seiner Zeitgenossen. Zeitungskritiken, Berichte, Notizen, Goethe und seine Werke betreffend, aus den Jahren 1802-1812*. Ed. Julius W. Braun. Berlin: Verlag von Friedrich Luckhardt, 1885, pp. 276-8.
  Rpt. of No. 1811-8.
  /RESEARCH: CHROMATICS/CHROMATICS

1885-19 **Ruge**, Sophus. "Die erste bildliche Darstellung von Höhenskalen der Gewächse." *Zeitschrift für wissenschaftliche Geographie*, 5 (1885), 136.
  /GEOGRAPHY

1885-20 **Springer**, Robert. "Goethes Verdienste um die Naturwissenschaften." In his *Essays zur Kritik und Philosophie und zur Goethe-Literatur*. Minden i. W.: J. C. C. Bruns' Verlag, 1885, pp. 240-67.
  Rpt. of No. 1866-7.
  /RECEPTION/GENERAL INTRODUCTION

1885-21 **Springer**, Robert. "Goethe und Graf von Sternberg." In his *Essays zur Kritik und Philosophie und zur Goethe-Literatur*. Minden i. W.: J. C. C. Bruns' Verlag, 1885, pp. 295-306.
  /STERNBERG, K VON/BOTANY/PALEONTOLOGY

1885-22 **Springer**, Robert. "Die naturwissenschaftlichen Anschauungen in Goethe's poetischen Werken." In his *Essays zur Kritik und Philosophie und zur Goethe-Literatur*. Minden i. W.: J. C. C. Bruns' Verlag, 1885, pp. 268-94.
  /WORKS: VARIOUS

1885-23 **Wd[?].**, A[?]. "[Review of:] Zur Farbenlehre, herausgegeben von Göthe. Im Verlag der Cottaischen Buchhandlung in Tübingen 1810. 2 Bde." In *Goethe im Urtheile seiner Zeitgenossen. Zeitungskritiken, Berichte, Notizen, Goethe und seine Werke betreffend, aus den Jahren 1802-1812*. Ed. Julius W. Braun. Berlin: Verlag von Friedrich Luckhardt, 1885, pp. 252-61.
  Rpt. of No. 1810-11.
  /REVIEW/CHROMATICS

1886-1 **Du Bois-Reymond**, Emil. "Goethe und kein Ende." In his *Reden: Erste Folge: Litteratur. Philosophie. Zeitgeschichte*. Leipzig: Verlag von Veit & Comp., 1886, pp. 418-47.
  Rpt. of No. 1882-7.

Rpt. 2nd edn. No. 1912-15.
"In der Aula der Berliner Universität am 15. October 1882 gehaltene Rectoratsrede."
/GENERAL INTRODUCTION

1886-2 **Fischer**, Kuno. "Goethe und Thomas Seebeck." In his *Erinnerungen an Moritz Seebeck wirkl. Geheimerath und Curator der Univesität Jena. Nebst einem Anhange: Goethe und Thomas Seebeck.* Heidelberg: Carl Winter's Universitätsbuchhandlung, 1886, pp. 117-50.
/SEEBECK, T/CHROMATICS

1886-3 **Frankl**, Ludw[ig]. Aug[ust]. "Graf Caspar Sternberg und Goethe. Eine Erinnerung." *Die Gegenwart: Wochenschrift für Literatur, Kunst und öffentliches Leben [Berlin]*, 30 (1886), 132-3.
Rpt. of No. 1842-7.
/STERNBERG, K VON/BOTANY/PALEONTOLOGY

1886-4 *****Geiger**, Karl. "Zu Goethes Fragment 'Die Natur'." *Archiv für Literaturgeschichte*, 14 (1886).
/WORKS: DIE NATUR

1886-5 **Haberlandt**, G[ottlieb]. "Goethes botanische Studien." *Humboldt: Monatsschrift für die gesamten Naturwissenschaften*, 5 (1886), 201-7.
/BOTANY

1886-6 **Loewenfeld**, Adolf. "Architektonisch-naturhistorisches Problem." *Die Natur: Zeitschrift zur Verbreitung naturwissenschaftlicher Kenntniß und Naturanschauung für Leser aller Stände*, NF 12 (1886), 556.
Cf. No. 1886-7.
/GEOLOGY

1886-7 **Müller**, Karl. "Zusatz des Herausgebers." *Die Natur: Zeitschrift zur Verbreitung naturwissenschaftlicher Kenntniß und Naturanschauung für Leser aller Stände*, NF 12 (1886), 556-8.
Addendum to No. 1886-6.
/GEOLOGY

1886-8 **Siewers**, E[?]. W. "Dichter und Naturforscher." *Die Gegenwart: Wochenschrift für Literatur, Kunst und öffentliches Leben [Berlin]*, 30 (1886), 211-14.
/GENERAL INTRODUCTION

1886-9 **Steiner**, Rudolf. *Grundlinien einer Erkenntnistheorie der Goetheschen Weltanschauung mit besonderer Rücksicht auf Schiller: Zugleich eine Zugabe zu Goethes "Naturwissenschaftlichen Schriften" in Kürschners "Deutscher National-Literatur".* Berlin/Stuttgart: Verlag von W. Spemann, 1886. iv, 92 pp.
    Rpt. Nos. 1924-35, 1949-173 and 1979-77.
    Trans. into English, No. 1940-17.
    Trans. into Spanish, No. 1962-33.
    Trans. into Italian, No. 1974-38.
    Trans. into Dutch, No. 1984-98.
    Trans. into French, No. 1985-102.
    Trans. into Portuguese, No. 1986-101.
    Cf. No. 1986-51.
    /EPISTEMOLOGY

1886-10 **Wiedersheim**, Robert. "Wirbeltheorie des Schädels." In his *Lehrbuch der vergleichenden Anatomi der Wirbelthiere auf Grundlage der Entwicklungsgeschichte.* 2nd edn. Jena: Verlag von Gustav Fischer, 1886, pp. 100-101.
    /ZOOLOGY/COMPARATIVE ANATOMY

1887-1 *****Child**, H[?]. "Goethe und die Blumen." *Der Zeitgeist [Beiblatt zum Berliner Tageblatt],* No. 35, 29 August 1887.
    /BOTANY

1887-2 **Goethe**, J. W. von. *Goethes Werke: Herausgegeben im Auftrage der Großherzogin Sophie von Sachsen.* 4 Parts. 133 vols. (in 143). Weimar: Hermann Böhlau/Hermann Böhlaus Nachfolger, 1887-1919.
    Individual vols. listed separately throughout.
    /EDITION

1887-3 **Haberland**, Maximilian. "Die Entwicklung der Lehre von der Metamorphose der Pflanzen von J. W. Goethe an bis auf die neueste Zeit." Neustrelitz: G. F. Spalding & Sohn, 1887. 16 pp.
    "Wissenschaftliche Beilage zum Programm der Realschule in Neustrelitz, Ostern 1887."
    /MORPHOLOGY/BOTANY/RECEPTION

1887-4 **Harnack**, Otto. "Goethes Naturbetrachtung." In his *Goethe in der Epoche seiner Vollendung (1805-1832).* Leipzig: J. C. Hinrichs'sche Buchhandlung, 1887, pp. 53-102.
    /NATURPHILOSOPHIE/METHOD

1887-5 **Harris**, W[?]. T. "Goethe as a Scientist." In *Poetry and Philosophy of Goethe: Comprising the lectures and extempore discussions before the Milwaukee literary school in August, 1886.* Ed. Marion V[ienna]. Dudley. Chicago: S. C. Griggs and Company, 1887. vi, 300 pp.
/GENERAL INTRODUCTION

1887-6 **MacAlister**, James. "Goethe as a Scientist." In *Poetry and Philosophy of Goethe. Comprising the Lectures and Extempore Discussions before the Milwaukee Literary School in August, 1886.* Ed. Marion V[ienna]. Dudley. Chicago: S. C. Griggs and Company, 1887, pp. 38-58.
"As Reported by the Milwaukee Sentinel."
Includes discussion by W. T. Harris, W. T. Hewitt, D. J. Snider, and the author.
/GENERAL INTRODUCTION

1887-7 **[Prem**, S[?]. M.] "Neue Beiträge zu Goethe's Beziehungen zu Deutschböhmen. 2. Der Kammmerbühl und das Goethedenkmal. Zu dem beigegebenen Bilde." *Literarisches Jahrbuch: Central-Organ für die wissenschaftlichen, literarischen und künstlerischen Interessen Nordwestböhmens und der deutschen Grenzlande*, 1 (1891), 33-7.
/GEOLOGY/PLACES: BÖHMEN

1887-8 **Schröer**, Karl Julius and Fr[?]. von **Rziha**. "Goethe und C. August im Bergwerk." *Chronik des Wiener Goethe-Vereins*, 2 (1887), 44.
/GEOLOGY/TECHNOLOGY/CARL AUGUST [GROSS-HERZOG VON WEIMAR]

1887-9 **[Steiner**, Rudolf.] "Goethes Farbenlehre und der Philosoph in Zombor." *Chronik des Wiener Goethe-Vereins*, 2, No. 11 (1887), 59-60.
/CHROMATICS/SCHMITT, E

1887-10 **Steiner**, R[udolf]. "Zur Farbenlehre." *Chronik des Wiener Goethe-Vereins*, 2, No. 7 (1887), 39-40.
/CHROMATICS

1888-1 **[anon.]** "Goethe und die Anlage des Bremer Hafens." *Norddeutsche Allgemeine Zeitung*, 28, No. 486 (14 October 1888), [1-2].
/MEYER, N/PLACES: BREMEN

1888-2 **Bendt**, Franz. "Goethe als Meteorologe." *Die Gegenwart: Wochenschrift für Literatur, Kunst und öffentliches Leben [Berlin]*, 33, No. 9 (1888), 134-6.
/METEOROLOGY

1888-3 **Bertheau**, Friedrich. "Göthe und seine Beziehungen zur schweizerischen Baumwoll-Industrie nebst dem Nachweiss dass unter Frau Susanna der Fabrikantenfrau in Wilhelm Meisters Wanderjahren Frau Barbara Schulthess von Zürich zu verstehen ist." Wetzikon: Aktienbuchdruckerei, 1888. 9 pp.
/TECHNOLOGY/WORKS: WILHELM MEISTERS WANDERJAHRE

1888-4 **Brauns**, David. "Das Problem des Serapeums von Pozzuoli." Leipzig: Wilhelm Engelmann, 1888. 15 pp.
Rpt. of No. 1888-5.
/GEOLOGY

1888-5 **Brauns**, David. "Das Problem des Serapeums von Pozzuoli." *Leopoldina: Amtliches Organ der Kaiserlichen Leopoldino-Carolinishen Deutschen Akademie der Naturforscher*, No. 24 (1888), 132-6; 150-52; 161-4; 189-92; 209-12.
Rpt. No. 1888-4.
/GEOLOGY

1888-6 [**Goethe**, J. W. von.] "Notizen zur Goethe-Literatur. II. Notizen Goethes über den Granit." Ed. Herm[ann]. Rollett. *Chronik des Wiener Goethe-Vereins*, 2, No. 12, 23 December 1888, 48.
Continuation of No. 1888-7.
/EDITION

1888-7 [**Goethe**, J. W. von.] "Notizen zur Goethe-Literatur. I. 'Zur Mineralogie und Geologie'." Ed. Herm[ann]. Rollett. *Chronik des Wiener Goethe-Vereins*, 3, No. 11, 30 November 1888, 44.
Cf. continuation, No. 1888-6.
/EDITION

1888-8 **Hellen**, Eduard von der. "Goethes Anteil an Lavaters Physiognomischen Fragmenten." Diss. Bonn. Frankfurt a/M: Literarische Anstalt Rütten & Loening, 1888. 35 pp.
Rpt. No. 1888-9.
/PHYSIOGNOMY/OSTEOLOGY

1888-9 **Hellen**, Eduard von der. "Goethes Anteil an Lavaters Physio-

gnomischen Fragmenten." Diss. Bonn. Frankfurt a/M: Literarische Anstalt Rütten & Loening, 1888. 255 pp.
Rpt. of No. 1888-8.
/PHYSIOGNOMY/OSTEOLOGY

1888-10 **Jordan**, Karl Friedr[ich]. "Goethe -- und noch immer kein Ende! Kritische Würdigung der Lehre Goethes von der Metamorphose der Pflanzen." Sammlung gemeinverständlicher wissenschaftlicher Vorträge, NS, Series 3, 52. Hamburg: Verlagsanstalt und Druckerei (vorm. J. F. Richter), 1888. 48 pp.
/MORPHOLOGY/BOTANY

1888-11 **Pfalz**, Franz. "Goethe und Schopenhauer." *Die Grenzboten. Zeitschrift für Politik, Litteratur und Kunst*, 47 (1888), 114-29; 172-81.
/SCHOPENHAUER, A

1888-12 **Reichel**, Eugen. "Lichtenberg und Goethe. Ein Beitrag zur Goethe-Forschung." *Die Gegenwart. Wochenschrift für Literatur, Kunst und öffentliches Leben*, 34, No. 27, 7 July 1888, 7-9; No. 28, 14 July 1888, 26-9.
/LICHTENBERG, G/CHROMATICS

1888-13 **Schwartzkopff**, Ernst. "Eine Studie über das Os intermaxillare." *Deutsche Monatsschrift für Zahnheilkunde*, 6 (1888), 129-34; 180-89.
/RESEARCH: OSTEOLOGY/OSTEOLOGY

1888-14 **Suess**, Eduard. "Der Serapis-Tempel bei Puzzuoli." In his *Das Antlitz der Erde*. 5 vols. Prag/Wien: F. Tempsky, 1888, II, 463-99.
/GEOLOGY

1888-15 **Thomas**, Calvin. "Goethe and the development hypothesis." *The Open Court. A Weekly Journal, Devoted to the Work of Conciliating Religion with Science*, 2, No. 29 (1888/1889), 815-8; No. 31, (1888/1889), 847-50.
/BIOLOGY: EVOLUTION/MORPHOLOGY/BIOLOGY

1888-16 **T[rebra**, Friedrich Wilhelm Heinrich] v[on]. "Lebensverhältnisse mit Ober-Berghauptmann von Trebra." *Goethe*, 9 (1888), 11-20; 83-4.
/TREBRA, F VON/GEOLOGY/MINERALOGY

1889-1 *[**anon.**] "Goethe und die Strumpfwirker." *Chemnitzer Tageblatt*,

No. 284 (1889).
/TECHNOLOGY

1889-2 **Bölsche**, Wilhelm. "Goethes Wahlverwandtschaften im Lichte moderner Naturwissenschaft." *Die Gesellschaft: Monatsschrift für Litteratur und Kunst*, September 1889, pp. 1330-40.
Rpt. No. 1979-13.
/WORKS: DIE WAHLVERWANDTSCHAFTEN

1889-3 **Brenning**, Emil. "Goethe's Stellung zur Wissenschaft." In his *Goethe nach Leben und Dichtung von Emil Brenning*. Biographieen zu der Sammlung klassischer Dichtungen. Gotha: Friedrich Andreas Perthes, 1889, pp. 91-101.
/GENERAL INTRODUCTION

1889-4 **Dilthey**, Wilhelm. "Zu Goethes Philosophie der Natur." *Archiv für Geschichte der Philosophie*, 2 (1889), 45-8.
/HERDER, J/SPINOZA, B

1889-5 **Francke**, Kuno. "Goethe und Cogswell." *Die Nation. Wochenschrift für Politik, Volkswirthschaft und Litteratur*, 7 (1889/1890), 614-15.
Trans. into English, No. 1890-4.
"Mit Goethes Brief an Cogswell vom 11. Aug. 1819."
/COGSWELL, J/MINERALOGY/GEOLOGY

1889-6 **Helmholtz**, Hermann Ludwig Ferdinand von. "Über Goethes naturwissenschaftliche Arbeiten: Vortrag gehalten in der Deutschen Gesellschaft zu Königsberg von A. [sic] Helmholtz. German Scientific Monographs Edited for American students, 1. New York: Henry Holt and Company F. W. Christern / Boston: Carl Schoenhof[, 1889]. ix, 43 pp.
Rpt. of No. 1853-8.
"With notes for American students by Oswald Seidensticker."
/GENERAL INTRODUCTION

1889-7 *****John**, Alois. "Goethe in Deutschböhmen." Eger: privately printed, 1889. 21 pp.
/GEOLOGY/PLACES: BÖHMEN

1889-8 **Schröer**[, Karl Julius]. "Goethe und ein Candidat der Theologie aus Ungarn." *Chronik des Wiener Goethe-Vereins*, 4 (1889), 7-11.
/FERJENTSEK, S/METEOROLOGY

1889-9 *__Schuster__, Arthur. "Goethes Farbenlehre." *Publications of the English Goethe Society*, 5 (1889), 141-51.
/CHROMATICS

1889-10 __Steiner__, Rudolf. "Ueber den Gewinn der Goethe-Studien durch die Weimarer Ausgabe in naturwissenschaftlicher Beziehung." *Chronik des Wiener Goethe-Vereins*, 3 (1889), 49-51.
Rpt. No. 1891-18.
/EDITIONS/GENERAL INTRODUCTION

1890-1 **Basedow**, Hans von. "Der Einfluß der Naturwissenschaft auf die Litteratur und deren Kunstprinzip. I. Goethe, Schiller und ihre Zeit." *Kritisches Jahrbuch*. *Beiträge zur Charakteristik der zeitgenössischen Litteratur sowie zur Verständigung über den modernen Realismus*, 1 (1890), 27-33.
/LITERARY THEORY/SCHILLER, F

1890-2 **Bock**, Alfred. "Goethe und Professor Wilbrand." *Frankfurter Zeitung*, No. 240, 28 August 1890.
Rpt. No. 1896-2.
/WILBRAND, J

1890-3 **Büsgen**, Moritz. "Über Goethes botanische Studien." *Goethe*, 11 (1890), 145-58.
/BOTANY

1890-4 **Francke**, Kuno. "Goethe and Cogswell." *The Harvard Monthly*, 10, No. 4 (1890), 132-7.
English trans. of No. 1889-5.
/COGSWELL, J/MINERALOGY/GEOLOGY

1890-5 **[Goethe**, J. W. von.] *Beiträge zur Optik: Zur Farbenlehre: Enthüllung der Theorie Newtons*. Vol. 3 of *Naturwissenschaftliche Schriften*. Ed., intro. and comm. Rudolf Steiner. Pref. K[arl]. J[ulius]. S[chrörer]. Kürschners Deutsche National-Literatur: Goethes Werke, vol. 33. Berlin /Stuttgart: Verlag von W. Spemann, 1890.
Rpt. of No. 1882-10.
/EDITION

1890-6 **Goethe**, J. W. von. *Zur Farbenlehre: Didaktischer Theil*. Vol. II.1 of the *Weimarer Ausgabe*. Weimar: Hermann Böhlau, 1890. xxxx, 399 pp.
Rpt. No. 1987-44.
/EDITION

1890-7 **Goethe**, J. W. von. *Zur Farbenlehre: Polemischer Theil*. Vol. II.2 of the *Weimarer Ausgabe*. Weimar: Hermann Böhlau, 1890. ix, 318 pp.
Rpt. No. 1987-47.
/EDITION

1890-8 **Grosse**, Eduard. "Goethe und die Newtonianer." *Velhagen & Klasings Neue Monatshefte*, 5 (1890/1891), 121-33.
/CHROMATICS/NEWTON, I

1890-9 **Haeckel**, Ernst. "Goethe on Evolution." *The Open Court. A weekly magazine devoted to the work of conciliating religion with science*, 4, No. 131, February 27 1890, 2111-14.
English trans. from No. 1870-3 [actually from 8th edn., 1889].
/BIOLOGY: EVOLUTION/RESEARCH: BIOLOGY/OKEN, L

1890-10 **Hertwig**, Oscar. "Ueber die Stellung des Kopfskelets zum Rumpfskelet." In his *Lehrbuch der Entwicklungsgeschichte des Menschen und der Wirbelthiere*. 3rd rev. edn. Jena: Verlag von Gustav Fischer, 1890, 520-26.
/RESEARCH: OSTEOLOGY/OSTEOLOGY/OKEN, L

1890-11 **Kerner von Marilaun**, Anton. "Metamorphosenlehre und natur-philosophische Spekulationen." In *Gestalt und Leben der Pflanze*. Vol. 1 of his *Pflanzenleben*. Leipzig/Wien: Verlag des Bibliographischen Instituts, 1890, pp. 8-14.
Rpt. No. 1896-10.
/MORPHOLOGY/BOTANY/NATURPHILOSOPHIE

1890-12 **Loeper**, Gustav von. "Zu Dichtung und Wahrheit 1." *Goethe*, 11 (1890), 174-5.
/STAUD[T], J/CHEMISTRY

1890-13 **Potonié**, Henry. "Die botanische (theoretische) Morphologie und Goethe." *Naturwissenschaftliche Wochenschrift*, 5 (1890), 46-8.
/BOTANY

1890-14 **Schuster**, A[rthur]. "Goethe's 'Farbenlehre'." *Publications of the English Goethe Society*, 5 (1890), 141-51.
/CHROMATICS

1890-15 **Weiss**, F. Ernest. "Goethe as a Naturalist." *Publications of the English Goethe Society*, 5 (1890), 43-66.
/GENERAL INTRODUCTION

1890-16 **Williamson**, W[?]. C. "On Goethe as botanist and osteologist." *Publications of the English Goethe Society*, 5 (1890), 127-40.
"Read at Owens College, Manchester, on March 30th, 1887."
/BOTANY/OSTEOLOGY/MORPHOLOGY/BIOLOGY

1891-1 **[anon.]** "Ein Beitrag Goethes zu den 'Ephemeriden' des Weimarer Geographischen Instituts." *Weimarische Zeitung*, No. 298, 20 December 1891.

/GEOGRAPHY

1891-2 *[anon.] "Naturwissenschaftliche Plaudereien. Goethes Farbenlehre." *Kölnische Zeitung [Beilage zur Sonntags-Ausgabe]*, No. 670,
16 August 1891.
/CHROMATICS

1891-3 **Gerber**, Paul Henry. "Goethe und noch immer kein Ende."
Sonntagsblatt Nr. 4 der Königsberger Hartungschen Zeitung, No. 21,
25 January 1891, [1-2].
/GENERAL INTRODUCTION

1891-4 **Goethe**, J. W. von. *Zur Morphologie: I. Theil*. Vol. II.6 of the
Weimarer Ausgabe. Weimar: Hermann Böhlau, 1891. viii, 452 pp.
Rpt. No. 1987-48.
/EDITION

1891-5 **Hager**, Herman. "Joseph Green Cogswells Beziehungen zu
Goethe." *Archiv für das Studium der neueren Sprachen und Lit-
teraturen*, 45, No. 87 (1891), 247-52.
/COGSWELL, J/MINERALOGY/GEOLOGY

1891-6 **Hauck**, Guido. "Technikers Faust-Erklärung." *Centralblatt der
Bauverwaltung*, 11 (1891), 123-7.
/TECHNOLOGY/WORKS: FAUST

1891-7 **Heuer**[, Otto]. "Goethe's elektrische Studien." *Elektricität:
Offizielle Zeitung der Internationalen Elektrotechnischen Ausstellung
Frankfurt am Main 1891*. Frankfurt am Main: Verlag von
Haasenstein & Vogler, 1891, pp. 39-40.
/PHYSICS/CHROMATICS

1891-8 **Potonié**, Henry. "Goethe ein Vorgänger Charles Darwin's?"
Naturwissenschaftliche Wochenschrift, 6, No. 38 (1891), 385-6.
/BIOLOGY: EVOLUTION/DARWIN, C

1891-9 [**Prem**, S[?]. M.] "Neue Beiträge zu Goethe's Beziehungen zu
Deutschböhmen. 2. Der Kammerbühl und das Goethedenkmal. Zu
dem beigegebenen Bilde." *Literarisches Jahrbuch. Centralorgan für
die wissenschaftlichen, literarischen und künstlerischen Interessen
Nordwestböhmens und der deutschen Grenzlande*, 1 (1891), 33-7.
/GEOLOGY/PLACES: DER KAMMERBÜHL

1891-10 **Ruland**, Carl. "Zu Goethes naturwissenschaftlichen Forsch-

ungen." *Goethe*, 12 (1891), 152-74.
/GENERAL INTRODUCTION

1891-11 **Schiff,** Emil. "Ueber Helmholtz' Goetherede in Weimar." *Die Nation. Wochenschrift für Politik, Volkswirtschaft und Litteratur*, 9 (1891/1892), 573-6.
Cf. No. 1892-10.
/HELMHOLTZ, H VON/RECEPTION

1891-12 **Schimmelbusch,** Walther. "Goethes Beschäftigung mit der Elektrizität. Eine zeitgemäße Betrachtung zu des Dichters 142. Geburtstag." *Didaskalia. Unterhaltungsblatt des Frankfurter Journals*, No. 200, 28 August 1891, 798-800.
/PHYSICS/CHROMATICS

1891-13 **Schopenhauer,** Arthur. *Commentatio exponens theoriam colorum physiologicam, eandemque primariam.* In his *Sämmtliche Werke in sechs Bänden.* Ed. Eduard Grisebach. Leipzig: Druck und Verlag von Philipp Reclam jun., 1891, VI, 111-73.
Rpt. of No. 1830-9.
2nd impression of this edn., [1895].
/RESEARCH: CHROMATICS/CHROMATICS

1891-14 **Schopenhauer,** Arthur. *Über das Sehn und die Farben. Eine Abhandlung.* In his *Sämmtliche Werke in sechs Bänden.* Ed. Eduard Grisebach. Leipzig: Druck und Verlag von Philipp Reclam jun., 1891, VI, 7-109.
Rpt. of No. 1816-4.
/RESEARCH: CHROMATICS/CHROMATICS

1891-15 **Schopenhauer,** Arthur. "Zur Farbenlehre." In *Parerga und Paralipomena: kleine philosophische Schriften.* Vol. 2 of his *Sämmtliche Werke in sechs Bänden.* Ed. Eduard Grisebach. Leipzig: Druck und Verlag von Philipp Reclam jun., 1891, pp. 195-204.
Rpt. of No. 1851-2.
2nd impression of this edn., [1895].
/CHROMATICS/RESEARCH: CHROMATICS

1891-16 **Schröer[,** Karl Julius]. "Altgraf Fugo Franz zu Salm und Goethe." *Chronik des Wiener Goethe-Vereins*, 5 (1891), 29-33.
/SALM, F ZU

1891-17 **Steiner,** Rudolf. "Gedanken zu dem handschriftlichen Nachlasse Goethes." *Chronik des Wiener Goethe-Vereins*, 5 (1891), 10-12.

/EDITIONS

1891-18 **Steiner**, Rudolf. "Über den Gewinn unserer Anschauungen von Goethes naturwissenschaftlichen Arbeiten durch die Publikationen des Goethe-Archivs." *Goethe*, 12 (1891), 190-210.
Rpt. of No. 1889-10.
/EDITION/GENERAL INTRODUCTION

1891-19 **Weiss**, F. Ernest. "Goethe as Naturalist." *Publications of the English Goethe Society*, 5 (1890), 43-66.
/GENERAL INTRODUCTION

1892-1 **[anon.]** "Ein Beitrag Goethes zu den 'Ephemeriden' des Weimarer Geographischen Instituts." *Mitteilungen der Kais. Königl. Geographischen Gesellschaft in Wien*, 35 (1892), 72-4.
/GEOGRAPHY/INSTITUTIONS: WEIMARER GEO-
GRAPHISCHES INSTITUT

1892-2 *****[anon.]** "Goethe und die Naturwissenschaften." *Sprudel. Centralblatt der Curorte in Österreich, Deutschland und der Schweiz*, 24, No. 9 (1892).
/GENERAL INTRODUCTION

1892-3 **[anon.]** "Previsioni di Goethe intorno alle future scoperte scientifice." *Minerva*, 2, 4, No. 8 (1892), 180-81.
Italian summary of No. 1892-10.
/HELMHOLTZ, H VON/GENERAL INTRODUCTION

1892-4 **[anon.]** "Was es außer Wasser noch regnet." *Beilage zur Allgemeinen Zeitung*, No. 250, 25 October 1892, 4-6.
/BOTANY

1892-5 **Bardeleben**, Karl von. "Goethe als Anatom." *Goethe*, 13 (1892), 163-80.
Rpt. No. 1895-1.
/ANATOMY

1892-6 **Goethe**, J. W. von. *Zur Morphologie: II. Theil.* Vol. II.7 of the *Weimarer Ausgabe.* Weimar: Hermann Böhlau, 1892. vi, 372 pp.
Rpt. No. 1987-49.
/EDITION

1892-7 **Goethe**, J. W. von. *Zur Naturwissenschaft überhaupt: Mineralogie und Geologie: I. Theil.* Vol. II.9 of the *Weimarer Aus-*

gabe. Weimar: Hermann Böhlau, 1892. vii, 409 pp.
Rpt. No. 1987-53.
/EDITION

1892-8 *Helmholtz, H[ermann]. von. "Goethe természettudományi sejtel-
mei. Ford.: Cz. A." *Természettudományi Közlöny*, 24 (1892), 526-
40.
Hungarian trans. of No. 1892-10.
/GENERAL INTRODUCTION

1892-9 Helmholtz, H[ermann]. von. *Goethe's Vorahnungen kommender
naturwissenschaftlicher Ideen*. Berlin: Verlag von Gebrüder Paetel,
1892. 55 pp.
Rpt. of No. 1892-10.
"Rede, gehalten an der Generalversammlung der Goethe-
Gesellschaft zu Weimar den 11. Juni 1892."
/GENERAL INTRODUCTION

1892-10 Helmholtz, H[ermann]. von. "Goethe's Vorahnungen
kommender naturwissenschaftlicher Ideen." *Deutsche Rundschau*, 72
(1892), 115-32.
Rpt. Nos. n.d.-20, 1892-9, 1892-11, 1896-7, 1903-15, 1917-24,
1925-17, 1932-149, 1971-19 and 1979-38.
Trans. into Hungarian, No. 1892-8.
Trans. into English, No. 1971-18.
Italian summary, No. 1892-3.
Cf. No. 1891-11.
Cf. No. 1892-15.
"Rede, gehalten in der Generalversammlung der Goethe-
Gesellschaft zu Weimar den 11. Juni 1892."
/GENERAL INTRODUCTION

1892-11 Helmholtz, H[ermann]. von. "Helmholtz über Goethe." *Didaskalia. Unterhaltungsblatt des Frankfurter Journals*, No. 142, 21 June
1892, 566-7; No. 143, 22 June 1892, 570-71.
Rpt. of No. 1892-10.
/GENERAL INTRODUCTION

1892-12 Kalischer, Salomon. "Weimarer Goethe-Ausgabe. Bericht der
Redactoren und Herausgeber. Zweite Abtheilung. Band 1.2."
Goethe, 13 (1892), 272-3.
/EDITIONS

1892-13 Leitzmann, Albert. "Georg Forsters Beziehungen zu Goethe

und Schiller und seine Verteidigung Schillers." *Archiv für das Studium der neueren Sprachen und Litteraturen*, 46, No. 88 (1892), 129-56.
/FORSTER, J

1892-14 ***Lungo**, Carlo del. "Meteorologia Goethiana [Goethean Meteorology]." *Rassegna Internazionale*, 1 June 1892 [1902?].
Rpt. No. 1902-6.
In Italian.
/METEOROLOGY/WORKS: LYRICS

1892-15 **Neumann-Hofer**, Otto. "Helmholtz auf dem Goethe-Tage." *Das Magazin für Litteratur*, 61, No. 27 (1892), 436-8.
Cf. No. 1892-10.
/HELMHOLTZ, H VON/RECEPTION

1892-16 ***Petermann**, Reinhard E. "Goethe als Meteorolog." *Die Presse*, No. 33, 2 February 1892.
/METEOROLOGY

1892-17 **Steiner**, Rudolf. "Weimarer Goethe-Ausgabe. Bericht der Redactoren und Herausgeber. Zweite Abtheilung. Band 6. 7." *Goethe*, 13 (1892), 273-4.
/EDITIONS

1892-18 **Suphan**, Bernhard. "Weimarer Goethe-Ausgabe. Bericht der Redactoren und Herausgeber. Zweite Abtheilung. Band 6. 7." *Goethe*, 13 (1892), 272.
/EDITIONS

1892-19 **Tyndall**, John. "1880. Goethe's 'Farbenlehre'." In his *New Fragments*. London: Longmans, Green, and Co., 1892, pp. 47-77.
Rpt. of No. 1880-12.
/CHROMATICS

1892-20 ***W[?].**, F. "Friedlieb Ferdinand Runge und sein Besuch bei Goethe." *Hamburgischer Correspondent*, No. 917, 29 December 1892; No. 920, 30 December 1892. Abendausgabe.
/RUNGE, F/CHEMISTRY

1892-21 **Wünsche**, Otto. "Goethe als Naturfreund und Naturforscher." *Jahresbericht des Vereins für Naturkunde zu Zwickau*, 1892, 1-35.
/CHROMATICS

1893-1 **Dorer**, Edmund. "Goethes Verhältnis zur Tierwelt." In his *Vermischte Aufsätze*. Vol. 3.2 of his *Nachgelassene Schriften*. Ed. Adolf Friedrich Graf von Schack. Dresden: Verlag von L. Ehlermann, 1893, pp. 121-46.
/ZOOLOGY

1893-2 **Friedel**, Ernst. "Märkische Geschiebe." *"Brandenburgia"*. *Monatsblatt der Gesellschaft für Heimatkunde der Provinz Brandenburg zu Berlin*, 1 (1892/1893), 242.
/GEOLOGY

1893-3 **Friedel**, Ernst. [Untitled.] *"Brandenburgia"*. *Monatsblatt der Gesellschaft für Heimatkunde der Provinz Brandenburg zu Berlin*, 1 (1892/1893), 146-53.
/GEOLOGY/PLACES: BRANDENBURG

1893-4 **Goethe**, J. W. von. *Zur Farbenlehre: Historischer Theil I*. Vol. II.3 of the *Weimarer Ausgabe*. Weimar: Hermann Böhlau, 1893. xxiv, 400 pp.
Rpt. No. 1987-45.
/EDITION

1893-5 **Goethe**, J. W. von. *Zur Morphologie: III. Theil*. Vol. II.8 of the *Weimarer Ausgabe*. Weimar: Hermann Böhlau, 1893. 362 pp.
Rpt. No. 1987-50.
/EDITION

1893-6 **Goethe**, J. W. von. *Zur Naturwissenschaft: Allgemeine Naturlehre: I. Theil*. Vol. II.11 of the *Weimarer Ausgabe*. Weimar: Hermann Böhlau, 1893. vii, 382 pp.
Rpt. No. 1987-51.
/EDITION

1893-7 **Günther**, Siegmund. "Der Kammerbühl. Eine vulkanistische Studie." *Der Ausland, Wochenschrift für Erd- und Völkerkunde*, 66 (1893), 353-5; 372-5.
/GEOLOGY/PLACES: BÖHMEN

1893-8 **Hellen**, Eduard von der. "Über die verschiedenen Zweige der hiesigen Thätigkeit. Ein Vortrag von Goethe." *Goethe*, 14 (1893), 3-26.
/EDITION/INSTITUTIONS: DIE FREITAGSGESELLSCHAFT

1893-9 **Kronfeld**, Ernst Moritz. "Goethe als Botaniker." In his *Bei Mut-

ter Grün. Wien: Verlag von Max Merlin[, 1893], pp. 13-23.
/BOTANY

1893-10 **Leitzmann**, Albert. "Zu Goethes Briefwechsel mit Georg Forster." *Vierteljahrschrift für Litteraturgeschichte*, 6 (1893), 152-6.
/FORSTER, G

1894-1 **Bailey**, G[?]. H. "Goethe as a student of chemistry." In *Transactions of the Manchester Goethe Society, 1886-1893*. Warrington: Mackie & Co., Limited, 1894, pp. 142-4.
/CHEMISTRY

1894-2 **Bardeleben**, Karl von. "Weimarer Goethe-Ausgabe. Bericht der Redactoren und Herausgeber. Zweite Abtheilung. Band 8." *Goethe*, 15 (1894), 315-17.
/COMPARATIVE ANATOMY

1894-3 **Becker**, Hermann. "Goethe als Geograph." Wissenschaftliche Beilage zum Jahresbericht der Margaretenschule zu Berlin. Berlin: R. Gaertners Verlagsbuchhandlung Hermann Heyfelder, 1894. 30 pp.
Cf. continuation, Nos. 1898-2 and 1904-.
/GEOGRAPHY

1894-4 ***Bock**, Alfred. "Goethe und Henrik Steffens." *Schlesische Zeitung*, No. 600 (1894).
/STEFFENS, H/NATURPHILOSOPHIE

1894-5 **Dilthey**, Wilhelm. "Aus der Zeit der Spinoza-Studien Goethe's." *Archiv für Geschichte der Philosophie*, 4 (1894), 317-41.
Rpt. No. 1914-4.
/NATURPHILOSOPHIE/SPINOZA, B

1894-6 **Friedel**, E[rnst]. "Nochmals Goethe und die Markgrafensteine." *"Brandenburgia". Monatsblatt der Gesellschaft für Heimatkunde der Provinz Brandenburg zu Berlin*, 3 (1894/1895), 95-6.
/GEOLOGY

1894-7 **Goethe**, J. W. von. *Zur Farbenlehre: Historischer Theil II*. Vol. II.4 of the *Weimarer Ausgabe*. Weimar: Hermann Böhlau, 1894. viii, 512 pp.
Rpt. No. 1987-46.
/EDITION

1894-8 **Goethe**, J. W. von. *Zur Naturwissenschaft überhaupt: Mineralogie und Geologie: II. Theil.* Vol. II.10 of the *Weimarer Ausgabe.* Weimar: Hermann Böhlau, 1894. viii, 282 pp.
Rpt. No. 1987-54.
/EDITION

1894-9 **Höfler**, Alois. "Einige nähere und fernere Ziele für die Weiterbildung des physikalischen Unterrichtes am Gymnasium." In *Tagblatt der 66. Versammlung Deutscher Naturforscher und Ärzte in Wien 1894.* Wien: Aus der kaiserlich-königlichen Hof- und Staatsdruckerei, 1894, p. 99.
Partial rpt. of No. 1895-4.
/PEDAGOGY/PHYSICS/CHROMATICS/OPTICS

1894-10 **[Höfler**, Alois.] "Goethes Naturleben in der Schule." *Chronik des Wiener Goethe-Vereins*, 8 [9] (1894), 29-31.
/PEDAGOGY/PHYSICS/CHROMATICS/OPTICS

1894-11 **Kareis**, Josef. "Goethe und die Elektricitätslehre." *Chronik des Wiener Goethe-Vereins*, 8 [9] (1894), 19.
Report on the lecture.
/PHYSICS/CHROMATICS

1894-12 **Kellner**, H[?]. C. "Goethes Dichtung 'Die Metamorphose der Pflanzen'." *Mittheilungen aus dem Goetheverein zu Zwickau [Beiblatt zum Zwickauer Tageblatt]*, 27 May 1894, 2-5.
"Festansprache. . .zur Frühlingsfeier im 'Goetheverein' den 27. April 1894."
/WORKS: LYRICS

1894-13 **Lippmann**, Edmund O. von. "Über einen naturwissenschaftlichen Aberglauben." *Abhandlungen der Naturforschenden Gesellschaft zu Halle*, 20 (1894), 1-14.
Rpt. No. 1906-17.
"Nach einem Vortrage gehalten in der Naturforschenden Gesellschaft zu Halle am 28. April 1894."
/WORKS: FAUST/ALCHEMY

1894-14 **Mann**, Albert. "Was bedeutet 'Metamorphose' in der Botanik? Diss. München. München: Druck von Val. Höfling, 1894. 40 pp.
/RESEARCH: MORPHOLOGY/RESEARCH: BOTANY

1894-15 **Meyer**, Alexander. "Goethe und die chemische Industrie." *Die Nation: Wochenschrift für Politik, Volkswirtschaft und Literatur*, 12

(1894/1895), 691-2.
/CHEMISTRY/STAUD[T], J

1894-16 **Meyer**, Richard M. "Goethe als Naturforscher." *Euphorion*, 1 (1894), 26-46.
Rpt. No. 1895-9.
/GENERAL INTRODUCTION

1894-17 **Osborn**, Henry Fairfield. "Johann Wolfgang Goethe was the greatest poet of Evolution. . ." In his *From the Greeks to Darwin: An Outline of the Development of the Evolution Idea*. Columbia University Biological Series, 1. New York/London: Macmillan and Co., 1894, 181-7.
2nd edn. 1899.
Frequent references to Goethe throughout the volume.
/BIOLOGY: EVOLUTION

1894-18 **Proft**, Ernst. "Kammerbühl und Eisenbühl, die Schicht-Vulkane des Egerer Beckens in Böhmen." *Jahrbuch der kaiserlich-königlichen Geologischen Reichsanstalt*, 44 (1894), 25-86.
/GEOLOGY

1894-19 **Rosenbach**, Ottomar. "Die Farbensirene und Bemerkungen über die Entstehung der Farben." In *Einundsiebzigster Jahres-Bericht der Schlesischen Gesellschaft für vaterländische Cultur*. Breslau: G. P. Aderholz' Buchhandlung, 1894, pp. 34-43.
Rpt. No. 1909-24.
/RESEARCH: CHROMATICS/CHROMATICS/RECEPTION

1894-20 **Schuster**, Arthur. "Goethe's theory of colour." In *Transactions of the Manchester Goethe Society, 1886-1893*. Warrington: Mackie & Co., 1894, pp. 137-8.
"Paper read 25th January 1888."
/CHROMATICS

1894-21 **Steiner**, Rudolf. "Zur Feier von Goethes Geburtstag. Goethes Naturanschauung gemäß den neuesten Veröffentlichungen des Goethe-Archivs." *Berichte des Freien Deutschen Hochstiftes in Frankfurt am Main*, NS 10 (1894), 1-18.
Rpt. No. 1979-75.
/GENERAL INTRODUCTION/EDITIONS

1894-22 **Vintschgau**, M[aximilian]. v[on]. "Physiologische Analyse eines ungewöhnlichen Falles partieller Farbenblindheit II." *Archiv für die*

gesammte Physiologie des Menschen und der Thiere, 57 (1894), 191-307.
/COLORBLINDNESS

1894-23 **Williamson**[, ?]. "Goethe as botanist." In *Transactions of the Manchester Goethe Society, 1886-1893*. Warrington: Mackie & Co., 1894, pp. 129-31.
/BOTANY

1894-24 **Wünsche**, Otto. "Goethe als Naturfreund und Naturforscher." *Jahresbericht des Vereins für Naturkunde zu Zwickau in Sachsen*, 1894, pp. 1-30.
"Vortrag gehalten im Verein für Naturkunde zu Zwickau."
/GENERAL INTRODUCTION

1895-1 **Bardeleben**, Karl von. "Goethe als Anatom." *Nord und Süd. Eine deutsche Monatsschrift*, 74 (1895), 46-60.
Rpt. of No. 1892-5.
Cf. Italian summary, No. 1896-1.
/ANATOMY

1895-2 **Goebel**, Karl (von). "Zur Geschichte unserer Kenntniss der Correlationserscheinungen. II." *Flora oder allgemeine Botanische Zeitung*, 81 (1895), 195-215.
/BOTANY/RESEARCH: BOTANY/SAINT-HILAIRE, G DE

1895-3 **Goedeke**, Karl. "Einleitung." In *Morphologie*. Vol. 32 of *Goethes Sämtliche Werke in 36 Bänden*. Stuttgart: Verlag der J. G. Cotta'schen Buchhandlung Nachfolger, 1895, v-xiv.
Rpt. of No. 1867-1.
/MORPHOLOGY/BIOLOGY

1895-4 **Höfler**, Alois. "Einige nähere und fernere Ziele für die Weiterbildung des physikalischen Unterrichtes am Gymnasium." *Zeitschrift für den Physikalischen und Chemischen Unterricht*, 8, No. 3 (1895), 123-33.
Partial rpt. No. 1894-9.
/PEDAGOGY/PHYSICS/CHROMATICS/OPTICS

1895-5 **Jastrowitz**, M[?]. "Historische Notiz über Aphasie." *Goethe*, 16 (1895), 192-3.
Rpt. of No. 1875-2.
/MEDICINE/PSYCHOLOGY

1895-6 **Krause**, Ernst [Sterne, Carus]. "Der Farbenreiz bei Menschen und Thieren. Eine Betrachtung zu Goethes Farbenlehre." *Sonntagsbeilage zur Vossischen Zeitung*, No. 17, 28 April 1895, cols. [8-11].
/CHROMATICS/RESEARCH: SENSORY PHYSIOLOGY

1895-7 **Lommel**, E[ugen]. von. "Eine optische Relique von Goethe." *Deutsche Revue über das gesamte nationale Leben der Gegenwart*, 20, No. 2 (1895), 44-8.
/CHROMATICS/HEGEL, G

1895-8 **May**, Walther. "Goethes Verhältniss zur Natur und ihrer Wissenschaft." *Verhandlungen des naturwissenschaftlichen Vereins in Karlsruhe*, 13 (1895/1900), 524-50.
/GENERAL INTRODUCTION

1895-9 **Meyer**, Richard M. "Goethe als Naturforscher." In his *Goethe*. Geisteshelden III, 1-3. Berlin: Hofmann & Co., 1895. xxxi, 628 pp. Rpt. of No. 1894-16.
/GENERAL INTRODUCTION

1895-10 **Meyer**, Richard M. "Goethes wissenschaftliche Arbeiten." In his *Goethe*. Geisteshelden III, 1-3. Berlin: Hofmann & Co., 1895, pp. 579-92.
/GENERAL INTRODUCTION

1895-11 **Mézières**, A[?]. "Coup d'oeil sur les travaux scientifiques de Goethe." In his *Les oeuvres expliquées par la vie 1749-1795*. Paris: Librairie Hachette et Cie., 1895, pp. 369-88.
/GENERAL INTRODUCTION

1895-12 ***Prochazka**, Vlad[?]. Jos[?]. "O geologicke sbirce J. W. Goetha z okoli Karlovyck Varu o museu Kralovstoi Ceskeho [On Goethe's Geological Collection in the Royal Bohemian Museum in Prag]." Prag, 1895.
In Czech.
/GOETHE'S COLLECTIONS/MINERALOGY/INSTITUTIONS: ROYAL BOHEMIAN MUSEUM, PRAGUE

1895-13 **Saccardo**, Pier' Andrea. "Goethe (Gio. Volfango)." In *La botanica in Italia: Materiali per la storia di questa scienza. Memorie del Reale Istituto Veneto di Scienze, Lettere ed Arti*, 25 (1895), 179.
In Italian.
/GENERAL INTRODUCTION

1895-14 **Saccardo**, Pier' Andrea. "Serra mobile della Palma di Goethe. (Ricostruita nel 1825.): Tecoma grandiflora *Delauny* (del Giappone). La Bignonia di Goethe [Moveable Greenhouse Goethe's Palm. (Reconstructed in 1825.): Tecoma grandiflora *Delauny* (from Japan). Goethe's Bignonia]." In his *L'orto botanico di Padova nel 1895 (Anno CCCL. dalla sua fondazione)*. Padova/Verona: Fratelli Drucker, 1895. 8 pp. + 8 plates.
    In Italian.
    /BOTANY/INSTITUTIONS: ORTO BOTANICO, PADOVA

1895-15 **Seuffert**, Bernhard. "Goethe an Carus." *Chronik des Wiener Goethe-Vereins*, 9 (1895), 46-7.
    /CARUS, C

1895-16 **Sieveking**, Heinrich. "Goethe und Schopenhauer." *Goethe*, 16 (1895), 209-13.
    /SCHOPENHAUER, A/CHROMATICS

1895-17 **Steiner**, Rudolf. "Goethes Beziehungen zur Versammlung deutscher Naturforscher und Aerzte in Berlin 1828, Nach einem Actenstück seines Archivs." *Goethe*, 16 (1895), 52-6.
    /RECEPTION/PLACES: BERLIN/EDITION/INSTITUTIONS: VERSAMMLUNG DEUTSCHER NATURFORSCHER UND AERZTE

1895-18 **Tyndall**, John. "Goethes Farbenlehre." In his *Fragmente: Neue Folge*. Braunschweig: Druck und Verlag von Friedrich Vieweg und Sohn, 1895, pp. 55-89.
    German trans. of No. 1880-12.
    /CHROMATICS

1895-19 **Vogel**, Carl. "Der Grossherzog Carl August, Goethe und Oken's Isis." *Chronik des Wiener Goethe-Vereins*, 9 (1895), 33-40.
    /CARL AUGUST [GROSSHERZOG VON WEIMAR]/OKEN, L

1895-20 **Wiener**, Chr[istian]. "Die Farbe der atmosphärischen Luft und Etwas über die Göthesche Farbenlehre." *Verhandlungen des Naturwissenschaftlichen Vereins in Karlsruhe*, 13 (1895-1900), 215-22.
    /CHROMATICS/RESEARCH: CHROMATICS

1895-21 **Witt**, Otto N. "Rundschau." *Prometheus. Illustrirte Wochenschrift über die Fortschritte in Gewerbe, Industrie und Wissenschaft*, 6

(1895), 188-90.
/STAUD[T], J/CHEMISTRY

1895-22 **Zellner**, Julius. "Goethe und Schopenhauer. Ein Beitrag zur Geschichte der Farbenlehre." *Chronik des Wiener Goethe-Vereins*, 9 (1895), 41-4.
/SCHOPENHAUER, A/CHROMATICS

1896-1 **[anon.]** "Goethe anatomista [Goethe as Anatomist]." *Minerva*, 6, 10, No. 7 (1896), 4-10.
Italian summary of No. 1895-1.
/ANATOMY

1896-2 **Bock**, Alfred. "Goethe und Professor Wilbrand." In his *Aus einer kleinen Universitätsstadt. Kulturgeschichtliche Bilder*. Giessen: Verlag von Emil Roth[, 1896], pp. 46-54.
Rpt. of No. 1890-2.
/WILBRAND, J

1896-3 **[Carus**, Carl Gustav.] "Ein Brief von Dr. G. Carus über Goethe." In *Ungedrucktes aus dem Goethe-Kreise. Mit vielen Facsimiles*. Ed. Gustav Ad[olf]. Müller. München: Verlagsbuchhandlung Seitz & Schauer, 1896, pp. 89-90.
/RECEPTION

1896-4 **Cohn**, Ferdinand. *Goethe als Botaniker*. In his *Die Pflanze. Vorträge aus dem Gebiete der Botanik*. 2nd exp. edn. Breslau: J. U. Kern's Verlag (Max Müller), 1896, pp. 77-155.
Rpt. of No. 1882-4.
/BOTANY

1896-5 **[Goethe**, J. W. von.] "Die Botanik unter dem Einflusse der Metamorphosenlehre. Goethes Versuch über die Metamorphose der Pflanzen. 1790." In *Erläuterte Abschnitte aus den Werken hervorragender Naturforscher aller Völker und Zeiten*. Ed. Friedrich Dannemann. Vol. 1 of his *Grundriss einer Geschichte der Naturwissenschaften: Zugleich eine Einführung in das Studium der naturwissenschaftlichen Literatur*. Leipzig: Verlag von Wilhelm Engelmann, 1896, pp. 194-8.
Rpt. Nos. 1902-11 and 1908-6.
/EDITION

1896-6 **Goethe**, J. W. von. *Zur Naturwissenschaft: Allgemeine Naturlehre: II. Theil*. Vol. II.12 of the *Weimarer Ausgabe*. Weimar:

Hermann Böhlaus Nachfolger, 1896. vii, 382 pp.
Rpt. No. 1987-52.
Contains name and subject indices to vols. II.6-II.12.
/EDITION

1896-7 **Helmholtz**, Hermann von. "Goethe's Vorahnungen kommender
naturwissenschaftlicher Ideen." In his *Vorträge und Reden*. 2 vols.
4th edn. Braunschweig: Friedrich Vieweg und Sohn, 1896, II, 337-
61.
Rpt. of No. 1892-10.
"Rede gehalten in der Generalversammlung der Goethe-
Gesellschaft zu Weimar 1892"
/GENERAL INTRODUCTION

1896-8 **Helmholtz**, H[ermann]. von. *Handbuch der Physiologischen
Optik*. 2nd rev. edn. Hamburg/Leipzig: Verlag von Leopold Voss,
1896. xix, 1334 pp.
/RESEARCH: OPTICS/RESEARCH: SENSORY PHYSIOL-
OGY

1896-9 **Helmholtz**, Hermann von. "Über Goethes naturwissenschaftliche
Arbeiten." In his *Vorträge und Reden*. 2 vols. 4th edn. Braun-
schweig: Friedrich Vieweg und Sohn, 1896, I, 23-47.
Rpt. of No. 1853-8.
"Vortrag gehalten zu Königsberg 1853."
/GENERAL INTRODUCTION

1896-10 **Kerner von Marilaun**, Anton. "Metamorphosenlehre und
naturphilosophische Spekulationen." In *Gestalt und Leben der
Pflanze*. Vol. 1 of his *Pflanzenleben*. 2nd rev. and exp. edn. Leip-
zig/Wien: Verlag des Bibliographischen Instituts, 1896, pp. 8-15.
Rpt. of No. 1890-11.
/MORPHOLOGY/BOTANY/NATURPHILOSOPHIE

1896-11 **Kraus**, Arnost V. "Goethovy prirodovedecke studie v Cechach
[Goethe's Scientific Studies in Bohemia]." In his *Goethe a Cechy*.
Prague: Kursíka a Kohouta, 1896, pp. 102-16.
In Czech.
/GEOLOGY/PLACES: BÖHMEN

1896-12 **Langguth**, Adolf. "Goethe als Wetterprophet." *Burschen-
schaftliche Blätter*, 9 (1896/1897), 310-13.
/METEOROLOGY

1896-13 **Lungo**, Carlo del. "Goethe scienziato [Goethe the Scientist]." *Nuova Antologia*, Series 4, 64, No. 148, 1 July 1896, 105-31. In Italian. /GENERAL INTRODUCTION

1896-14 **Schwalbe**, J[ulius]. "Zur Geschichte der 'plastischen Anatomie'." *Deutsche Medizinische Wochenschrift*, 22 (1896), 761-2. /ANATOMY

1896-15 ***Zellner**, Julius. "Goethe und Schopenhauer. Ein Beitrag zur Geschichte der Farbenlehre." *Chronik des Wiener Goethe-Vereins*, 9 (1896), 41-44. /CHROMATICS/SCHOPENHAUER, A

1897-1 [anon.] "Aus dem botanischen Garten in Padua. Zwei Bilder zur italienischen Reise." *Chronik des Wiener Goethe-Vereins*, 11 (1897), 20-22. /BOTANY/INSTITUTIONS: ORTO BOTANICO, PADOVA

1897-2 [anon.] "Die Goethe-Palme in Padua." *Die Gartenlaube: Illustriertes Familienblatt*, No. 29 (1897), 500. /BOTANY/INSTITUTIONS: ORTO BOTANICO, PADOVA

1897-3 *[anon.] "Goethe und der Panamakanal." *Frankfurter Zeitung*, No. 93 (1897). /TECHNOLOGY

1897-4 ***Barewicz**, Witwold. "Goethes Naturgefühl." *Programm des Franz-Josef-Gymnasiums in Drohobycz (Galizien)*, 1897. /NATURPHILOSOPHIE

1897-5 **Goethe**, J. W. von. *Chromatik*. Vol. II.5.1 of the *Weimarer Ausgabe*. Weimar: Hermann Böhlaus Nachfolger, 1897. x, 479 pp. Rpt. No. 1987-36. /EDITION

1897-6 ***Goethe**, J. W. von. *Materialien zur Farbenlehre (Schluß): Entoptische Farben: Paralipomena zur Chromatik: Nachträge: Sprüche in Prosa: Nachträge zu den naturwissenschaftlichen Schriften*. Vol. 5 of *Naturwissenschaftliche Schriften*. Ed., intro. and comm. Rudolf Steiner. Pref. K[arl]. J[ulius]. S[chrörer]. Kürschners Deutsche National-Literatur: Goethes Werke, vol. 33. Berlin/Stuttgart: Verlag von W. Spemann, 1897. Rpt. of No. 1882-10.

/EDITION

1897-7 *Goethe, J. W. von. *Zur Farbenlehre II: Materialien zur Ge-schichte der Farbenlehre.* Vol. 4 of *Naturwissenschaftliche Schriften.* Ed., intro. and comm. Rudolf Steiner. Pref. K[arl]. J[ulius]. S[chrörer]. Kürschners Deutsche National-Literatur: Goethes Werke, vol. 33. Berlin/Stuttgart: Verlag von W. Spemann, 1897.
Rpt. of No. 1882-10.
/EDITION

1897-8 Ilwof, Franz. "Goethe und die industrielle Revolution am Ende des 18. Jahrhunderts." *Chronik des Wiener Goethe-Vereins,* 11 (1897), 43-4.
/TECHNOLOGY

1897-9 Leitzmann, Albert. "Briefwechsel zwischen Goethe und Lichten-berg." *Goethe,* 18 (1897), 32-48.
/EDITION/LICHTENBERG, G/CHROMATICS

1897-10 [Potonié, H(enry).] "Dr. H. Potonié: Die Metamorphose der Pflanzen im Lichte palaeontologischer Thatsachen." In "Der siebente naturwissenschaftliche Feriencursus für Lehrer an höheren Schulen, abgehalten in Berlin vom 29. September bis 9. October 1897. Bericht auf Grund eingegangener Beiträge durch Prof. Dr. B. Schwalbe." *Naturwissenschaftliche Wochenschrift,* 12 (1897), 608-14.
/RECEPTION/RESEARCH: BOTANY/RESEARCH: MOR-PHOLOGY

1897-11 Schwalbe, J[ulius]. "Zu 'Goethe und die plastische Anatomie.'" *Goethe,* 18 (1897), 282-3.
/ANATOMY

1897-12 Steiner, Rudolf. *Goethes Weltanschauung.* Weimar: Verlag von Emil Felber, 1897. x, 206 pp.
Rpt. No. 1921-27, 1963-34 and 1979-76.
Trans. into Italian, No. 1925-31.
Trans. into English, Nos. 1928-50 and 1985-101.
Trans. (partial) into Dutch, No. 1983-99.
Trans. into Dutch, No. 1983-100.
Trans. into French, No. 1985-100.
Cf. No. 1982-25.
/GENERAL INTRODUCTION/HEGEL, G/NATUR-PHILOSOPHIE

1898-1 [anon.] "Zwei Goethe-Pflanzen in Padua." *Vom Fels zum Meer [Beilage: Der Sammler]*, 17, No. 17 (1898), 31-32.
/BOTANY/INSTITUTIONS: ORTO BOTANICO, PADOVA

1898-2 **Becker**, Hermann. "Goethe als Geograph." In *Wissenschaftliche Beilage zum Jahresbericht der IX. Städtischen Realschule zu Berlin. Programm No. 125.* Berlin: R. Gaertners Verlagsbuchhandlung Hermann Heyfelder, 1898, pp. 1-29.
Continuation of No. 1894-3.
Cf. Continuation, No. 1904-6.
/GEOGRAPHY

1898-3 **Biedermann**, W[oldemar]. Fr[ei]h[er]r. v[on]. "Berichtigung zum 9. Bande von Goethes Tagebüchern." *Goethe*, 19 (1898), 295-6.
/EDITIONS/THIENEMANN, A/ZOOLOGY

1898-4 **Cossmann**, Paul Nikolaus. "Goethes Naturteleologie." *Euphorion: Zeitschrift für Literaturgeschichte*, 5 (1898), 694-705.
/NATURPHILOSOPHIE

1898-5 **Dove**, Alfred. "Goethe unter den Naturforschern." In his *Ausgewählte Schriften vornehmlich historischen Inhalts.* Leipzig: Verlag von Duncker & Humblot, 1898, pp. 495-502.
Rpt. of No. 1874-3.
/GENERAL INTRODUCTION/RECEPTION

1898-6 **Driesmans**, Heinrich. "Ein naturwissenschaftlich gebildeter Berliner Oberlehrer." In his *Die Plastische Kraft in Kunst, Wissenschaft und Leben.* Leipzig: Druck und Verlag von C. G. Naumann, 1898, pp. 128-30.
/MORPHOLOGY/PEDAGOGY

1898-7 **Goebel**, K[arl]. "Morphologie und Organographie." In *Allgemeine Organographie.* Pt. I of his *Organographie der Pflanzen insbesondere der Archegoniaten und Samenpflanzen.* Jena: Verlag von Gustav Fischer, 1898, pp. 1-9.
/RESEARCH: BOTANY/RESEARCH: MORPHOLOGY
/BOTANY/MORPHOLOGY

1898-8 **Hederich**, Reinhard. *Goethe und die physikalische Geographie.* Münchener Geographische Studien, 5. München: Theodor Ackermann Königlicher Hof-Buchhändler, 1898. 66 pp.
/GEOGRAPHY

1898-9 **John**, Victor. "Quetelet bei Goethe." In *Festgabe für Johannes Conrad. Zur Feier des 25-jährigen Bestehens des staatswissenschaftlichen Seminars zu Halle a. S.* Ed. H[?]. Paasche. Sammlung nationalökonomischer und statistischer Abhandlungen des staatswissenschaftlichen Seminars zu Halle a. S., 20. Jena: Verlag von Gustav Fischer, 1898, pp. 311-34.
/QUETELET, A

1898-10 **Kerner von Marilaun**, Anton. "Goethes Verhältnis zur Pflanzenwelt." *Chronik des Wiener Goethe-Vereins*, 12 (1898), 22-4. "Aus einem Vortrage, gehalten am 21. März 1898. . ."
/BOTANY

1898-11 **Möbius**, Paul Julius. *Ueber das Pathologische bei Goethe.* Leipzig: Verlag von Johann Ambrosius Barth, 1898. vi, 208 pp. Rpt. Nos. 1903-21 and 1982-123.
/PATHOLOGY/MORPHOLOGY

1898-12 **Müller**, Erich. "Goethe und die Medicin." *Die Heilkunde: Monatsschrift für praktische Medicin*, 3 (1898/1899), 718-21. Cf. continuation, No. 1899-28.
/MEDICINE

1898-13 **Peine**, Selmar. "Goethe in Freiberg." *Mitteilungen des Freiberger Altertumsvereins mit Bildern aus Freibergs Vergangenheit*, 35 (1898), 116-18.
/GEOLOGY/PLACES: FREIBERG

1898-14 **Schüddekopf**, Carl. "Die Freitagsgesellschaft. Eine Erläuterung zum Briefwechsel mit Schiller." *Goethe*, 19 (1898), 14-19.
/INSTITUTIONS: DIE FREITAGSGESELLSCHAFT /SCHILLER, F

1898-15 **Vorländer**, Karl. "Goethe und Kant." *Goethe*, 19 (1898), 167-85.
/KANT, I/NATURPHILOSOPHIE/PHILOSOPHY

1899-1 ***Anderlind**, Leo. "Goethes Beziehungen zur Land- und Forstwirtschaft." *Leipziger Zeitung*, Wissenschaftliche Beilage, No. 98 (1899), 413-16.
/AGRONOMY/FORESTRY

1899-2 *[anon.] "Goethe als Physiker." *Wiener Abendpost*, No. 218 (1899).

/PHYSICS/OPTICS/CHROMATICS

1899-3   *[anon.]   "Goethe, Karl August und die Gasbeleuchtung."
Frankfurter Zeitung, No. 299, [1899?].
/TECHNOLOGY

1899-4   *[anon.]   "Goethe und Chladni." *Frankfurter Zeitung*, No. 283,
2. Morgenblatt, 1899.
/CHLADNI, E/ACOUSTICS/MUSIC THEORY

1899-5   *[anon.]   "J. W. Döbereiner. Eine Goethe-Erinnerung."
Frankfurter Zeitung, No. 167, 2. Morgenblatt, 1899.
/DÖBEREINER, J/CHEMISTRY

1899-6   **Arleth**, Emil.   "Einige Bemerkungen zu Goethes Thätigkeit als
Naturforscher." In *Goethe-Festschrift zum 150. Geburtstage des
Dichters*. Ed. August Ströbel. Prag: Verlag der Lese- und
Redehalle, 1899, pp. 97-101.
"Herausgegeben von der Lese- und Redehalle der deutschen
Studenten in Prag."
/GENERAL INTRODUCTION

1899-7   **Bernays**, Michael.   "Über Goethes Briefwechsel mit den
Gebrüdern von Humboldt. Herausgegeben von T[homas]. Fr.
Bratranek. Leipzig: F. A. Brockhaus, 1876." In his *Zur neueren und
neuesten Literaturgeschichte*. Vol. 4 of his *Schriften zur Kritik und
Literaturgeschichte*. Ed. Georg Wittkowski. Berlin: B. Behr's Ver-
lag (E. Bock), 1899, pp. 362-4.
Rev. of No. 1876-3.
/EDITION/HUMBOLDT, A VON/HUMBOLDT, W VON

1899-8   **Faller**, Arthur.   "Göthe als Naturforscher." *Aus der Heimat.
Eine naturwissenschaftliche Zeitschrift. Organ des deutschen Lehrer-
Vereins für Naturkunde*, 12 (1899), 97-103; 145-50.
/GENERAL INTRODUCTION

1899-9   **Geiger**, Ludwig.   "Goethes Geburtstag im Jahre 1826 wurde in
Bonn durch ein Festmahl gefeiert, . . ." *Goethe*, 20 (1899), 274-5.
/NEES VON ESENBECK, C/RECEPTION

1899-10   **Gerber**, Paul Henry.   "Goethe als Mediziner." *Wiener Medicinische Wochenschrift*, 49 (1899), 2001-5; 2061-5.
/MEDICINE

1899-11 [**Goethe**, J. W. von.] "Priroda [Die Natur]." *Zhizn'*, 9, No. 6
(1899), 1-2.
/TRANSLATION: RUSSIAN

1899-12 [**Goethe**, J. W. von.] "Sammlung zur Kenntniss der Gebirge von
und um Karlsbad angezeigt und erläutert von Herrn Geheimerath von
Goethe." Supplement to *Neues Jahrbuch für Mineralogie, Geologie
und Paleontologie*, 2 (1899). 28 pp.
/EDITION

1899-13 *****Grosse**, W[ilhelm?]. "Goethe als Naturforscher." *Weser-
Zeitung*, 27-31 August 1899.
/GENERAL INTRODUCTION

1899-14 **Haeckel**, Ernst. "Transformismus. Goethe." In his *Die
Welträthsel. Gemeinverständliche Studien über Monistische
Philosophie*. Bonn: Verlag von Emil Strauß, 1899, pp. 86-88.
Rpt. 1899ff.
Trans. into English, No. 1900-6.
/BIOLOGY: EVOLUTION/COMPARATIVE ANATOMY

1899-15 **Harnack**, Otto. "Ueber Goethe's Monadenlehre." In his *Essais
und Studien zur Literaturgeschichte*. Braunschweig: Friedrich
Vieweg und Sohn, 1899, pp. 281-6.
/NATURPHILOSOPHIE/PHILOSOPHY/LEIBNIZ, G

1899-16 **Helmholtz**, H[ermann]. von. "Über Goethe's naturwissen-
schaftliche Arbeiten: Vortrag gehalten in der Deutschen Gesellschaft
zu Königsberg." New York: H[enry]. Holt and Company/Boston:
C[arl]. Schoenhof[, 1899]. ix, 43 pp.
Rpt. of No. 1853-8.
"With notes for American students by Oswald Seidensticker."
/GENERAL INTRODUCTION

1899-17 *****Holthof**, Carl. "Goethes Naturanschauung mit besonderer
Berücksichtigung seiner Stellung zu Darwin." *Frankfurter Zeitung*,
No. 231, 31 August 1899.
/BIOLOGY: EVOLUTION/DARWIN, C/GENERAL INTRO-
DUCTION

1899-18 *****John**, Victor. "Goethe e Quetelet [Goethe and Quetelet]."
Estratto della Riforma sociale, 9, No. 4, Sec. ser. (1899). 14 pp.
In Italian.
/QUETELET, A/ASTRONOMY

1899-19 **Kalischer**, S[alomon]. "Weimarer Goethe-Ausgabe. Goethes Werke. Herausgegeben im Auftrage der Großherzogin Sophie von Sachsen. Weimar, H. Böhlaus Nachfolger. Bericht der Redactoren und Herausgeber." *Goethe*, 20 (1899), 285-6.
/EDITIONS

1899-20 **Knoblauch**, A[ugust]. "Wissenschaftliche Sitzung zur Feier von Goethes 150. Geburtstage am Freitag, den 25. August 1899. 1. Senckenberg und Goethe. Einleitende Worte des I. Direktors." *Bericht der Senckenbergischen naturforschenden Gesellschaft in Frankfurt am Main*, 1899, pp. 119-23.
/SENCKENBERG, J/MEDICINE

1899-21 **König**, Walter. "Goethes optische Studien." Frankfurt a. M.: C. Naumann's Druckerei, 1899. 32 pp.
   Rpt. No. 1899-22.
   "Festrede zur Feier von Goethes 150. Geburtstag gehalten am 26. August 1899 im Hörsaal des Physikalischen Vereins."
/OPTICS/CHROMATICS/HERING, E

1899-22 **König**, Walter. "Goethes optische Studien." *Physikalische Zeitschrift*, 1, No. 42 (1899/1900), 454-63; No. 43 (1899/1900), 467-70.
   Rpt. of No. 1899-21.
/OPTICS/CHROMATICS/HERING, E

1899-23 **Lo Re**, Antonio. "Goethe scienziato [Goethe the Scientist]." *Scienza e diletto*, 8, No. 39 (1899), 1-2.
   In Italian.
/GENERAL INTRODUCTION

1899-24 **Lungo**, Carlo del. "L'evoluzione in due poesie di W. Goethe [Evolution in Two Works by Goethe]." *Rivista d'Italia*, 2, No. 8 (1899), 664-77.
/BIOLOGY: EVOLUTION

1899-25 ***Malkowsky**, Georg. "Goethes Farbenlehre und die moderne Malerei." *Moderne Kunst*, 13 (1899), No. 14.
/CHROMATICS/FINE ARTS/RESEARCH: CHROMATICS /RESEARCH: FINE ARTS

1899-26 **Möbius**, Martin. "Goethe als Botaniker." *Die Gartenwelt: Illustriertes Wochenblatt für den gesamten Gartenbau*, 3, No. 48, 27

August 1899, 560-73; No. 49, 3 September 1899, 584-6; No. 49, 10 September 1899, 597-9.

    Rpt. No. 1899-27.

    "Zum 150. Geburtstage des Dichters (28. August)."

    /BOTANY

1899-27 **Möbius**, Martin. "Goethe als Botaniker." *Natur und Haus: Illustrierte Zeitschrift für alle Naturfreunde*, 8 (1899/1900), 9-13; 31-4; 44-6.

    Rpt. of No. 1899-26.

    "Zum 150. Geburtstage des Dichters."

    /BOTANY

1899-28 **Müller**, Erich. "Goethe und die Medicin." *Die Heilkunde: Monatsschrift für praktische Medicin*, 4 (1899/1900), 24-7; 94-6; 280-82.

    Continuation of No. 1898-12.

    /MEDICINE

1899-29 **Potonié**, H[enry]. "Die morphologische Herkunft des pflanzlichen Blattes und der Blattarten. Ein Gedenkblatt zu Goethe's 150. Geburtstage, 28 Aug. 1749-1899." *Naturwissenschaftliche Wochenschrift*, 14 (1899), 405-15.

    "Nach einem vor der Gesellschaft naturforschender Freunde zu Berlin am 18. Juli 1899 gehaltenen Vortrage."

    /RESEARCH: MORPHOLOGY/RESEARCH: BOTANY

1899-30 **Potonié**, H[enry]. "Über die morphologische Herkunft der pflanzlichen Blattarten." *Sitzungsberichte der Gesellschaft naturforschender Freunde zu Berlin*, 1899, 139-59.

    /RESEARCH: MORPHOLOGY/RESEARCH: BOTANY

1899-31 **Reichenbach**, Heinrich. "Goethe und die Biologie." *Bericht der Senckenbergischen naturforschenden Gesellschaft in Frankfurt am Main*, 1899, 124-55.

    "Wissenschaftliche Sitzung zur Feier von Goethes 150. Geburtstage am Freitag, den 25. August 1899."

    /BIOLOGY

1899-32 ***Sarschef**, Ruben. "Goethe und Samuel Thomas von Sömmering." *Frankfurter Nachrichten*, August 1899, pp. 2219-20; 2235-7.

    /SÖMMERING, S

1899-33 **Schultz**, Paul. "Arthur Schopenhauer's Abhandlung: 'Ueber das

Sehen und die Farben'." *Archiv für Physiologie. Physiologische Abteilung des Archivs für Anatomie und Physiologie [Supplement-Band]*, 1899, pp. 510-33.
/CHROMATICS/SCHOPENHAUER, A/YOUNG, T /HELMHOLTZ, H VON

1899-34 **Stilling**, Jacob. "[Ü]ber Goethes Farbenlehre." In *Straßburger Goethe-Vorträge. Zum Besten des für Straßburg geplanten Denkmals des jungen Goethe*, Straßburg: Verlag von Karl J. Trübner, 1899, pp. 147-73.
　　　Rpt. 2nd edn. 1899.
　　　/CHROMATICS/HERING, E

1899-35 *****Sudhoff**, Karl. "Goethe und Johannes Müller." *Düsseldorfer neueste Nachrichten*, 15, No. 233 (1899).
　　　/MÜLLER, J/CHROMATICS/SENSORY PHYSIOLOGY

1899-36 **Valentin**, Veit. "Wolken in Vision und Wissenschaft bei Goethe. Ein Beitrag zu Goethes hundertfünfzigster Geburtstagsfeier." *Neue Jahrbücher für das klassische Altertum Geschichte und deutsche Literatur*, 2 (1899), 385-401.
　　　/METEOROLOGY

1899-37 *****Weinhold**[, ?]. "Goethe im Erzgebirge und Vogtland. 'Glück auf!'." *Organ des Erzgebirgs-Vereins*, No. 9, September 1899, 134-9.
　　　/GEOLOGY

1899-38 **Weizsäcker**, Paul. "Goethe und der Steindruck." In *Goethe-Festschrift zum 150. Geburtstage des Dichters*. Ed. August Ströbel. Prag: Verlag der Lese- und Redehalle, 1899, pp. 180-89.
　　　/TECHNOLOGY

1900-1 **Bode**, Wilhelm. "Goethe als Landmann." *Das Land: Zeitschrift für die sozialen und volkstümlichen Angelegenheiten auf dem Lande*, 8 (1900), 373-6.
/FORESTRY

1900-2 **Braß**, Friedrich. "Goethes Anschauung der Natur, die Grundlage seiner sittlichen und ästhetischen Anschauungen in Entwicklung und Wandlung." Leipzig: B. G. Teubner, 1900. 40 pp.
Rpt. of No. 1900-3.
"Beilage zum Programm für die Realschule zu Cottbus."
/NATURPHILOSOPHIE/GENERAL INTRODUCTION

1900-3 **Braß**, Friedrich. "Goethes Anschauung der Natur, die Grundlage seiner sittlichen und ästhetischen Anschauungen in Entwicklung und Wandlung." In Braß, Friedrich, Paul Lorentz and P. Meyer. *Aus dem Goethejahr*. Leipzig: B. G. Teubner, 1900, pp. 1-40.
Rpt. No. 1900-2.
"Beilage zum Programm für die Realschule zu Cottbus."
/NATURPHILOSOPHIE/GENERAL INTRODUCTION

1900-4 **Cohn**, Hermann. "Goethe über den Impfzwang." *Wochenschrift für Therapie und Hygiene des Auges*, 4 (1900/1901), 411-12.
Rpt. Nos. 1901-3 and 1902-5.
/IMMUNOLOGY

1900-5 **Gerber**, Paul Henry. *Goethe's Beziehungen zur Medicin. Ein populärer Vortrag, erweitert, mit Litteratur und Anmerkungen versehen, nebst Goethe's Geburts- und Todesanzeige*. Berlin: Verlag von S. Karger, 1900. 87 pp.
/MEDICINE

1900-6 **Haeckel**, Ernst. "(Transformism: Goethe)." In his *The Riddle of the Universe at the Close of the Nineteenth Century*. Trans. Joseph McCabe. New York/London: Harper & Brothers, 1900, pp. 74-6.
English trans. of No. 1899-14.
/BIOLOGY: EVOLUTION/COMPARATIVE ANATOMY

1900-7 **Helmholtz**, H[ermann]. von. "Le idee e le opere scientifiche di Goethe." Trans. C. Del Lungo. *La Rassegna Nazionale*, 115 (1900), 574-91.
Italian trans. of No. 1853-8.
/GENERAL INTRODUCTION

1900-8 **Janota**, Eduard (der Ältere). "Goethe als Naturforscher im

nordwestlichen Böhmen." *Pharmaceutische Post*, 33 (1900), 735-9.
/GEOLOGY/PLACES: BÖHMEN

1900-9 **Laube**, Gustav C. "Goethes Beziehungen zu Deutsch-Böhmen. Ein Vortrag, gehalten am 22. November 1899." In *Bericht der Lese- und Redehalle der deutschen Studenten in Prag über das Jahr 1899*. Prag: Verlag der Lese- und Redehalle der deutschen Studenten, 1900, pp. 15-23.
/GEOLOGY/MINERALOGY/PLACES: BÖHMEN

1900-10 **May**, Walther. "Goethe und Alexander von Humboldt." *Verhandlungen des Naturwissenschaftlichen Vereins in Karlsruhe*, 14 (1900/1901), 3-30.
/HUMBOLDT, A VON

1900-11 **Molisch**, Hans. "Goethe als Naturforscher." In *Bericht der Lese- und Redehalle der deutschen Studenten in Prag über das Jahr 1899*. Prag: Verlag des deutschen Vereines zur Verbreitung gemeinnütziger Kenntnisse in Prag, 1900, pp. 5-14.
Rpt. No. 1900-12.
"Rede, gehalten bei der Goethefeier der Lese- und Redehalle der deutschen Studenten in Prag, am 22. November 1899."
/GENERAL INTRODUCTION

1900-12 **Molisch**, Hans. "Goethe als Naturforscher." Sammlung gemeinnütziger Vorträge, 256. Prag: Verlag des deutschen Vereines zur Verbreitung gemeinnütziger Kenntnisse in Prag, 1900. 10 pp.
Rpt. of No. 1900-11.
/GENERAL INTRODUCTION

1900-13 **Schiff**, Julius. "Goethes naturwissenschaftliche Forschungen und ihre Bedeutung für den naturwissenschaftlichen Unterricht." In *Programm des städtischen Johannes-Gymnasiums zu Breslau für das Schuljahr von Ostern 1899 bis Ostern 1900*. Breslau: Grass, Barth & Co., 1900, pp. 3-32.
/CHROMATICS

1900-14 **Steiner**, Rudolf. "Goethe und die Mathematik." *Das Magazin für Literatur*, 69 (1900), 226-8.
Rpt. Nos. 1900-15.
/MATHEMATICS

1900-15 ***Steiner**, Rudolf. "Goethe und die Mathematik." *Frankfurter Zeitung*, No. 239 (1900) [1901?].

Rpt. of No. 1900-14.
/MATHEMATICS

1900-16 **Vogel**, Heinrich. "Goethe in seinen Beziehungen zu Apothekern." *Apotheker-Zeitung*, 15 (1900), 525-6; 533-4; 541-2.
/PHARMACOLOGY/CHEMISTRY

1901-1 *[anon.] "Goethe und L. A. J. Quetelet." *Frankfurter Zeitung*, No. 183, Abendblatt, 1901.
/QUETELET, L

1901-2 **Bliedner**, A[rno]. *Goethe und die Urpflanze.* Frankfurt a/M.: Literarische Anstalt Rütten & Loening, 1901. iv, 75 pp.
/BOTANY

1901-3 *Cohn, Hermann. "Goethe über den Impfzwang." *Frankfurter Zeitung*, No. 246, 5 September 1901.
Rpt. of No. 1900-4.
/IMMUNOLOGY

1901-4 **Dennert**, Eberhard. "Haeckel und Goethe." In his *Die Wahrheit über Ernst Haeckel und seine "Welträtsel".* Halle a. S./Bremen: C. Ed. Müller's Verlagsbuchhandlung Max Grosse, 1901, pp. 40-50.
/HAECKEL, E/BIOLOGY: EVOLUTION

1901-5 **Driesmans**, Heinrich. "Goethes Farbenlehre ein Stück germanischer Weltanschauung. Der Goethisch-Newtonische Farbenstreit ein Rassenstreit." In his *Die Wahlverwandtschaften der deutschen Blutmischung.* Pt. 2 [3] of *Die Kulturgeschichte der Rasseninstinkte.* Leipzig: Diederichs, 1901, pp. 67-71.
Rpt. No. 1914-5.
/CHROMATICS

1901-6 **Eimer**, Theodor. "Goethe über den Zwischenkiefer." In his *Vergleichend-anatomisch-physiologische Untersuchungen über das Skelett der Wirbeltiere.* Pt. 3 of *Die Entstehung der Arten auf Grund von Vererben erworbener Eigenschaften nach den Gesetzen organischen Wachsens.* Leipzig: Verlag von Wilhelm Engelmann, 1901, pp. 101-5.
/OSTEOLOGY/COMPARATIVE ANATOMY

1901-7 **Freytag**, Gustav. "Goethe und der Scharfrichter Huß zu Eger." In his *Vermischte Aufsätze aus den Jahren 1848 bis 1894. Erster Band.* Ed. Ernst Elster. Leipzig: Verlag von S. Hirzel, 1901, pp.

56-62.
    Rpt. of No. 1853-1.
    /HUß, K/MINERALOGY

1901-8 **Hauffen**, Adolf. "Goethe und der Egerer Magistratsrat Grüner. Mit einem ungedruckten Briefe Goethes und mit einer Bildtafel." *Deutsche Arbeit. Monatsschrift für das geistige Leben der Deutschen in Böhmen*, 1 (1901/1902), 31-8.
    /GRÜNER, J/MINERALOGY

1901-9 **Kalischer**, Salomon. "Nochmals Goethe und die Mathematik." *Berliner Tageblatt*, 30, No. 463 (12 September 1901)[, 2-3].
    /MATHEMATICS

1901-10 **Kalischer**, Salomon. "Warum erscheint uns der Himmel blau?" *Das Weltall: Illustrierte Zeitschrift für Astronomie und verwandte Gebiete*, 2 (1901/1902), 254.
    /CHROMATICS

1901-11 **Kraushar**, Alexander. "Goethe i Humboldt w gronie czlonkow Towarzystwa Warszawskiego Przyjaciol Nauk (1829-1830) [Goethe and Humboldt in the Circle of the Members of the Warsaw Society of the Friends of Learning]." *Tygodnik Illustrowany [Warszawa]*, No. 22, 19 May 1901, 425-7.
    In Polish.
    /HUMBOLDT, A VON/INSTITUTIONS: TOWARZYSTWA PRZYJACIOL NAUK [WARSZAWA]

1901-12 **Lippmann**, Edmund O von. "Goethe's Farbenlehre." *Zeitschrift für Naturwissenschaften: Organ des naturwissenschaftlichen Vereins für Sachsen und Thüringen*, 74 (1901), 17-43.
    "Vortrag gehalten im 'Naturwissenschaftlichen Vereine' [Stuttgart]."
    /CHROMATICS

1901-13 ***Meurer**, H[?]. "Der Doktor-Ingenieur und Goethe." *Frankfurter Zeitung*, No. 245 (1901), Abendblatt.
    /TECHNOLOGY

1901-14 **Meyer**, Richard M. "Goethe als Psycholog." *Goethe*, 22 (1901), 1*-26*.
    "Festvortrag gehalten in der 16. Generalversammlung der Goethe-Gesellschaft in Weimar am 1. Juni 1901."
    /PSYCHOLOGY

1901-15 **Plath**, Margarethe. "Der Goethe-Schellingsche Plan eines philo-sophischen Naturgedichtes. Eine Studie zu Goethes 'Gott und Welt'." *Preußische Jahrbücher*, 106 (1901), 44-74.
/NATURPHILOSOPHIE/SCHELLING, F VON/WORKS: LYRICS

1901-16 **Schlieper**, Hans. "Emanuel Swedenborgs System der Natur-philosophie, besonders in seiner Beziehung zu Goethe-Herderschen Anschauungen." Diss. Berlin. Berlin: Gustav Schade (Otto Francke)[, 1901].
/NATURPHILOSOPHIE/SWEDENBORG, E/HERDER, J

1901-17 **Seiling**, Max. "Goethe 'und' Haeckel." *Die Gesellschaft. Münchener Halbmonatsschrift für Kunst und Kultur*, 17, No. 3 (1901), 10-16.
/HAECKEL, E/BIOLOGY: EVOLUTION

1901-18 **Siebeck**, Herman. "Goethe als Denker." Fromanns Klassiker der Philosophie. Stuttgart: Fr. Frommanns Verlag (E. Hauff), 1902. 244 pp.
/NATURPHILOSOPHIE/SPINOZA, B/BIOLOGY: EVOLUTION/SCHELLING, F VON

1901-19 **Steiner**, Rudolf. "Goethe und die Medizin." *Wiener klinische Rundschau*, 15, No. 2 (1901), 24-6.
Rpt. No. 1932-309.
/MEDICINE

1901-20 **Stieda**, Wilhelm. "Goethe und die Porzellan-Fabrik zu Ilmenau." *Goethe*, 22 (1901), 224-51.
/TECHNOLOGY/PLACES: ILMENAU

1901-21 **Vogel**, Theodor. "Goethes Schema einer allgemeinen Natur-lehre." *Neue Jahrbücher für das klassische Altertum Geschichte und deutsche Litteratur*, 4 (1901), 63-9.
/PHILOSOPHY/BIOLOGY

1901-22 **Wiesner**, Julius. "Goethes Urpflanze." *Die Zeit. Wiener Wochenschrift für Politik, Volkswirtschaft, Wissenschaft und Kunst*, 29/30, No. 366, 5 October 1901, 6-8; No. 367, 12 October 1901, 24-5.
Rpt. No. 1910-19.
/BOTANY

1902-1 *[anon.] "F. J. Gall über Goethes Kopf." *Reichenberger Zeitung*, 26 June 1902.
/GALL, F/PHRENOLOGY

1902-2 *[anon.] "Goethe und Franz Josef Gall." *Frankfurter Zeitung*, No. 166 and 170, 1902.
/GALL, F/PHRENOLOGY

1902-3 **Briefwechsel** *zwischen J. W. v. Goethe und Kaspar Graf v. Sternberg. (1820-1832)*. Ed. August Sauer. Vol. 1 of *Ausgewählte Werke des Grafen Kaspar von Sternberg*. Bibliothek deutscher Schriftsteller aus Böhmen, 13. Prag: J. G. Calve'sche k. u. k. Hof- u. Universitäts-Buchhandlung, 1902. li, 434 pp.
"Herausgegeben im Auftrage der Gesellschaft zur Förderung deutscher Wissenschaft, Kunst und Literatur in Böhmen."
/STERNBERG, K/BOTANY/PAEONTOLOGY

1902-4 **Cartellieri**, Josef. "Das Eger-Franzensbader Becken. Eine geologische Übersicht." In *Marienbad, Franzensbad, Teplitz-Schönau, Johannisbad, Liebwerda, Bilin, Giesshübl, Sauerbrunn, Krondorf, Neudorf*. Ed. E. Heinrich Kisch. N. p.: n. p., pp. 121-47.
/GEOLOGY/STERNBERG, K

1902-5 **Cohn**, Hermann. "Goethe über den Impfzwang." *Goethe*, 23 (1902), 216-18.
Rpt. of No. 1900-4.
/IMMUNOLOGY

1902-6 **Del Lungo**, Carlo. "Meteorologia goethiana [Goethean Meteorology]." *Rassegna Internazionale*, 3, No. 9 (1902), fasc. 5, 233-9.
Rpt. No. 1892-14.
In Italian.
Includes the poem "In onore di Howard," pp. 237-9.
/METEOROLOGY/WORKS: LYRICS

1902-7 **Distel**, Theodor. "Hahnemann und Goethe, 1829 mit einander verglichen." *Deutsche Medicinische Wochenschrift*, 28 (1902), 580.
/HAHNEMANN, C

1902-8 **Ebstein**, Erich. "Goethe über die Fettleibigkeit." *Deutsche Medicinische Wochenschrift*, 28 (1902), 887.
/PHYSIOLOGY

1902-9 **Fischer**, F[?]. "Goethe über Irrenanstalten und Geistes-krankheiten." *Psychiatrisch-Neurologische Wochenschrift*, 4 (1902/1903), 473-5.
Rpt. No. 1903-6.
/PSYCHOLOGY

1902-10 **Friedel**, Ernst. "Goethe als Zeuge gegen das Automobil." *"Brandenburgia"*. *Monatsblatt der Gesellschaft für Heimatkunde der Provinz Brandenburg zu Berlin*, 11 (1902/1903), 82-3.
/TECHNOLOGY

1902-11 **[Goethe, J. W. von]**. "Die Botanik unter dem Einflusse der Metamorphosenlehre. Goethe's Versuch über die Metamorphose der Pflanzen. 1790." In *Erläuterte Abschnitte aus den Werken hervorragender Naturforscher aller Völker und Zeiten*. Ed. Friedrich Dannemann. Vol. 1 of his *Grundriss einer Geschichte der Naturwissenschaften: Zugleich eine Einführung in das Studium der naturwissenschaftlichen Litteratur*. 2nd rev. and exp. edn. Leipzig: Verlag von Wilhelm Engelmann, 1902, pp. 217-21.
Rpt. of No. 1896-5.
/BOTANY/RECEPTION

1902-12 **Haeckel**, Ernst. "Darwins, Goethes ock Lamarcks natursyn." In *Två Föredrag af Ernst Haeckel*. Trans. K. E. F. Stockholm: Wahlström & Widstrand[, 1902], pp. 55-97.
Swedish trans. of No. 1882-14.
/BIOLOGY: EVOLUTION/DARWIN, C/LAMARCK, J DE

1902-13 **Haeckel**, Ernst. "Die Naturanschauung von Darwin, Goethe und Lamarck." In his *Gemeinverständliche Vorträge und Abhandlungen aus dem Gebiete der Entwicklungslehre*. 6 vols. 2nd exp. edn. Bonn: Verlag von Emil Strauß, 1902, pp. 217-80.
Rpt. of No. 1882-14.
/BIOLOGY: EVOLUTION/DARWIN, C/LAMARCK, J DE

1902-14 **Kalischer**, Salomo. "Warum erscheint uns der Himmel blau?" *Das Weltall: Illustrierte Zeitschrift für Astronomie und verwandte Gebiete*, 2 (1902), 254.
/CHROMATICS/RAYLEIGH, LORD [STRUTT, J]

1902-15 **Kon [Cohn]**, F[erdinand]. "Gëte kak botanik." Trans. and comm. I. Baranovskogo. *Naychnie obozrenie*, cp. 6, No. 6 (1902), pt. 1, 207-30; No. 7, pp. 205-23; No. 8, pp. 215-21; No. 9, pp. 125-

40.

Russian trans. of No. 1881-2.
[Zhitomirskaia 3825]
/BOTANY

1902-16 **Potonié**, Henry. "Ein Blick in die Geschichte der botanischen Morphologie mit besonderer Rücksicht auf die Pericaulom-Theorie." *Naturwissenschaftliche Wochenschrift*, 18 [NS 2], No. 1, 5 October 1902, 3-8; No. 2, 12 October 1902, 13-15; No. 3, 19 October 1902, 25-8.
    Exp. rpt. Nos. 1903-27 and 1912-21.
    /RESEARCH: BOTANY/RESEARCH: MORPHOLOGY

1902-17 **Potonié**, Henry. "Die Pericaulom-Theorie." *Berichte der deutschen Botanischen Gesellschaft*, 20 (1902), 502-20.
    /RESEARCH: BOTANY/RESEARCH: MORPHOLOGY

1902-18 **Schaerffenberg**, Paul. "Goethes Farbenlehre. Zum 28. August." *Unterhaltungsbeilage zur Täglichen Rundschau [Berlin]*, No. 201, 28 August 1902, 802-3.
    /CHROMATICS

1902-19 **Schwann**, Mathieu. "Die Goethe-Sphinx." *Sonntagsbeilage No. 1 zur Vossischen Zeitung No. 7 [Berlin]*, 5 January 1902, 3-5; 11-13.
    /BIOLOGY: EVOLUTION/MORPHOLOGY/HAECKEL, E/DARWIN, C

1902-20 **Stettner**, Thomas. "Goethe und die Münchner Lithographie." *Zeitschrift für Bücherfreunde: Monatshefte für Bibliophilie und verwandte Interessen*, 6 (1902/1903), 196-201.
    Rpt. No. 1929-64.
    /TECHNOLOGY

1902-21 *****Türkel**, Siegfried. "Goethe als Psychiater." *Wiener Morgen-Zeitung*, No. 290 (1902).
    /PSYCHIATRY

1902-22 *****Vogler**, P[?]. "Goethes Metamorphose der Pflanzen." *Neue Zürcher Zeitung*, No. 242, 1902.
    /BOTANY/MORPHOLOGY

1902-23 *****Wilke**, Arthur. "Goethes Farbenlehre. Eine Darstellung für die Goethe-Gemeinde." *Berliner Tageblatt [Beiblatt: Zeitgeist]*, No. 7, 17 February 1902.

175

/CHROMATICS

1902-24 **Wirkner**, Wenzel. "Goethe als Naturforscher in Karlsbad 1806." In *Festschrift zur 74. Versammlung Deutscher Naturforscher und Aerzte*. Karlsbad: [n.p.], 1902, p. 707.
/GEOLOGY/PLACES: KARLSBAD/WIRKNER, W

1903-1 [**anon.**] "Morphologie." *Chronik des Wiener Goethe-Vereins*, 17 (1903), 17.
/MORPHOLOGY/BURDACH, K

1903-2 **Del Lungo**, Carlo. *Goethe ed Helmholtz [Goethe and Helmholtz]*. Piccola biblioteca di scienze moderne, 73. Milano/Roma/Firenze: Fratelli Bocca Editori, 1903. 161 pp.
Cf. No. 1903-10.
In Italian.
/HELMHOLTZ, H VON

1903-3 **Döll**, Heinrich. *Goethe und Schopenhauer: Ein Beitrag zur Entwicklungsgeschichte der Schopenhauerschen Philosophie*. Berlin: Ernst Hofmann & Co., 1903. 73 pp.
Originally Inauguraldissertation Giessen.
/SCHOPENHAUER, A/CHROMATICS

1903-4 **Dreher**, Eugen. "Goethe's Bedeutung als Naturforscher." In his *Philosophische Abhandlungen*. Berlin: v. Decker, 1903, pp. 125-38.
Cf. No. 1904-20.
Rpt. of No. 1880-4.
"Vortrag, gehalten in der 'Deutschen Gesellschaft' zu Berlin."
/GENERAL INTRODUCTION

1903-5 **Driesmans**, Heinrich. "Das Gesetz Goethe's in der Menschenbildung und Rassenkreuzung." *Die Gegenwart: Wochenschrift für Literatur, Kunst und öffentliches Leben*, 63 (1903), 183-6.
/ANATOMY/GENETICS

1903-6 *****Fischer**, F[?]. "Goethe über Irrenanstalten und Geisteskrankheiten." *Frankfurter Zeitung*, No. 44, 13 February 1903.
Rpt. of No. 1902-9.
/PSYCHOLOGY

1903-7 **Geiger**, Ludwig. "Ein wenig bekannter Freund Goethes." *Goethe*, 24 (1903), 256-61.
/LANGERMANN, J/MEDICINE

1903-8 *Gnad, E[?]. "Goethe und Graf Sternberg." *Wiener Abendpost*, No. 36 (1903).
/STERNBERG, K/BOTANY/PALEONTOLOGY

1903-9 [Goethe, J. W. von.] "Diese, ob schon ehrenvolle Aufnahme unserer Bemühungen mußte uns doch bedenklich scheinen indem da wo von Gestalt und Umgestaltung eigentlich zu sprechen ist. . ." In "Die Goethe-Autographen der Münchener Hof- und Staatsbibliothek." Ed. Erich Petzet. *Goethe*, 24 (1903), 61-2.
/EDITION

1903-10 [Goethe, J. W. von.] "La natura [Die Natur]." In Del Lungo, Carlo. *Goethe ed Helmholtz*. Piccola biblioteca di scienze moderne, 73. Milano/Roma/Firenze: Fratelli Bocca Editori, 1903, pp. 153-5. "libera versione" [Avanzi].
/TRANSLATION: ITALIAN

1903-11 [Goethe, J. W. von.] *Studi scientifici sulle origini, affinità e transformazione degli esseri [Scientific Studies on the Origins, Affinities, and Transformations of Creatures]*. Trans. and pref. Giuseppe e Giovanni Monti. Torino: Bocca, 1903. 149 pp.
Cf. No. 1903-23.
/TRANSLATION: ITALIAN

1903-12 Hansen, A[dolph]. "Goethe oder Linné, . . ." *Erste Beilage zur Vossischen Zeitung [Morgen-Ausgabe]*, No. 553, 26 November 1903[, 1].
/BOTANY/LINNAEUS [LINNÉ], C

1903-13 Hansen, A[dolph]. "Linné oder Goethe?" *Vossische Zeitung [Berlin] [Morgen-Ausgabe]*, No. 497, 23 October 1903[, 2-3].
/BOTANY/LINNAEUS [LINNÉ], C

1903-14 Heisterbergk[, ?]. "Ein eigenhändiges Pseudonym Goethes." *Goethe*, 24 (1903), 253-4.
/GEOLOGY/PLACES: HARZ/TECHNOLOGY

1903-15 Helmholtz, Hermann von. "Goethe's Vorahnungen kommender naturwissenschaftlicher Ideen." In his *Vorträge und Reden*. 2 vols. 5th edn. Braunschweig: Druck und Verlag von Friedrich Vieweg und Sohn, 1903, pp. 335-61.
Rpt. of No. 1892-10.
"Rede gehalten in Generalversammlung der Goethe-Gesellschaft

zu Weimar 1892."
/GENERAL INTRODUCTION

1903-16 **Helmholtz**, Hermann von. "Ueber Goethes naturwissenschaft-
liche Arbeiten." In his *Vorträge und Reden*. 2 vols. 5th edn.
Braunschweig: Druck und Verlag von Friedrich Vieweg und Sohn,
1903, pp. 23-47.
Rpt. of No. 1853-8.
"Vortrag gehalten zu Königsberg 1853."
/GENERAL INTRODUCTION

1903-17 **Kahlbaum**, Georg W. A. "Goethe und Berzelius in Karlsbad."
*Janus. Archives internationales pour l'Histoire de la Médicine et la
Géographie Médicale*, 8 (1903), 86-7; 251-4.
/BERZELIUS, J VON/CHEMISTRY

1903-18 [**Kalischer**, Salomon.] ["Es ist doch eine sonderbare Art. . ."]
Zweite Beilage zur Vossischen Zeitung, No. 458, 30 September 1903[,
1].
Response to No. 1903-32.
/BOTANY/LINNAEUS [LINNÉ], C

1903-19 **Kohut**, Adolph. "Goethe als Naturforscher." In his *Ernstes und
Heiteres von berühmten Aerzten, Apothekern und Naturforschern*.
Berlin: Berlinische Verlagsanstalt[, 1903], pp. 129-53.
/GENERAL INTRODUCTION

1903-20 *****Lewes**, G[eorge]. H[enry]. "Goethe als Naturforscher." In his
Goethes Leben und Werke. Trans. Julius Frese. 2 vols. 18th edn.
Stuttgart: Verlag von Carl Krabbe, 1903, II, ?.
Rpt. of No. 1857-4.
/GENERAL INTRODUCTION

1903-21 **Möbius**, Paul Julius. "Goethe über das Pathologische." In his
Goethe, I. Theil. Vol. 2 of his *Ausgewählte Werke*. Leipzig: Verlag
von Johann Ambrosius Barth, 1903, pp. 1-160.
Rpt. of No. 1898-11.
/PATHOLOGY

1903-22 **Möbius**, P[aul]. J[ulius]. "Goethe und Gall." In his *Goethe: II.
Theil*. Vol. III of his *Ausgewählte Werke*. Leipzig: Verlag von
Johann Ambrosius Barth, 1903, pp. 209-60.
/GALL, F/PHRENOLOGY

1903-23 **Monti**, Giuseppe. "Prefazione." In [Goethe, J. W. von.] *Studi scientifici sulle origini, affinità e transformazione degli esseri [Scientific Studies on the Origins, Affinities, and Transformations of Creatures].* Trans. and pref. Giuseppe e Giovanni Monti. Torino: Bocca, 1903, pp. 5-30.
In Italian.
/GENERAL INTRODUCTION

1903-24 **Neumeister**, Georg. "Goethe als Arzt." *Unterhaltungsbeilage, Abend-Blatt: Tägliche Rundschau: Unabhängige Zeitung für nationale Politik*, 23, No. 400 (1903), 797-8.
/MEDICINE

1903-25 **Paladino**, Giovanni. "Volfango Goethe naturalista. Appunti [Goethe the Naturalist. Notes]." *Il Pungolo*, 10, 8-9 May 1903, 3.
In Italian.
/GENERAL INTRODUCTION

1903-26 **Peltzer**, Alfred. "Die ästhetische Bedeutung von Goethes Farbenlehre." Heidelberg: Carl Winter's Universitätsbuchhandlung, 1903. 47 pp.
/CHROMATICS/AESTHETICS

1903-27 **Potonié**, Henry. "Ein Blick in die Geschichte der botanischen Morphologie und die Pericaulom-Theorie." Jena: Verlag von Gustav Fischer, 1903. 45 pp.
Exp. rpt. of No. 1902-16.
/RESEARCH: BOTANY/RESEARCH: MORPHOLOGY

1903-28 **Seiling**, Max. "Goethe und der Materialismus." *Psychische Studien*, 30 (1903), 223-32; 362-8; 422-8; 751-8.
/NATURPHILOSOPHIE

1903-29 *****Stettner**, Thomas. "Ärztliche Tischgenossen Goethes." *Neue medizinische Presse*, 3 (1903), 197ff.
/MEDICINE

1903-30 *****Warming**, Eugenius. [On the Current Over-Valuing of Goethe.] *Aftenposten [Christiania]*, 4 November 1903.
In Norwegian?
/BOTANY?

1903-31 **Wasielewski**, Waldemar von. *Goethe und die Descendenzlehre.* Frankfurt am Main: Literarische Anstalt Rütten & Loening, 1903. 61

pp.
/BIOLOGY: EVOLUTION/HAECKEL, E/DARWIN, C

1903-32 *Wille, Nordal. ["Goethe oder Linné. Eine Antwort an die Vossische Zeitung.]" *Aftenposten [Christiania]*, November 1903.
Cf. response, No. 1903-18.
/BOTANY/LINNAEUS [LINNÉ], C

1904-1 [anon.] "Goethe im Urteil französischer Naturforscher." *Beilage zur Allgemeinen Zeitung*, No. 34 (1904), pp. 270-71.
/NATURPHILOSOPHIE

1904-2 [anon.] "Goethe und die Naturwissenschaft der Gegenwart." *Düsseldorfer Zeitung*, 13 September 1904.
/GENERAL INTRODUCTION

1904-3 *[anon.] "Notes et Analyses: Goethe, Darwin et Lamarck; Chronique: Goethe et les rayons N." *Revue des Idées*, 15 mars 1904.
/BIOLOGY: EVOLUTION/DARWIN, C/LAMARCK, J DE

1904-4 Baldensperger, Fernand. "Physiciens et naturalistes." In his *Goethe en France: étude de littérature comparée*. Paris: Librairie Hachette, 1904, pp. 195-209.
2nd edn. 1920.
Reception of Goethe's scientific work by French scientists.
/RECEPTION

1904-5 Bauch, Bruno. "Ueber Goethes philosophische Weltanschauung." *Preußische Jahrbücher*, 115 (1904), 518-29.
/NATURPHILOSOPHIE/PHILOSOPHY/METHOD

1904-6 Becker, Hermann. "Goethe als Geograph." In *Wissenschaftliche Beilage zum Jahresbericht der IX. Städtischen Realschule zu Berlin*. Programm No. 138. Berlin: Weidmannsche Buchhandlung, 1904. 28 pp.
Continuation of Nos. 1894-3 and 1898-2.
/GEOGRAPHY

1904-7 Bölsche, Wilhelm. "Ein versteinertes Tier und ein lebendiger Gedanke." In his *Weltblick. Gedanken zu Natur und Kunst*. 3rd edn. Dresden: Verlag von Carl Reißner, 1904, pp. 43-82.
/BIOLOGY/MORPHOLOGY

1904-8 Bruntsch, Friedrich Max. ["Herders Idee der Entwicklung bei

Goethe und Carl Ritter."] In his *Die Idee der Entwicklung bei Herder. (Von geographischen Gesichtspunkten aus betrachtet).* Diss. Leipzig. [Leipzig:] Robert Raab, 1904, pp. 79-87.
/BIOLOGY: EVOLUTION/HERDER, J/RITTER, C

1904-9 **Distel**, Theodor. "Die Goethe Feier bei Loder in Moskau am 28. August 1829." *Goethe*, 25 (1904), 244.
/RECEPTION/LODER, J/MEDICINE

1904-10 **Distel**, Theodor. "Zu Goethes Zoologie." *Goethe*, 25 (1904), 243.
/ZOOLOGY

1904-11 **Fischl**, Friedrich. "Goethe in Marienbad." In *Sammlung Gemeinnütziger Vorträge.* Prag: J. G. Calve'sche k. u. k. Hof- und Universitäts-Buchhandlung, 1904, pp. 139-58.
"Herausgegeben vom Deutschen Vereine zur Verbreitung gemeinnütziger Kenntnisse in Prag."
/GEOLOGY/MINERALOGY/PLACES: MARIENBAD

1904-12 **G[eiger]**, L[udwig]. "Zu dem Aufsatz: Ein wenig bekannter Freund Goethes. . ." *Goethe*, 25 (1904), 257.
/LANGERMANN, J/MEDICINE

1904-13 ***Girard**, A[?]. *Controverses transformistes: Goethe, Darwin et Lamarck.* Paris: ?, 1904.
/BIOLOGY: EVOLUTION/DARWIN, C/LAMARCK, J DE

1904-14 **Goethe[, J. W. von].** "Naturwissenschaft." *Goethes kleinere Aufsätze.* Sel. W. v. Seidlitz. München: Verlagsanstalt F. Bruckmann A.-G., 1904, pp. 299-343.
/EDITION: SELECTIONS

1904-15 **Goethe**, J. W. von. *Nachträge zu Band 6-12.* Vol. II.13 of the *Weimarer Ausgabe.* Weimar: Hermann Böhlaus Nachfolger, 1904. x, 565 pp.
Rpt. No. 1987-38.
/EDITION: SELECTIONS

1904-16 **Gräntz**, Fritz. "Goethe und die Naturwissenschaft der Gegenwart." *Westermanns illustrierte deutsche Monatshefte für das gesamte geistige Leben der Gegenwart,* 96 (1904), 782-90.
/GENERAL INTRODUCTION

1904-17 **Grünstein**, Leo. "Goethe, Merck und Camper. (Aus ungedruckten Briefen Mercks and Peter und Adrien Camper.)" *Neue Freie Presse. Morgenblatt*, No. 14392, 18 September 1904, 36-7.
/MERCK, J/CAMPER, P/OSTEOLOGY

1904-18 **Hansen**, A[dolph]. "Die angebliche Abhängigkeit der Goetheschen Metamorphosenlehre von Linné." *Goethe*, 25 (1904), 128-41.
/BOTANY/LINNAEUS [LINNÉ], C

1904-19 **Helmholtz**, Hermann von. "Über Goethes naturwissenschaftliche Arbeiten. Hermann v. Helmholtz. Vorträge u. Reden. 4. Aufl. Bd. 1. Braunsch. Vieweg & Sohn, 1896. S. 25-30." In *Lesebuch zur Einführung in die Kenntnis Deutschlands und seines Lebens. Für ausländische Studierende und für die oberste Stufe höherer Lehranstalten des In- und Auslandes.* Berlin: Weidmannsche Buchhandlung, 1904, pp. 177-83.
    Partial rpt. of No. 1853-8.
/GENERAL INTRODUCTION

1904-20 ***Hirzel**, Salomon. "Goethe als Naturforscher." *Frankfurter Zeitung*, No. 44, 13 February 1904.
    Cf. No. 1903-4.
/GENERAL INTRODUCTION/DREHER, E

1904-21 **Kalischer**, Salomon. "Goethe als Naturforscher." In Bielschowsky, Albert. *Goethe: Sein Leben und seine Werke.* 2 vols. München: C. H. Beck'sche Verlagsbuchhandlung Oskar Beck, 1904, pp. 412-61.
/GENERAL INTRODUCTION

1904-22 **Kareis**, Josef. "Goethes Elektrizitätsforschung." *Österreichische Rundschau*, 1 (1904/1905), 460-72.
/PHYSICS/CHROMATICS

1904-23 **Laué**, Walter. *Gedanken zu Goethes Faust. -- Schiller und die Farbenlehre.* Breslau: Verlagsanstalt v. S. Schottländer/Leipzig: E. F. Steinacker, 1904. 210 pp.
/CHROMATICS/SCHILLER, F/WORKS: FAUST

1904-24 **Lippmann**, E[dmund O.] v[on]. "Zur Farbenlehre." *Goethe*, 25 (1904), 237.
    Rpt. No. 1906-18.
/CHROMATICS

1904-25 **May**, Walther. "Goethe und Darwin." In his *Goethe. Humboldt. Darwin. Haeckel: Vier Vorträge.* Berlin-Steglitz: Verlag Enno Quehl, 1904, pp. 49-148.
2nd edn. 1906.
/DARWIN, C/BIOLOGY: EVOLUTION

1904-26 **Miessner**, Wilhelm. "Goethes Naturanschauung." *Internationale Literatur- und Musikberichte*, 11 (1904), 172-3.
/GENERAL INTRODUCTION

1904-27 *****Ricek-Gerolding**, L[?]. G. "Goethe und die deutsche Abstammungslehre." *Deutsches Tageblatt [Wien]*, No. 5, 1904.
/BIOLOGY: EVOLUTION

1904-28 *****Schenk**, Paul. "Goethe und Darwin." *Hamburger Nachrichten*, Belletristisch-Literarische Beilage No. 35, 28 August 1904.
/DARWIN, C/BIOLOGY: EVOLUTION

1904-29 **Seiling**, Max. *Goethe und der Materialismus.* Leipzig: Druck und Verlag von Oswald Mutze, 1904. 154 pp.
/NATURPHILOSOPHIE

1904-30 **Weidlich**, Karl. "Wann und warum sehen wir Farben? Ein Beitrag zur Farbenlehre." Leipzig: Buchdruckerei von J. J. Weber, 1904. 44 pp.
/RESEARCH: CHROMATICS/CHROMATICS

1904-31 **Ziegler**, H[einrich]. E[rnst]. "Goethes biologische Studien. Nach einem von Professor Ernst Haeckel am 17. Juni in Jena gehaltenen Vortrage." *Frankfurter Zeitung*, 28 June 1904.
/BIOLOGY/HAECKEL, E

1905-1 **Achelis**, Th[?]. "Naturforschung." In his *Was sagt Goethe? Ein Goethe-Brevier.* Bücher der Weisheit und Schönheit. Stuttgart: Greiner und Pfeifer[, 1905], pp. 135-56.
/GENERAL INTRODUCTION/METHOD/MORPHOLOGY

1905-2 *****[anon.]** "Ein Ausflug Goethes nach Zinnwald und Altenberg." *Teplitz-Schönauer Anzeiger*, 44, No. 106 (1905).
/GEOLOGY

1905-3 *****[anon.]** "Goethe's Forecast of an Atlantic-Pacific Canal." *The Critic*, 47 (1905), 210-11.
/TECHNOLOGY

1905-4 **Baumgarten**, P[aul]. v[on]. "Goethes Naturstudien, insbesondere in darwinistischer Beleuchtung." *Deutsche Revue*, 30 (1905), 302-12.
/BIOLOGY/BIOLOGY: EVOLUTION/DARWIN, C

1905-5 **Bölsche**, Wilhelm. ["Goethe und Haeckel."] In his *Naturgeheimnis*. Jena/Leipzig: Eugen Diederichs Verlag, 1905, pp. 157-79.
/HAECKEL, E/BIOLOGY: EVOLUTION

1905-6 *****Bölsche**, Wilhelm. "Die leuchtende Pflanze." *Über Land und Meer*, 1 November 1905.
Partial rpt. No. 1905-7.
/BOTANY/CHROMATICS

1905-7 *****Bölsche**, Wilhelm. "Die leuchtende Pflanze und Goethes Farbenlehre." *Frankfurter Zeitung [1. Morgenblatt]*, 4 November 1905.
Partial rpt. of No. 1905-6.
/BOTANY/CHROMATICS

1905-8 **Bossert**, A[dolphe]. "Die Farbentheorie." In his *Schopenhauer als Mensch und Philosoph*. Dresden: Verlag von Carl Reißner, 1905, pp. 64-83.
/SCHOPENHAUER, A/CHROMATICS

1905-9 **Bossert**, A[dolphe]. "Schopenhauer und Goethe." In his *Schopenhauer als Mensch und Philosoph*. Dresden: Verlag von Carl Reißner, 1905, pp. 50-63.
/SCHOPENHAUER, A/CHROMATICS

1905-10 **Burckhardt**, C. A. H[ugo]. *Goethes Unterhaltungen mit Friedrich Soret*. Weimar: Hermann Böhlaus Nachfolger, 1905. xvii, 158 pp.
"Nach dem französischen Texte als eine bedeutend vermehrte und verbesserte Ausgabe des dritten Teils der Eckermannschen Gespräche"
/SORET, F/MINERALOGY

1905-11 **Chamberlain**, Houston Stewart. "Goethe (Idee und Erfahrung): Mit einem Exkurs über die Metamorphosenlehre." In his *Immanuel Kant: Die Persönlichkeit als Einführung in das Werk*. München: Verlagsanstalt F. Bruckmann, 1905, pp. 89-171.
/NATURPHILOSOPHIE/EPISTEMOLOGY/MORPHOLOGY

1905-12 **Cohn**, Jonas. "Das Kantische Element in Goethes Weltanschauung. Schillers philosophischer Einfluß auf Goethe." *Kant-Studien*, 10 (1905), 286-345.
/NATURPHILOSOPHIE/EPISTEMOLOGY/KANT, I

1905-13 **[Goethe**, J. W. von.] *Goethes Naturphilosophie.* Taschenausgaben der 'Philosophischen Bibliothek', 16. Leipzig: Verlag von Felix Meiner, 1905. 85 [157-241] pp.
Partial rpt. of No. 1905-14.
/EDITION: SELECTIONS/GENERAL INTRODUCTION

1905-14 **[Goethe**, J. W. von.] *Goethes Philosophie aus seinen Werken. Ein Buch für jeden gebildeten Deutschen.* Ed. and intro. Max Heynacher. Philosophische Bibliothek, 109. Leipzig: Verlag der Dürr'schen Buchhandlung, 1905. viii, 428 pp.
Partial rpt. No. 1905-13.
/EDITION: SELECTIONS/GENERAL INTRODUCTION

1905-15 **Goethe**[, J. W. von]. *Philosophie der Farben.* Taschenausgaben der 'Philosophischen Bibliothek', 35. Leipzig: Verlag von Felix Meiner[, 1905]. 50 [219-68] pp.
Rpt. of No. 1905-14.
/EDITION: SELECTION

1905-16 **Haeckel**, Ernst. "Ueber die Biologie in Jena während des 19. Jahrhunderts." *Jenaische Zeitschrift für Naturwissenschaft*, 39 [NS 32] (1905), 713-26.
"Vortrag, gehalten in der Sitzung der Medizinisch-naturwissenschaftlichen Gesellschaft zu Jena am 17. Juni 1904."
/OSTEOLOGY/COMPARATIVE ANATOMY/BIOLOGY

1905-17 **Helmholtz**, Hermann von. "Über Goethes naturwissenschaftliche Arbeiten. Hermann v. Helmholtz. Vorträge u. Reden. 4. Aufl. Bd. 1. Braunsch. Vieweg & Sohn, 1896. S. 25-30." In *Lesebuch zur Einführung in die Kenntnis Deutschlands und seines Lebens. Für ausländische Studierende und für die oberste Stufe höherer Lehranstalten des In- und Auslandes.* 2nd edn. Berlin: Weidmannsche Buchhandlung, 1904, pp. 216-21.
Partial rpt. of No. 1853-8.
/GENERAL INTRODUCTION

1905-18 **Kronfeld**, Adolf. "Goethe und Haeckel." *Das freie Wort: Frankfurter Halbmonatsschrift für Fortschritt auf allen Gebieten des geistigen Lebens*, 4, No. 12 (1905), 453-63.

/HAECKEL, E/BIOLOGY: EVOLUTION

1905-19 **M[?]**, A. "Goethe und Schopenhauer über die Luftschiffer." *Königlich privilegirte Berlinische Zeitung von Staats- und gelehrten Sachen. Vossische Zeitung*, No. 605, 27 December 1905, 1.
/TECHNOLOGY

1905-20 **Morris**, Max. "Weimarer Goethe-Ausgabe. Bericht der Redaktoren und Herausgeber. Band II 13." *Goethe*, 26 (1905), 312-15.
/EDITION

1905-21 **Prack**, Adolf. "Goethe über Schelling." *Österreichisch-Ungarische Revue*, 33 (1905), 65-79; 143-59.
/SCHELLING, F VON/NATURPHILOSOPHIE

1905-22 **Rádl**, Emanuel. "J. W. von Goethe." In his *Geschichte der biologischen Theorien seit dem Ende des siebzehnten Jahrhunderts.* Pt. I. Leipzig: Verlag von Wilhelm Engelmann, 1905, pp. 263-70.
/BIOLOGY/OSTEOLOGY

1905-23 **Schneider**, Hermann. "Goethe's naturphilosophische Leitgedanken. Eine Einführung in die naturwissenschaftlichen Werke." Berlin: Gose & Tetzlaff Verlagsbuchhandlung[, 1905].
/NATURPHILOSOPHIE/METHOD/GENERAL INTRODUCTION

1905-24 **Teichl**, Robert. "Goethe und Georg Graf von Buquoy." *Chronik des Wiener Goethe-Vereins*, 19 (1905), 17-30.
/BUQUOY, G VON/NATURPHILOSOPHIE

1905-25 **Velenovsky**, Josef. "Was versteht man unter Pflanzenmorphologie und welches ist ihr Verhältnis zu den verwandten Wissenschaften." In *Vergleichende Morphologie der Pflanzen. I. Teil.* Prag: Verlagsbuchhandlung von Fr. Rivnác, 1905, pp. 1-7.
Cf. Supplement, No. 1913-35.
/RESEARCH: MORPHOLOGY/RESEARCH: BOTANY/MORPHOLOGY/BOTANY

1906-1 **[anon.]** "Goethe als Bergwerkskommisar." *Berliner Tageblatt und Handelszeitung [Morgen-Ausgabe]*, 35, No. 415 (1906)[, 2-3].
/GEOLOGY/TECHNOLOGY

1906-2 **[anon.]** "Goethe als Mineraloge." *Kölnische Volkszeitung*, 28 June 1906.

/GEOLOGY

1906-3 [**anon.**] "Goethe as mineralogist and geologist." *Nature: A Weekly Illustrated Journal of Science*, 75 (1906/1907), 176-7.
/GEOLOGY/LINCK, G

1906-4 **Bernt**, Friedrich. "Goethes Farbenlehre." *Beilage zur Weimarischen Zeitung*, Nos. 11, 15 and 20, 14 January 1906.
/CHROMATICS

1906-5 **Bölsche**, Wilhelm. "Leuchtende Pflanzen. Naturwissenschaftliche Plauderei." *Über Land und Meer*, 95 (1906), 6.
/BOTANY/CHROMATICS

1906-6 **Brass**, Arnold. *Untersuchungen über das Licht und die Farben.* Osterwieck/Harz: Verlag von Zickfeldt, 1906. vi, 192 pp.
/RESEARCH: CHROMATICS/CHROMATICS/NEWTON, I

1906-7 **Dalberg**, G. K. L. Huberti del. "Goethe und die Heilkunde." *Die Heilkunde: Monatsschrift für practische Medicin*, January/February 1906, 19-25; 69-73.
/MEDICINE

1906-8 **Dalberg**, G. K. L. Huberti del. "Medicinisches von und über Goethe." *Die medicinische Woche und Balneologische Centralzeitung*, Nos. 20-22, 1906, pp. 222-4; 236-8; 246-8.
/MEDICINE

1906-9 **Feldhaus**, Franz M. "Goethe und die Luftschiffahrt." *Illustrierte Aeronautische Mitteilungen: Deutsche Zeitschrift für Luftschiffahrt*, 10 (1906), 297-99.
/TECHNOLOGY

1906-10 **Förster**, Brix. "Methode und Ziel in Goethes naturphilosophischer Forschung." *Goethe*, 27 (1906), 226-42.
/NATURPHILOSOPHIE/METHOD/EPISTEMOLOGY

1906-11 **Goethe**, J. W. von. *Paralipomena zu Band 1-5: Register zu Band 1-5, 2. Abtheilung.* Vol. II.5.2 of the *Weimarer Ausgabe.* Weimar: Hermann Böhlaus Nachfolger, 1906. xix, 532 pp.
    Rpt. No. 1987-41.
/EDITION: SELECTIONS

1906-12 "**Goethes** Unterhaltungen mit Friedrich Soret." In *Stunden mit*

Goethe: Für die Freunde seiner Kunst und Weisheit. Ed. Wilhelm Bode. Berlin: Ernst Siegfried Mittler und Sohn, 1906, vol. 2, 50-57.
/SORET, F/MINERALOGY

1906-13 **Hansen**, A[dolph]. "Goethes Metamorphose der Pflanzen." *Goethe*, 27 (1906), 207-25.
/BOTANY/MORPHOLOGY

1906-14 **John**, Alois. "Goethe und der Kammerbühl." In *Goethe-Festschrift aus Anlass der Enthüllung des Goethe-Denkmals in Franzensbad am 9. September 1906.* Ed. Alois John. Franzensbad: Verlag der Kurverwaltung in Franzensbad, 1906, pp. 47-60.
/GEOLOGY

1906-15 *****Krüger-Westend**, Hermann. "Goethe und Joachim Jungius." *Hamburger Nachrichten*, Beilage No. 11, 18 March 1906.
/JUNGIUS, J

1906-16 **Linck**, Gottlob. "Goethes Verhältnis zur Mineralogie und Geognosie." Jena: Verlag von Gustav Fischer, 1906. 48 pp.
"Rede gehalten zur Feier der akademischen Preisverteilung am 16. Juni 1906."
/GEOLOGY

1906-17 **Lippmann**, Edmund O. von. "Alraun und schwarzer Hund; ein naturwissenschaftlicher Aberglaube." In his *Abhandlungen und Vorträge zur Geschichte der Naturwissenschaften.* Leipzig: Verlag von Veit & Co., 1906, pp. 190-204.
Rpt. of No. 1894-13.
/ALCHEMY/WORKS: FAUST

1906-18 **Lippmann**, Edmund O. von. "Goethes Farbenlehre." In his *Abhandlungen und Vorträge zur Geschichte der Naturwissenschaften.* Leipzig: Verlag von Veit & Co., 1906, pp. 219-46.
Rpt. of No. 1904-24.
/CHROMATICS

1906-19 **Magnus**, Rudolf. *Goethe als Naturforscher: Vorlesungen gehalten im Sommer-Semester 1906 an der Universität Heidelberg.* Leipzig: Verlag von Johann Ambrosius Barth, 1906. vii, 336 pp.
Trans. into English, No. 1949-111.
/GENERAL INTRODUCTION

1906-20 **Milch**, Ludwig. "Goethe und die Geologie." In *Stunden mit*

Goethe: Für die Freunde seiner Kunst und Weisheit. Ed. Wilhelm
Bode. Berlin: Ernst Siegfried Mittler und Sohn, 1906, vol. II, pp.
102-27.
/GEOLOGY

1906-21 **Mulert**[, ?]. "Goethes Entdeckung des Zwischenkiefers beim
Menschen." In *Naturwissenschaftliche Gesellschaft "Isis" in Meissen.
Mitteilungen aus den Sitzungen des Vereinsjahres 1906/1907.*
Meißen: Druck von C. E. Klinkicht & Sohn, pp. 35-40.
/OSTEOLOGY/COMPARATIVE ANATOMY

1906-22 **Reukauf**, Edmund. "Goethe als Mikroskopiker." *Aus der
Natur: Zeitschrift für alle Naturfreunde*, 2 (1906/1907), 449-58.
Rev. rpt. No. 1912-22.
/GOETHE'S APPARATUS/GOETHE'S COLLECTIONS
/MICROSCOPY

1907-1 **Bliedner**, A[rno]. "Ein Symbol des höchsten Alters." *Stunden
mit Goethe: Für die Freunde seiner Kunst und Weisheit.* Ed. Wilhelm
Bode. Berlin: Ernst Siegfried Mittler und Sohn, 1907, vol. III, pp.
145-7.
/BOTANY

1907-2 **Bölsche**, Wilhelm. "Goethe und der Elefant." *Die Woche:
Moderne Illustrierte Zeitschrift*, 3, No. 28 (1907), 1222-4.
/ZOOLOGY

1907-3 **[Bölsche**, Wilhelm?]. "Goethe und die Fliegen." *Berliner Zeitung
am Mittag: Berliner Zeitung*, 31, No. 274, 22 November 1907[, 8].
/ZOOLOGY/BOTANY

1907-4 **Börnstein**, Richard. "Aus Goethes Meteorologie." *Meteorologische Zeitschrift*, 24 (1907), 241-7.
/METEOROLOGY

1907-5 **Börnstein**, Richard. "Goethes Meteorologie." *Deutsche Revue
[Stuttgart and Leipzig]*, 32 (1907), 106-19.
/METEOROLOGY

1907-6 **Boucke**, Ewald A. *Goethes Weltanschauung auf historischer
Grundlage. Ein Beitrag zur Geschichte der dynamischen Denk-
richtung und Gegensatzlehre.* Stuttgart: Fr. Frommanns Verlag (E.
Hauff), 1907. xxi, 459 pp.
/METEOROLOGY/CHROMATICS/NATURPHILSOPHIE

1907-7 **Ettlinger**, J[?]. "Goethe und Georg Forster." *Vossische Zeitung*, No. 262, 7 June 1907.
/FORSTER, J/NATURPHILOSOPHIE

1907-8 **G[eiger]**., L[udwig]. "Zu Goethe und Langermann." *Goethe*, 28 (1907), 250-51.
/LANGERMANN, J/MEDICINE

1907-9 [**Goethe**, J. W. von.] "La metamorfosi delle piante." Trans. Giovanni Castelli. Siena: Lazzeri, 1907. 26 pp.
Extract from the *Rivista Italiana di Scienze Naturali*, 26 (1906).
/TRANSLATION: ITALIAN

1907-10 **Gräf**, Hans Gerhard. "Goetheerinnerungen im nordwestlichen Böhmen." *Die Grenzboten: Zeitschrift für Politik, Literatur und Kunst*, 66 (1907), 13-28; 133-44.
/GEOLOGY/PLACES: BÖHMEN

1907-11 [**H?**, J. R.] "Goethe als Naturforscher." *Die Grenzboten: Zeitschrift für Politik, Literatur und Kunst*, 66 (1907), 107-8.
/GENERAL INTRODUCTION

1907-12 **Hansen**, Adolph. *Goethes Metamorphose der Pflanzen: Geschichte einer botanischen Hypothese.* 2 pts. Giessen: Verlag von Alfred Tölpelmann, 1907. xi, 380 pp.; [8] pp., 28 plates.
/BOTANY/MORPHOLOGY/RECEPTION/INFLUENCES /BATSCH, A

1907-13 **Hansen**, Adolph. "Haeckels 'Welträtsel' und Herders Weltanschauung." Giessen: Verlag von Alfred Töpelmann (vormals J. Ricker), 1907. 40 pp.
/HAECKEL, E/HERDER, J/NATURPHILOSOPHIE /BIOLOGY: EVOLUTION

1907-14 **Henkel**, Hermann. "Goethe und die Natur. Ein Überblick." Wernigerode: B. Angerstein, 1907. 16 pp.
/GENERAL INTRODUCTION

1907-15 **Johannsen**, Wilhelm Ludvig. "Om Goethes Naturforskning [On Goethe's Scientific Research]." *Dansk Tidsskrift. Ny Raekke: Gads Danske Magasin 1906-1907.* Kobenhavn: Nielsen & Lydiche (Axel Simmelkiaer), May 1907, pp. 670-80.
In Danish.

/GENERAL INTRODUCTION

1907-16 John, Alois. "Der Goethestein im Egerlande. (1895)." In his *Egerländer Heimatsbuch: Gesammelte Aufsätze*. Eger: Georg Adler, 1907, pp. 101-5.
/GEOLOGY

1907-17 John, Alois. "Der Kammerbühl und das Goethe-Denkmal. (1891)." In his *Egerländer Heimatsbuch: Gesammelte Aufsätze*. Eger: Georg Adler, 1907, pp. 105-8.
/GEOLOGY

1907-18 Kalischer, S[alomon]. "Goethes Metamorphose der Pflanzen." *Deutsche Literaturzeitung*, 28, No. 39 (1907), cols. 2437-2442.
/BOTANY

1907-19 Milch, L[udwig]. "Die Beziehungen K. C. v. Leonhard's zu Goethe." *Neues Jahrbuch für Mineralogie, Geologie und Paläontologie*, 1907, 169-80.
/LEONHARD, K/MINERALOGY

1907-20 Lippmann, Edmund O. von. "Encheiresis Naturae." *Chemiker-Zeitung*, 31 (1907), 172; 461-3.
Rpt. Nos. 1908-17 and 1913-20.
/WORKS: FAUST/CHEMISTRY

1907-21 Nägele, E[?]. "Das 'Neue Jahrbuch' von 1807-1907." *Neues Jahrbuch für Mineralogie, Geologie und Paläontologie*, 1907, vii-xviii.
/GEOLOGY

1907-22 *Petsch, Robert. "Goethe als Naturforscher." *Nationalzeitung*, Sonntagsbeilage 13 (1907).
/GENERAL INTRODUCTION

1907-23 S[?]. "Goethe und die deutschen Apotheker." *Apotheker Zeitung*, 22, No. 71 (1907), 745-7.
/PHARMACOLOGY/RECEPTION

1907-24 Schelling, F[riedrich]. W. J. [von]. "Ueber den Ursprung des allgemeinen Organismus." In his *Schriften zur Naturphilosophie*. Vol. 1 of his *Werke. Auswahl in drei Bänden*. Pref. Arthur Drews. Ed. and intro. Otto Weiß. Leipzig: Fritz Eckardt Verlag, 1907, pp. 441-679.

Rpt. of No. 1798-2.
/BOTANY/MORPHOLOGY/OPTICS/RESEARCH: BIOLOGY

1907-25 **Speck**, Johannes. "Der Entwicklungsgedanke bei Goethe." Cammin i. Pom.: Fermazin & Knauff, 1907. 32 pp.
/NATURPHILOSOPHIE/BIOLOGY: EVOLUTION

1907-26 **Sticker**, Georg. "Goethes Metamorphose der Pflanzen." *Hochland: Monatsschrift für alle Gebiete des Wissens, der Literatur und Kunst*, 5 (1907/1908), 91-4.
/BOTANY/MORPHOLOGY

1907-27 **Tschermak[-Seysenegg]**, Armin von. "Über das Verhältnis von Gegenfarbe, Kompensationsfarbe und Kontrastfarbe." *Archiv für die gesammte Physiologie des Menschen und der Tiere*, 117 (1907), 473-96.
/RESEARCH: CHROMATICS

1907-28 **Weber**, Max Maria Freiherr von. "Goethe und die Dampfmaschine: Aphorisme." In his *Aus der Welt der Arbeit: Gesammelte Schriften*. Berlin: G. Grote'sche Verlagsbuchhandlung, 1907, pp. 271-9.
Rpt. of No. 1865-7.
/TECHNOLOGY

1907-29 **Welten**, Heinz. "Goethe als Botaniker." *Vossische Zeitung [Morgen-Ausgabe]*, No. 271, 13 June 1907[, 2-3].
/BOTANY

1907-30 **Worm**, Walter. "Stomatologisches bei Goethe." *Deutsche Monatsschrift für Zahnheilkunde*, 25 (1907), 563-5.
/STOMATOLOGY

1908-1 **[anon.]** "'Alles ist aus dem Wasser entsprungen,'. . ." In *Stunden mit Goethe*. Ed. Wilhelm Bode. Berlin: E. S. Mittler & Sohn, 1908, pp. 144-6.
/NATURPHILOSOPHIE

1908-2 **Bardeleben**, Karl von. "Der Schädel oder Kopfskelett." In his *Das Skelett*. Pt. II of *Die Anatomie des Menschen*. Aus Natur und Geisteswelt, 202. Leipzig: Druck und Verlag von B. G. Teubner, 1908, pp. 35-55.
/OSTEOLOGY/ANATOMY

1908-3 **Bode**, Wilhelm. "Die ersten Luftballons in Weimar." *Stunden mit Goethe*, 4 (1908), 58-63.
/TECHNOLOGY

1908-4 **Bruck**, W[?]. F. "Goethe und die Botanik." *Preußische Jahrbücher*, 131 (1908), 29-36.
/BOTANY/HANSEN, A

1908-5 **Chamberlain**, Houston Stewart. "Goethe, Linné und die exakte Wissenschaft der Natur." In *Wiesener-Festschrift*. Ed. K. Linsbauer. Wien: Verlagsbuchhandlung Carl Konegen (Ernst Stülpnagel), 1908, pp. 225-38.
Rpt. No. 1925-6.
/BOTANY/LINNAEUS [LINNÉ], C/METHOD

1908-6 [**Goethe**, J. W. von.] "Die Botanik unter dem Einflusse der Metamorphosenlehre. Goethe's Versuch über die Metamorphose der Pflanzen. 1790." In *Aus der Werkstatt grosser Forscher: Allgemeinverständliche erläuterte Abschnitte aus den Werken hervorragender Naturforscher aller Völker und Zeiten.* Ed. Friedrich Dannemann. Vol. 1 of his *Grundriss einer Geschichte der Naturwissenschaften: Zugleich eine Einführung in das Studium der naturwissenschaftlichen Litteratur.* 3rd rev. and exp. edn. Leipzig: Verlag von Wilhelm Engelmann, 1908, pp. 227-31.
Rpt. of No. 1896-5.
/EDITION

1908-7 [**Goethe**, J. W. von.] "Johann Wolfgang Goethe." In *Herder. -- Die Stürmer und Dränger. -- Goethe. Johann Peter Hebel.* Vol. 4 of *Aus der deutschen Literatur. Dichtungen in Poesie und Prosa ausgewählt für Schule und Haus.* Ed. Johannes Meyer. Berlin: Verlag von Gerdes & Hödel, 1908, pp. 185-554.
"Ausgewählt von Direktor Dr. Wasserzieher in Neuwied."
/EDITION: SELECTIONS

1908-8 [**Goethe**, J. W. von.] "Schriften und Aufsätze zur Naturwissenschaft." In *Herder. -- Die Stürmer und Dränger. -- Goethe. Johann Peter Hebel.* Vol. 4 of *Aus der deutschen Literatur. Dichtungen in Poesie und Prosa ausgewählt für Schule und Haus.* Ed. Johannes Meyer. Berlin: Verlag von Gerdes & Hödel, 1908, pp. 507-54.
/EDITION: SELECTIONS

1908-9 **Grünbaum**, Herbert. "Die chemische Verwandtschaftslehre in Goethes Wahlverwandtschaften." *Chemiker-Zeitung*, 32 (1908),

1173-84.
/CHEMISTRY

1908-10 *Hoffmann, K[?]. O. "Goethe als Geolog." *Zeitschrift für Mineralogie, Geologie und Paläontologie*, 2, No. 7 (1908).
/GEOLOGY

1908-11 Ilwof, Franz. "Das Wetterschießen bei Goethe." *Chronik des Wiener Goethe-Vereins*, 21 (1908), 14-15.
/METEOROLOGY

1908-12 *Karrig, O[tto]. "Goethe und die Vogelwelt." *Hamburger Nachrichten [Sonntagsbeilage]*, No. 13, 1908.
/ORNITHOLOGY?

1908-13 Kerner von Marilaun, Anton. "Goethes Verhältnis zur Pflanzenwelt." In Kronfeld, M[?]. *Anton Kerner von Marilaun: Leben und Arbeit eines deutschen Naturforschers*. Intro. R. von Wettstein. Leipzig: Chr. Herm. Tauchnitz, 1908, pp.
/BOTANY

1908-14 Kerner von Marilaun, Anton. "Goethe und Darwin." In Kronfeld, M[?]. *Anton Kerner von Marilaun: Leben und Arbeit eines deutschen Naturforschers*. Intro. R. von Wettstein. Leipzig: Chr. Herm. Tauchnitz, 1908, pp. 215-24.
    Rpt. of No. 1880-9.
/DARWIN, C/BIOLOGY: EVOLUTION

1908-15 Lavater, J[ohann]. C[aspar]. *Physiognomische Fragmente zur Beförderung der Menschenkenntniß und Menschenliebe*. 4 vols. Leipzig/Winterthur 1775-1778. Berlin: H. Barsdorf, 1908.
    Photomech. rpt. of No. 1776-1.
/PHYSIOGNOMY

1908-16 Lienhard, F[riedrich]. "Goethe II. 2. Der Naturforscher." *Wege nach Weimar*, 6, No. 8 (1908), 66-85.
/GENERAL INTRODUCTION

1908-17 Lippmann, Edmund O. von. "Encheiresis Naturae." *Goethe*, 29 (1908), 163-4.
    Rpt. of No. 1907-20.
/WORKS: FAUST/CHEMISTRY

1908-18 Lippmann, Edmund O. v[on]. "Über Sinn und Herkunft des

Wortes 'Encheiresis naturae' in Goethes Faust." In *Verhandlungen der Berliner Gesellschaft für Geschichte der Medizin und der Naturwissenschaften. Mitteilungen zur Geschichte der Medizin und der Naturwissenschaften*, 7 (1908), 343.
/WORKS: FAUST/CHEMISTRY

1908-19 **Marschik-Brünn**, Samuel. "Goethe als Technolog." *Das Wissen für Alle: Populär-wissenschaftliche Wochenschrift*, No. 21-23 (1908), 321-4; 334-40; 353-7.
/TECHNOLOGY

1908-20 **Meyer**, Adolf. "Goethe und Helmholtz." *Preußische Jahrbücher*, 130 (1908), 191-214.
/HELMHOLTZ, H VON

1908-21 **Mießner**, Wilhelm. "Friedrich Wilhelm Schelling. Ein Goethephilosoph." *Die Gegenwart*, 73, No. 36 (1908), 150-53.
/SCHELLING, F VON/NATURPHILOSOPHIE

1908-22 **Milch**, L[udwig]. "Goethes Beziehungen zu dem Mineralogen Karl Caesar von Leonhard." *Neues Jahrbuch für Mineralogie, Geologie und Paläontologie*, 1907, 169-80.
/LEONHARD, K/MINERALOGY

1908-23 **Münz**, Bernhard. "Aus der Leidensgeschichte der Farbenlehre." *Stunden mit Goethe*, 4 (1908), 268-74.
/CHROMATICS/LÖVY, H

1908-24 **Oppel**, Eduard. "Goethe und Rousseau als Botaniker." *Badische Schulzeitung. Organ des Badischen Lehrer-Vereins, des Witwenund Waisenstifts und des Pestalozzi-Vereins*, 48, No. 20 (1908), 305-7.
/BOTANY/ROUSSEAU, J

1908-25 **Raehlmann**, Eduard. "Der simultane Kontrast im Farbensehen." *Zeitschrift für Augenheilkunde*, 19 (1908), 1-16.
/RESEARCH: CHROMATICS/CHROMATICS

1908-26 *****Schneider**, Hermann. "Goethes Prosahymnus 'Die Natur'." *Archiv für das Studium der neueren Sprachen und Literaturen*, 62, 120 (1908).
/WORKS: DIE NATUR

1908-27 **Teutenberg**, Ad[?]. "Goethe und die Luftschiffahrt." *Illustrierte*

Aeronautische Mitteilungen: Deutsche Zeitschrift für Luftschiffahrt, 12 (1908), 524-8.
/TECHNOLOGY

1908-28 *Teutenberg, Ad[?]. "Goethe über Luftballons und Luftschiffahrt." *Hannoverscher Courier*, No. 27 (1908), 691.
/TECHNOLOGY

1908-29 Utitz, Emil. *Grundzüge der ästhetischen Farbenlehre.* Stuttgart: Verlag von Ferdinand Enke, 1908. viii, 156 pp.
/RESEARCH: CHROMATICS/CHROMATICS

1908-30 Wasserzieher, Ernst. "Goethe als Naturforscher." *Beilage zum 4. Jahresbericht der städtischen höheren Mädchenschule und Lehrerinnen-Seminars zu Neuwied am Rhein.* Neuwied: Druck der Strüder'schen Buchdruckerei, 1908. 20 pp.
Rpt. No. 1908-31.
/GENERAL INTRODUCTION

1908-31 Wasserzieher, Ernst. "Goethe als Naturforscher." In *Herder -- Die Stürmer und Dränger -- Goethe: Johann Peter Hebel.* Vol. 4 of *Einführung in die deutsche Literatur. Dichtungen in Poesie und Prosa erläutert für Schule und Haus.* Ed. Johannes Meyer. Berlin: Verlag von Gerdes & Hödel, 1908, pp. 664-76.
Rpt. of No. 1908-30.
/GENERAL INTRODUCTION

1908-32 Weidel, Karl. "Goethes Naturbetrachtung." *Montagsblatt: Wissenschaftliche Wochenbeilage der Magdeburgischen Zeitung: Organ für Heimatskunde*, 60 (1908), 190-92; 196-7; 205-7; 213-15.
/GENERAL INTRODUCTION

1909-1 [anon.] "Das Blitzen der Blüten." *Düsseldorfer Zeitung*, 8 May 1909.
/BOTANY

1909-2 *[anon.] "Goethe und Alexander von Humboldt." *Hamburger Fremdenblatt*, No. 104 (1909).
/HUMBOLDT, A VON

1909-3 *[anon.] "Goethe und F. A. Reuß." *Prager Tageblatt*, No. 359, 30 December 1909.
/REUß, F/MINERALOGY

1909-4 [**anon.**] "Goethe und der Panamakanal." *Königlich privilegirte Berlinische Zeitung von Staats- und gelehrten Sachen. Vossische Zeitung*, No. 384, 18 August 1909, 1.
/TECHNOLOGY

1909-5 [**anon.**] "Goethe und die Physiker." *Kölnische Volkszeitung. Literaturblatt*, No. 320, 27 June 1909.
/CHROMATICS

1909-6 [**anon.**] "Naturwissenschaft." *Kölnische Zeitung*, 3 June 1909. Contains brief review of No. 1909-18.
/REVIEW/DARWIN, C/BIOLOGY: EVOLUTION

1909-7 *[**anon.**] "Oerstedt, Schiller und Goethe." *Frankfurter Zeitung*, No. 190, 2. Morgenblatt, 11 July 1909.
/OERSTEDT, H/SCHILLER, F/NATURPHILOSOPHIE

1909-8 ***Brod**, Max. "Farbenlehre." *März: Halbmonatsschrift für deutsche Kultur*, 3, No. 4 (1909), 484-6.
/CHROMATICS

1909-9 **Förster**, Brix. "Goethes Naturwissenschaftliche Philosophie und Weltanschauung." Annaberg: Grasers Verlag (Richard Liesche), 1909. iv, 127 pp.
/GENERAL INTRODUCTION/NATURPHILOSOPHIE
/METHOD/EPISTEMOLOGY

1909-10 *[**Fränkel**, Ludwig?]. "Goethe und die Brüder Humboldt." *Münchener Neueste Nachrichten*, No. 405, 31 August 1909.
/HUMBOLDT, A VON/HUMBOLDT, W VON

1909-11 [**Goethe**, J. W. von.] "Jährlicher unterthänigster Bericht über den Zustand der Museen und anderer wissenschaftlicher Anstalten zu Jena." *Goethe*, 30 (1909), 21-37.
/EDITION

1909-12 **Goethes** *Briefwechsel mit Wilhelm und Alexander v. Humboldt*. Ed. Ludwig Geiger. Berlin: Hans Bondy, 1909. xxx, 359 pp.
/HUMBOLDT, A VON/WORKS: CORRESPONDENCE

1909-13 **Hoppe**, Hugo. "Goethe als Naturforscher (Nach seinen Reiseberichten). I." Goethe, 30 (1909), 141-53.
Cf. continuation, No. 1911-22.
/GENERAL INTRODUCTION

1909-14 **Kohut**, Adolf. "Alexander v. Humboldt und Goethe." *Neue Freie Presse. Morgenblatt*, No. 16061, 9 May 1909, 32-4.
/HUMBOLDT, A VON

1909-15 *****Krüger-Westend**, Hermann. "Goethe und die Luftschiffahrt." *Altonaer Tageblatt u. Ottensener Nachrichten*, Unterhaltungsbeilage zum 28. August 1909.
/TECHNOLOGY

1909-16 **M[?].**, [?]. "Goethe als Botaniker." *Chronik des Wiener Goethe-Vereins*, 24 (1910), 15.
/BOTANY/HANSEN, A

1909-17 **Morris**, Max and Erich **Schmidt**. "Zur Naturwissenschaft." In *Goethes Werke in sechs Bänden*. Ed. Erich Schmidt. Leipzig: Insel-Verlag, 1909, VI, 510-14.
2nd edn. 1910.
/GENERAL INTRODUCTION

1909-18 **Otto**, Rudolf. "Goethe und Darwin." *Freie Bayerische Schulzeitung*, 10 (1909), 30-32.
Cf. review, No. 1909-6.
/DARWIN, C/BIOLOGY: EVOLUTION

1909-19 **Otto**, Rudolf. "Goethe und Darwin: Darwinismus und Religion." Abhandlungen der Friesschen Schule. Göttingen: Vandenhoeck & Ruprecht, 1909, pp. 3-13.
Rev. Max Morris, *Euphorion*, 19 (1912), 401-2.
/DARWIN, C/BIOLOGY: EVOLUTION/THEOLOGY

1909-20 **Rádl**, Emanuel. "Die Lehre von der Metamorphose." In his *Geschichte der Entwicklungstheorien in der Biologie des XIX. Jahrhunderts*. Pt. II of *Geschichte der biologischen Theorien*. Leipzig: Verlag von Wilhelm Engelmann, 1909, pp. 25-31.
/BOTANY/MORPHOLOGY

1909-21 **Rádl**, Emanuel. "Die Schönheit der lebendigen Natur. Goethes und Humboldts Ansichten." In his *Geschichte der Entwicklungstheorien in der Biologie des XIX. Jahrhunderts*. Pt. II of *Geschichte der biologischen Theorien*. Leipzig: Verlag von Wilhelm Engelmann, 1909, pp. 245-6.
/NATURPHILOSOPHIE/HUMBOLDT, A VON

1909-22 **Rádl**, Emanuel. "Spiraltheorie." In his *Geschichte der Entwicklungstheorien in der Biologie des XIX. Jahrhunderts*. Pt. II of *Geschichte der biologischen Theorien*. Leipzig: Verlag von Wilhelm Engelmann, 1909, pp. 24-5.
/BOTANY/MORPHOLOGY

1909-23 *****Reys**, J[?]. H. O. "Goethe en Camper als voorloopers van Darwin [Goethe and Camper as Predecessors of Darwin]." *Vragen van den dag*, 24 July 1909.
In Dutch.
/CAMPER, P/DARWIN, C/BIOLOGY

1909-24 **Rosenbach**, Ottomar. "Die Farbensirene und Bemerkungen über die Entstehung der Farben." In *Klinisch-experimentelle Abhandlungen; Arbeiten vermischten Inhalts: Briefe: Nachlaß*. Vol. 2 of *Ausgewählte Abhandlungen von Ottomar Rosenbach*. Ed. Walter Guttmann. Leipzig: Verlag von Johann Ambrosius Barth, 1909, pp. 413-20.
Rpt. of No. 1894-19.
/RESEARCH: CHROMATICS/CHROMATICS/RECEPTION

1909-25 *****S[?].**, [?] v[on]. "Goethes Metamorphose der Pflanzen." *Hamburgischer Correspondent: Liter[arische] Beilage*, No. 1.
/BOTANY/HANSEN, A

1909-26 **Schiff**, Julius. "Eine Begegnung zwischen Goethe und Berzelius." *Schlesische Gesellschaft für vaterländische Cultur*, II. Abteilung, Naturwissenschaften, 86 (1908), 50-53.
Rpt. exp. edn. No. 1910-16.
/BERZELIUS, J [VON]/CHEMISTRY

1909-27 **Seiling**, Max. "Goethe 'und' Haeckel." *Glauben und Wissen: Blätter zur Verteidigung und Vertiefung der christlichen Weltanschauung*, 7, No. 7 (1909), 241-8.
/HAECKEL, E/BIOLOGY: EVOLUTION/THEOLOGY

1909-28 **Semper**, Max. "Zu Goethes Entwurf: Bildung der Erde." *Goethe*, 30 (1909), 231-3.
/GEOLOGY

1910-1 **Bachmann**, E[?]. "Goethe und Berzelius auf dem Kammerbühl." *Reclams Universum. Moderne Illustrierte Wochenschrift*, 26, No. 48 (1910), 1221-3.
/BERZELIUS, J VON/PLACES: DER KAMMERBÜHL

1910-2 *****Berger**, Ernst. "Goethes Farbenlehre und die modernen Theorien." *Kunst für Alle*, 26 (1910/1911), 133-41.
/CHROMATICS/FINE ARTS

1910-3 **Engel**, Eduard. "Goethes Weltanschauung. Naturwissenschaft, Philosophie, Religion." In his *Goethe: Der Mann und das Werk.* Berlin: Concordia Deutsche Verlags-Anstalt Hermann Ehbock, 1910, pp. 477-93.
/GENERAL INTRODUCTION

1910-4 **Geitel**, Max. "Die Technik im Spiegel Goethescher Prosa und Poesie." *Die Welt der Technik, Illustriertes Fachblatt für die Fortschritte in Technik, Industrie und Kunstgewerbe*, 72 (1910), 22-6; 42-5.
/TECHNOLOGY/WORKS: VARIOUS

1910-5 **Goethe**[, J. W. von.] "Höhen der alten und neuen Welt bildlich verglichen." Weimar: Hof-Buchdruckerei, 1910. [4] pp.
Rpt. of No. 1813-1.
"Aus Bertuchs Allgemeinen Geographischen Ephemeriden (Mai 1813) in 100 Exemplaren zur 25. Generalversammlung der Goethe-Gesellschaft am 18. Juni 1910 besonders abgedruckt von Leonard L. Mackall."
/EDITION

1910-6 **Goethe**[, J. W. von] [**Tobler**, Georg Christoph]. "Die Natur: Ein Hymnus." Leipzig: Insel Verlag, 1910. [16] pp.
/EDITION

1910-7 **Grosse**[, Eduard]. "Goethe als Physiker" *Der Tag: Illustrierter Teil*, No. 209, 7 September 1910[, 4].
/CHROMATICS

1910-8 **Grosse**[, Wilhelm?]. "Goethe als Meteorologe." *Der Tag: Illustrierter Teil*, No. 209, 7 September 1910[, 4].
/METEOROLOGY

1910-9 **Kahle**, P[?]. "Zu Goethes erster Brockenfahrt." *Der Harz. Vereinsblatt des Harzklubs*, 17 (1910), cols. 7-10.

/CHROMATICS/PLACES: DER BROCKEN

1910-10 **Kritzinger**, H[?]. H. "Über eine von Goethe im Jahre 1828 beobachtete Planetenkonstellation." *Himmel und Erde: Illustrierte Naturwissenschaftliche Monatsschrift*, 22 (1910), 186-8.
/ASTRONOMY

1910-11 **Lippmann**, Edmund O. von. "Goethes Farbenlehre." *Chronik des Wiener Goethe-Vereins*, 24 (1910), 22-3.
"Referat eines Vortrags v. 1. Februar 1910."
/CHROMATICS

1910-12 **Lucerna**, Camilla. *Das Märchen: Goethes Naturphilosophie als Kunstwerk*. Leipzig: Fritz Eckardt Verlag, 1910. viii, 191 pp.
/WORKS: DAS MÄRCHEN/NATURPHILOSOPHIE

1910-13 **Meyerhof**, Otto. "Über Goethes Methode der Naturforschung." Abhandlungen der Fries'schen Schule, 3. Göttingen: Vandenhoeck & Rupprecht, 1910. 55 pp.
Rev. Max Morris, *Euphorion*, 19 (1912), 401-2.
/METHOD

1910-14 **Milch**, Ludwig. "Zur Entstehung der Aufsätze: 'Geologische Probleme und Versuch ihrer Auflösung' und 'Verschiedene Bekenntnisse'." *Goethe*, 31 (1910), 136-54.
/GEOLOGY

1910-15 *****Ruben**, L[?]. "Goethes Methode der Naturforschung." *Literatur und Wissenschaft. Monatliche Beilage der Heidelberger Zeitung*, July 1910.
/METHOD/NATURPHILOSOPHIE

1910-16 **Schiff**, Julius. "Eine Begegnung zwischen Goethe und Berzelius." In *Stunden mit Goethe: Für die Freunde seiner Kunst und Weisheit*. Ed. Wilhelm Bode. Berlin: E. S. Mittler & Sohn, 1910, VI, 92-100.
Rpt. exp. edn. of No. 1909-26.
/BERZELIUS, J VON/CHEMISTRY

1910-17 **Schmidt**, W[ilhelm]. "Goethes Farbenlehre und die Dreifarbenphotographie (Zur Erinnerung an den 16. Mai 1810)." *Photographische Rundschau und Photographisches Centralblatt: Zeitschrift für Freunde der Photographie*, 24 (1910), 176-80.
/TECHNOLOGY/RESEARCH: CHROMATICS

1910-18 **Wasielewski**, Waldemar von. *Goethes meteorologische Studien.* Leipzig: Insel-Verlag, 1910. viii, 89 pp. Rev. Max Morris, *Euphorion*, 19 (1912), 397.
/METEOROLOGY/GOETHE'S COLLECTIONS

1910-19 **Wiesner**, Julius. "Goethes Urpflanze. (1901)." In his *Natur -- Geist -- Technik: Ausgewählte Reden, Vorträge und Essays.* Leipzig: Verlag von Wilhelm Engelmann, 1910, pp. 312-29. Rpt. of No. 1901-22.
/BOTANY

1911-1 **[anon.]** "Johann Wolfgang von Goethe: His Relation to Science and the Useful Arts." *Scientific American Supplement*, 72, No. 1855 (1911), 56.
/TECHNOLOGY/GENERAL INTRODUCTION

1911-2 **Biedenkapp**, Georg. "Watt, Darwins Großvater und Goethe." In his *James Watt und die Erfindung der Dampfmaschine: Eine biographische Skizze.* Stuttgart: Verlag der Technischen Monatshefte Franckh'sche Verlagshandlung, 1911, pp. 51-3.
/BIOLOGY/WATT, J/DARWIN, E

1911-3 **Bleek**, Walter van der. "Giordano Bruno -- Goethe." In his *Giordano Bruno--Goethe und das Christusproblem: Naturwissenschaft und Bibel.* Berlin: Verlag Neues Leben Wilhelm Borngraeber, 1911, pp. 65-163; 165-91.
/BRUNO, G/THEOLOGY/HISTORY OF SCIENCE

1911-4 **Dannemann**, Friedrich. "[Metamorphose der Pflanzen.]" In Dannemann, Friedrich. *Das Emporblühen der modernen Naturwissenschaften bis zur Entdeckung des Energieprinzipes.* Vol. 3 of *Die Naturwissenschaften in ihrer Entwicklung und in ihrem Zusammenhange dargestellt.* Leipzig: Verlag von Wilhelm Engelmann, 1911, pp. 357-9.
/MORPHOLOGY/BOTANY/RECEPTION

1911-5 ***Dees**[, ?]. "Goethes Ansichten über Arbeitstherapie." *Allgemeine Zeitschrift für Psychiatrie und psychisch-gerichtliche Medizin*, 68 (1911), 117ff.
/MEDICINE

1911-6 **Friedländer**, Salomo. "Goethe contra Newton." *Die Aktion*, 1 (1911), 722-3.

/CHROMATICS/NEWTON, I

1911-7 **Geitel**, Max. *Entlegene Spuren Goethes: Goethes Beziehungen zu der Mathematik, Physik, Chemie und deren Anwendung in der Technik, zum technischen Unterricht und zum Patentwesen.* München/Berlin: Druck und Verlag von R. Oldenbourg, 1911. viii, 215 pp.
    Rev. Payer v. Thurn, *Chronik des Wiener Goethe-Vereins*, 26 (1912), 44.
    Rev. Georg Witkowski, *Lit. Echo*, 15 (1912/1913), col. 1622.
    /GENERAL INTRODUCTION/TECHNOLOGY

1911-8 **Geitel**, Max. "Goethe als Techniker." *Die Welt der Technik*, 73 (1911), 3-7; 29-34.
    /TECHNOLOGY

1911-9 **Geitel**, Max. "Goethe als Techniker und Arbeitsminister." *Berliner Volks-Zeitung mit Täglichem Unterhaltungs-Blatt*, 59, No. 143 (1911), 2-3.
    /TECHNOLOGY

1911-10 **Geitel**, Max. "Goethe in seinen Beziehungen zur Technik." *Fünfte Beilage zur Vossischen Zeitung*, No. 288, 15 June 1911, 1.
    Rpt. No. 1911-11
    /TECHNOLOGY

1911-11 **Geitel**, Max. "Goethe in seinen Beziehungen zur Technik." *Verhandlungen des Vereins zur Beförderung des Gewerbefleißes*, 90 (1911), 348-70.
    Rpt. of No. 1911-10.
    /TECHNOLOGY

1911-12 **Geitel**, Max. "Goethe in seinen Beziehungen zur Technik und als Arbeitsminister Karl Augusts von Weimar." *Annalen für Gewerbe und Bauwesen*, 68 (1911), 148-60.
    Rpt. No. 1911-13.
    /TECHNOLOGY

1911-13 **Geitel**, Max. "Goethe in seinen Beziehungen zur Technik und als Arbeitsminister Karl Augusts von Weimar." *Unterhaltungs-Beilage der Deutschen Nachrichten, Berliner Tageszeitung*, 5, No. 73 (1911), 1.
    Rpt. of No. 1911-12.
    /TECHNOLOGY

1911-14 **Geitel**, Max. "Goethes Beziehungen zu der Luftschiffahrt." *Automobil- und Flugtechnische Zeitschrift*, 14 (1911), 17-18.
/TECHNOLOGY

1911-15 *__Grabein__, Paul. "Goethe als Bergmann." *Dortmunder Zeitung*, 5 April 1911.
/GEOLOGY/TECHNOLOGY

1911-16 **Gräf**, Hans Gerhard. *Goethe in Berka an der Ilm. Mit ungedruckten Briefen des Badeinspektors Schütz an Goethe.* Weimar: Verlag von Gustav Kiepenhauer, 1911. vi, 92 pp.
/PLACES: BERKA AN DER ILM/MEDICINE

1911-17 **Hecht**, Georg. "Goethe und Darwin." *Xenien: Eine Monatsschrift für literarische Ästhetik und Kritik*, 4 (1911), 268-75.
/DARWIN, C/BIOLOGY: EVOLUTION

1911-18 *__Helmers__, Heinrich. "Goethe als Techniker." *Anhalt. Staats-Anzeiger*, No. 284 (1911).
Rpt. Nos. 1911-19 and 1911-20.
/TECHNOLOGY

1911-19 *__Helmers__, Heinrich. "Goethe als Techniker." *Breslauer Zeitung*, No. 808 (1911).
Rpt. of No. 1911-18.
/TECHNOLOGY

1911-20 *__Helmers__, Heinrich. "Goethe als Techniker." *Düsseldorfer Zeitung*, 15 November 1911.
Rpt. of No. 1911-18.
/TECHNOLOGY

1911-21 **Hirsch**, Gottwald Chr[?]. "Goethe als Biologe." *Annalen der Naturphilosophie*, 11 (1911/1912), 307-61.
/BIOLOGY

1911-22 **Hoppe**, Hugo. "Goethe als Naturforscher (Nach seinen Reiseberichten). II." *Goethe*, 32 (1911), 130-53.
Continuation of No. 1909-13.
/GENERAL INTRODUCTION

1911-23 **Köbke**, P[?]. "Aus Jacob Berzelius: Själfbiografiska Anteckningar." *Goethe*, 32 (1911), 31.

204

/BERZELIUS, J VON/CHEMISTRY

1911-24 **Kohlbrugge**, J[acob]. H[ermann]. F[riedrich]. "Goethe als vergelijkend anatom [Goethe as a Comparative Anatomist]." *De Gids*, 75 (1911), 117-37.
Trans. into German, No. 1913-17.
In Dutch.
/COMPARATIVE ANATOMY

1911-25 **Kohlbrugge**, J[acob]. H[ermann]. F[riedrich]. "Was Goethe's natuurbeschouwing eene teleologische of eene mechanische? [Was Goethe's View of Nature Teleological or Mechanistic?]" *De Gids*, 75 (1911), 504-26.
In Dutch.
/NATURPHILOSOPHIE/PHILOSOPHY

1911-26 **Lucerna**, Camilla. "Goethes Naturphilosophie als Kunstwerk." *Annalen der Naturphilosophie*, 10 (1911), 192-206.
/WORKS: DAS MÄRCHEN/NATURPHILOSOPHIE

1911-27 **Möbius**, P[aul]. J[ulius]. "Bemerkungen zur Farbenlehre." In *Schopenhauer*. Vol. 4 of his *Ausgewählte Werke*. 3rd edn. Leipzig: Verlag von Johann Ambrosius Barth, 1911, pp. 273-82.
/CHROMATICS/SCHOPENHAUER, A/RECEPTION

1911-28 **Potonié**, Henry and Erich A. **Metze**. "Über Goethe's Stellung zur Deszendenztheorie." *Naturwissenschaftliche Wochenschrift*, NS 10, No. 32 (1911), 512.
/BIOLOGY: EVOLUTION/DARWIN, C

1911-29 **Runge**, F[riedlieb]. F[erdinand]. "Mein Besuch bei Goethe im Jahre 1819." In *Stunden mit Goethe: Für die Freunde seiner Kunst und Weisheit*. Ed. Wilhelm Bode. Berlin: E. S. Mittler & Sohn, 1911, 7, 29-44.
Rpt. of No. 1867-5.
/CHEMISTRY

1911-30 **Schelenz**, Hermann. "Sömmering und Goethe in der Casseler Anatomie." *Berliner Klinische Wochenschrift. Organ für praktische Aerzte*, 48 (1911), 649-51.
/SÖMMERING, S [VON]/MEDICINE

1911-31 **Schelling**, F[riedrich]. W[ilhelm]. J[oseph von]. "Ueber den Ursprung des allgemeinen Organismus." In his *Von der Weltseele*.

Ed. Otto Weiss. Philosophische Bibliothek, 133c. Leipzig: F. Meiner, 1911.
Rpt. of 1798-2.
/BOTANY/MORPHOLOGY/OPTICS/RESEARCH: BIOLOGY

1911-32 **Schiff**, Julius. "Alexander v. Humboldt in seinen Beziehungen zu Goethe." In *Stunden mit Goethe: Für die Freunde seiner Kunst und Weisheit*. Ed. Wilhelm Bode. Berlin: E. S. Mittler & Sohn, 1911, 7, 10-28.
/HUMBOLDT, A VON

1911-33 **Schiff**, Julius. "Der Chemiker J. W. Döbereiner und seine Beziehungen zu Goethe." In *Festschrift zur Jahrhundertfeier der Universität Breslau am 2. August 1911*. Breslau: Verlag von Trewendt & Granier[, 1911], 93-109.
"herausgegeben vom Schlesischen Philologenverein"
/DÖBEREINER, J/CHEMISTRY

1911-34 **Schuster**, Julius. "Goethes physisch-chemisch-mechanisches Problem." *Berichte der Deutschen Botanischen Gesellschaft*, 29 (1911), 722-8.
/CHEMISTRY

1911-35 **Semper**, Max. "Bemerkungen über Geschichte der Geologie und daraus resultierende Lehren." *Geologische Rundschau: Zeitschrift für allgemeine Geologie*, 2 (1911), 263-77.
/RESEARCH: GEOLOGY/GEOLOGY/RECEPTION

1911-36 **Wasiliewski**, Waldemar von. "Einleitung zu Goethes naturwissenschaftlichen Schriften." In *Goethes Werke. Vollständige Ausgabe*. 40 vols. Intro. and comm. Karl Alt. Berlin/Leipzig /Wien/Stuttgart: Bong, 1911, XXXVI, i-cxxi.
/GENERAL INTRODUCTION

1912-1 [anon.] "Goethe e la gomma scientifica [Goethe and Synthetic Rubber]." *Il Marzocco*, 17, No. 27 (1912), 5.
In Italian.
From the "Pall Mall Gazette."
/TECHNOLOGY

1912-2 [anon.] "Goethe und die 'Chymie'. Zu Goethes Todestag (28. August)." *Mainzer Tageblatt*, 26 August 1912.
/CHEMISTRY

1912-3 [anon.] "Goethe und die 'Chymie'. Zu Goethes Todestag (28. August)." *Täglicher Anzeiger, Elberfeld*, 29 August 1912.
/CHEMISTRY

1912-4 [anon.] "Goethe und die 'Chymie'. Zu Goethes Todestag (28. August)." *Tägliche Unterhaltungsbeilage zur Deutschen Tageszeitung*, 19, No. 199 (1912), 1-2.
/CHEMISTRY

1912-5 **Bois-Reymond**, Emil du. "Goethe und kein Ende." In *Reden von Emil du Bois-Reymond in zwei Bänden*. 2nd rev. and exp. edn. 2 vols. Leipzig: Verlag von Veit & Comp., 1912, II, pp. 157-83.
    Rpt. of No. 1886-1.
    "In der Aula der Berliner Universität am 15. Oktober 1882 gehaltene Rektoratsrede."
/GENERAL INTRODUCTION

1912-6 **Cann Lippincott**, R[?]. C. "Goethe's meteorology." *Quarterly Journal of the Royal Meteorological Society [London]*, 37, No. 165 (1912), 69.
/METEOROLOGY

1912-7 **Chamberlain**, Houston Stewart. "Der Naturforscher." In his *Goethe*. München: F. Bruckmann, 1912, pp. 241-387.
/GENERAL INTRODUCTION

1912-8 **Ebstein**, Erich. "Goethe über die Ursache der verschiedenen Länge der Schwänze." *Archiv für Geschichte der Naturwissenschaften und der Technik*, [3] (1912), 242.
/OSTEOLOGY/COMPARATIVE ANATOMY

1912-10 **Ebstein**, Erich. "Lichtenberg und Goethe über die Theorie der Farben." *Archiv für die Geschichte der Naturwissenschaften und der Technik*, 3, No. 1 (1912), 71-8.
/LICHTENBERG, G/CHROMATICS

1912-11 **Hahn**, F[?].-L[?]. "Goethe biologiste, médicin, psychologue et mystique: Etude et mystique: Etude psycho-pathologique." *Répertoire de Médecine internationale*, 2, No. 21 (1912), 22-7.
/BIOLOGY/MEDICINE/PSYCHOLOGY

1912-12 **Hirsch**, Gottwald Chr[?]. "Goethe als Biologe." *Annalen der Naturphilosophie*, 11, No. 4 (1912), 307-72.
/BIOLOGY

1912-13 *Kirchner, V[?]. "Haeckel und Goethe." *Geisteskampf der Gegenwart*, 48 (1912), 5-15.
/HAECKEL, E/DARWIN, C/BIOLOGY: EVOLUTION

1912-14 Kronenberg, M[oritz]. "Goethe." In his *Die Blütezeit des deutschen Idealismus: Von Kant bis Hegel*. Vol. 2 of his *Geschichte des Deutschen Idealismus*. München: C. H. Beck'sche Verlagsbuchhandlung Oskar Beck, pp. 389-423.
/NATURPHILOSOPHIE/MORPHOLOGY

1912-15 Morris, Max. "Anmerkungen." In *Schriften zur Naturwissenschaft*. Part 1. Intro. and notes Max Morris. Vol. 39 of *Goethes sämtliche Werke. Jubiläums-Ausgabe in 40 Bänden*. Ed. Eduard von der Hellen. Stuttgart and Berlin: J. G. Cotta'sche Buchhandlung Nachfolger[, 1912], pp. 345-81.
/GENERAL INTRODUCTION

1912-16 Morris, Max. "Anmerkungen." In *Schriften zur Naturwissenschaft*. Part 2. Intro. and notes Max Morris. Vol. 40 of *Goethes sämtliche Werke. Jubiläums-Ausgabe in 40 Bänden*. Ed. Eduard von der Hellen. Stuttgart and Berlin: J. G. Cotta'sche Buchhandlung Nachfolger[, 1912], pp. 323-43.
/GENERAL INTRODUCTION

1912-17 Morris, Max. "Einleitung." In *Schriften zur Naturwissenschaft*. Part 1. Intro. and notes Max Morris. Vol. 39 of *Goethes sämtliche Werke. Jubiläums-Ausgabe in 40 Bänden*. Ed. Eduard von der Hellen. Stuttgart and Berlin: J. G. Cotta'sche Buchhandlung Nachfolger[, 1912], pp. v-lii.
/GENERAL INTRODUCTION

1912-18 Morris, Max. "Goethe als Geologe." In *Schriften zur Naturwissenschaft*. Part 2. Intro. and notes Max Morris. Vol. 40 of *Goethes sämtliche Werke. Jubiläums-Ausgabe in 40 Bänden*. Ed. Eduard von der Hellen. Stuttgart and Berlin: J. G. Cotta'sche Buchhandlung Nachfolger[, 1912], pp. v-xx.
/GEOLOGY

1912-19 Morris, Max. "Goethe als Meteorologe." In *Schriften zur Naturwissenschaft*. Part 2. Intro. and notes Max Morris. Vol. 40 of *Goethes sämtliche Werke. Jubiläums-Ausgabe in 40 Bänden*. Ed. Eduard von der Hellen. Stuttgart and Berlin: J. G. Cotta'sche Buchhandlung Nachfolger[, 1912], pp. xx-xxviii.

/METEOROLOGY

1912-20 **Morris**, Max. "Goethes Farbenlehre." In *Schriften zur Natur-wissenschaft*. Part 2. Intro. and notes Max Morris. Vol. 40 of *Goethes sämtliche Werke. Jubiläums-Ausgabe in 40 Bänden*. Ed. Eduard von der Hellen. Stuttgart and Berlin: J. G. Cotta'sche Buchhandlung Nachfolger[, 1912], pp. xxxviii-l.
/CHROMATICS

1912-21 **Potonié**, Henry. "Historisches und Kritisches." In his *Grundlinien der Pflanzen-Morphologie im Lichte der Palaeontologie*. 2nd rev. edn. Jena: Verlag von Gustav Fischer, 1912, pp. 30-67.
Exp. rpt. of No. 1902-16.
/RESEARCH: BOTANY/RESEARCH: MORPHOLOGY

1912-22 **Reukauf**, Edmund. "Goethe als Mikroskopiker." *Mikrokosmos: Zeitschrift für praktische Arbeit auf dem Gebiet der Naturwissenschaften*, 6 (1912/1913), 163-5.
Rev. rpt. of No. 1906-22.
/GOETHE'S APPARATUS/GOETHE'S COLLECTIONS/MICROSCOPY

1912-23 *****Riedinger**, Franz. "Zur Beurteilung Schopenhauers durch Goethe in Eckermanns Gesprächen." *Das Wissen*, 6, No. 7 (1912).
/SCHOPENHAUER, A/CHROMATICS

1912-24 **Rotten**, Elisabeth. "Goethes Urphänomen und die platonische Idee." Diss. Marburg. Marburg, 1912. 53 pp.
Rpt. No. 1913-28.
Cf. response, No. 1914-28.
/NATURPHILOSOPHIE/PLATO

1912-25 **Schiff**, Julius. "Goethes chemische Berater und Freunde." *Deutsche Rundschau*, 38 (1912), 450-66.
Rpt. No. 1912-26.
/CHEMISTRY/DÖBEREINER, J

1912-26 **Schiff**, Julius. "Goethes chemische Berater und Freunde." *Halbmonatshefte der Deutschen Rundschau*, 3, No. 18 (1912), 453-69.
Rpt. of No. 1912-25.
/CHEMISTRY/BERZELIUS, J VON/DÖBEREINER, J/EINSIEDEL, A VON/GÖTTLING, J/MITSCHERLICH, E/RITTER, J/ROSE, H /SCHERER, A/SIEWER, ?

1912-27 **Semper**, Max. "Diluvium und prähistorische Menschheit bei Goethe und seinen Zeitgenossen." *Goethe*, 34 (1912), 21-33.
Rpt. of No. 1912-28.
/GEOLOGY

1912-28 **Semper**, Max. "Diluvium und prähistorische Menschheit bei Goethe und seinen Zeitgenossen." *Korrespondenz-Blatt der Deutschen Gesellschaft für Anthropologie, Ethnologie und Urgeschichte*, 43 (1912), 56-7.
Rpt. No. 1912-27.
/GEOLOGY

1912-29 **Stegemann**, Herbert. "Goethes Naturanschauung." *Tägliche Unterhaltungsbeilage zur Deutschen Tageszeitung*, 19, No. 143, 21 June 1912[, 2-3]; No. 144, 22 June 1912[, 2-3].
/NATURPHILOSOPHIE

1912-30 **Strachan**, R[?]. "Goethe's Meteorology." *Quarterly Journal of the Royal Meteorological Society [London]*, 38, No. 164 (1912), 314-16.
/METEOROLOGY

1912-31 **Urban**, Michael. "Goethe in Marienbad." *Prager Medizinische Wochenschrift*, 37 (1912), 352-9.
/GEOLOGY/PLACES: MARIENBAD

1912-32 **Urban**, Michael. "Graf Kaspar Sternberg und Marienbad." *Prager Medizinische Wochenschrift*, 37 (1912), 596-9.
/STERNBERG, K VON/PLACES: MARIENBAD /BOTANY/PALEONTOLOGY

1912-33 **Voigt**, Julius. *Goethe und Ilmenau*. Leipzig: Xenien-Verlag, 1912. 392 pp.
/GEOLOGY/TECHNOLOGY

1912-34 **Wasielewski**, Waldemar von. "Über Goethes naturwissenschaftliche Arbeiten, insbesondere die Farbenlehre." *Kosmos: Handweiser für Naturfreunde und Zentralblatt für das naturwissenschaftliche Bildungs- und Sammelwesen*, 9 (1912), 245-9.
/CHROMATICS/GENERAL INTRODUCTION

1912-35 **Zellner**, Julius. "Zur Spiraltendenz der Vegetation. (Mit einem ungedruckten Briefe von K. von Martius an Goethe.)" *Chronik des*

Wiener Goethe-Vereins, 26 (1912), 41-3.
/BOTANY/MARTIUS, K [VON]

1913-2 **Benecke**, Wilhelm. "Goethe. Begriff der 'Metamorphose' bei Goethe und seinen Vorgängern. Begriff der 'Metamorphose' in der heutigen Pflanzenmorphologie. Phylogenetische Grundlage der 'Metamorphose'. Metamorphose in der Ontogenie." In his *Morphologie und Entwicklungsgeschichte der Pflanzen. Die Kultur der Gegenwart: ihre Entwicklung und ihre Ziele*, Pt. 3, Section 4, vol. 2. Leipzig/Berlin: Druck und Verlag B. G. Teubner, 1913, pp. 185-92.
/MORPHOLOGY/RECEPTION/RESEARCH: MOR-PHOLOGY/BOTANY/RESEARCH: BOTANY

1913-3 **Blume**, Rudolf. "Die Medizin in Goethes 'Faust'." *Akademische Mitteilungen: Organ für die gesamten Interessen der Studentenschaft and der Albert-Ludwigs-Universität in Freiburg i. Br.*, NF 13 (1913), 48-9; 52-3.
Rpt. No. 1913-4.
/MEDICINE/WORKS: FAUST

1913-4 **Blume**, Rudolf. "Zur Medizin in Goethes 'Faust'." *Goethe*, 34 (1913), 197-8.
Rpt. of No. 1913-3.
/MEDICINE/WORKS: FAUST

1913-5 **Ebstein**, Erich. "Goethes Anteil an der Lehre von der Aphasie." *Zeitschrift für die gesamte Neurologie und Psychiatrie*, 17 (1913), 58-64.
/NEUROLOGY

1913-6 **Ebstein**, Erich. "Goethe über den Zwischenkiefer." *Archiv für Geschichte der Naturwissenschaften und der Technik*, 4 (1913), 167-8.
/OSTEOLOGY/COMPARATIVE ANATOMY

1913-7 **Ebstein**, Erich. "Goethe über die Beziehungen der Schilddrüse zu den weiblichen Geschlechtsorganen." *Mitteilungen zur Geschichte der Medizin und der Naturwissenschaften*, 12 (1913), 125-6.
/PHYSIOLOGY

1913-8 **Ebstein**, Erich. "Goethe über die Ursache der verschiedenen Länge der Schwänze." *Archiv für Geschichte der Naturwissenschaften und der Technik*, 1913, No. 4, 242.
/COMPARATIVE ANATOMY

1913-9 **Goebel**, K[arl von]. "Allgemeines über den Begriff Umbildung oder Metamorphose." In his *Allgemeine Organographie*. Pt. 1 of *Organographie der Pflanzen insbesondere der Archegoniaten und Samenpflanzen*. 2nd rev. edn. Jena: Verlag von Gustav Fischer, 1913, pp. 313-17.
/RESEARCH: MORPHOLOGY/RESEARCH: BOTANY
/MORPHOLOGY/BOTANY

1913-10 **Hansen**, A[dolph]. "Goethe der Natur-Erforscher." *Goethe*, 34 (1913), 15-20.
/GENERAL INTRODUCTION

1913-11 **Hertz**, Wilhelm. *Goethes Naturphilosophie im Faust: Ein Beitrag zur Erklärung der Dichtung von Wilhelm Hertz*. Mittlers Goethe-Bücherei. Berlin: Ernst Siegfried Mittler und Sohn, 1913. x, 162.
/NATURPHILOSOPHIE/WORKS: FAUST

1913-12 **Hertz**, Wilhelm. "Machen und Entstehen. Zur Naturphilosophie im 'Faust'." In *Stunden mit Goethe: Für die Freunde seiner Kunst und Weisheit*. Ed. Wilhelm Bode. Berlin: Ernst Siegfried Mittler und Sohn, 1913, IX, pp. 37-62.
/NATURPHILOSOPHIE/WORKS: FAUST

1913-13 **House**, Roy Temple. "Goethe and the Chemists." *Popular Science Monthly*, 82 (1913), 332-7.
/CHEMISTRY/BUCHHOLZ, H/GÖTTLING, J
/DÖBEREINER, J

1913-14 **Kaemmerer**, Paul. "Die künstlerische, soziale und wirtschaftliche Bedeutung einer Wissenschaft der Maltechnik." *Technische Mitteilungen für Malerei*, 29 (1913/1914), 7-10.
/CHROMATICS/RESEARCH: FINE ARTS

1913-15 **Kaemmerer**, Paul. "Das Licht und seine Wirkungen: ein formales Gesetz des Intellekts: eine Erkenntnis a priori." *Jahrbuch der Schopenhauer-Gesellschaft*, 2 (1913), 126-40.
/CHROMATICS/OPTICS/SCHOPENHAUER, A/RESEARCH:
CHROMATICS/RESEARCH: OPTICS

1913-16 **Kerner von Marilaun**, Anton and Adolph **Hansen**. "Die Metamorphosenlehren und die Morphologie." In their *Der Bau und die lebendigen Eigenschaften der Pflanzen (Zellenlehre und Biologie der*

Ernährung). Vol. 1 of *Pflanzenleben*. 3rd rev. edn. Leipzig/Wien: Bibliographisches Institut
/RESEARCH: MORPHOLOGY/RESEARCH: BOTANY

1913-17 **Kohlbrugge**, J[acob]. H[ermann]. F[riedrich]. *Historisch-kritische Studien über Goethe als Naturforscher*. Würzburg: Curt Kabitzsch, 1913. v, 154 pp.
German trans. of No. 1911-24.
Rev. Richard Meszlény, *Grenzbote*, 72 (1913), 610.
Rev. Max Semper, *Frankfurter Zeitung*, 4 May 1918.
/GENERAL INTRODUCTION/GEOLOGY/COMPARATIVE ANATOMY

1913-18 **Kohut**, Adolph. "Goethes Beziehungen zu Franzensbad." *Goethe*, 34 (1913), 101-17.
/GEOLOGY/PLACES: FRANZENSBAD

1913-19 **Lindner**, Albert. "Goethe in der Saline zu Sulza." In *Stunden mit Goethe: Für die Freunde seiner Kunst und Weisheit*. Ed. Wilhelm Bode. Berlin: Ernst Siegfried Mittler und Sohn, 1913, IX, pp. 208-19.
/GEOLOGY

1913-20 **Lippmann**, Edmund O. von. "Encheiresis naturae." In his *Abhandlungen und Vorträge zur Geschichte der Naturwissenschaften*. 2 vols. Leipzig: Verlag von Veit & Comp., 1913, pp. 439-49.
Rpt. of No. 1907-20.
/WORKS: FAUST/CHEMISTRY

1913-21 **Lorenz**, Richard and A[?]. **Höchberg**. "Die Stellung Goethes in der Geschichte der Entdeckung des photographischen Effekts." *Archiv für die Geschichte der Naturwissenschaften und der Technik*, 4 (1913), 323-7.
/CHEMISTRY

1913-22 **May**, Walther. "Der Sinn der Pflanzenmetamorphose bei Goethe." *Die Naturwissenschaften: Wochenschrift für die Fortschritte der Naturwissenschaften, der Medizin, und der Technik*, 1 (1913), 982-5.
Cf. No. 1913-29.
/MORPHOLOGY/BOTANY

1913-23 **Mayer**, Karl. "Dendrologische Notizen aus dem botanischen Garten in Padua." *Mitteilungen der Deutschen Dendrologischen*

Gesellschaft, 1913, pp. 315-16.
/BOTANY/INSTITUTIONS: ORTO BOTANICO, PADOVA

1913-24 **Moeller**, G[?]. H. "Goethe als Naturforscher." *Abhandlungen und Bericht LIII des Vereins für Naturkunde zu Cassel e. V. über das 74.-76. Vereinsjahr 1909-1912.* Ed. B. Schaefer. Cassel: Verlag des Vereins, 1913, pp. 1-43.
"Vortrag im Naturwissenschaftlichen Verein Schweinfurt am Mittwoch, den 20. Januar 1909."
/GENERAL INTRODUCTION

1913-25 ***Reitmayer**, C[?]. A. "Goethe als Seetierbeobachter." *Blätter für Terrarien- und Aquarienkunde*, 24 (1913), 200.
/OCEANOGRAPHY

1913-26 ***Reukauf**, E[?]. "Goethe und das Mikroskop." *Mikrokosmos*, 6 (1913), 234-9.
/MICROSCOPY/GOETHE'S APPARATUS

1913-27 **Riedinger**, Franz. "Über die Auslegung einer vermeintlich sich auf Schopenhauer beziehenden Stelle in Eckermanns Gesprächen mit Goethe." *Jahrbuch der Schopenhauer-Gesellschaft*, 2 (1913), 182-8.
/SCHOPENHAUER, A/CHROMATICS

1913-28 **Rotten**, Elisabeth. *Goethes Urphänomen und die platonische Idee.* Philosophische Arbeiten herausgegeben von Hermann Cohen in Berlin und Paul Natorp in Marburg, 8.1. Giessen: Verlag von Alfred Töpelmann (vormals J. Ricker), 1913. iv, 132 pp.
Exp. rpt. of No. 1912-24.
/NATURPHILOSOPHIE/PLATO

1913-29 **Schneider**, Karl Camillo. "Zu Herrn Prof. Mays Artikel: Der Sinn der Pflanzenmetamorphose bei Goethe." *Die Naturwissenschaft*, 1 (1913), 1101.
Cf. No. 1913-22.
/MORPHOLOGY/BOTANY

1913-30 **Scholz**, Heinrich. "Goethes Urphänomen." *Preussische Jahrbücher*, 154 (1913), 327-33.
/METHOD

1913-31 **Semper**, Max. "Goethe als Naturforscher: Eine Ausstellung im Senckenberg-Museum." *Frankfurter Zeitung*, 4 May 1913.
In Mappe III E 61/C20: "Goethe und die Naturwissenschaften.

Zeitungsausschnitte 1913 -" at the Frankfurter Goethe-Museum.
/EXHIBITION

1913-32 **Siegel**, Carl. "Goethe." In his *Geschichte der deutschen Natur-philosophie*. Leipzig: Akademische Verlagsgesellschaft, 1913, pp. 150-81.
/NATURPHILOSOPHIE

1913-33 **Totzauer**, Robert J. "Goethes geologische Sammlungen aus Böhmen im Stifte Tepl." *Lotos. Naturwissenschaftliche Zeitschrift*, 61 (1913), 169-80; 211-24; 233-47.
/GOETHE'S COLLECTIONS/GEOLOGY/INSTITUTIONS: STIFT TEPL

1913-34 **Tschermak-Seysenegg**, Armin von. "Die führenden Ideen der Physiologie der Gegenwart." *Münchener medizinische Wochenschrift*, 60 (1913), 2328-32.
/RESEARCH: CHROMATICS/RESEARCH: PHYSIOLOGY

1913-35 **Velenovsky**, Josef. *Vergleichende Morphologie der Pflanzen. IV. Teil (Supplement)*. Prag: Verlagsbuchhandlung von Fr. Rivnác, 1913. 224 pp.
Supplement to No. 1905-25.
/RESEARCH: MORPHOLOGY/RESEARCH: BOTANY /MORPHOLOGY/BOTANY

1913-36 **Zellner**, Julius. 9 "Zur Spiraltendenz der Vegetation. (Mit einem ungedruckten Briefe von K. v. Martius an Goethe.)" *Chronik des Wiener Goethe-Vereins*, 26 (1912), 41-3.
/MARTIUS, K [VON]/BOTANY

1913-37 **Zimmermann**, Felix. "Die Wiederspiegelung der Technik in der deutschen Dichtung von Goethe bis zur Gegenwart." Inaug.-Diss. Leipzig. Dresden: Druck von W. Ulrich, 1913. 159 pp.
L of C PT 134.I4Z5
/TECHNOLOGY

1914-1 **[anon.]** "Eine österreichische Stimme über Goethe." *Chronik des Wiener Goethe-Vereins*, 27, No. 5/6 (1914), 44.
/MINERALOGY/PLACES: KARLSBAD

1914-1a **Briefwechsel** *zwischen Goethe und Johann Wolfgang Döbereiner (1810-1830)*. Ed. and comm. Julius Schiff. Weimar: Hermann

Böhlaus Nachfolger, 1914. xxxv, 144 pp.
/DÖBEREINER, J/CHEMISTRY

1914-2 **Buchner**, Georg. "Zu Goethes Farbenlehre." *Münchner Kunsttechnische Blätter: Beilage zur "Werkstatt der Kunst"*, 10, No. 16 (1914), 78-9; No. 23 (1914), 107-8.
/CHROMATICS

1914-3 **Bulle**, Ferdinand. " Zur Struktur des Pantheismus: Die Kategorie der Totalität in Goethes naturwissenschaftlichen Schriften." *Euphorion*, 21 (1914), 156-82.
/NATURPHILOSOPHIE/EPISTEMOLOGY

1914-4 **Dilthey**, Wilhelm. "Aus der Zeit der Spinozastudien Goethes." In his *Weltanschauung und Analyse des Menschen seit Reinaissance und Reformation*. Vol. 2 of his *Gesammelte Schriften*. Leipzig/Berlin: Verlag von B. G. Teubner, 1914, II, 391-415.
Rpt. of No. 1894-5.
/NATURPHILOSOPHIE/SPINOZA, B

1914-5 **Driesmans**, Heinrich. "Goethes Farbenlehre, ein Stück germanischer Weltanschauung." *Technische Mitteilungen für Malerei*, 31, No. 15 (1914/1915), 133-5.
Rpt. of No. 1901-5.
Cf. Nos. 1916-22 and -41.
/CHROMATICS

1914-6 *****Emrich**, Arnold. "Goethe and Schopenhauer on Mathematics." *Open Court*, 28 (1914), 521-8.
/MATHEMATICS/SCHOPENHAUER, A

1914-7 *****[Goethe**, J. W. von.] "Priroda [Natur]." Trans. A[?]. G. Genkel'. In E. Gekkel' [Haeckel]. *Estestvennaia istoriia mirotvoreniia*, 1914, pp. 14-18.
[Zhitomirskaia 2192]
/TRANSLATION: RUSSIAN

1914-8 **Gräf**, Hans Gerhard. "Louis Strohmeyer bei Goethe. Ein Nachtrag zu 'Goethes Gesprächen'." *Goethe*, 1 (1914), 145-51.
/STROMEYER, L/MEDICINE

1914-9 **Hansen**, Adolph. "Die Aufstellung von Goethe's naturwissenschaftlichen Sammlungen im Neubau des Goethehauses zu Weimar." *Die Naturwissenschaften: Wochenschrift für die Fortschritte der*

Naturwissenschaften, der Medizin und der Technik, 2 (1914), 575-81.
/GOETHE'S COLLECTIONS/EXHIBITION

1914-10 **Hansen**, Adolph. "Goethe's naturwissenschaftliche Sammlungen im Neubau des Goethehauses zu Weimar." *Naturwissenschaftliche Wochenschrift*, 29 [NS 13] (1914), 577-9.
/GOETHE'S COLLECTIONS

1914-11 **Heyse**, Paul. "Goethe als Naturforscher." In his *Gedichte von Paul Heyse*. 2 vols in one. 9th edn. Stuttgart/Berlin: J. G. Cotta'sche Buchhandlung Nachfolger, 1914, I, 253.
A poem.
/GENERAL INTRODUCTION

1914-12 **Himmelbaur**, Wolfgang, Otto **Storch** and Alfred **Himmelbauer**. "Goethe als Naturforscher." *Wochenschrift für Volksbildung: Urania*, 7, No. 1/3 (1914), 9-12; No. 4/6 (1914), 21-4; No. 7 (1914), 42-5.
/GENERAL INTRODUCTION

1914-13 **Hoppe**, J[ohannes]. "Bemerkung zu Horns Artikel über Goethes Farbenlehre." *Technische Mitteilungen für Malerei*, 31, No. 11 (1914/1915), 98.
Response to No. 1914-16.
/CHROMATICS/HORN, C

1914-14 **Hoppe**, J[ohannes]. "Glossen." *Technische Mitteilungen für Malerei*, 31, No. 15 (1914/1915), 130-31.
Response to Horn's many articles published in the same journal in 1914.
/CHROMATICS/HORN, C

1914-15 **Horn**, Carl. "Die Erhaltung der Energie (Wechsel-Folge von Systole und Diastole) als 2. Urphänomen der Energetik." *Technische Mitteilungen für Malerei*, 31, No. 15 (1914/1915), 131-2; No. 16 (1914/1915), 138-40; No. 17 (1914/1915), 150-51.
/RESEARCH: PHYSICS/RESEARCH: CHROMATICS /PHYSICS/CHROMATICS

1914-16 **Horn**, Carl. "Geschichtliche Materialien zur Diskussion über Goethes Farbenlehre." *Technische Mitteilungen für Malerei*, 31, No. 5 (1914/1915), 37-9; No. 6 (1914/1915), 54-6; No. 7 (1914/1915), 62-3.
Cf. response, No. 1914-13.
/CHROMATICS/RECEPTION/HISTORY OF SCIENCE

1914-17 **Horn**, Carl. *Goethe als Energetiker: Verglichen mit den Energetikern Robert Mayer, Ottomar Rosenbach, Ernst Mach.* Leipzig: Verlag von Johann Ambrosius Barth, 1914. 91 pp.
/PHYSICS/CHROMATICS/MAYER, R/ROSENBACH, O
/MACH, E

1914-18 **Horn**, Carl. "Goethes Farbenlehre und die Physik der Gegenwart." *Technische Mitteilungen für Malerei*, 31, No. 1 (1914/1915), 2-4.
/CHROMATICS/PHYSICS/RECEPTION

1914-19 **Horn**, Carl. "Systole-Diastole (Er. . ., Ent. . .) als Erstes Urphänomen der Energetik." *Technische Mitteilungen für Malerei*, 31, No. 11 (1914/1915), 98-100; No. 12, (1914/1915), 106-8; No. 13 (1914/1915), 114-15.
/RESEARCH: PHYSICS/RESEARCH: CHROMATICS-
/PHYSICS /CHROMATICS

1914-20 **Horn**, Carl. "Das 'Weiß' der Physiker: Eine Anfrage an die Maler." *Technische Mitteilungen für Malerei*, 31, No. 21 (1914/1915), 180.
/RESEARCH: CHROMATICS/CHROMATICS/FINE ARTS

1914-21 **Kaemmerer**, Paul. "Licht-Raum: das Urbild (platonische Idee) der Materie und Energie." *Technische Mitteilungen für Malerei*, 31, No. 19-24 (1914/1915), 161-4; 171-3; 177-9; 187-8; 194-7; 204-7.
Cf. continuations, Nos. 1915-37 and 1916-44.
/RESEARCH: PHYSICS/RESEARCH: CHROMATICS

1914-22 **Kaemmerer**, Paul. "Das 'Weiß' der Physiker: Eine Antwort und Anfrage an die Physiker." *Technische Mitteilungen für Malerei*, 31, No. 24 (1914/1915), 201-3.
Cf. continuation, No. 1915-41.
/RESEARCH: CHROMATICS/CHROMATICS

1914-23 **König**, Berthold. "Goethes Homunculus." *Oesterreichische Chemiker-Zeitung*, 28 (1914), 250-57.
/ALCHEMY/WORKS: FAUST

1914-24 **Kohlbrugge**, J[?]. H. F. "Goethes Stellung zum Entwicklungsgedanken." *Die Naturwissenschaften: Wochenschrift für die Fortschritte der Naturwissenschaften, der Medizin, und der Technik*, 2 (1914), 849-54.

/BIOLOGY: EVOLUTION

1914-25 **Kohlbrugge**, J[?]. H. F. "Historisch-kritische Studien über Goethe als Naturforscher." *Zoologische Annalen*, 2 (1914), 213-16. Rev. E. Radl, *Isis*, 2 (1914), 123-16.
/GENERAL INTRODUCTION

1914-26 **Kühn**, Hugo. "Goethe und der Ilmenauer Bergbau." In his *Kulturgeschichtliche Bilder aus Thüringen*. Leipzig: Dieterich'sche Verlagsbuchhandlung, 1914, pp. 35-40.
/TECHNOLOGY/GEOLOGY

1914-27 **Lehrs**, Philipp. "Goethes naturwissenschaftliche Sammlungen." *Frankfurter Zeitung*, No. 104, 15 April 1914.
/GOETHE'S COLLECTIONS

1914-28 **Misch**, Georg. "Goethe, Plato, Kant. Eine Kritik." *Logos*, 5 (1914/1915), 276-89.
Response to No. 1912-24.
/PLATO/KANT, I/NATURPHILOSOPHIE

1914-29 ***Mühlethaler**, J[?]. "Goethes wissenschaftliche Methode und ihre Bedeutung für die heutige Forschung." *Nord und Süd*, 149 (1914), 56-72.
/METHOD

1914-30 **Müller**, Oskar. "Goethes 'Entdeckung' des Zwischenkieferknochens." *Wissenschaftliche Beilage der Leipziger Zeitung*, No. 25, 20 June 1914, 97-8.
/OSTEOLOGY/COMPARATIVE ANATOMY

1914-31 **Petersen**, Peter. *Goethe und Aristoteles*. Berlin/ Braunschweig/Hamburg: Verlag von George Westermann, 1914. iv, 58 pp.
/ARISTOTLE/NATURPHILOSOPHIE

1914-32 **Schopper**, Alfred. "Reußisches in Goethes Sammlungen." Gera: Geraer Verlagsanstalt und Druckerei, 1914. 8 pp.
"Abdruck as Nr. 131 der Fürstl. Reuß-Geraer Zeitung vom 7. Juni 1914."
/GOETHE'S COLLECTIONS/PLACES: REUSS

1914-33 **Semper**, Max. *Die geologischen Studien Goethes: Beiträge zur Biographie Goethes und zur Geschichte und Methodenlehre der Geologie*. Leipzig: Verlag von Veit u. Comp., 1914. xii, 389 pp.

"Bearbeitet im Auftrag des Goethe-National-Museums in Weimar: herausgegeben mit der Unterstützung der Goethe-Gesellschaft und der Rheinischen Gesellschaft für wissenschaftliche Forschung."
/GEOLOGY

1914-34 **Siegel**, Carl. "Goethe und die spekulative Naturphilosophie." *Kant-Studien*, 19 (1914), 488-96.
"Vortrag im Wiener Goethe-Verein, gehalten am 10. Januar 1914."
/NATURPHILOSOPHIE

1914-35 **Speyerer**, Kurt. "Goethes physikalische Sammlungen im Neubau des Weimarer Goethehauses." *Geschichtsblätter für Technik, Industrie und Gewerbe*, 1 (1914), 134-42.
/GOETHE'S COLLECTIONS/GOETHE'S APPARATUS

1914-36 ***Stein**, Robert. "Goethes naturwissenschaftliche Sammlungen." *Literarische Beilage der Kölnischen Volks-Zeitung*, 13 April 1916.
/GOETHE'S COLLECTIONS/GOETHE'S APPARATUS

1914-37 **Thomas**, Friedrich A. W. "Die Deutung der 'blitzenden Blüten' bei Schleiermacher und Goethe." In his *Das Elisabeth Linné-Phänomen (sogennantes Blitzen der Blüten) und seine Deutungen: Zur Anregung und Aufklärung, zunächst für Botaniker und Blumenfreunde.* Jena: Verlag von Gustav Fischer, 1914, pp. 32-9.
/CHROMATICS/RESEARCH: CHROMATICS/BOTANY /RESEARCH: BOTANY /SCHLEIERMACHER, F

1914-38 ***Tibal**, A[?]. "Goethe et les sciences de la nature." *Revue du Mois*, 19 Febr. 1914.
/GENERAL INTRODUCTION

1914-39 **Zaunick**, Rudolph. "Goethe und Vicq-d'Azyr. Ein Beitrag zur Zwischenkieferfrage." *Mathematisch-Naturwissenschaftliche Blätter*, 11, No. 1/2 (1914), 2-4.
/OSTEOLOGY/COMPARATIVE ANATOMY/VICQ D'AZYR, F

1914-40 **Ziegler**, Theobald. "Goethe und die Natur." In his *Goethes Welt- und Lebensanschauung.* Berlin: Georg Reimer, 1914, pp. 40-53.
/NATURPHILOSOPHIE

1915-1 [anon.] "Aus den uns zugegangenen zustimmenden Äußerungen zu dem in den 'T. M. f. M.' geführten Kampfe für Goethes Licht- und Farbenlehre." *Technische Mitteilungen für Malerei*, 32 (1915/1916), 154-5.
/CHROMATICS/RESEARCH: CHROMATICS

1915-2 [anon.] "Die Finsternis als Naturkraft: Nachtrag zu dem Aufsatz in Nr. 15. Jg. XXXII." *Technische Mitteilungen für Malerei*, 15 (1915/1916), 200.
Cf. No. 1915-17.
/CHROMATICS/ROSENBACH, O/BRASS, A

1915-3 [anon.] "Goethes Selbstbekenntnis und seine Forderung an die Nachwelt." *Technische Mitteilungen für Malerei*, 32, No. 10/11 (1915), 73-4.
/CHROMATICS

1915-4 [anon.] "H. von Helmholtz über Goethes Farbenlehre." *Münchner Kunsttechnische Blätter*, 11, Nos. 13-15, 5-19 April 1915, 56-8; 62-3; 68-70.
/CHROMATICS/HELMHOLTZ, H VON

1915-5 *Bergmann, Ernst. "Goethe und der fliegende Mensch." *Der Tag*, No. 263 (1915).
/TECHNOLOGY

1915-6 Bücken, Ernst. "Die Grundlagen der Goetheschen Tonlehre." *Technische Mitteilungen für Malerei*, 32, No. 16/17 (1915/1916), 137-9.
/MUSICOLOGY

1915-7 Carus, Paul. *Goethe, with special consideration of his Philosophy*. Chicago: Open Court Publishing Co., 1915. xi, 357 pp.
/GENERAL INTRODUCTION/PHILOSOPHY

1915-8 Dupré, Fr[?]. "Goethe und die Chemie." *Das Polytechnikum [Köthner Akademische Blätter]*, 8 (1915/1916), 81-3; 90-91.
Cf. continuation, No. 1916-13.
/CHEMISTRY

1915-9 F[?].-D[?], [?]. "Die Farbenfibel von Wilhelm Ostwald." *Münchner Kunsttechnische Blätter*, 13, No. 19, 11 June 1917, 110-12.
Rpt. of No. 1915-10.

/CHROMATICS/OSTWALD, W/RESEARCH: CHROMATICS

1915-10 *F[?].-D[?], [?]. "Die Farbenfibel von Wilhelm Ostwald." *Neue Züricher Zeitung*, 22 February 1917.
Rpt. No. 1915-9.
/CHROMATICS/OSTWALD, W/RESEARCH: CHROMATICS

1915-11 **Fritzsche**, Günther. "Der Zwischenkiefer im Lichte der anatomisch-geschichtlichen Forschung." *Deutsche Zahnärztliche Wochenschrift*, 18 (1915), 309-13; 325-7; 333-6.
/RESEARCH: OSTEOLOGY/RESEARCH: COMPARATIVE ANATOMY

1915-12 *[**Goethe**, J. W. von.] "Goethes Regeln für Badereisen." *Kölner Zeitung*, 3 June 1915, No. 664.
/MEDICINE

1915-13 **Henning**, Hans. "Goethe." In *Ernst Mach als Philosoph, Physiker und Psycholog: Eine Monographie*. Leipzig: Verlag von Johann Ambrosius Barth, 1915, pp. 166-74.
/MACH, E/PHILOSOPHY

1915-14 **Hoppe**, Joh[annes]. "Beiträge zur Erörterung der Frage, ob die heute geltende Lehre von Licht und Farbe abzuschaffen sei." *Technische Mitteilungen für Malerei*, 32, No. 14/15 (1915/1916), 121-2.
Cf. response, No. 1915-33.
/CHROMATICS/RESEARCH: CHROMATICS/HORN, C/KÄMMERER, P

1915-15 **Horn**, Carl. "Die bisherige Lichteinheit und Lichtmessung (Subjektive oder objektive Photometrie?)." *Technische Mitteilungen für Malerei*, 32 (1915/1916), 5-8.
/RESEARCH: PHYSICS/CHROMATICS

1915-16 **Horn**[, Carl]. "'Brechbarkeit' oder: 'Energie und Transformator'?" *Technische Mitteilungen für Malerei*, 32 (1915 /1916), 198-200.
/RESEARCH: PHYSICS/RESEARCH: CHROMATICS

1915-17 **Horn**, Carl. "Die Finsternis als Natur-Kraft. Wirkendes Licht -->, gegen (rück)wirkende Finsternis <--." *Technische Mitteilungen für Malerei*, 32, No. 15 (1915/1916), 130-32.
Cf. Nos. 1915-2 and 1915-33.
/RESEARCH: PHYSICS/RESEARCH: CHROMATICS

/CHROMATICS

1915-18 **Horn[, Carl]**. "Goethe-Journalistik oder Goethe-Forschung?"
Technische Mitteilungen für Malerei, 32 (1915/1916), 145.
/CHROMATICS

1915-19 **Horn, Carl**. "Die Lichtelektrizität an festen Körpern, Gasen und
Farbstoffen, ± Elektrische Wirkungen durch Belichtung --> und
Verdunklung <--." *Technische Mitteilungen für Malerei*, 32, No.
10/11 [Goethe-Nummer] (1915/1916), 77-81.
/RESEARCH: PHYSICS/RESEARCH: CHROMATICS

1915-20 **Horn, Carl**. "Licht -- Finsternis, Leichte -- Schwere, Wärme --
Kälte usw. --> <-- als verwandte Naturkräfte und -- Gegenkräfte."
Technische Mitteilungen für Malerei, 32, No. 16/17 (1915/1916),
143-5.
/RESEARCH: PHYSICS/RESEARCH: CHROMATICS

1915-21 **Horn[, Carl]**. "Licht--Jupiter Goethe?" *Technische Mitteilungen
für Malerei*, 32 (1915/1916), 150-51.
/CHROMATICS

1915-22 **Horn, Carl**. "Die Maler, die Physiker und das Licht: Ein Wort
zur gegenseitigen Verständigung." *Technische Mitteilungen für
Malerei*, 32, No. 13 (1915/1916), 114-15.
Rpt. No. 1916-32.
/RESEARCH: CHROMATICS/RESEARCH:
PHYSICS/RESEARCH: FINE ARTS

1915-23 **Horn, Carl**. "Die Physiker, die Physiologen und das Licht."
Technische Mitteilungen für Malerei, 32, No. 14 (1915/1916), 124-6.
/RESEARCH: PHYSICS/RESEARCH: CHROMATICS
/RESEARCH: PHYSIOLOGY/CHROMATICS

1915-24 **Horn[, Carl]**. "Robert Mayer--Goethe: Zwei Ehrenpflichten der
deutschen Wissenschaft." *Technische Mitteilungen für Malerei*, 32,
No. 10/11 [Goethe-Nummer], (1915 /1916), 75-6.
/PHYSICS/CHROMATICS/MAYER, R

1915-25 **Horn[, Carl]**. "(Stoffloser) Lichtäther oder (stofflicher)
Lichtwiderstand?" *Technische Mitteilungen für Malerei*, 32, No.
22/23 (1915/1916), 197-8.
/RESEARCH: PHYSICS/RESEARCH: CHROMATICS
/CHROMATICS

1915-26 **Horn**, Carl. "Tatsachen-Material zur Dynamik des Lichtes."
Technische Mitteilungen für Malerei, 32, No. 2 (1915/1916), 9; No. 3
(1915/1916), 17; No. 4 (1915/1916), 25; No. 5 (1915/1916), 33; No.
6 (1915/1916), 41; No. 7 (1915/ 1916), 49; No. 8 (1915/1916), 61;
No. 9 (1915/1916), 65.
/RESEARCH: PHYSICS/RESEARCH: CHROMATICS
/CHROMATICS

1915-27 **Horn**, Carl. "Was fehlt unserer heutigen Chaos-Physik im
Vergleich zu Goethes Ordnungs- und Analogie-Physik?" *Technische
Mitteilungen für Malerei*, 32, No. 18/19 (1915/1916), 167-9; No. 20
(1915/1916), 176-8; No. 21 (1915/1916), 189-91.
/RESEARCH: PHYSICS/RESEARCH: CHROMATICS
/PHYSICS /CHROMATICS/METHOD

1915-28 **Horn**[, Carl]. "Weitere Anerkennungen von Goethes Farben-
lehre durch die Fachwissenschaft." *Technische Mitteilungen für
Malerei*, 32, No. 10/11 [Goethe-Nummer] (1915/1916), 76-7.
/CHROMATICS/RECEPTION/RESEARCH: CHROMATICS

1915-29 **Horn**[, Carl]-**Kaemmerer**[, Paul]. "Goethes Selbstbekenntnis
und seine Forderung an die Nachwelt." *Technische Mitteilungen für
Malerei*, 32, No. 10/11 [Goethe-Nummer] (1915 /1916), 73-4.
/CHROMATICS

1915-30 **Horn**[, Carl]-**Kaemmerer**[, Paul]. "Welches sind die Unter-
schiede zwischen Goethes und Newtons Licht- und Farbenlehre?"
Technische Mitteilungen für Malerei, 32 (1915/1916), 74-5.
/CHROMATICS/NEWTON, I

1915-31 **Horn**[, Carl]-**Kaemmerer**[, Paul]. "Zur Antwort des Herrn
Geh. Rats Dr. Wilhelm Ostwald auf die in Nr. 14 an ihn gerichtete
Frage: Goethes oder Newtons Licht- und Farbenlehre?" *Technische
Mitteilungen für Malerei*, 32, No. 18/19 (1915 /1916), 163-7.
/CHROMATICS/OSTWALD, W/NEWTON, I

1915-32 **Kaemmerer**, Paul. "An unsere Leser! (Zum 32. Jahrgang der
Techn. Mitt.)" *Technische Mitteilungen für Malerei*, 32 (1915/1916),
1-2.
/CHROMATICS/RESEARCH: CHROMATICS/RESEARCH:
FINE ARTS

1915-33 **Kaemmerer**, Paul. "Beantwortung der oben angeführten Fragen

Dr. Hoppes." *Technische Mitteilungen für Malerei*, 32, 15 (1915/1916), 132-4.
>Response to No. 1915-14.
>Cf. No. 1915-17.
>/CHROMATICS/HOPPE, J

1915-34 **Kaemmerer**, Paul. "Für die Kunstanschauungen Meier-Graefes?" *Technische Mitteilungen für Malerei*, 32, No. 10/11 [Goethe-Nummer] (1915/1916), 81-94.
>/MEIER-GRAEFE, J/CHROMATICS/FINE ARTS/NEWTON, I /NIETZSCHE, F

1915-35 **Kaemmerer**, Paul. "Goethe--Kant--Dürer oder Meier-Graefe? Eine Anfrage an Herrn Prof. Lovis Corinth." *Technische Mitteilungen für Malerei*, 32, No. 14 (1915/1916), 122-4.
>/CORINTH, L/CHROMATICS/NEWTON, I/MEIER-GRAEFE, J/KANT, I /DÜRER, A

1915-36 **Kaemmerer**, Paul. "Goethes oder Newtons Licht- und Farbenlehre? Eine öffentliche Anfrage an Herrn Geheimrat Wilhelm Ostwald." *Technische Mitteilungen für Malerei*, 32, No. 14 (1915/1916), 121-2.
>/CHROMATICS/NEWTON, I/OSTWALD, W

1915-37 **Kaemmerer**, Paul. "Licht-Raum: das Urbild (platonische Idee) der Materie und Energie." *Technische Mitteilungen für Malerei*, 32, Nos. 2-9; 13, 15-23 (1915/1916), 13-15; 22-4; 27-30; 36-8; 43-5; 52-4; 62-3; 67-70; 115-17; 135-6; 146-50; 169-72; 178-81; 194-5; 204-5.
>Continuation of No. 1914-21.
>Continuation No. 1916-44.
>/RESEARCH: PHYSICS/RESEARCH: CHROMATICS

1915-38 **Kaemmerer**, Paul. "Newtons angebliche Herstellung des Weißen aus Farbstoffen." *Technische Mitteilungen für Malerei*, 32, No. 10/11 [Goethe-Nummer] (1915/1916), 94-103.
>/CHROMATICS/NEWTON, I

1915-39 **Kaemmerer**, Paul. "Goethes oder Newtons Farbenlehre? (Eine öffentliche Anfrage an Herrn Geheimrat Wilhelm Ostwald.)." *Technische Mitteilungen für Malerei*, 32 (1915 /1916), 201.
>/CHROMATICS/NEWTON, I/OSTWALD, W

1915-40 **Kaemmerer**, Paul. "Überschwenglichkeiten oder Wahrheit? Ein Beitrag zu deutscher Kunstwissenschaft, Kunstkritik, und

Kunstschriftstellerei." *Technische Mitteilungen für Malerei*, 32 (1915/1916), 126-8.
/MEIER-GRAEFE, J/CHROMATICS/NEWTON, I

1915-41 **[Kaemmerer**, Paul.] "Das 'Weiß' der Physiker." *Technische Mitteilungen für Malerei*, 32, No. 2 (1915/1916), 16.
Continuation of No. 1914-22.
/RESEARCH: CHROMATICS/CHROMATICS

1915-42 **Lüdecke**, F[?]. "Goethes naturwissenschaftliche Sammlungen." *Technik und Wirtschaft*, 8 (1915), 254.
/GOETHE'S COLLECTIONS

1915-43 **Meyer**, O[?]. E. "Goethe und die Geologie." *Schlesische Zeitung*, No. 307, 1915.
/GEOLOGY

1915-44 **Ostwald**, Wilhelm. "Goethes oder Newtons Licht- und Farbenlehre?" (Mitgeteilt von Horn-Kaemmerer.) *Technische Mitteilungen für Malerei*, 32 (1915/1916), 163.
/CHROMATICS/NEWTON, I

1915-45 **P[?]**, E. "Goethes Farbenlehre in Münchener Ausgabe." *Bund Deutscher Decorationsmaler*, 6, No. 4, 15 February 1917, 40-41.
/CHROMATICS/EDITIONS

1915-46 ***P[?]**, E. "Goethes Farbenlehre in Münchener Ausgabe." *Münchener Zeitung*.
/CHROMATICS/EDITIONS

1915-47 **Piening**, August. "Tatsächliches zu Goethes Farbenlehre!" *Technische Mitteilungen für Malerei*, 32, No. 1 (1915/1916), 3-5; No. 2 (1915/1916), 10-13; No. 3 (1915/1916), 19-22.
/CHROMATICS/RESEARCH: CHROMATICS

1915-48 **Rádl**, Emanuel. "Idealistische Morphologie in Deutschland. Goethes Morphologie." In "Zur Geschichte der Biologie von Linné bis Darwin." In his *Allgemeine Biologie*. Leipzig/Berlin: Verlag von B. G. Teubner, 1915, IV.1, 5-6.
/MORPHOLOGY/BIOLOGY/METHOD

1915-49 **Schäfer**, C[äsar]. "Goethes Anteil an der Lehre von der Pflanzenmetamorphose." *Verhandlungen des Naturwissenschaftlichen Vereins zu Hamburg im Jahre 1915*, 23 (1916), lvii-lviii.

/BOTANY/MORPHOLOGY

1915-50 **Schiff**, Julius. "Ein Beitrag zur Geschichte des Quecksilbers und der Quecksilberverbindungen (im Anschluß an den Goethe-Knebel-Döbereinerschen Briefwechsel)." *Archiv für die Geschichte der Naturwissenschaften und der Technik*, 5 (1915), 390-97.
/CHEMISTRY/WORKS: CORRESPONDENCE/KNEBEL, K/DÖBEREINER, J

1915-51 *****Sirks**, M[?]. J. "Altes und Neues über Bestäubung und Befruchtung der höheren Pflanzen." *Naturwissenschaftliche Wochenschrift*, NS 14 (1915), 729-74.
/BOTANY

1915-52 *****Strunz**, Franz. "Über Alchemie und Goethe." *Literarisches Echo*, 18 (1915/1916), cols. 401-6.
/ALCHEMY

1915-53 "**Zur Wiederauferstehung** von Goethes Farbenlehre 1810 /1915." *Technische Mitteilungen für Malerei*, 32, No. 10/11 (1915).
Cf. Nos. 1915-3, -19, -24, -28, -29, -34 and -38.
"Beilage zu der Goethe-Nummer 1915."
/COLLECTION

1916-1 **[anon.]** "A. Bericht über die Versammlung des bayer. Mathematiker-Vereins vom 2. Juni 1917 im Hörsaal Nr. 366 der Techn. Hochschule München. B. Gegenbericht über den Versammlungsverlauf seitens der Vorstandschaft des bayer. Mathematiker-Vereins." *Technische Mitteilungen für Malerei*, 33 (1916 /1917), 173-88.
Cf. continuation, No. 1917-1.
/CHROMATICS/RESEARCH: CHROMATICS/INSTITUTIONS: BAYERISCHER MATHEMATIKER-VEREIN

1916-2 *****[anon.]** "Aus den Anerkennungen und Anregungen für unseren Kampf um Goethes Farbenlehre." *Technische Mitteilungen für Malerei*, 33 (1916/1917), 96.
/CHROMATICS/RESEARCH: CHROMATICS

1916-3 *****[anon.]** "Eine Friedensfeier in London mit Newtons 'weissestem Weiss'." *Technische Mitteilungen für Malerei*, 33 (1916/1917), 77-8.
/CHROMATICS

1916-4 *[anon.] "Goethe, dem Genius der Deutschen Licht- und Farben-forschung zur Wiederkehr seines Todestages." *Technische Mitteilungen für Malerei*, 33 (1916/1917), 134.
/CHROMATICS

1916-5 **Berger**, Dorothea. "Goethe als Vertreter der Länderkunde im 18. Jahrhundert. Ein Beitrag zu Goethes Schaffen, ein Beitrag zur Geschichte der Länderkunde." Diss. Greifswald. Greifswald: Emil Hartmann, 1916. 111 pp.
/GEOGRAPHY

1916-6 **B[erger**, Ernst]. "Goethes 'Farbenlehre' und der Feldzug von 1792." *Münchner Kunsttechnische Blätter: Beilage zur "Werkstatt der Kunst"*, 12, No. 9 (1916), 39-40.
/CHROMATICS/WORKS: AUTOBIOGRAPHICAL WRITINGS

1916-7 **[Berger**, Ernst.] "Eine neue Lösung des Streites zwischen Goethe und Newton." *Münchner Kunsttechnische Blätter: Beilage zur "Werkstatt der Kunst"*, 13, No. 2, 16 October 1916, 7-8; No. 3, 30 October 1916, 13-15; No. 4, 3 November 1916, 19-21; 27 November 1916, 25-7; No. 5/6, 11 December 1916, 31-2.
/CHROMATICS/NEWTON, I

1916-8 **Berger**, Ernst. "Schopenhauers Farbentheorie und sein Briefwechsel mit Goethe. Eine Jahrhundert-Erinnerung." *Münchner Kunsttechnische Blätter: Beilage zur "Werkstatt der Kunst"*, 12, No. 13, 20 March 1916; No. 14, 3 April 1916; No. 15, 17 April 1916, 59-60; 65-7; 71-2.
/SCHOPENHAUER, A/CHROMATICS/WORKS: CORRESPONDENCE

1916-9 **Cassirer**, Ernst. "Goethe." In *Freiheit und Form: Studien zur deutschen Geistesgeschichte*. Berlin: Ernst Cassirer, 1916, pp. 269-414.
/NATURPHILOSOPHIE/METHOD/PHILOSOPHY

1916-10 **Deetjen**, Werner. "Die Geschichte eines Teleskops. Mit ungedrückten Dokumenten von Lichtenberg, Kästner und Goethe." *Hannoversche Geschichtsblätter*, 19 (1916), 412-18.
/OPTICS/EDITION

1916-11 **Driesmans**, Heinrich. "Denkreinigung vor Sprachreinigung: Zur Wiedereinführung Goetheschen Sprachgeistes in die Wissenschaft und

das Leben." *Die Tat: Monatsschrift für die Zukunft deutscher Kultur*, 1, No. 2 (1916/1917), 134-42.
/CHROMATICS

1916-12 **Dühring**, Eugen. "Ueber Philosophie und heutige Schopenhauerei." *Personalist und Emanzipator: Monatsschrift für actionsfähige Geisteshaltung und gegen corrupte Wissenschaft*, No. 364, December 1916, 2906-9.
/SCHOPENHAUER, A/CHROMATICS

1916-13 *****Dupré**, Fr[?]. "Goethe und die Chemie." *Das Polytechnikum [Köthner Akademische Blätter]*, 9 (1916/1917), 4-5.
Continuation of No. 1915-7.
/CHEMISTRY

1916-14 **Dyroff**, Adolf. "Beziehungen zu Goethe, Görres, Johannes Müller." In *Carl Jos. Windischmann (1775-1839) und sein Kreis*. Köln: Kommissionsverlag und Druck von J. P. Bachem, 1916, pp. 76-85.
/WINDISCHMANN, K/MEDICINE/NATURPHILOSOPHIE

1916-15 **Feldhaus**, Franz M. "Goethe und die Vaucansonschen Automaten." *Geschichtsblätter für Technik, Industrie und Gewerbe*, 3 (1916), 165-6.
/TECHNOLOGY

1916-16 **Fritzsche**, Günther. "Goethe und die Anatomie." *Deutsche Monatsschrift für Zahnheilkunde*, 34 (1916), 184-220.
/OSTEOLOGY/ANATOMY/GENERAL INTRODUCTION

1916-17 **Goethe**[, J. W. von]. "Ausgewählte Kapitel aus Goethes Farbenlehre." Ed. Horn-Marlin. *Bund Deutscher Decorationsmaler: Fachzeitschrift für das Malergewerbe*, 5 (1916), 121-4; 129-31; 137-9; 146-7; 153-4; 163-5; 169-70; 177-9; 187-9.
Rpt. No. 1917-21.
/EDITION: SELECTIONS

1916-18 **Gundolf**, Friedrich. "Mathematik." In his *Goethe*. Berlin: Georg Bondi, 1916, pp. 413-17.
Cf. No. 1926-13.
/MATHEMATICS

1916-19 **Gundolf**, Friedrich. "Natur." In his *Goethe*. Berlin: Georg Bondi, 1916, pp. 376-81.

Cf. No. 1926-13.
/GENERAL INTRODUCTION

1916-20 **Hansen**, Adolph. "Goethes Herbarium." *Kosmos: Handweiser für Naturfreunde und Zentralblatt für das naturwissenschaftliche Bildungs- und Sammelwesen*, 13 (1916), 63-5.
/GOETHE'S COLLECTIONS/BOTANY

1916-21 **Hansen**, Adolph. "Die sachlichen und philosophischen Grundlagen von Goethes Morphologie (Metamorphose der Pflanzen und Osteologie): zugleich ein Beitrag zur Kritik der morphologischen Begriffsbildung." *Bericht der Oberhessischen Gesellschaft für Natur- und Heilkunde zu Giessen*, Naturwissenschaftliche Abteilung, NS 7 (1916/1919), 1-200.
/MORPHOLOGY/OSTEOLOGY/PHILOSOPHY/METHOD

1916-22 **Hoppe**, J[ohannes]. "Goethes Farbenlehre, ein Stück germanischer Weltanschauung?" *Technische Mitteilungen für Malerei*, 33, No. 5/6 (1916/1917), 33-6; No. 7/8 (1916/1917), 48-50.
Cf. No. 1914-5.
/CHROMATICS

1916-23 **Horn**[, Carl]. "Eine Anfrage an Herrn Prof. Ernst Berger." *Technische Mitteilungen für Malerei*, 33, No. 1 (1916/1917), 8.
/CHROMATICS

1916-24 **Horn**, K[C]arl. "Die dringend nötige Reform der Lichtlehre und unsere heutigen physikalischen Schulbücher. Forderungen zur Beseitigung der in unseren optischen Lehrbüchern enthaltenen, experimentellen Lücken und Irrtümer." *Technische Mitteilungen für Malerei*, 33, No. 14/15 (1916/1917), 97-101, 113-19; No. 16/17 (1916/1917), 134-7; No. 18/20 (1916/1917), 165-70.
Cf. continuation, No. 1917-25.
/RESEARCH: OPTICS/RESEARCH: CHROMATICS
/PEDAGOGY /OPTICS/CHROMATICS

1916-25 **Horn**, K[C]arl. "Fachdiskussionen zur Farbenlehre und zum Deutschen Farbenbuch." *Technische Mitteilungen für Malerei*, 33, No. 9/11 (1916/1917), 58-61.
/RESEARCH: CHROMATICS/RESEARCH: FINE ARTS

1916-26 **Horn**[, Carl.] "Geschäftliches zur eingeleiteten Diskussion über Goethes Farbenlehre." *Technische Mitteilungen für Malerei*, 33, No. 21/22 (1916/1917), 170-71.

/CHROMATICS

1916-27 **Horn**, K[C]arl. "Goethes Lichtlehre." *Bund Deutscher Decorationsmaler: Fachzeitschrift für das Malergewerbe*, 5 (1916), 117-18.
Rpt. of No. 1916-28.
/CHROMATICS/OPTICS/PHYSICS

1916-28 **Horn**, K[C]arl. "Goethes Lichtlehre." *Die Tat: Monatsschrift für die Zukunft deutscher Kultur*, 8, No. 4 (1916/ 1917), 378-80.
Rpt. No. 1916-27.
/CHROMATICS/OPTICS/PHYSICS

1916-29 **Horn**[, Carl]. "Goethe und Arnold Brass: Eine wichtige elektrische Analogie zu den Licht-Versuchen von Arnold Brass." *Technische Mitteilungen für Malerei*, 33, No. 12/13 (1916/1917), 94-5.
/CHROMATICS/BRASS, A/RESEARCH: PHYSICS

1916-30 **Horn**, K[C]arl. "Lichtlehre, Farbenlehre und absolutes Maßsystem: Zu W. Ostwald's 'absolutem System der Farben'." *Technische Mitteilungen für Malerei*, 33, No. 3/4 (1916/1917), 21-22; No. 5/6 (1916/1917), 36-40; No. 7/8 (1916/1917), 50-52; 14/15 (1916/1917), 105-6.
/RESEARCH: PHYSICS/RESEARCH: CHROMATICS/OSTWALD, W

1916-31 **Horn**, Carl. "Lichtphysik und Deutsches Farbenbuch." *Bund Deutscher Decorationsmaler: Fachzeitschrift für das Malergewerbe*, 5, No. 4 (1916), 35-6.
/RESEARCH: PHYSICS/RESEARCH: CHROMATICS /CHROMATICS /FINE ARTS

1916-32 **Horn**, Carl. "Die Maler, die Physiker und das Licht. Ein Wort zu gegenseitiger Verständigung." *Bund Deutscher Decorationsmaler: Fachzeitschrift für das Malergewerbe*, 5, No. 2 (1916), 18-20.
Rpt. of No. 1915-22.
/RESEARCH: CHROMATICS/RESEARCH: PHYSICS/RESEARCH: FINE ARTS

1916-33 **Horn**, K[C]arl. "Professor Ernst Berger und seine Behauptungen über Goethes Farbenphysik." *Technische Mitteilungen für Malerei*, 33, No. 9/11 (1916/1917), 72-4.
/CHROMATICS/BERGER, E

1916-34 **Horn**, K[C]arl. "Weimar gegen Goethe -- Goethe gegen Weimar. Zum gegenwärtigen Kampf um das Licht." *Technische Mitteilungen für Malerei*, 33, 18/20 (1916/1917), 137.
/CHROMATICS/RECEPTION

1916-35 **Horn**[, Carl]. "Zahl der Farben nach Ostwald und Goethe." *Technische Mitteilungen für Malerei*, 33 (1916/ 1917), 95-6.
/CHROMATICS/OSTWALD, W

1916-36 **Horn**[, Carl]. "Zur Antwort des Herrn Prof. Ernst Berger auf meine Anfrage in Nr. 1 XXXIII. Jahrgang." *Technische Mitteilungen für Malerei*, 33, No. 3/4 (1916/1917), 22-3.
/CHROMATICS

1916-37 **Horn**[, Carl]-**Kaemmerer**[, Paul]. "Die Farbenlehre -- das bin Ich: Ein Protest gegen Wilhelm Ostwald." *Technische Mitteilungen für Malerei*, 33, No. 12/13 (1916/1917), 84-6.
/CHROMATICS/OSTWALD, W/RESEARCH: CHROMATICS

1916-38 **Horn-Marlin**, Carl. "Ausgewählte Kapitel aus Goethes Farben-lehre. (Bearbeitet von Horn-Marlin)." *Bund Deutscher Dekorativ-Maler*, 5 (1916), 121-4; 129-31; 137-9; 146-7; 153-4; 163-5; 169-70; 177-9; 187-9.
/EDITION: SELECTIONS/CHROMATICS

1916-39 [**Kaemmerer**, Paul.] "Goethe, dem Genius der deutschen Licht- und Farbenforschung zur 85. Wiederkehr seines Todestages (22. März 1832) (22. März 1917)." *Technische Mitteilungen für Malerei*, 33, No. 18/20 (1916/1917), 134.
Signed: "Die Schriftleitung."
/CHROMATICS

1916-40 [**Kaemmerer**, Paul.] "Goethe-Raehlmann und die Deutsche Goethe-Gesellschaft." *Technische Mitteilungen für Malerei*, 33, No. 12/13 (1916/1917), 82.
Signed: "Die Schriftleitung."
/CHROMATICS/RAEHLMANN, E/INSTITUTIONS: GOETHE-GESELLSCHAFT

1916-41 **Kaemmerer**, Paul. "Goethes Farbenlehre, ein Stück german-ischer Weltanschauung! Eine persönliche Erklärung." *Technische Mitteilungen für Malerei*, 33, No. 9/11 (1916/ 1917), 62-4.
Response to No. 1914-5.
/CHROMATICS

1916-42 **Kaemmerer**, Paul. "Goethes Farbenlehre und die Möglichkeit, Blinden das Sehvermögen wiederzugeben." *Technische Mitteilungen für Malerei*, 33, No. 14/15 (1916/1917), 106-7; No. 16-17 (1916/1917), 127-30.
The conclusion never appeared.
/CHROMATICS/SENSORY PHYSIOLOGY

1916-43 **Kaemmerer**, Paul. "Goethe und die deutschen 'Fachgenossen' unter sich." *Technische Mitteilungen für Malerei*, 33, No. 9/11 (1916/1917), 64-72.
/CHROMATICS/RECEPTION

1916-44 **Kaemmerer**, Paul. "Licht -- Raum: das Urbild (platonische Idee) der Materie und Energie." *Technische Mitteilungen für Malerei*, 33, Nos. 2-8; 12/13 (1916/1917), 17-20; 25-8; 40-42; 54-6; 92-4.
Coninuation of No. 1915-37.
Incomplete; promised continuation never appeared.
/RESEARCH: PHYSICS/RESEARCH: CHROMATICS

1916-45 **Kaemmerer**, Paul. "Maler-Physiker contra Mathematiker-Physiker und das Goethe-Invalidentum in Weimar. Eine Entgegnung auf die Licht- und Farben-Physik Dr. Speyerers." *Technische Mitteilungen für Malerei*, 33, No. 18/20 (1916/1917), 147-60.
Promised continuation never appeared.
/RECEPTION/RESEARCH: CHROMATICS/SPEYERER, ?

1916-46 **Kaemmerer**, Paul. "Professor Ernst Berger contra Goethe, Newton, Schopenhauer, Leonardo da Vinci." *Technische Mitteilungen für Malerei*, 33, No. 9/11 (1916/1917), 74-7.
/CHROMATICS/BERGER, E/NEWTON, I/SCHOPEN-HAUER, A/DA VINCI, L

1916-47 [**Kaemmerer**, Paul.] "Ein Unglücksfall beim Triumph deutscher Forscherarbeit während des Weltkrieges." *Technische Mitteilungen für Malerei*, 33, No. 12/13 (1916/1917), 82-4.
Signed: "Die Schriftleitung."
/RESEARCH: CHROMATICS/RECEPTION

1916-48 **Kaemmerer**, Paul. "Die Unterschiede im Schwarz und im Weiß: Eine Entgegnung und ein Beitrag zu den begrifflichen und formalen Grundlagen des Deutschen Farbenbuches." *Technische Mitteilungen für Malerei*, 33, No. 1/2 (1916/1917), 6-8; 15-17.

/RESEARCH: CHROMATICS/RESEARCH: FINE ARTS

1916-49 **Kistner**, Adolf. "Goethes physikalische Apparate." *Central-Zeitung für Optik und Mechanik Elektrotechnik und verwandte Berufszweige*, 37 (1916), 139-40; 153-4.
/GOETHE'S COLLECTIONS

1916-50 **Krais**, Paul. "Über die Farben." *Färber-Zeitung [Berlin]*, 27 (1916), 113-14.
/RESEARCH: CHROMATICS/CHROMATICS

1916-51 **Orth**, Johannes. "Das biologische Problem in Goethes Wahlver-wandtschaften." *Sitzungsberichte der Königlich Preussischen Akademie der Wissenschaften*, 1916, pp. 1197; 1198-1212.
/BIOLOGY/WORKS: DIE WAHLVERWANDTSCHAFTEN

1916-52 **Raehlmann**, Eduard. "Goethes Farbenlehre." *Goethe*, 3 (1916), 3-40.
　　　　Rev. [anon.], "Das neue Goethe-Jahrbuch," n.p., 1916. [In Mappe III E 21/C91: "Goethe und die Farbenlehre 1913-. Sammelmappe Zeitungsausschnitte" at the Frankfurter Goethe-Museum.]
/CHROMATICS

1916-53 **Russell**, E[duard]. S[tuart]. "Goethe." In his *Form and Function: A Contribution to the History of Animal Morphology*. London: John Murray, 1916, pp. 45-51.
/MORPHOLOGY

1916-54 **Schmidkunz**, Hans. "Farbentheorien." *Münchner Kunsttechnische Blätter*, 13, No. 3 (1916), 15-16; No. 4 (1916), 21-3; No. 5 (1916), 27-8; No. 6 (1916), 32-4.
RESEARCH: CHROMATICS/CHROMATICS

1916-55 **Schmiedel**, Oskar. "Goethe und die 'Fraunhoferschen Linien'." *Technische Mitteilungen für Malerei*, 33 (1916 /1917), 143-5.
/CHROMATICS/KRAIS, P/HOPPE, J

1916-56 **Speyrer**, K[urt]. "Gegen der Physik der Herren Horn und Kaemmerer." *Technische Mitteilungen für Malerei*, 33, No. 16 /17 (1916/1917), 120-26.
　　　　Cf. No. 1916-57.
　　　　Promised continuation never appeared.
/RESEARCH: CHROMATICS/RESEARCH:

PHYSICS/CHROMATICS/HORN, C/KAEMMERER, J

1916-57 **Speyrer**, K[urt]. "Vorläufige Bemerkung zur Entgegnung der Herren Horn und Kaemmerer." *Technische Mitteilungen für Malerei*, 33, No. 21/22 (1916/1917), 171-2.
Cf. No. 1916-56.
/RESEARCH: CHROMATICS/RESEARCH: PHYSICS/CHROMATICS /HORN, C/KAEMMERER, J

1916-58 **Stein**, Robert. "Chemie." *Geschichtsblätter für Technik, Industrie und Gewerbe*, 3 (1916), 176-8.
/CHEMISTRY

1916-59 **Stein**, Robert. "Die von Goethe entworfenen Tabellen." In "Übersichtstafeln für Natur- und Heilkunde." *Mitteilungen zur Geschichte der Medizin und der Naturwissenschaften*, 15 (1916), 94; 97-8.
/EDITION

1916-60 ***Turóczi-Trostler**, József. "Goethe mint természettudos [Goethe as a Scientist]." Természettudományi füzetekböl. Temesvár: Hunyadi kny, 1916. 38 pp.
In Hungarian.
/GENERAL INTRODUCTION

1916-61 **Weihe**, Carl. "Physiologische und Spektral-Farben. Ein Beitrag zu Goethes Farbenlehre." *Sonntagsbeilage zur Vossischen Zeitung*, No. 35, 27 August 1916, 238-9.
/CHROMATICS

1916-62 **Wendriner**, Hans. "Ein balneologisches Gutachten Goethes nebst anderen historischen Bemerkungen über die Gründung des Bades Berka." *Zeitschrift für Balneologie Klimatologie und Kurort-Hygiene*, 9 (1916/1917), 163-72.
/MEDICINE

1916-63 **Wohlbold**, H[ans]. "Nachforschung nach Goethes Methode -- ein geistiges Kriegsziel." *Technische Mitteilungen für Malerei*, 33, No. 1 (1916/1917), pp. 3-5.
/CHROMATICS/RESEARCH: CHROMATICS

1916-64 **Zeitler**, Julius. "Farbenlehre." In *Goethe-Handbuch*. Ed. Julius Zeitler. 3 vols. Stuttgart: J. B. Metzlersche Buchhandlung in Stuttgart, 1916, I, 531-35.

/CHROMATICS

1917-1 **[anon.]** "A. Bericht über die Versammlung des bayer. Mathematiker-Vereins vom 2. Juni 1917 im Hörsaal Nr. 366 der Techn. Hochschule München. B. Gegenbericht über den Versammlungsverlauf seitens der Vorstandschaft des bayer. Mathematiker-Vereins." *Technische Mitteilungen für Malerei*, 34, No. 1/2 (1916/1917), 3-12.
 Continuation of No. 1916-1.
 /CHROMATICS/RESEARCH: CHROMATICS/INSTITUTIONS: BAYERISCHER MATHEMATIKER-VEREIN

1917-2 **[anon.]** "Goethe oder Newton." *Münchener Zeitung*, No. 160, 13 June 1917.
 /CHROMATICS/NEWTON, I

1917-3 **[anon.]** "Goethesche Farbenlehre." *Die Naturwissenschaften*, 5 (1917), 355-6.
 /CHROMATICS

1917-4 **[anon.]** "Goethes Farbenlehre in Münchner Ausgabe." *Bund deutscher Dekorativ-Maler*, 6 (1917), 40-41.
 /CHROMATICS/RESEARCH: CHROMATICS

1917-5 **[anon.]** "Neupapier aus Altpapier." *Wochenblatt für Papierfabrikation*, 48 (1917), 62.
 /TECHNOLOGY/ECOLOGY

1917-6 **Barthel**, Ernst. "Goethe über seine Farbenlehre." *Das Reich*, 2 (1917/1918), 777-81.
 /CHROMATICS/NEWTON, I

1917-7 **Barthel**, Ernst. "Der Grundirrtum der jetzigen Naturwissenschaft im allgemeinen und der bisherigen Farbenlehre im besonderen." *Technische Mitteilungen für Malerei*, 34, No. 9-11 (1917/1918), 61-2.
 /RESEARCH: CHROMATICS/CHROMATICS/HISTORY OF SCIENCE

1917-8 **Barthel**, Ernst. "In Sachen des absoluten Farbensystems." *Zeitschrift für den Physikalischen und Chemischen Unterricht*, 30 (1917), 51-2.
 /RESEARCH: CHROMATICS/CHROMATICS

1917-9 **Barthel**, Ernst. "In Sachen der Goetheschen Farbenlehre." *Das*

literarische Echo [Berlin], 19 (1917), cols. 1046-1052.
/CHROMATICS/NEWTON, I

1917-10 **Barthel**, Ernst. "Ein interessantes Rechenexempel." *Technische Mitteilungen für Malerei*, 34, No. 3-4 (1917/1918), 24.
/CHROMATICS/NEWTON, I

1917-11 **Barthel**, Ernst. "Was ist ein Schatten?" *Technische Mitteilungen für Malerei*, 34, No. 7-8 (1917/1918), 44-5.
/RESEARCH: CHROMATICS/CHROMATICS/NEWTON, I

1917-12 **Barthel**, Ernst. "Was Newtons Theorie nicht aufklären kann." *Technische Mitteilungen für Malerei*, 34, No. 5-6 (1917/1918), 29.
/CHROMATICS/NEWTON, I/RESEARCH: CHROMATICS

1917-13 **Barthel**, Ernst. "Ein Wort zur Klärung der Farbenbegriffe im Streit um Goethes Farbenlehre." *Technische Mitteilungen für Malerei*, 34, No. 1-2 (1917/1918), 12.
/CHROMATICS/NEWTON, I

1917-14 **B[arthel].**, E[rnst]. "Zum Streit über Goethes Farbenlehre." *Münchner Kunsttechnische Blätter: Beilage zur "Werkstatt der Kunst"*, 13, No. 23, 27 August 1917, 138.
/CHROMATICS/NEWTON, I

1917-15 **Barthel**, Ernst. "Die Zwickmühle." *Technische Mitteilungen für Malerei*, 34, No. 5-6 (1917/1918), 28-9.
/CHROMATICS

1917-16 **Belyi**, Andrei [Boris **Bugaev**]. *Rudol'f Shteiner i Gete v mirovozzrenii sovremennocti [Rudolf Steiner and Goethe: Philosophical Contemporaries]*. Moskva: "Dukhovnoe znanie," 1917. viii, 344 pp.
In Russian.
Rev. E. Alapin, *Kniga i revoliutsiia*, 13, No. 1 (1921), 69.
/STEINER, R/METHOD/EPISTEMOLOGY

1917-17 **Einstein**, A[lbert]. Review of: Helmholtz, Hermann von. *Zwei Vorträge über Goethe: Goethes naturwissenschaftliche Arbeiten: Goethes Vorahnungen kommender naturwissenschaftlicher Ideen*. Braunschweig: Fr. Vieweg & Sohn, 1917. *Die Naturwissenschaften: Wochenschrift für die Fortschritte der Naturwissenschaften, der Medizin, und der Technik*, 5 (1917), 675.
Cf. No. 1917-24.

/CHROMATICS/RECEPTION/REVIEW/HELMHOLTZ, H
VON

1917-18 **Feldhaus**, Franz M. "Goethe über Erfinden und Patentwesen."
Geschichtsblätter für Technik, Industrie und Gewerbe, 4 (1917), 228.
/TECHNOLOGY

1917-19 **Franz**, V[iktor]. "Goethes Zikaden und Heuschrecken."
Naturwissenschaftliche Wochenschrift, 32 [NS 16] (1917), 496.
/ENTOMOLOGY

1917-20 **Glatzel**, Paul. "Goethes Anschauungen über Optik in neuer
Beleuchtung." *Central-Zeitung für Optik und Mechanik: Elektrotechnik und verwandte Berufszweige*, 38, No. 13 (1917), 154-5.
/CHROMATICS

1917-21 *****Goethe**[, J. W. von]. "Goethes Farbenlehre in Auswahl für
Maler. Ed. Horn-Marlin. München: Hochschulbuchhandlung Max
Hueber, 1917.
Rpt. of No. 1916-17.
"Bearbeitet von Horn-Marlin für den Bund deutscher Dekorationsmaler."
/EDTION: SELECTIONS

1917-22 **Goethe**[, J. W. von] [**Tobler**, Georg Christoph]. "Natur. Ein
Fragment." [Leibniz: Breitkopf & Härtel, 1910.] [12] pp.
/EDITION

1917-23 **Goethes** *Briefwechsel mit Joseph Sebastian Grüner und Joseph
Stanislaus Zauper (1820-1832)*. Ed. August Sauer. Intro. Josef Nadler. Bibliothek deutscher Schriftsteller aus Böhmen, 17. Prag: J. G.
Calve'sche k. u. k. Hof- u. Universitäts-Buchhandlung, 1917. ci, 535
pp.
/WORKS: CORRESPONDENCE/GRÜNER, J/ZAUPER, J

1917-24 **Helmholtz**, Hermann v[on]. *Goethe's naturwissenschaftliche
Arbeiten: Goethe's Vorahnungen kommender naturwissenschaftlicher
Ideen*. Braunschweig: Friedr[ich]. Vieweg u. Sohn, 1917. 64 pp.
Rpt. of Nos. 1853-8 and 1892-10.
Rev. A[lbert]. Einstein, No. 1917-17.
/GENERAL INTRODUCTION

1917-25 **Horn**, K[C]arl. "Die dringend nötige Reform der Lichtlehre und
unsere heutigen physikalischen Schulbücher. Forderungen zur Be-

seitigung der in unseren optischen Lehrbüchern enthaltenen, experimentellen Lücken und Irrtümer." *Technische Mitteilungen für Malerei*, 34, No. 7/8 (1917/1918), 39-42.
Continuation of No. 1916-24.
/RESEARCH: OPTICS/RESEARCH: CHROMATICS /PEDAGOGY/OPTICS /CHROMATICS

1917-26 **Horn**, K[C]arl. "Lichtlehre ($<=>$) Doehlemannsche Optik oder Ponceletsche Optik? Hochschuloptik oder Volksoptik?" *Technische Mitteilungen für Malerei*, 34, No. 7/8 (1917/1918), 42-3.
/RESEARCH: OPTICS/CHROMATICS/DOEHLMANN, ?/PONCELET, J

1917-27 **Horn**, K[C]arl. "$\pm$ Rand und $\pm$ Blende. Polare Teilbilder und Totalbild: Grundversuche zur physikalischen Bilderlehre nach dem Prinzip der Dualität." *Technische Mitteilungen für Malerei*, 34, No. 9/11 (1917/1918), 53-9; 12/14 (1917/1918), 72-5.
/RESEARCH: CHROMATICS/RESEARCH: OPTICS

1917-28 **Horn**, K[C]arl. "Der polare Aufbau von Goethes Lichtfinsternislehre und Weltanschauung: Doppelspaltig angelegte Texte und Bilder aus seiner Farbenlehre." *Technische Mitteilungen für Malerei*, No. 15/16 (1917/1918), 87-9.
/CHROMATICS/EDITION: SELECTIONS/PHILOSOPHY

1917-29 **Horn**, K[C]arl. "W. Ostwalds Farbenfibel -- ein Triumph deutscher Forscherarbeit?" *Bund Deutscher Decorationsmaler: Fachzeitschrift für das Malergewerbe*, 6, No. 3 (1917), 30-32; No. 5 (1917), 50-51.
/CHROMATICS/OSTWALD, W

1917-30 **Horn**, K[C]arl. "Zehn interessante optische, physikalische und malerische Streitfragen. Zu den Ausführungen der Hochschulprofessoren in der Sitzung des Bayr. Mathematiker-Vereins vom 2. Juni." *Technische Mitteilungen für Malerei*, 34, No. 3/4 (1917/1918), 13-18; No. 5/6 (1917/1918), 25-7.
/RESEARCH: CHROMATICS/CHROMATICS/INSTITUTIONS: BAYERISCHER MATHEMATIKER-VEREIN

1917-31 **K[?].**, W[?]. ["Der Goetheschen Farbenlehre hat sich. . ."] *Die Naturwissenschaften: Wochenschrift für die Fortschritte der Naturwissenschaften, der Medizin, und der Technik*, 5, No. 21, 25 May 1917, 355-6.
/CHROMATICS

1917-32 **Kaemmerer**[, Paul]. "Eine Äußerung Prof. Dörners." *Technische Mitteilungen für Malerei*, No. 5/6 (1917/1918), 27-8.
/CHROMATICS/DÖRNER, ?

1917-33 **Kaemmerer**, Paul. "Goethe und die Deutschen, daß Gott erbarm! Kritik an der Versammlung des Bayer. Mathematiker-Vereins." *Technische Mitteilungen für Malerei*, 34, Nos. 3-11 (1917/1918), 18-24; 30; 45-7; 62-64.
Continuation, No. 1917-34.
/CHROMATICS/INSTITUTIONS: BAYERISCHER MATHEMATIKER-VEREIN

1917-34 **Kaemmerer**, Paul. "Goethe und Leonardo da Vinci: Als Fortsetzung des Aufsatzes: 'Goethe und die Deutschen, daß Gott erbarm!" *Technische Mitteilungen für Malerei*, 34, No. 12/14 (1917/1918), 77-82.
Continuation of No. 1917-33.
/CHROMATICS/RECEPTION/DA VINCI, L

1917-35 **Kaemmerer**, Paul. "Zur Reformation der Lichtlehre: Den beiden deutschen Reformatioren des geistigen und physischen Lichtes, den Kämpfern für die geistige Freiheit des deutschen Volkes: Goethe und Luther." *Technische Mitteilungen für Malerei*, No. 9/11 (1917/1918), 51-3.
/CHROMATICS/RECEPTION/LUTHER, M

1917-36 **Raehlmann**, E[duard]. "Goethes Farbenlehre und die Naturwissenschaft." *Naturwissenschaftliche Wochenschrift*, 32 [NS 16], No. 43 (1917), 601-5.
/CHROMATICS

1917-37 **Schelenz**, Hermann. "Goethe-Apotheken." *Pharmazeutische Zeitung*, 62 (1917), 681-2.
/CHEMISTRY

1917-38 **Schelenz**, Hermann. "Tee-Ersatz." *Prometheus: Illustrierte Wochenschrift über die Fortschritte in Gewerbe, Industrie und Wissenschaft*, 28 (1917), 735-6.
/CHEMISTRY

1917-39 **Sommerfeld**, A[rnold]. "Goethes Farbenlehre im Urteile der Zeit." *Deutsche Revue*, 42 (1917), 100-106.
/CHROMATICS/RECEPTION

1917-40 **Stein**, Robert. "Goethes Übersichtstafeln." *Das literarische Echo: Halbmonatsschrift für Literaturfreunde [Berlin]*, 19 (1917), cols. 1306-1319.
/EDITION

1917-41 ***Stein**, Robert. "Ein Irrtum in Goethes 'Naturwissenschaftlichen Entwicklungsgang' -- Chemie." *Allgemeine Zeitung*, 1917, pp. 402ff. and 412ff.
/CHEMISTRY

1917-42 **Stein**, Robert. "Naturgeschichts-Unterricht im 18. Jahrhundert und Goethes botanisches Studium." *Mitteilungen zur Geschichte der Medizin und der Naturwissenschaften*, 16 (1917), 135-42.
/BOTANY/PEDAGOGY

1917-43 **Stein**, Robert. "Reines Deutsch und fremdsprachige Fachausdrücke." *Geschichtsblätter für Technik, Industrie und Gewerbe*, 4 (1917), 243-5.
/CHEMISTRY

1917-44 **Strunz**, Franz. *Goethe als Naturforscher*. Urania-Bücherei, 15. Wien: Verlag des Volksbildungshauses Wiener Urania, 1917. 97 pp.
/GENERAL INTRODUCTION

1917-45 **Weniger**, Ludwig. "'Wär nicht das Auge sonnenhaft'." *Neue Jahrbücher für das klassische Altertum: Geschichte und deutsche Literatur und für Pädagogik*, 39 (1917), 238-53.
/CHROMATICS/EPISTEMOLOGY/PLOTINUS/MANILIUS/BÖHME, J/THEOLOGY

1917-46 **Wohlbold**, H[ans]. "Goethe--Newton." *Das Reich*, 2 (1917-/1918), 57-69.
/CHROMATICS/NEWTON, I

1917-47 **Wohlbold**, H[ans]. "Grundsätzliches zur Farbenlehre." *Das Reich*, 2 (1917/1918), 639-59.
/CHROMATICS/RESEARCH: CHROMATICS

1917-48 **Wohlbold**, H[ans]. "Die Physik, die Urphänomene und die Geisteswissenschaft." *Das Reich*, 2 (1917/1918), 426-47.
/CHROMATICS/NEWTON, I

1917-49 **Zell**, Theodor. "Goethe als Tierbeobachter." *Zur Guten Stunde:*

Illustrierte Zeitschrift, 2 (1917), 468-70.
/ZOOLOGY

1917-50 *Zint, Hans. "Goethe und Schopenhauer." *Ber. 6 Gen-Vers.*
Schopenhauer-Ges. Danzig: 1917, pp. 9-10.
/CHROMATICS/SCHOPENHAUER, A

1918-1 **Barthel**, Ernst. "Goethes Farbenlehre." *Nord und Süd*, 43, No.
167 (1918), 76-9.
/CHROMATICS

1918-2 **Barthel**, Ernst. "Goethes Farbenlehre, ein Werk der Zukunft."
Deutsche Revue, 43, No. 3 (1918), 181-8.
/CHROMATICS/SCHOPENHAUER, A/NEWTON, I

1918-3 **Ebstein**, Erich. "Zur Geschichte des Tee- und Kaffee-Ersatzes."
Mitteilungen zur Geschichte der Medizin und der Naturwissen-
schaften, 17 (1918), 158.
/CHEMISTRY

1918-4 **Engelhardt**, Victor. "Dichter, Philosoph, Physiker und
Physiologe über die Farben." *Das Weltall: Bildgeschmückte*
Halbmonatsschrift für Astronomie und verwandte Gebiete, 19, No. 5/6
(1918/1919) 37-43.
/CHROMATICS/RECEPTION/SCHOPENHAUER, A /NEW-
TON, I/HELMHOLTZ, H VON

1918-5 **Feldhaus**, Franz M. "Die Zauberuhr des Magus von Helmstedt."
Geschichtsblätter für Technik und Industrie, 5 (1918), 277-8.
/TECHNOLOGY/BEIREIS, G

1918-6 **Hirschberg**, J[ulius]. "Goethe und die Farbenlehre." In his *Ge-*
schichte der Augenheilkunde. Vol. 15.1 of *Handbuch der gesamten*
Augenheilkunde. Ed. A. Graefe et al. 2nd rev. edn. Berlin: Verlag
von Julius Springer, 1918, pp. 18-25.
/CHROMATICS/RECEPTION

1918-7 **Küster**, Ernst. "Albertus Magnus und Goethe." *Die Naturwis-*
senschaften: Wochenschrift für die Fortschritte der Naturwissen-
schaften, der Medizin, und der Technik, 6 (1918), 137-9.
/ALBERTUS MAGNUS/BOTANY

1918-8 **Lerch**, Eugen. "Goethe und Schopenhauer." *Norddeutsche*
Allgemeine Zeitung, Morgen-Ausgabe, 57, No. 438, 28 August 1918[,

2].
/SCHOPENHAUER, A/CHROMATICS

1918-9 **Lubosch**, Wilhelm. "Goethe's Rezension des Werkes von Pander und d'Alton und eine dunkle Textstelle in ihr. In his "Über Pander und D'Altons Vergleichende Osteologie der Säugetiere. Ein Kapitel aus der Naturphilsophie. Festschrift zum siebzigsten Geburtstage von Ernst Stahl in Jena." *Flora oder Allgemeine Zeitung*, 11/12 [111/112] (1918), 668-702; 670-74.
/OSTEOLOGY/COMPARATIVE ANATOMY/PANDER, H/D'ALTON, E

1918-10 **Merbach**, Paul Alfred. "Allerlei Technisches im Briefwechsel des Herzogs-Großherzogs Carl August mit Goethe." *Geschichtsblätter für Technik, Industrie und Gewerbe*, 5 (1918), 129-37.
/TECHNOLOGY/WORKS: CORRESPONDENCE/CARL AUGUST [GROSSHERZOG VON WEIMAR]

1918-11 **Ostwald**, Wilhelm. *Goethe, Schopenhauer und die Farbenlehre.* Leipzig: Verlag Unesma, 1918. vi, 145 pp.
Rpt. 1918.
/CHROMATICS/SCHOPENHAUER, A

1918-12 **Ostwald**, Wilhelm. "Goethes Farbenlehre." In his *Mathematische Farbenlehre*. Bk. 1 of *Die Farbenlehre*. Leipzig: Verlag Unesma, 1918, p. 106.
Rpt. No. 1918-13.
/CHROMATICS/RESEARCH: CHROMATICS

1918-13 **Ostwald**, Wilhelm. "Die Stellung der Farbenlehre im Gebäude der Wissenschaft." *Technische Mitteilungen für Malerei*, 35 (1918/1919), 4-6.
Rpt. of No. 1918-12.
/RESEARCH: CHROMATICS/HISTORY OF SCIENCE

1918-14 **Stein**, Robert. "Goethes Weinflaschen-Ausblühung und Göttlings Probierkabinett. Eine chemiegeschichtliche Untersuchung." *Archiv für die Geschichte der Naturwissenschaften und der Technik*, 8 (1918), 187-205.
/GOETHE'S COLLECTIONS/CHEMISTRY

1918-15 **Wohlbold**, Hans. "Goethe und die Deszendenztheorie." *Das Reich [München/Heidelberg]*, 3 (1918), 195-217.
/BIOLOGY: EVOLUTION

1918-16 **Zint**, Hans. "Goethe und Schopenhauer in ihrer Stellung zur Farbenlehre." *Mitteilungen zur Geschichte der Medizin und der Naturwissenschaften*, 17 (1918), 177.
/CHROMATICS/SCHOPENHAUER, A

1918-17 **Zint**, Hans. [Untitled precis of a lecture on 31 May 1917.] *Jahrbuch der Schopenhauer-Gesellschaft*, 7 (1918), 285.
/SCHOPENHAUER, A/CHROMATICS

1919-1 **André**, Hans. *Goethes Morphologie (Metamorphose der Pflanzen und Osteologie): Ein Beitrag zum sachlichen und philosophischen Verständnis und zur Kritik der morphologischen Begriffsbildung.* Giessen: Verlag von Alfred Töpelmann, 1919. 200 pp.
/MORPHOLOGY/BOTANY/OSTEOLOGY/RESEARCH: MORPHOLOGY

1919-2 **Chamberlain**, Houston Stewart. "Grundlagen, Kant, Goethe: Goethe und Linné." In his *Lebenswege meines Denkens*. München: F. Bruckmann, 1919, pp. 140-48.
/BOTANY/KANT, I/LINNAEUS [LINNÉ], C

1919-3 **Doebber**, Adolph. "Goethe und sein Gut Ober-Roßla: Nach den Akten im Goethe- und Schiller-Archiv und im Geh. Haupt- und Staats-Archiv zu Weimar." *Goethe*, 6 (1919), 195-239.
/AGRONOMY/PLACES: OBER-ROßLA

1919-4 **Feldhaus**, Franz M. "Goethe, Pustkusten und der Pusterich." *Geschichtsblätter für Technik und Industrie*, 6 (1919), 189-90.
/TECHNOLOGY

1919-5 **Kries**, Johannes von. "Goethe als Naturforscher." *Die Naturwissenschaften: Wochenschrift für die Fortschritte der Naturwissenschaften, der Medizin, und der Technik*, 7 (1919), 835-7.
Rpt. Nos. 1920-13.
Cf. rev. edn. No. 1924-23.
"Vortrag [Selbstreferat], gehalten bei der Tagung der Goethe-Gesellschaft zu Weimar am 28. September 1919."
/GENERAL INTRODUCTION

1919-6 **Lippmann**, Edmund O. "Goethe und die Zuckerfabrikation." *Die Deutsche Zuckerindustrie*, 44 (1919), 5-7.
Rpt. No. 1923-15.
/CHEMISTRY/TECHNOLOGY

1919-7 **Lubosch**, Wilhelm. "Was verdankt die vergleichend-anatomische Wissenschaft den Arbeiten Goethes?" *Goethe*, 6 (1919), 157-91.
/COMPARATIVE ANATOMY

1919-8 **Möbius**, Martin. "Die Begründung der Pflanzengeographie durch Alexander von Humboldt." *Naturwissenschaftliche Wochenschrift*, 34, NF 18 (1919), 521-6.
/GEOGRAPHY/BOTANY

1919-9 **Molisch**, Hans. "Goethe als Naturforscher." In his *Populäre biologische Vorträge*. Jena: Verlag von Gustav Fischer, 1920, pp. 1-13.
/GENERAL INTRODUCTION

1919-10 **Ostwald**, Wilhelm. *Einführung in die Farbenlehre*. Bücher der Naturwissenschaft, 26. Reclams Universal Bibliothek, 6041-6044. Leipzig: Druck und Verlag von Philipp Reclam jun., 1919. 174 pp.
/RESEARCH: CHROMATICS/CHROMATICS

1919-11 *****Radovanovic**[, ?]. "Gete kao naucnik [Goethe as a Scientist]." *Misao [Belgrade]*, 29 (1919), 168ff.
In Serbo-Croatian.
/GENERAL INTRODUCTION

1919-12 **Salewski**, Will. "Goethe als wissenschaftlicher Revolutionär." *Freideutsche Jugend: Monatsschrift für das junge Deutschland*, 5, No. 7 (1919), 289-97.
Cf. response, No. 1919-15.
/NATURPHILOSOPHIE

1919-13 **Schelenz**, Hermann. "Goethe, der Dichter-Naturkundige, über heil-naturkundliche Dinge." *Berichte der Deutschen Pharmazeutischen Gesellschaft*, 29 (1919), 123-33.
/PHARMACOLOGY

1919-14 **Schips**, M[?]. "Die Idee vom Typus und ihre Bedeutung für Morphologie und Systematik." *Naturwissenschaftliche Wochenschrift*, 34 [NS 18] (1919), 401-7.
RESEARCH: BIOLOGY/RESEARCH: MORPHOLOGY /BIOLOGY/MORPHOLOGY

1919-15 **Schultz-Hencke**, Harald. "Goethe und die moderne Naturerkenntnis: Eine Entgegnung." *Freideutsche Jugend*, 5 (1919), 439-43.

Response to No. 1919-12.
/NATURPHILOSOPHIE

1919-16 **Stein**, Walter Johannes. *Die moderne naturwissenschaftliche Vorstellungsart und die Weltanschauung Goethes: wie sie Rudolf Steiner vertritt.* Konstanz: Wölfing, 1919. 115 pp.
Rpt. No. 1921-23.
/METHOD/EPISTEMOLOGY/STEINER, R

1919-17 **Whyte**, L[ancelot]. L[aw]. "Goethe's Single View of Nature and Man." *German Life and Letters*, July 1919, 287-97.
/PHILOSOPHY/GENERAL INTRODUCTION

1919-18 **Wohlbold**, Hans. "Zur Metamorphosenlehre." *Das Reich*, 4 (1919), 152-76.
/MORPHOLOGY/BOTANY

1920-1 **[anon.]** "Kleine Chronik: Die Idee der Metamorphose." N.p.: n.p., 1 January 1920.
In "Mappe zu Goethes naturwissenschaftlichem Werk," Deutsches Literaturarchiv, Marbach.
/ALBERTUS MAGNUS

1920-2 **Berendt**, Hans. "Goethe und Schelling." In *Festschrift für Berthold Litzmann zum 60. Geburtstag 18. 4. 1917 im Auftrage der Literarhistorischen Gesellschaft Bonn*. Ed. Carl Enders. Bonn: Friedrich Cohen, 1920, pp. 77-104.
Rpt. No. 1921-2.
/SCHELLING, F VON/NATURPHILSOPHIE

1920-3 **Carré**, Jean-Marie. "Les études scientifiques de Goethe, le physicien, le botaniste, le zoologiste." In his *Goethe en Angleterre*. Paris: Librairie Plon[, 1920], pp. 270-73.
2nd edn. [1925].
/GENERAL INTRODUCTION/BOTANY/ZOOLOGY

1920-4 **Dennert**, Friedrich, ed. *Goethe und der Harz*. Harzer Heimatbücher, 2. Quedlinburg: Verlag Harzer Heimatbücher, 1920. 184 pp.
2nd rev. and exp. edn. No. 1927-12.
/GEOLOGY/PLACES: HARZ

1920-5 **Dietert**, Friedrich. *Goethe im Harz: Goethes Harzreisen in seinen Tagebüchern, Briefen, Dichtungen*. Wernigerode and Chorin: Deutscher Kultur- und Heimatverlag, 1920. 91 pp.
2nd rev. and exp. edn. No. 1927-14.
/GEOLOGY/PLACES: HARZ

1920-6 **Franz**, Viktor. "Goethes Bedeutung für die Naturforschung." *Illustrirte Zeitung*, 155, No. 4025, 19 August 1920, 215.
/GENERAL INTRODUCTION/RECEPTION

1920-7 **Gëte**. *Bor'ba za realisticheskoe mirovozzrenie [Goethe. The Battle for a Realistic World-View]*. Sel. and trans. V. O. Likhtenshtadta. Ed. and intro. A. Bogdanova. Trudy sots. akademii. Petersbyrg: Gocizdat, 1920. xii, 500 pp.
Cf. No. 1920-8.
[Zhitomirskaia 51]
"Soderzh.: Likhtenshtadt V. O. Gete -- myslitel'. -- Gete. Stat'i i fragmenty. [Razdely]: Morfologiia. -- Ucheniie o tsvetakh. -- Teoriia poznaniia. -- Materialy dlia biografii Gete kak

estestvoispytatelia i filosofa. [Zhitomirskaia].
/TRANSLATION: RUSSIAN

1920-8 **Goethe**[, J. W. von] [Tobler, Georg?]. "Die Natur: Fragment aus dem Tiefurter Journal. Ed. Hermann Leicht. München-Pullach: Paul Stangl Verlag[, 1920]. 30 pp.
/EDITION

1920-9 **[Goethe**, J. W. von.] "Znachitel'nyi stimul ot odnogo metkogo slova [Bedeutende Fördernis durch ein einziges geistreiches Wort]." In *Gëte. Bor'ba za realisticheskoe mirovozzrenie [Goethe. The Battle for a Realistic World-View]*. Sel. and trans. V. O. Likhtenshtadta. Ed. and intro. A. Bogdanova. Trudy sots. akademii. Petersbyrg: Gocizdat, 1920, pp.
[Zhitomirskaia 2061]
/TRANSLATION: RUSSIAN

1920-10 **Harms**, H[ermann]. "Goethes Beobachtung über die Sprossmetamorphose der Opuntien." *Monatsschrift für Kakteenkunde*, 30 (1920), 188-9.
/BOTANY

1920-11 **Hauer**, Josef Matthias. *Vom Wesen des Musikalischen*. Leipzig/Wien: Waldheim-Eberle, 1920. 66 pp.
Rpt. 1923 and 1966.
/RESEARCH: MUSICOLOGY

1920-12 **Hunger**, Rudolf. "Zur Kunsterziehung in der Schule. Ein Kapitel aus Goethes Farbenlehre." *Zeitschrift für Deutschkunde*, 34 (1920), 55-75.
/CHROMATICS/PEDAGOGY

1920-13 **Kries**, Johannes von. "Goethe als Naturforscher." *Goethe*, 7 (1920), 3-44.
Rpt. of No. 1919-5.
/GENERAL INTRODUCTION

1920-14 **Lippmann**, Edmund O. von. "Der Stein der Weisen und Homunculus, zwei alchemistische Probleme in Goethes Faust." *Chemiker-Zeitung*, 44 (1920), 213-14.
Rpt. No. 1923-16.
/ALCHEMY/WORKS: FAUST/HISTORY OF SCIENCE

1920-15 **Michel**, Ernst. *Weltanschauung und Naturdeutung: Vorlesungen*

über Goethes Naturanschauung. Jena: Eugen Diederichs, 1920. 92 pp.
>   Partial rpt., No. 1927-38.
>   /METHOD/EPISTEMOLOGY

1920-16 **Molisch**, Hans. "Goethe, Darwin und die Spiraltendenz im Pflanzenreiche." *Naturwissenschaftliche Wochenschrift*, NF 19 (1920), 625-9.
>   /BOTANY/DARWIN, C/MORPHOLOGY

1920-17 **Nordenskiöld**, Erik. "Goethe." In his *Biologins historia: II: Biologin under 1600 -- och 1700 talen.* Helsingfors: Holger Schildt/Stockholm: Björck & Börjeson, 1921, pp. 225-34.
>   Trans. into German, No. 1926-31.
>   Trans. into Finnish, No. 1927-45.
>   Trans. into English, No. 1928-35.
>   In Swedish.
>   /BIOLOGY/HISTORY OF SCIENCE

1920-18 **Ostwald**, Wilhelm. "Die Farbenpsychologie." *Deutsche Psychologie*, 3, No. 1 (1920/1921), 1-40.
>   /RESEARCH: CHROMATICS/RESEARCH: PSYCHOLOGY

1921-1 **Barthel**, Ernst. "Das Verhältnis der Schopenhauerschen zur Goetheschen Farbenlehre." *Archiv für Geschichte der Philosophie*, 33 [NS 26], No. 1/2 (1921), 60-66.
>   /CHROMATICS/SCHOPENHAUER, A

1921-2 **Berendt**, Hans. "Goethe und Schelling." In *Festschrift für Berthold Litzmann zum 60. Geburtstag 18. 4. 1917 im Auftrage der Literarhistorischen Gesellschaft Bonn.* Ed. Carl Enders. Berlin: G. Grot'sche Verlagsbuchhandlung, 1921, pp. 77-104.
>   Rpt. of No. 1920-2.
>   /SCHELLING, F VON/NATURPHILSOPHIE

1921-3 **Bornmüller**, Johannes. "Ginkgo biloba L. vom sogenannten Goethe'schen Exemplar am Fürstenhaus in Weimar." *Mitteilungen des Thüringischen Vereins*, NF 35 (1921), 9.
>   /BOTANY

1921-4 **Cassirer**, Ernst. "Goethe und die mathematische Physik. Eine erkenntnistheoretische Studie." In his *Idee und Gestalt: Goethe / Schiller / Hölderlin / Kleist: Fünf Aufsätze.* Berlin: Bruno Cassirer, 1921, pp. 27-76.

Rpt. Nos. 1924-6 and 1981-9.
/CHROMATICS/NEWTON, I/EPISTEMOLOGY

1921-5 **Deetjen**, Werner. "Goethes Mitarbeit an dem naturhistorischen Bilder- und Lesebuch von Jakob Glatz." *Jahrbuch der Sammlung Kippenberg*, 1 (1921), 178-80.
/GLATZ, J/PEDAGOGY

1921-6 **Engel**, Eduard. "Goethes Weltanschauung. Naturwissenschaft, Philosophie, Religion." In his *Goethe: Der Mann und das Werk*. 2 vols. 11th rev. edn. Hamburg/Braunschweig/Berlin: Verlag von Georg Westermann, 1921, pp. 713-36.
/GENERAL INTRODUCTION/PHILOSOPHY

1921-7 **Ferrari**, Giuseppe Michele. "Goethe naturalista [Goethe the Naturalist]." *L'Arduo*, 1, No. 12, S.II (1921), 439-60.
In Italian.
/GENERAL INTRODUCTION

1921-8 **II Führer** *durch den Sammlungsanbau des Goethe-Hauses: Mit dem Grundriß des I. und II. Obergeschosses*. Amtliche Ausgabe. [Weimar:] Das Goethe-Nationalmuseum in Weimar[, 1921]. 94 pp.
Rpt. 2nd edn. 1922.
/GOETHE'S COLLECTIONS

1921-9 **[Goethe**, Johann Wolfgang von.] *Goethes naturwissenschaftliche Schriften*. Vol. 1. Ed and intro. Rudolf Steiner. Vol. 33 of *Goethes Werke*. Vol. 114 of *Deutsche National-Literatur: Historisch kritische Ausgabe*. Ed. Joseph Kürschner. Stuttgart/Berlin/Leipzig: Union Deutsche Verlagsgesellschaft[, 1921]. lxxxiv, 472 pp.
Rpt. of No. 1882-10.
/EDITION

1921-10 **[Goethe**, Johann Wolfgang von.] *Goethes naturwissenschaftliche Schriften*. Vol. 2. Ed and intro. Rudolf Steiner. Vol. 34 of *Goethes Werke*. Vol. 115 of *Deutsche National-Literatur: Historisch kritische Ausgabe*. Ed. Joseph Kürschner. Stuttgart/Berlin/Leipzig: Union Deutsche Verlagsgesellschaft[, 1921]. lxxiv, 403 pp.
Rpt. of No. 1884-5.
/EDITION

1921-11 **[Goethe**, Johann Wolfgang von.] *Goethes naturwissenschaftliche Schriften*. Vol. 3. Ed and intro. Rudolf Steiner. Vol. 35 of *Goethes Werke*. Vol. 116 of *Deutsche National-Literatur: Historisch kritische*

Ausgabe. Ed. Joseph Kürschner. Stuttgart/Berlin/Leipzig: Union Deutsche Verlagsgesellschaft[, 1921]. xxxii, 540 pp.
Rpt. of No. 1884-6.
/EDITION

1921-12 [**Goethe**, Johann Wolfgang von.] *Goethes naturwissenschaftliche Schriften.* Vol. 4.1. Ed and intro. Rudolf Steiner. Vol. 36.1 of *Goethes Werke.* Vol. 117.1 of *Deutsche National-Literatur: Historisch kritische Ausgabe.* Ed. Joseph Kürschner. Stuttgart/Berlin/Leipzig: Union Deutsche Verlagsgesellschaft[, 1921]. xvi, 341 pp.
/EDITION

1921-13 [**Goethe**, Johann Wolfgang von.] *Goethes naturwissenschaftliche Schriften.* Vol. 4.2. Ed and intro. Rudolf Steiner. Vol. 36.2 of *Goethes Werke.* Vol. 117.2 of *Deutsche National-Literatur: Historisch kritische Ausgabe.* Ed. Joseph Kürschner. Stuttgart/Berlin/Leipzig: Union Deutsche Verlagsgesellschaft[, 1921]. 660 pp.
/EDITION

1921-14 **Hansen**, A[dolph]. "Zur Metamorphosenlehre." *Naturwissenschaftliche Wochenschrift*, 20 (1921), 7-8.
/BOTANY/RESEARCH: BOTANY

1921-15 **Hayata**, Bunzo. "An Interpretation of Goethe's Blatt in his 'Metamorphose der Pflanzen', as an Explanation of the Principle of Natural Classification." In [Japanese title:] *Icones Plantarum Formosanarum nec non et Contributiones ad Floram Formosanam. Or, Icones of the Plants of Formosa, and Materials for a Flora of the Island, based on a Study of the Collections of the Botanical Survey of the Government of Formosa.* Taihoku: Bureau of Productive Industries, Government of Formosa, 1921, X, 75-95.
/BOTANY/RECEPTION: JAPAN

1921-16 **Klinckowstroem**, Graf Carl von. "Goethe und Ritter. (Mit Ritters Briefen an Goethe)." *Goethe*, 8 (1921), 135-51.
/RITTER, J/NATURPHILOSOPHIE/CHROMATICS

1921-17 **Lakon**, Georg. "Goethes Physiologische Erklärung der Pflanzenmetamorphose als moderne Hypothese von dem Einfluß der Ernährung auf Entwicklung und Gestaltung der Pflanze." *Beihefte zum Botanischen Centralblatt. Original-Arbeiten. Erste Abteilung: Anatomie, Histologie, Morphologie und Physiologie der Pflanzen*, 38

(1921), 158-81.
/BOTANY/PHYSIOLOGY/MORPHOLOGY

1921-18 **Martell**, Paul. "Goethe und die Technik." *Die Braunschweiger G. N. C.-Monatsschrift*, No. 2 (1921), 99-104. Rpt. Nos. 1925-23, 1927-35 and 1929-40.
/TECHNOLOGY

1921-19 **Möbius**, M[artin]. "Zur Metamorphose der Pflanzen." *Naturwissenschaftliche Wochenschrift*, NF 20 (1921), 739-42.
/BOTANY/RESEARCH: BOTANY/MORPHOLOGY

1921-20 **Riemer**, Friedrich Wilhelm. "Farbenlehre." In *Friedrich Wilhelm Riemer Mitteilungen über Goethe*. Ed. Arthur Pollmer. Leipzig: Insel-Verlag, 1921, pp. 226-8. Rpt. of No. 1841-12.
/CHROMATICS

1921-21 **Riemer**, Friedrich Wilhelm. "(Über ein geologisches Basrelief von Goethe)." In Friedrich Wilhelm Riemer. *Mitteilungen über Goethe*. Leipzig: Insel-Verlag, 1921, p. 343.
/GEOLOGY

1921-22 **Schwebsch**, Erich. "Rudolf Steiner und Goethe." In *Vom Lebenswerk Rudolf Steiners: Eine Hoffnung neuer Kultur*. Ed. Friedrich Rittelmeyer. München: Chr. Kaiser Verlag, 1921, pp. 241-72.
/STEINER, R/RECEPTION

1921-23 **Stein**, Walter Johannes. *Die moderne naturwissenschaftliche Vorstellungsart und die Weltanschauung Goethes, wie sie Rudolf Steiner vertritt. Historisch-kritische Beiträge zur Entwicklung der neuren Philosophie*. Diss. Wien. Wissenschaft und Zukunft. N.p.: Der kommende Tag AG Verlag, 1921. 116 pp. Rpt. of No. 1919-16. Rpt. No. 1985-99.
/METHOD/EPISTEMOLOGY/STEINER, R

1921-24 **Steiner**, Rudolf. "Die Entstehung der Metamorphosenlehre. Über das Wesen und die Bedeutung von Goethes Schriften über organische Bildung." In *Goethes Naturwissenschaftliche Schriften*. Ed. Rudolf Steiner. Stuttgart/Leipzig/Berlin: Union Deutsche Verlagsgesellschaft[, 1921], I, xx-xxxiv; lii-lxxvii; lxxviii-lxxxiv.
/MORPHOLOGY/BIOLOGY/BOTANY/ZOOLOGY

1921-25 **Steiner**, Rudolf. "Die Entstehung von Goethes Gedanken über die Bildung der Tiere." In *Goethes Naturwissenschaftliche Schriften*. Ed. Rudolf Steiner. Stuttgart/Leipzig/Berlin: Union Deutsche Verlagsgesellschaft[, 1921], I, xxxiv-lii.
    Rpt. of No. 1882-23.
    Rpt. No. 1926-33.
    /ZOOLOGY/MORPHOLOGY

1921-26 **Steiner**, Rudolf. "Das geologische Grundprinzip Goethes." In *Goethes Naturwissenschaftliche Schriften*. Ed. Rudolf Steiner. Stuttgart/Leipzig/Berlin: Union Deutsche Verlagsgesellschaft[, 1921], II, lix-lxxiii.
    /GEOLOGY

1921-27 **Steiner**, Rudolf. *Goethes Weltanschauung*. 5th-12th edn. Berlin: Philosophisch-Anthroposophischer Verlag, 1921. 175 pp.
    Rpt. of No. 1897-12.
    /GENERAL INTRODUCTION/HEGEL, G/NATURPHIL-OSOPHIE

1921-28 **Steiner**, Rudolf. "Goethe und die Mathematik." In *Goethes Naturwissenschaftliche Schriften*. Ed. Rudolf Steiner. Stuttgart/Leipzig/ Berlin: Union Deutsche Verlagsgesellschaft[, 1921], II, lxvii, lxix.
    Rpt. Nos. 1926-38, 1932-310 and 1948-41.
    /MATHEMATICS

1921-29 **Steiner**, Rudolf. "Die meteorologischen Vorstellungen Goethes." In *Goethes Naturwissenschaftliche Schriften*. Ed. Rudolf Steiner. 4 vols. Stuttgart, Berlin, Leipzig: Union Deutsche Verlagsgesellschaft[, 1921], pp. lxxiii-lxxiv.
    /METEOROLOGY

1921-30 **Troxler**, Ignaz Paul Vital. *Blicke in das Wesen des Menschen*. Goetheanum Bücherei. Ed. and intro. Hans Erhard Lauer. Stuttgart: Der kommende Tag A.-G./Verlag, 1921. 154 pp.
    /RESEARCH: ANTHROPOLOGY/RESEARCH: PSYCHOLOGY

1921-31 ***Urban**, Henry F. "Curie, Einstein und Goethe." *Berliner Lokal-Anzeiger*, No. 282, 17 June 1921.
    /CURIE, M/EINSTEIN, A

1921-32 **Wahl**, Hans. "Goethe im Gärtnerhaus am Botanischen Garten 1817-1830. Führer durch die Goethezimmer." Jena: G. Neuenhahn, 1921. 16 pp.
/BOTANY/PLACES: BOTANISCHER GARTEN, JENA

1922-1 **[anon.]** "Goetheanismus." *Die Drei*, 2 (1922/1923), 585-6; 674-5.
/NATURPHILOSOPHIE/METHOD

1922-2 **[anon.]** -"Ko-te tui yu tzu-jan k'o-hsueh chih kung-hsien [Goethe's Contribution to Natural Science]." *Hsueh-teng [Study Lamp]*, 25 March 1922.
In Chinese.
/GENERAL INTRODUCTION

1922-3 **Barthel**, Ernst. *Goethes Wissenschaftslehre in ihrer modernen Tragweite*. Bonn: Verlag von Friedrich Cohen, 1922. 119 pp.
/EPISTEMOLOGY/METHOD/NATURPHILOSOPHIE

1922-4 **Behme**, Friedrich. "Goethe im Obertale." In his *Das Okertal*. Pt. III of his *Geologischer Harzführer*. 4th rev. edn. Hannover: Hahnsche Buchhandlung, 1922, pp. 31-7.
/GEOLOGY/PLACES: HARZ

1922-5 **Bopp**, Walter. "Goethes Morphologie als Versuch einer reinen Phänomenologie des Organischen." *Zeitschrift für die Geschichte der Anatomie*, Abt. 3, 24 (1922), 657-85.
/MORPHOLOGY/PHENOMENOLOGY

1922-6 **Braun**, Otto. "Goethe und Schelling: Eine Studie." *Goethe*, 9 (1922), 199-214.
/SCHELLING, F VON/NATURPHILOSOPHIE

1922-7 **Carus**, Carl Gustav. "Frommsein und Pietismus. Fragment eines vor ungefähr 30 Jahren an einen Freund nach L. . . . . . geschriebenen Briefes." *Die Drei*, 2 (1922/1923), 592-5.
Rpt. of No. 1848-1.
Under the rubric "Goetheanismus."
"Aus seinem Werke: 'Mnemosyne, Blätter aus Gedenk- und Tagebüchern.' 1848."
/NATURPHILOSOPHIE

1922-8 **Carus**, Carl Gustav. "Sein -- Nichtsein. Aus einem Briefe an einen Freund im Jahre 1817." *Die Drei*, 2 (1922/ 1923), 596-7.

Under the rubric "Goetheanismus."
/NATURPHILOSOPHIE

1922-9 **Chamberlain**, Houston Stewart. "Grundlagen, Kant, Goethe / Goethe und Linné." In his *Lebenswege meines Denkens*. 2nd edn. München: F. Bruckmann, 1922, 140-48.
/KANT, I/EPISTEMOLOGY/LINNAEUS [LINNÉ], C
/BOTANY

1922-10 *****Diergart**, Paul. "Auf unbeachteten Pfaden Goethes in Straßburg." *Bonner Zeitung: Beilage Hochschule u. Wissenschaft*, No. 5, 24 July 1922.
Rpt. No. 1927-13.
/PLACES: STRAßBURG/SPIELMANN, J

1922-11 **F[?].**, H[?]. H. "Astronomisches vom Gesichtspunkt Goethescher Naturanschauung." *Die Drei: Monatsschrift für Anthroposophie Dreigliederung und Goetheanismus*, 2 (1922), 449-54.
/ASTRONOMY

1922-12 **Feldhaus**, Franz M. "Irrtümer im 'Faust'." *Geschichtsblätter für Technik und Industrie*, 9 (1922), 97-8.
/TECHNOLOGY/WORKS: FAUST

1922-13 **Francke**, Otto. "Eine Begegnung des Mineralogen Christian Samuel Weiß mit Goethe." *Goethe*, 9 (1922), 282-4.
/WEIß, C/MINERALOGY

1922-14 **Frei**, Hans Heinrich. "Die Schöpfung des Menschen: von Karl Snell, ordentl. Professor der Mathematik und Physik an der Universität Jena. 1863: Eine Würdigung." *Die Drei*, 2 (1922/1923), 945-56.
Under the rubric "Goetheanismus."
/NATURPHILOSOPHIE

1922-15 **Fricke**, Hermann. "Die tägliche Doppelschwingung des Luftdrucks als Wirkung der Schwerkraft." *Meteorologische Zeitschrift*, 39 (1922), 247-8.
/METEOROLOGY

1922-16 *****Goethe**, J. W. von. "Goethe: Natur." Illustr. Sascha Kronburg. Wien/Leipzig: Wiener Graphische Werkstätte, 1922. 13 pp.
Frankfurter Goethe-Museum III E 60.
/EDITION

1922-17 [**Goethe**, J. W. von.] *Goethes Philosophie aus seinen Werken. Ein Bild für jeden gebildeten Deutschen.* Ed. and intro. Max Heynacher. 2nd revised edn. Philosophische Bibliothek, 109. Leipzig: Verlag von Felix Meiner, 1922. cxxxi, 319 pp.
      Cf. Nos. 1922-23 and 1922-24.
      /EDITION: SELECTIONS

1922-18 **Goethe**[, J. W. von] [Tobler, Georg?]. "Hymne an die Natur." Illustr. Joseph Iberz. Die Drucke der Schönen Rarität. Hamburg: Harms Verlag[, 1922].
      /EDITION

1922-19 **Goethe**[, J. W. von] [Tobler, Georg?]. "Natur." Wien/ Leipzig: Verlag der Wiener Graphischen Werkstätte, 1922. 13 pp.
      /EDITION

1922-20 **Grävell**, F[riedrich]. *Goethe im Recht gegen Newton.* Ed. and intro. Guenther Wachsmuth. Stuttgart: Der kommende Tag A.-G. Verlag, 1922. xix, 207 pp.
      Rpt. of No. 1857-3.
      /CHROMATICS/NEWTON, I

1922-21 *****Hartenstein**, Gustav. "Goethe über den Zwischenkiefer und einen pathologischen Befund am Oberkiefer." Diss. Freiburg i. Br. 1922.
      Cf. No. 1922-22.
      /OSTEOLOGY/PATHOLOGY

1922-22 *****Hertenstein**, Gustav. "Goethe über den Zwischenkiefer und einen pathologischen Befund am Oberkiefer." Med. Diss. Freiburg 1922. 15 pp.
      Cf. No. 1922-21.
      Typescript.
      /OSTEOLOGY/PATHOLOGY

1922-23 **Heynacher**, Max. "Die Farbenlehre." In *Goethes Philosophie aus seinen Werken. Ein Buch für jeden gebildeten Deutschen.* Ed. and intro. Max Heynacher. 2nd revised edn. Philosophische Bibliothek, 109. Leipzig: Verlag von Felix Meiner, 1922, pp. lxxxiv-lxxxviii.
      /CHROMATICS/PHILOSOPHY

1922-24 **Heynacher**, Max. "Die Metamorphose der Tiere und Pflanzen."

In *Goethes Philosophie aus seinen Werken. Ein Bild für jeden gebildeten Deutschen.* Ed. and intro. Max Heynacher. 2nd revised edn. Philosophische Bibliothek, 109. Leipzig: Verlag von Felix Meiner, 1922, pp. xli-xlv.
/CHROMATICS/PHILOSOPHY

1922-25 **Kalkhof**, Josef. "Das Leben eines Goetheanisten: Gotthilf Heinrich Schubert: (26. IV 1780 bis 31. VII 1860)." *Die Drei*, 2 (1922/1923), 850-55.
Under the rubric "Goetheanismus."
/SCHUBERT, G/NATURPHILOSOPHIE

1922-26 *****Kuo**, Mo-jo. ["The Merits of J. W. Goethe in the Natural Sciences."] [*Lantern of Study*], 23 March 1922.
In Chinese.
/GENERAL INTRODUCTION

1922-27 **List**, Friedrich. "Goethes durchgewachsene Birne: (Ein familiengeschichtlicher und literarhistorischer Beitrag zu Goethes morphologischen Studien): Hans Gerhard Gräf zu seiner Wiedergenesung dargebracht." *Goethe*, 9 (1922), 277-81.
/MORPHOLOGY/BOTANY/PATHOLOGY

1922-28 **Maier**, Rudolf E. "Das Urphänomen der Lichtbeugung: Mitteilungen aus 'Der kommende Tag': Wissenschaftliches Forschungsinstitut." *Die Drei*, 2 (1922/1923), 926-37.
Under the rubric "Goetheanismus."
/RESEARCH: OPTICS/RESEARCH: CHROMATICS

1922-29 **Oken**, Lorenz. "Die farbigen Schatten, ihr Entstehen und Gesetz von Heinrich Zschokke. (Rezension.)." *Die Drei*, 2 (1922/1923), 694-5.
Rpt. of No. 1826-11.
"Vorlesung, gehalten in der Naturforschenden Gesellschaft zu Aarau 1826. Bei Sauerländer."
/RESEARCH: CHROMATICS/CHROMATICS/ZSCHOKKE, H/REVIEW

1922-30 **Oken**, Lorenz[?]. "Merkwürdige Phänomene. (Rezension.)." *Die Drei*, 2 (1922/1923), 676-93.
Rpt. of No. 1818-10.
Under the rubric "Goetheanismus."
/REVIEW/CHROMATICS/RESEARCH: CHROMATICS/NEWTON, I

1922-31 **Paucker**, C[?]. J. A. "Ideen zu einer Theosophie." *Die Drei*, 2 (1922/1923), 587-91.
Orig. publ. 1819.
Under the rubric "Goetheanismus."
/NATURPHILOSOPHIE

1922-32 **Podestà**, Hans. "Goethes und Schillers Anteil." In his *Physiologische Farbenlehre*. Vol. 4 of his *Die Farbenlehre: In fünf Büchern*. Leipzig: Verlag Unesma, 1922, p. 172.
/COLORBLINDNESS/SCHILLER, F

1922-33 **Puchtinger**, Franz. "Goethes mineralogische Studien und der Steinschneider Müller." In his *Goethe in Karlsbad*. Karlsbad und Leipzig: Walther Heinrich, 1922, pp. 139-56.
/GEOLOGY/MÜLLER, C

1922-34 **Schiff**, Julius. "Mignon, Ottilie, Makarie im Lichte der Goetheschen Naturphilosophie." *Goethe*, 9 (1922), 133-47.
/NATURPHILOSOPHIE/WORKS: WILHELM MEISTERS LEHRJAHRE /WORKS: DIE WAHLVERWANDT-SCHAFTEN/WORKS: WILHELM MEISTERS WANDER-JAHRE

1922-35 **Siebeck**, Herman. "Die Natur." In his *Goethe als Denker*. Fromanns Klassiker der Philosophie, 15. Stuttgart: Fr. Fromanns Verlag (H. Kurtz), 1922, pp. 62-117.
/NATURPHILOSOPHIE

1922-36 ***Speyrer**, Kurt. "Goethes Sammlungen zur Physik und Chemie." In *Führer durch das Goethe-Nationalmuseum II*. Weimar, 1922, 6-25.
/EXHIBITION/GOETHE'S COLLECTIONS/CHROMA-TICS/CHEMISTRY

1922-37 **Steffen**, Albert. "Vorträge Rudolf Steiners über das Wesen der Farben." *Die Drei (Wochenschrift für Anthroposophie)*, 2 (1922/1923), 802-16.
/STEINER, R/RESEARCH: CHROMATICS/CHROMATICS

1922-38 **Stein**, W[alther]. J[ohannes]. "Goetheanismus. Ein Blatt aus dem Nachlass von Wilhelm Heinrich Preuss. (Unveröffentlicht.)" *Die Drei*, 2 (1922/1923), 266-7.
/PREUSS, W/NATURPHILOSOPHIE

1922-39 **Sticker**, Georg. "Goethes Morphologie und Metamorphosenlehre." *Fortschritte der Medizin*, 40 (1922), xv-xvii.
/MORPHOLOGY

1922-40 **Strakosch**, Alexander. "Agnostische Wissenschaft und ihre
sozialen Folgen, erläutert an Ostwalds Farbenlehre." *Die Drei:
Monatsschrift für Anthroposophie und Dreigliederung*, 1 (1922), 989-
1000.
/OSTWALD, W/RESEARCH: CHROMATICS/CHROMA-
TICS/METHOD/PHILOSOPHY

1922-41 *****Sudhoff**, Karl. "Goethe und die Anfänge der deutschen Natur-
forscherversammlung." *Leipziger Neueste Nachrichten*, 19 Sept.
1922.
/INSTITUTIONS: DEUTSCHE NATURFORSCHERVER-
SAMMLUNG

1922-42 **Troll**, Wilhelm. "Goethes Naturanschauung in seinen Gedichten." *Naturwissenschaftliche Wochenschrift*, 37 [NS 21] (1922),
313-17.
/NATURPHILOSOPHIE/GENERAL INTRODUCTION

1922-43 **Uehli**, Ernst and Eugen **Kolisko**. "Zur Wiederbelebung des
'Goetheanismus'." *Die Drei: Monatsschrift für Anthroposophie und
Dreigliederung*, 1, No. 12 (1922), 1177-83.
Contains an excerpt from F. S. Voigt's *System der Natur und
ihre Geschichte* (1823).
/VOIGT, F/RECEPTION/NATURPHILOSOPHIE

1922-44 **Usteri**, A[?]. "Eine vergessene Blattstellungstheorie." *Die Drei:
Monatsschrift für Anthroposophie und Dreigliederung*, 2 (1922/1923),
455-9.
Under the rubric "Goetheanismus."
/RESEARCH: BOTANY/RESEARCH: MORPHOLOGY

1922-45 **Waaser**, Friedrich. "Grundsätzliches zu Goethes Metamorphosenlehre." *Naturwissenschaftliche Wochenschrift*, NF 21 (1922), 473-
9.
/MORPHOLOGY

1922-46 **Wachsmuth**, Günther. "Introduction" to Grävell, Friedrich.
Goethe im Recht gegen Newton. Stuttgart: Der kommende Tag, 1922.
/CHROMATICS

1922-47 **Wessely**, Karl. "Goethes und Schopenhauers Stellung in der Geschichte der Lehre von den Gesichtsempfindungen." Berlin: Verlag von Julius Springer, 1922. 43 pp.
"Rektoratsrede anlässlich der 340. Stiftungsfeier der Universität Würzburg gehalten in der Aula am 11. Mai 1922."
/CHROMATICS/SCHOPENHAUER, A/HISTORY OF SCIENCE

1922-48 *****Wohlbold**, Hans. "Raumerlebnis und Farbenlehre." Stuttgart: Der kommende Tag, 1922. 41 pp.
/RESEARCH: CHROMATICS/RESEARCH: PSYCHOLOGY

1922-49 **Worm**, Walter. "Stomatologisches bei Goethe." Berlin: Berlinische Verlagsanstalt, 1922. 44 pp.
/STOMATOLOGY

1922-50 *****Zell**, Th[eodor]. "Goethe und die Naturwissenschaften." *Der Tag*, No. 262, 25 August 1922.
/GENERAL INTRODUCTION

1922-51 **Zinkernagel**, Franz. "Goethes Ur-Meister und der Typusgedanke: Eine akademische Rede." Zürich: Verlag Seldwyla, 1922. 30 pp.
/MORPHOLOGY/WORKS: WILHELM MEISTERS THEATRALISCHE SENDUNG/LITERARY THEORY

1923-1 **Almquist**, E[?]. "Linné und das natürliche Pflanzensystem." *Botanische Jahrbücher für Systematik, Pflanzengeschichte und Pflanzengeographie*, 58 (1923), 1-14.
Cf. esp. pp. 7-9, "Goethes Anschauungen."
/BOTANY/LINNAEUS [LINNÉ], C

1923-2 **B[?]**. "Ein endlich erfüllter Wunsch Goethes." *Deutsche Allgemeine Zeitung, Süddeutsche Ausgabe*, 21 October 1923.
In Mappe III E 61/C20: "Goethe und die Naturwissenschaften. Zeitungsausschnitte 1913 -" at the Frankfurter Goethe-Museum.
/CHROMATICS

1923-3 **Barthel**, Ernst. *Goethes Relativitätstheorie der Farbe: Nebst einer musikästhetischen Parallele*. Bonn: Verlag von Friedrich Cohen, 1923. 72 pp.
/CHROMATICS/RESEARCH: CHROMATICS/RESEARCH:

MUSIC THEORY

1923-4 **Bode**, Wilhelm. "Erdschöpfung, Faust, Metamorphose und ein Söhnchen: Winter 1789/90." In his *Goethes Leben [VII.]: 1787-1790 Rom und Weimar*. Berlin: E. S. Mittler & Sohn, 1923, pp. 271-300.
/GEOLOGY/WORKS: FAUST/MORPHOLOGY

1923-5 *****Bopp**, Walter. "Goethes Morphologie als Versuch einer reinen Phänomenologie des Organischen." Diss. Heidelberg 1923.
Rpt. No. 1923-6.
/MORPHOLOGY/EPISTEMOLOGY/NATURPHILOSOPHIE

1923-6 **Bopp**, Walter. "Goethes Morphologie als Versuch einer reinen Phänomenologie des Organischen." *Ergebnisse der Anatomie und Entwicklungsgeschichte*, 24 (1923), 657-85.
Rpt. of No. 1923-5.
/MORPHOLOGY/EPISTEMOLOGY/NATURPHILOSOPHIE

1923-7 **Buber**, L[?]. "Goethe in Karlsbad." *Unser Egerland: Monatsschrift für Heimaterkundung und Heimatpflege*, 27 (1923), 79-80.
/GEOLOGY/PLACES: KARLSBAD

1923-8 *****Funk**, Heinrich. "Georg Christoph Tobler, der Verfasser des pseudogoethischen Hymnus 'Die Natur'." *Zürcher Taschenbücher auf das Jahr 1924*, NS 24 (1923).
Frankfurter Goethe-Museum III E 60 / C2
/TOBLER, G

1923-9 **[Goethe**, J. W. von.] "Goethes Aufenthalt im Egerlande im Jahre 1823." *Unser Egerland: Monatsschrift für Heimaterkundung und Heimatpflege*, 27 (1923), 70-78.
/EDITION/GEOLOGY/PLACES: EGERLAND

1923-10 **Haberlandt**, Gottlieb. "Goethe und die Pflanzenphysiologie. Bernhard Seuffert zum siebzigsten Geburtstag am 23. Mai 1923 gewidmet." Leipzig: Verlag von Max Weg, 1923. 21 pp.
/BOTANY/PHYSIOLOGY

1923-11 **Haldane**, Richard Burdon Viscount. "Goethe as a Thinker." *Contemporary Review*, 12A (1923), 137-48.
Rpt. No. 1924-21.
Trans. into German, No. 1924-20.
/NATURPHILOSOPHIE/PHILOSOPHY

1923-12 **Hauer**, Josef Matthias. "Goethes Farbenlehre." In his *Deutung des Melos: Eine Frage an die Künstler und Denker unserer Zeit.* Leipzig/Wien/Zürich: E. P. Tal, 1923.
/CHROMATICS/RESEARCH: MUSIC THEORY

1923-13 **Kalkhof**, Josef. "Goetheanismus. Das Leben eines Goetheanisten Gotthilf Heinrich Schubert (26. IV. 1780 bis 31. VII. 1860)." *Die Drei: Monatsschrift für Anthroposophie: Dreigliederung und Goetheanismus*, 2, No. 10/11 (1923), 850-55.
/SCHUBERT, G/NATURPHILOSOPHIE

1923-14 **Lasaulx**, Ernst von. "Die Sühnopfer der Griechen und Römer und ihr Verhältnis zu dem einen auf Golgotha: Ein Beitrag zur Religionsphilosophie." (Stellenweise gekürzt.)" *Die Drei*, 3 (1923), 147-60.
Under the rubric "Goetheanismus."
/NATURPHILOSOPHIE

1923-15 **Lippmann**, Edmund O. "Goethe und die Zuckerfabrikation." In his *Beiträge zur Geschichte der Naturwissenschaften und der Technik.* Berlin: Verlag von Julius Springer, 1923, pp. 275-81.
Rpt. of No. 1919-6.
/CHEMISTRY/TECHNOLOGY

1923-16 **Lippmann**, Edmund O. von. "Der Stein der Weisen und Homunculus, zwei alchemistische Probleme in Goethes Faust." In his *Beiträge zur Geschichte der Naturwissenschaften und der Technik.* Berlin: Verlag von Juius Springer, 1923, pp. 251-5.
Rpt. of No. 1920-14.
/ALCHEMY/WORKS: FAUST/HISTORY OF SCIENCE

1923-17 ***Maier**, Rudolf. "Das Urphänomen der Lichtbeugung." *Die Drei*, 2, No. 12 (1923).
/RESEARCH: OPTICS

1923-18 ***Maier**, Rudolf. *Der Villardsche Versuch.* Stuttgart: Der kommende Tag, 1923.
/RESEARCH: PHYSICS/VILLARD, P

1923-19 **Mendel**, Kurt. "Goethe und der Impfzwang." *Deutsche medizinische Wochenschrift*, 49 (1923), 557.
/MEDICINE

1923-20 **Noggler**, Josef. "Goethe in seinen Beziehungen zu Pharmazeuten." *Pharmazeutische Monatshefte*, 4 (1923), 82-8; 101-5; 125-8. "Vortrag, gehalten in der Oesterr. pharmazeutischen Gesellschaft in Wien am 22. März 1923."
/PHARMACOLOGY/CHEMISTRY

1923-21 **Schiff**, Julius. "Eine Niederschrift des Chemikers J. W. Döbereiner für Goethe und die Grossherzogin Maria Paulowna." *Die Naturwissenschaften: Wochenschrift für die Fortschritte der Naturwissenschaften, der Medizin, und der Technik*, 11 (1923), 89-90.
/DÖBEREINER, J/CHEMISTRY

1923-22 **Schiff**, Julius. "Unveröffentlichte chemische Dokumente aus dem Goethe- und Schiller-Archiv in Weimar." *Chemiker-Zeitung*, 47 (1923), 385-6.
/CHEMISTRY/DÖBEREINER, J

1923-23 **Schopenhauer**, Arthur. "Ueber das Sehn und die Farben." In *Arthur Schopenhauers sämtliche Werke*. Ed. Paul Deussen. München: R. Piper & Co., 1923, VI, 5-87.
Rpt. of No. 1816-4.
/RESEARCH: CHROMATICS

1923-24 *****Schüphaus**, Emilie. "Die psychologisch-optischen Untersuchungen in Goethes Farbenlehre." Diss. Münster 1923.
/CHROMATICS/OPTICS/PSYCHOLOGY

1923-25 **Sonnefeld**, A[?]. "Die optischen Studien von Goethe: 'Zur Farbenlehre'." *Optische Rundschau und Photo-Optiker*, 23 (1923), 170-78.
/CHROMATICS

1923-26 **Steffen**, Albert. "Vorträge Rudolf Steiners über das Wesen der Farben gehalten am Goetheanum." *Die Drei: Monatsschrift für Anthroposophie Dreigliederung und Goetheanismus*, 2, No. 10/11 (1923), 802-16.
/RESEARCH: CHROMATICS/STEINER, R

1923-27 *****Steiner**, Rudolf. "Goethe und die Mathematik." *Das Goetheanum*, 26 August 1923.
Rpt. of No. 1921-28.
/MATHEMATICS

1923-28 *****Steiner**, Rudolf. "Goethe und Goetheanum." *Das Goethe-

anum, 25 March 1923.
   Rpt. No. 1932-311.
   /ANTHROPOSOPHY/MORPHOLOGY/EPISTEMOLOGY

1923-29 **Uexküll**, J[akob Baron]. v[on]. "Die Stellung der Naturforscher
   zu Goethes Gott-Natur." *Die Tat: Monatsschrift für die Zukunft
   deutscher Kultur*, 15, No. 7 (1923/1924), 492-506.
   /RECEPTION/GENERAL INTRODUCTION/NATUR-
   PHILOSOPHIE

1923-30 **Wien**, Wilhelm. "Goethe und die Physik." Leipzig: Verlag von
   Johann Ambrosius Barth, 1923. 39 pp.
   Rpt. No. 1930-57.
   "Vortrag gehalten in der Münchener Universität am 9. Mai
   1923."
   Rev. P. Volkmann, *Annalen der Philosophie*, 4 (1924), 101-2.
   /CHROMATICS/NEWTON, I

1924-1 "**Abdruck** einer Kupferplatte aus Goethes Nachlaß mit dem nach
   Goethes Entwurf (1806) gestochenen Siegel der Naturforschenden
   Gesellschaft zu Jena. Für Herrn Prof. Dr. Anton Kippenberg einmal
   abgezogen und mit den herzlichsten Glückwünschen des Goethe-
   Nationalmuseums am 22. Mai. 1924 überreicht von Hans Wahl."
   n.p.: privately printed[, 1924]. 1 pg.
   /INSTITUTIONS: NATURFORSCHENDE GESELLSCHAFT
   ZU JENA

1924-2 **Arendt**, Th[?]. "Vom Brockengespenst." *Meteorologische
   Zeitschrift*, 41 (1924), 280-82.
   "LIX. Band der 'Zeitschrift der Österr. Gesellschaft für
   Meteorologie' 1924."
   /METEOROLOGY/OPTICS

1924-3 **Barthel**, Ernst. "Goethes Farbenlehre und das negative Spek-
   trum." *Kölnische Zeitung*, No. 606, 28 August 1924, Beilage.
   Rpt. No. 1925-1.
   /CHROMATICS/RESEARCH: CHROMATICS

1924-4 **Brauer**, Kurt. "Goethes Briefwechsel mit Wackenroder." In
   *Studien zur Geschichte der Chemie: Festgabe Edmund O. v.
   Lippmann zum siebzigsten Geburtstage dargebracht aus nah und fern
   und im Auftrage der Deutschen Gesellschaft für Geschichte der
   Medizin und der Naturwissenschaften*. Berlin: Verlag von Julius
   Springer, 1927, pp. 159-75.

/WACKENRODER, H/CHEMISTRY/WORKS: COR-
RESPONDENCE

1924-5 **Brauer**, Kurt. "Goethe und die Chemie. (Der Briefwechsel zwischen Goethe und Wackenroder.)" *Zeitschrift für angewandte Chemie*,
37 (1924), 185-9.
Cf. No. 1924-4.
/CHEMISTRY/WACKENRODER, H

1924-6 **Cassirer**, Ernst. "Goethe und die mathematische Physik. Eine
erkenntnistheoretische Studie." In his *Idee und Gestalt: Goethe /
Schiller / Hölderlin / Kleist: Fünf Aufsätze*. 2nd edn. Berlin: Bruno
Cassirer, 1921, pp. 33-80.
Rpt. of No. 1921-4.
Rpt. No. 1975-7.
/CHROMATICS/NEWTON, I/EPISTEMOLOGY

1924-7 *****Di Tella**, O[?]. "Di Goethe e la fisica [Goethe and Physics]." *La
cultura*, No. 4, 1924-1925.
In Italian.
/CHROMATICS

1924-8 **Epstein**, Paul. "Goethe und die exakte Naturforschung."
*Festschrift zur Jahrhundertfeier des Physikalischen Vereins [Frankfurt
a. M.]*, 1924, pp. 18-35.
/CHROMATICS/NEWTON, I/RESEARCH: CHROMATICS

1924-9 **Epstein**, Paul. "Goethe und die Mathematik." *Goethe*, 10 (1924),
76-102.
"Vortrag, gehalten am 10. Dezember 1922 in der Gesellschaft
der Freunde des Goethemuseums zu Frankfurt a. M."
/MATHEMATICS

1924-10 **Gebhardt**, Martin. "Goethe als dichtender Physiker." *Das
Schönburgische Geistervariété*. Waldenburger Schriften, 4. Privately
printed, 1924, pp. 105-17.
Rpt. Nos. 1925-11 and 1925-12.
"Privatdruck für Seine Durchlaucht den Fürsten Günther von
Schönburg-Waldenburg von Georg Minde-Pouet heraus-
gegeben in 100 nummerierten Exemplaren 1925."
/CHROMATICS

1924-11 **Glockner**, Hermann. "Das philosophische Problem in Goethes
Farbenlehre. Ein Vortrag." Beiträge zur Philosophie, 11. Heidel-

berg: Carl Winter's Universitätsbuchhandlung, 1924. 32 pp.
Rpt. No. 1966-9.
Trans. into Italian, No. 1981-18.
/CHROMATICS/AESTHETICS

1924-12 **Goethe**[, J. W. von]. *Die Metamorphose der Pflanzen.* Ed. with
the original illustrations by Julius Schuster. Berlin: W. Junk, 1924.
iii, 145 pp.
Rev. M[?], "Die Originalillustrationen zu Goethes Metamorphose der Pflanzen," *Deutsche Allgemeine Zeitung,
Süddeutsche Ausgabe*, 30 October 1923. [In Mappe III E
61/C20: "Goethe und die Naturwissenschaften. Zeitungsausschnitte 1913 -" at the Frankfurter Goethe-Museum.]
Rev. [anon.], *Deutsche Allgemeine Zeitung, Süddeutsche Ausgabe*, 16 March 1924. [In Mappe III E 61/C20: "Goethe und
die Naturwissenschaften. Zeitungsausschnitte 1913 -" at the
Frankfurter Goethe-Museum.]
Rev. Wilhelm Junk, "Das Missgeschick Goethes. Zu dem
Stuttgarter Goethe-Fund," *Berliner Tageblatt*, 12 September
1928. [In Mappe III E 61/C20: "Goethe und die Naturwissenschaften. Zeitungsausschnitte 1913 -" at the Frankfurter
Goethe-Museum.]
/EDITION

1924-13 [**Goethe**, J. W. von.] *Die schönsten Essays von Goethe.* Bücher
der Bildung, 5. München: Albert Langen[, 1924]. 230 pp.
Rpt. No. 1931-17.
Contains several sections on science.
/EDITION: SELECTIONS

1924-14 **Goethe**, J. W. von. *Ur Goethes Tankenvärld. Urval ur Goethes
filosofiska skrifter.* Ed. and intro. Alf Ahlberg. Berömda filosofer,
27. Stockholm: Björk & Björesson, 1924. 180 pp.
Contains several of the scientific essays.
/TRANSLATION: SWEDISH

1924-15 **Goethe**, J. W. v[on]. and Lorenz **Oken**. *Die Wirbelmetamor-
phose des Schädels von J. W. v. Goethe und Lorenz Oken.* Intro.
H[ans]. Wohlbold. München: Pflügerverlag, 1924. 83 pp.
Rpt. of No. 1807-5.
Cf. No. 1924-38.
/EDITION/RESEARCH: OSTEOLOGY/RESEARCH: MOR-
PHOLOGY

1924-16 **Gräf**, Hans Gerhard. "Naturwissenschaft." In "Goethe und Schweden: Ein Versuch." In his *Goethe: Skizzen zu des Dichters Leben und Werken*. Leipzig: H. Haessel Verlag, 1924, pp. 105-14.
/RECEPTION/PLACES: SWEDEN

1924-17 **Haberlandt**, Gottlieb. "Goethe und die Pflanzenphysiologie." *Die Naturwissenschaften: Wochenschrift für die Fortschritte der reinen und der angewandten Naturwissenschaften*, 12 (1924), 267.
"Sitzungsberichte der Preußischen Akademie der Wissenschaften. 1923."
/BOTANY/PHYSIOLOGY

1924-18 **Haeberlin**, Carl. "Goethe und die Zellenlehre." *Deutsche Allgemeine Zeitung, Süddeutsche Ausgabe*, 22 April 1924.
In Mappe III E 61/C20: "Goethe und die Naturwissenschaften. Zeitungsausschnitte 1913 -" at the Frankfurter Goethe-Museum.
/HISTOLOGY

1924-19 **Haeckel**, Ernst. "Die Naturanschauung von Darwin, Goethe und Lamarck (1882)." In *Gemeinverständliche Werke*. Vol. 5 of his *Vorträge und Abhandlungen*. Ed. Heinrich Schmidt-Jena. Leipzig: Alfred Kröner/Berlin: Carl Henschel Verlag[, 1924], pp. 291-331.
/BIOLOGY: EVOLUTION/DARWIN, C/LAMARCK, J DE

1924-20 **Haldane**, [Richard Burdon] Viscount. "Goethe als Denker." Heidelberger Akten der Portheim-Stiftung, 7. Materialien zur Naturphilosophie, 3. Heidelberg: Carl Winters Universitätsbuchhandlung, 1924. 16 pp.
German trans. of Nos. 1923-11.
/NATURPHILOSOPHIE/PHILOSOPHY

1924-21 **Haldane**, Richard Burdon Viscount. "Goethe as a Thinker. Presidential Address." *Publications of the English Goethe Society*, NS 1 (1924), 1-19.
Rpt. of No. 1923-11.
Trans. into German, No. 1924-20.
/NATURPHILOSOPHIE/PHILOSOPHY

1924-22 **Heyse**, Paul. "Goethe als Naturforscher." In *Hadrian: Alkibiades: Gedichte und Übersetzungen*. Vol. III.5 of his *Gesammelte Werke*. Stuttgart/Berlin/Grunewald: J. G. Cottasche Buchhandlung Nachfolger[, 1924], p. 604.
A poem.

/GENERAL INTRODUCTION

1924-23 **Kries**, Johannes von. *Goethe als Psycholog*. Philosophie und Geschichte: Eine Sammlung von Vorträgen und Schriften aus dem Gebiet der Philosophie und Geschichte, 5. Tübingen: Verlag von J. C. B. Mohr (Paul Siebeck), 1924. 52 pp.
Cf. No. 1919-5.
/PSYCHOLOGY/GENERAL INTRODUCTION

1924-24 **Kronenberg**, M[oritz]. "Goethes Naturanschauung." *Die Naturwissenschaften: Wochenschrift für die Fortschritte der reinen und der angewandten Naturwissenschaften*, 12, No. 44 (1924), 911-14.
/NATURPHILOSOPHIE/PHILOSOPHY

1924-25 **Lohmann**, W[?]. "Die naturwissenschaftlichen Schriften Goethes in ihrer zeitlichen Folge als Ausdruck seiner Innenentwicklung und als Grundlage für die Komposition seiner Novellenwerke." *Die Drei: Monatsschrift für Anthroposophie Dreigliederung und Goetheanismus*, 4 (1924), 333-45.
/GENERAL INTRODUCTION/BIOGRAPHY/WORKS: NOVELLEN

1924-26 **Lohmann**, W[?]. "The Study of Goethe and the Continuation of his Work." *Anthroposophical Movement: News for English-speaking Members of the Anthroposophical Society*, 1 (1924), 14-15.
/GENERAL INTRODUCTION

1924-27 **Mahnke**, Dietrich. *Leibniz und Goethe: Die Harmonie ihrer Weltansichten*. Weisheit und Tat. Eine Folge philosophischer Schriften, 4. Erfurt: Verlag Kurt Stenger, 1924. 82 pp.
/LEIBNIZ, G/NATURPHILOSOPHIE/PHILO-SOPHY/SPINOZA, B

1924-28 **Mamlock**, G[?]. "Goethes Naturweg." *Berliner Tageblatt und Handels-Zeitung [Morgen-Ausgabe]*, 53, No. 38, 23 January 1924[, 2].
/GENERAL INTRODUCTION

1924-29 **Neumann**, Ernst Wilh[elm]. "Goethe und Schopenhauer in ihrem Verhältnis zur Farbenlehre." *Natur: Illustrierte Halbmonatsschrift für Naturfreunde*, 15 (1924), 243-4.
/CHROMATICS

1924-30 *Ostwald, Wilhelm. "Goethe und die Farben." *Neue Freie Presse [Wien]*, 28 December 1924; 4 January 1925.
/CHROMATICS

1924-31 *R[?]. "Goethes durchgewachsene Blumen." *Der Tag*, No. 211, 2 September 1924.
/BOTANY

1924-32 Schickler, Eberhard. "Metamorphosen." *Die Drei: Monatsschrift für Anthroposophie Dreigliederung und Goetheanismus*, 3, No. 12 (1924), 951-4.
/RESEARCH: MORPHOLOGY

1924-33 *Schulz, Hans. "Die Stellung der physiologischen Optik." *Deutsche optische Wochenschrift*, 10 (1924), 371-2.
/CHROMATICS

1924-34 Schuster, Julius. "Goethe als botanischer Zeichner. Zum 28. August 1924." *Der Kunstwanderer: Halbmonatsschrift für Alte und Neue Kunst, für Kunstmarkt und Sammelwesen*, 6 (1924), 338-41.
/BOTANY

1924-35 Steiner, Rudolf. *Grundlinien einer Erkenntnistheorie der Goetheschen Weltanschauung mit besonderer Rücksicht auf Schiller*. 2nd exp. edn. Philosophisch-Anthroposophische Bibliothek. Dornach/Schweiz: Philosophisch-Anthroposophischer Verlag, 1924. xiii, 112 pp.
Rpt. of No. 1886-9.
/EPISTEMOLOGY

1924-36 Wachsmuth, Guenther. "Grundlagen einer neuen Farbenlehre." In his *Die ätherischen Bildekräfte im Kosmos, Erde und Mensch*. Goetheanum Bücherei, 14. Stuttgart: Der kommende Tag, 1924, pp. 155-63.
/RESEARCH: CHROMATICS/STEINER, R/ANTHRO-
POSOPHY

1924-37 Wohlbold, H[ans]. "Die Farben der Pflanzen." *Die Drei: Monatsschrift für Anthroposophie Dreigliederung und Goetheanismus*, 3, No. 12 (1924), 936-50.
/RESEARCH: BOTANY/RESEARCH: CHROMATICS

1924-38 Wohlbold, H[ans]. "Zur Einführung." In *Die Wirbelmeta-morphose des Schädels von J. W. v. Goethe und Lorenz Oken*. Intro.

H[ans]. Wohlbold. München: Pflügerverlag, 1924, pp. 5-44.
/OSTEOLOGY/MORPHOLOGY/RESEARCH: OSTEOL-
OGY/RESEARCH: MORPHOLOGY

1925-1 **Barthel**, Ernst. "Goethes Farbenlehre und das negative Spek-
trum." *Geisteskultur: Monatshefte der Comenius-Gesellschaft für
Geisteskultur und Volksbildung*, 34 (1925), 138-41.
Rpt. of No. 1924-3.
/CHROMATICS/RESEARCH: CHROMATICS

1925-2 [**Barthel**, Ernst?]. "Von Goethes Farbenlehre." *Antäus: Blätter
für neues Wirklichkeitsdenken*, No. 3, 1 February 1925, 38-9.
Rpt. No. 1925-3.
/CHROMATICS

1925-3 [**Barthel**, Ernst?]. "Von Goethes Farbenlehre." *Mannheimer
Tageblatt*, 17 February 1925.
Rpt. of No. 1925-2.
/CHROMATICS

1925-4 **Becker**, Bernhard. *Goethes Reise nach Harbke und Helmstedt.*
Helmstedt: Verlag von J. C. Schmidt, 1925. 52 pp.
/BOTANY/BEIREIS, G/VELTHEIM, GRAF VON

1925-5 **Bode**, Wilhelm. "Staatsdiener, Naturforscher, Dichter und
Denker 1784." In his *Goethes Leben [V.]: 1781-1786: Pegasus im
Joche.* Berlin: E. S. Mittler & Sohn, 1925, pp. 186-243.
/GENERAL INTRODUCTION

1925-6 **Chamberlain**, Houston Stewart. "Goethe, Linné und die exakte
Wissenschaft der Natur." In his *Rasse und Persönlichkeit.* München,
1925, pp. 112-25.
Rpt. of No. 1908-5.
/BOTANY/LINNAEUS [LINNÉ], C/METHOD

1925-7 **Christiansen**, Werner. "Über zwei aufgefundene Schriftstücke."
Euphorion, 26 (1925), 257-9.
/EDITION/BOTANY/CARL AUGUST [GROSSHERZOG VON
WEIMAR]/ VOIGT, F

1925-8 *****Claus**, H[?]. "Beiträge zur Geschichte der geologischen
Forschung in Thüringen." *Beiträge zur Geologie von Thüringen*, 1,
No. 2 (1925), 11-12.
/GEOLOGY/PLACES: THÜRINGEN

1925-9 **Drevermann**, Fritz. "Goethe und seine Stellung zur Geologie." In *Aus Natur und Museum: 55. Bericht der Senckenbergischen Natur-forschenden Gesellschaft. Heft 2.* Frankfurt a. M.: Selbstverlag der Senckenbergischen Naturforschenden Gesellschaft, 1925, pp. 45-55.
/GEOLOGY

1925-10 **Franz**, Viktor. "Zur Kennzeichnung der allgemeinen Entwick-lungsrichtungen des Organismenreiches." *Zeitschrift für induktive Abstammungs- und Vererbungslehre*, 36 (1925), 33-58.
/RESEARCH: BIOLOGY/RESEARCH: MORPHOLOGY

1925-11 **Gebhardt**, Martin. "Goethe als dichtender Physiker." *Unterrichtsblätter für Mathematik und Naturwissenschaften*, 31 (1925), 76-7.
Rpt. of No. 1924-10.
/CHROMATICS

1925-12 **Gebhardt**, Martin. "Goethe als dichtender Physiker." *Die Naturwissenschaften*, 13 (1925), 464-7; 464-5.
Rpt. of No. 1924-10.
"27. Hauptversammlung des Deutschen Vereins zur Förderung des mathematischen und naturwissenschaftlichen Unterrichts."
/CHROMATICS

1925-13 **Gebhardt**, Martin. "Goethe im Physikunterricht." *Zeitschrift für den Physikalischen und Chemischen Unterricht*, 38 (1925), 1-5; 57-67.
/CHROMATICS/PEDAGOGY

1925-14 **Goethe**[, J. W. von]. *Goethes naturwissenschaftliche Schriften. Band I.* Leipzig: Insel-Verlag[, 1925]. 885 pp.
/EDITION

1925-15 **Goethe**[, J. W. von]. *Goethes naturwissenschaftliche Schriften. Band II.* Leipzig: Insel-Verlag[, 1925]. 698 pp.
/EDITION

1925-16 **Goethe**[, J. W. von]. *Die Metamorphose der Pflanzen.* Leipzig: Insel-Verlag[, 1925]. 64 pp.
/EDITION

1925-17 **Helmholtz**, Hermann von. "Goethes Vorahnungen kommender naturwissenschaftlicher Ideen." In his *Natur und Naturwissenschaft.*

Bücher der Bildung, 11. München: Albert Langen[, 1925], pp. 137-65.

Rpt. of No. 1892-10.
"Rede, gehalten in der Generalversammlung der Goethe-Gesellschaft zu Weimar 1892."
/GENERAL INTRODUCTION

1925-18 *Ipsen, Gunther. "Goethes naturwissenschaftliche Erkenntnis." In *Das Inselschiff*, 6, No. 3 (1925).
/GENERAL INTRODUCTION

1925-19 Jacobshagen, Eduard. *Allgemeine vergleichende Formenlehre der Tiere*. Leipzig: Klinkhrdt Verlag, 1925. vii, 258 pp.
Contains numerous references to Goethe.
/ZOOLOGY/MORPHOLOGY

1925-20 Kistner, A[dolf]. "Johann Wolfgang von Goethe." In *Deutsche Meister der Naturwissenschaft*. Vol. 1 of his *Deutsche Meister der Naturwissenschaft und Technik*. 2nd exp. edn. München: Verlag Josef Kösel & Friedrich Pustet, 1925, pp. 54-73.
/GENERAL INTRODUCTION

1925-21 Koch, Franz. *Goethe und Plotin*. Leipzig: Verlagsbuchhandlung J. J. Weber, 1925. 263 pp.
/PLOTINUS/NATURPHILOSOPHIE/PHILOSOPHY/IN-FLUENCES

1925-22 *Kritzinger, H[?]. H. "Die Sterne, Goethe und wir." *Der Türmer*, 28 (1925/1926), 150-54.
/ASTRONOMY

1925-23 Martell, Paul. "Goethe und die Technik." *Das Werk: Monatsblätter der Montangruppe der Siemens-Rheinelbe-Schuckert-Union*, 4 (1925), 697-700.
Rpt. of No. 1921-18.
/TECHNOLOGY

1925-24 Meß, Friedrich. "Goethe und Beireis oder das mißlungene Genie." *Pflüger. Monatsschrift für die Heimat*, 2 (1925), 148-52; 248-50; 297-300.
/BEIREIS, G/MEDICINE/NATURPHILOSOPHIE /TECH-NOLOGY

1925-25 *Pongrácz, Sándor. "Goethe emléke a paleontologiában

[Goethe's Influence on Paleontology]." *Természettudományi Közlöny*, 1925, 374-81.
  In Hungarian.
  /PALEONTOLOGY/GEOLOGY

1925-26 **Schiff**, Julius. "Bildung und Umbildung im Pflanzenreiche." *Paul Kellers Monatsblätter: Die Bergstadt*, 14, vol. 1 (1925/1926), 391-7.
  /BOTANY/MORPHOLOGY

1925-27 **Schiff**, Julius. "Goethe, die Schlesische Vaterländische Gesellschaft und die ersten meteorologischen Beobachtungen auf der Schneekoppe." *Der Wandrer im Riesengebirge: Organ des Riesen- und Iser-Gebirgs-Vereins*, 45 (1925), 218-20.
  /METEOROLOGY/INSTITUTIONS: SCHLESISCHE VATERLÄNDISCHE GESELLSCHAFT/MÜLLER, C/BRANDES, H

1925-28 **Schiff**, Julius. "Goethe und Döbereiner über die Schwefelwässer von Berka." *Chemiker-Zeitung*, 49 (1925), 681-2.
  /GEOLOGY/DÖBEREINER, J

1925-29 **Schiff**, Julius. "J. S. C. Schweigger und sein Briefwechsel mit Goethe." *Die Naturwissenschaften: Wochenschrift für die Fortschritte der reinen und der angewandten Naturwissenschaften*, 13 (1925), 555-9.
  /SCHWEIGGER, J/CHROMATICS

1925-30 **Schiff**, Julius. "Zur Goethe-Arbeit der deutschen Naturforscher." *Die Naturwissenschaften: Wochenschrift für die Fortschritte der reinen und der angewandten Naturwissenschaften*, 13 (1925), 533-4.
  /RECEPTION/INFLUENCES

1925-31 ***Steiner**, Rudolfo [Rudolf]. *La Concezione Goethianan del Mondo*. Trans. U. Tommasini. Scrittori Italiani e Stranieri: Filosofia, 236. Lanciano: G. Carabba Edit. Tip, 1925.
  Italian trans. of No. 1897-12.
  /GENERAL INTRODUCTION/HEGEL, G/NATUR-PHILOSOPHIE

1925-32 **Totzauer**, Robert. "Entstehungsgeschichte der Stift Tepler geologischen Goethe-Sammlung." In *Beiträqe zur Geschichte des Stiftes Tepl*. 2 vols. Marienbad: Buchdruckerei und Verlag "Eger-

land," 1925, II, 259-79.
  Rpt. No. 1932-329.
  /GOETHE'S COLLECTIONS/GEOLOGY

1925-33 **Troll**, Wilhelm. "Gestalt und Gesetz. Versuch einer geistesge-
schichtlichen Grundlegung der morphologischen und physiologischen
Forschung." *Flora oder Allgemeine Botanische Zeitung*, NS 18/19
(1925), 536-65.
  Rpt. No. 1941-29.
  /RESEARCH: MORPHOLOGY/RESEARCH: PHYSIOL-
  OGY/NATURPHILOSOPHIE

1925-34 **Wagner**, Wilhelm. "Goethe und der geologische Aufbau des
Rochusbergs bei Bingen." *Notizblatt des Vereins für Erdkunde
[Darmstadt]*, 5, No. 8 (1925), 224-31.
  /GEOLOGY/PLACES: ROCHUSBERG

1926-1 **Bassermann-Jordan**, Ernst von. "Goethe und die Automaten."
Die Uhrmacherkunst, 51 (1926), 745-8.
  /BEIREIS, G/TECHNOLOGY

1926-2 **Bassermann-Jordan**, Ernst von. "Goethe und die Uhren." *Die
Uhrmacherkunst*, 51 (1926), 59-62; 77-9.
  /TECHNOLOGY

1926-3 **Bode**, Wilhelm. "Goethes Camera obscura [illustration]." In
1790-1794 Vereinsamung. Vol. 8 of his *Goethes Leben*. Berlin: E.
S. Mittler & Sohn, 1926, p. 40.
  /GOETHE'S APPARATUS

1926-4 **Carus**, Carl Gustav. *Symbolik der menschlichen Gestalt*. Ed.
Theodor Lessing. Celle: Niels Kampmann Verlag, 1926. 534 pp.
  Rpt. of No. 1841-2.
  /RESEARCH: ANTHROPOLOGY/NATURPHILOSOPHIE

1926-5 **Carus**, Carl Gustav. "Die Urpflanze." Bernoulli, Chr. and
H[ans]. Kern. *Romantische Naturphilsophie*. Jena: Eugen
Diederichs, 1926, pp. 381-6.
  Partial rpt. of No. 1861-3.
  /BOTANY/RESEARCH: BOTANY/NATURPHILOSOPHIE

1926-6 **Carus**, Carl Gustav. *Zwölf Briefe über das Erdleben*. Ed.
Christoph Bernouilli and Hans Kern. Celle: Niels Kampmann Verlag, 1926. 248 pp.

Rpt. of 1841-3.
/NATURPHILOSOPHIE

1926-7 **Clemm**, Walther Claus. "Der Arzt in Goethe." *Ärztliche Rundschau*, 36 (1926), 61-3.
/MEDICINE

1926-8 [**Goethe**, J. W. von.] *Goethes Farbenlehre*. Ed. and intro. Gunther Ipsen. Leipzig: Insel-Verlag[, 1926]. xxxvi, 686 pp.
Cf. No. 1926-16.
/EDITION

1926-9 [**Goethe**, J. W. von.] *Goethes Morphologische Schriften*. Sel. and intro. Wilhelm Troll. Jena: Eugen Diederichs Verlag, 1926. 486 pp.
Rpt. "Neue Sonderausgabe" 1932.
Cf. No. 1926-41.
Cf. No. 1927-64.
/EDITION: SELECTIONS

1926-10 *[**Goethe**, J. W. von.] *Zur Farbenlehre*. Vol. 2 of *Goethes Schriften zur Naturwissenschaft*. Ed. and intro. Richard Müller-Freienfels. Berlin: Volksverband der Bücherfreunde Wegweiser-Verlag, 1926.
Cf. No. 1926-29.
/EDITION

1926-11 **Grohmann**, Gerbert. "Neue Wege zum Verständnis der Pflanzenfamilien dargestellt am Beispiel der Gräser." *Gäa-Sophia: Jahrbuch der naturwissenschaftlichen Sektion der Freien Hochschule für Geisteswissenschaft am Goetheanum*, 1 (1926), 235-45.
/RESEARCH: BOTANY

1926-12 **Grünewald**, Max. "Wie kam Goethe zur Entdeckung des menschlichen Zwischenkiefers?" *Aus der Heimat [Stuttgart]*, 39, No. 2 (1926), 17-19.
Rpt. No. 1927-19.
/OSTEOLOGY

1926-13 **Gundolf**, Friedrich. "Goethe als Naturforscher." In *Im Umkreis der exakten Naturwissenschaften*. Ed. Eugen Stock and Hans Heinrich Schmidt-Voigt. Diesterwegs Deutschkunde. Frankfurt a. M.: Verlag Moritz Diesterweg, 1926, pp. 118-22.
Cf. Nos. 1916-18 and -19.

/GENERAL INTRODUCTION

1926-14 **Gutbier**, Alexander. *Goethe, Großherzog Carl August und die Chemie in Jena*. Jenaer Akademische Reden, 2. Jena: Verlag von Gustav Fischer, 1926. vi, 66 pp.
"Rede gehalten zur Feier der akademischen Preisverteilung am 19. Juni 1926 von Dr. Alexander Gutbier o. ö. Professor der Chemie derzeit. Rektor der thüringischen Landesuniversität Jena: Mit einem neu aufgefundenen Brief Döbereiners an Goethe."
/CHEMISTRY/CARL AUGUST [GROSSHERZOG VON WEIMAR] /PLACES: JENA

1926-15 **Helmholtz**, Hermann v[on]. "Über Goethes naturwissenschaftliche Arbeiten." Ed. and comm. P[aul]. Zühlke. Velhagen u. Klasings deutsche Lesebogen: Materialien zum Arbeitsunterricht an höheren Schulen, 4. Bielefeld/Leipzig: Verlag von Velhagen u. Klasing, 1926. 24 pp.
Rpt. of No. 1853-8.
/GENERAL INTRODUCTION

1926-16 **Ipsen**, Gunther. "Die Begründung der Geisteswissenschaft. Eine Einleitung in Goethes Farbenlehre." In [Goethe, J. W. von.] *Goethes Farbenlehre*. Ed. and intro. Gunther Ipsen. Leipzig: Insel-Verlag[, 1926], pp. i-xxxvi.
/CHROMATICS/PHILOSOPHY

1926-17 **Ipsen**, Gunther. "Nachwort des Herausgebers." In *Goethes naturwissenschaftliche Schriften*. Vol. 2. Leipzig: Insel-Verlag[, 1926], pp. 685-96.
/GENERAL INTRODUCTION

1926-18 **John**, Alois. "Der 'Egeran' bei Haslau." *Unser Egerland: Monatsschrift für Heimaterkundung und Heimatpflege*, 30 (1926), 126-7.
/GEOLOGY/PLACES: HASLAU

1926-19 **John**, Alois. "Der Goethestein bei Haslau." *Unser Egerland: Monatsschrift für Heimaterkundung und Heimatpflege*, 30 (1926), 125-6.
/GEOLOGY/PLACES: HASLAU

1926-20 **Kasten**, Hans. "Ein Samenkorn Goethischer Naturkenntnis Colutea arborescens." Bremen[: Buchhandlung Otto Melcher], 1926.

13 pp.
/BOTANY

1926-21 **Kirschmann**, August. "Das umgekehrte Spektrum und seine Farben, sowie seine Bedeutung für die optische Wissenschaft." *Licht und Farbe*, 2 (1926), 411-42.
/CHROMATICS/OPTICS

1926-22 *****König**, Josef. "Das Urphänomen bei Goethe." In his *Der Begriff der Institution*. Halle (Saale), 1926.
/METHOD

1926-23 **Kühn**, Lenore. "Goethes Naturanschauung in seinen morphologischen Schriften." *Die Frau: Organ des Bundes Deutsche Frauenvereine: Monatsschrift für das gesamte Frauenleben unserer Zeit*, 34, No. 3 (1926/1927), 147-50.
/MORPHOLOGY

1926-24 **Lampa**, Anton. "Goethe und das Wetter." *Der Pflug*, December 1926, 65-70.
/METEOROLOGY

1926-25 **Landau**, Paul. "Goethe als Gartenfreund." In his *Gartenglück von einst*. Berlin-Westend: Verlag der Gartenschönheit, 1926, pp. 109-16.
/BOTANY

1926-26 **Leitzmann**, Albert. "Der Kosakenhetman in Goethes 'Farbenlehre'." *Goethe*, 12 (1926), 310-11.
/CHROMATICS

1926-27 **Leser**, Hermann. "Zu Goethes Naturansicht." *Beiträge zur Philosophie des deutschen Idealismus*, 4, No. 2 (1926/ 1927), 1-19.
/NATURPHILOSOPHIE

1926-28 **Martell**, P[aul]. "Goethes Farbenlehre." *Central-Zeitung für Optik und Mechanik Elektrotechnik undn verwandte Berufszweige*, 47 (1926), 331-2.
/CHROMATICS

1926-29 **Müller-Freienfels**, Richard. "Einleitung." In [J. W. von Goethe.] *Zur Farbenlehre*. Vol. 2 of *Goethes Schriften zur Naturwissenschaft*. Ed. and intro. Richard Müller-Freienfels. Berlin: Volksverband der Bücherfreunde Wegweiser-Verlag, 1926, pp. v-

xxxvii.
/CHROMATICS

1926-30 **Müller-Freienfels**, Richard. "Einleitung." In [J. W. von Goethe.] *Zur Morphologie*. Vol. 1 of *Goethes Schriften zur Naturwissenschaft*. Ed. and intro. Richard Müller-Freienfels. Berlin: Volksverband der Bücherfreunde Wegweiser-Verlag, 1926, pp. v-lvi.
/MORPHOLOGY/BIOLOGY

1926-31 **Nordenskiöld**, Erik. "Goethe." In his *Geschichte der Biologie: Ein Überblick*. Trans. Guido Schneider. Jena: Verlag von Gustav Fischer, 1926, pp. 282-9.
German trans. of No. 1920-17.
/BIOLOGY/HISTORY OF SCIENCE

1926-32 **Schiff**, Julius. "Wolken und Wolkensymbolik." *Paul Kellers Monatsblätter*, 15 (1926/1927), 57-64.
/METEOROLOGY/HOWARD, L

1926-33 **Steiner**, Rudolf. "Die Entstehung von Goethes Gedanken über die Bildung der Tiere." In *Goethes Naturwissenschaftliche Schriften*. Ed. Rudolf Steiner. Dornach: Philosophischer-Anthroposophischer Verlag am Goetheanum, 1926, 25-48.
Rpt. of No. 1921-25.
/ZOOLOGY/MORPHOLOGY

1926-34 **Steiner**, Rudolf. "Das geologische Grundprinzip Goethes." In his *Goethes naturwissenschaftliche Schriften*. Dornach: Philosophischer-Anthroposophischer Verlag am Goetheanum, 1926, pp. 184-9.
/GEOLOGY

1926-35 **Steiner**, Rudolf. "Die meteorologischen Vorstellungen Goethes." In his *Goethes naturwissenschaftliche Schriften*. Dornach: Philosophischer-Anthroposophischer Verlag am Goetheanum, 1926, pp. 190-92.
/METEOROLOGY

1926-36 *****Steiner**, Rudolf. *Goethe als Denker und Forscher*. Dornach: Philosophischer-Anthroposophischer Verlag am Goetheanum, 1926.
/GENERAL INTRODUCTION

1926-37 **Steiner**, Rudolf. *Goethes naturwissenschaftliche Schriften*. Dornach: Philosophischer-Anthroposophischer Verlag am

Goetheanum, 1926. 264 pp.
Rpts. Nos. 1962-31 and 1987-107.
Rpt. exp. edn. No. 1962-32.
Cf. Nos. 1926-33, -34, -35 and -38.
Trans. into Italian, No. 1944-16.
Trans. into English, No. 1950-72.
Trans. into Portuguese, No. 1984-97.
/GENERAL INTRODUCTION

1926-38 **Steiner**, Rudolf. "Goethe und die Mathematik." In his *Goethes naturwissenschaftliche Schriften*. Dornach: Philosophischer-Anthroposophischer Verlag am Goetheanum, 1926, pp. 180-183.
Rpt. of No. 1921-28.
/MATHEMATICS

1926-39 **Trillich**, Heinrich. "Die Entstehung der Keilglasfarben: Forschungsergebnisse zur Grundlage der Farbennormung." *Technische Mitteilungen für Malerei*, 42 (1926), 219-29.
/CHROMATICS

1926-40 **Troll**, Wilhelm. "Goethe und die Physik." *Die Tat: Monatsschrift für die Zukunft deutscher Kultur*, 18, No. 9 (1926), 693-704.
/METHOD/CHROMATICS/EPISTEMOLOGY

1926-41 **Troll**, Wilhelm. "Goethe in seinem Verhältnis zur Natur: Eine Einführung des Herausgebers." In [Goethe, J. W. von]. *Goethes Morphologische Schriften*. Ed. and intro. Wilhelm Troll. Jena: Eugen Diederichs Verlag, 1926, pp. 13-104.
Partial rpt. No. 1927-64.
/NATURPHILOSOPHIE/GENERAL INTRODUCTION /MORPHOLOGY /SPINOZA, B/SCHILLER, F/LINNAEUS [LINNÉ], C

1926-42 **Usteri**, A[?]. "Mensch und Pflanze." *Gäa-Sophia: Jahrbuch der naturwissenschaftlichen Sektion der Freien Hochschule für Geisteswissenschaft am Goetheanum*, 1 (1926), 157-99.
/RESEARCH: BOTANY

1926-43 **Usteri**, A[?]. "Pflanzen und Steine." *Gäa-Sophia: Jahrbuch der naturwissenschaftlichen Sektion der Freien Hochschule für Geisteswissenschaft am Goetheanum*, 1 (1926), 200-234.
/RESEARCH: BOTANY/RESEARCH: GEOLOGY

1926-44 **Winderlich**, Rudolf. "Ein merkwürdiger Satz aus Goethes Farbenlehre." *Naturwissenschaftliche Monatshefte für den biologischen
chemischen geographischen und geologischen Unterricht*, 23 (1926),
244.
/CHROMATICS

1926-45 **Wohlbold**, H[ans]. "Die Farben der Tiere." *Gäa-Sophia: Jahr-
buch der naturwissenschaftlichen Sektion der Freien Hochschule für
Geisteswissenschaft am Goetheanum*, 1 (1926), 246-53.
/RESEARCH: ZOOLOGY/RESEARCH: CHROMATICS

1926-46 **Wohlbold**, H[ans]. "Goethe als Naturforscher in seiner
Bedeutung für die Gegenwart." *Die Tat: Monatsschrift für die
Zukunft deutscher Kultur*, 18, No. 1 (1926/1927), 17-32.
/GENERAL INTRODUCTION

1926-47 **Zeylmans van Emmichoven**, F[?]. W. "Die Bedeutung von
Goethes Art der Naturbetrachtung für die Heilkunst. I." *Natura:
Zeitschrift zur Erweiterung der Heilkunst nach geistes-
wissenschaftlicher Menschenkunde*, 1 (1926/1927), 21-8.
/MEDICINE/OSTEOLOGY

1926-48 **Zeylmans van Emmichoven**, F[?]. W. "Die Bedeutung von
Goethes Art der Naturbetrachtung für die Heilkunst. II." *Natura:
Zeitschrift zur Erweiterung der Heilkunst nach geisteswissenschaft-
licher Menschenkunde*, 1 (1926/1927), 61-8.
/MEDICINE/OSTEOLOGY

1927-1 **Abel**, Adam. "Goethe [Georg Tobler?]. Die Natur."
Umschrieben von Adam Abel. Istist-Bücher, 7. München: Paul
Stangl Verlag, 1927. 49 pp.
Frankfurter Goethe-Museum III E 60/d1.
/EDITION

1927-2 **[anon.]** "Goethe und die Glastechnik." *Glastechnische Berichte*,
5 (1927), 298.
/TECHNOLOGY

1927-3 **Bacmeister**[, W(?).]. "Goethes Beziehungen zur Ornithologie."
*Jahreshefte des Vereins für vaterländische Naturkunde in
Württemberg*, 83 (1927), lxxxi-lxxxii.
/ORNITHOLOGY

1927-4 **Baravalle**, Hermann von. "Formen und Formbildung im Reich

des Organischen." *Gäa-Sophia: Jahrbuch der naturwissenschaftlichen Sektion der Freien Hochschule für Geisteswissenschaft am Goetheanum*, 2 (1927), 36-54.
/MORPHOLOGY/MATHEMATICS

1927-5 **Barthel**, Ernst. "Die Gegenwartsbedeutung der Goetheschen Farbenlehre." *Archiv für Geschichte der Mathematik, der Naturwissenschaften und der Technik*, 10 (1927/1928), 363-5.
/CHROMATICS/RESEARCH: CHROMATICS

1927-6 **Barthel**, Ernst. "Die Zukunftsbedeutung der Goetheschen Farbenlehre." *Annalen der Philosophie und philosophischen Kritik*, 6 (1927), 297-302.
/CHROMATICS/RESEARCH: CHROMATICS

1927-7 **Bockholt**, Grete. "Metamorphosen am Skelett." *Natura: Zeitschrift zur Erweiterung der Heilkunst nach geisteswissenschaftlicher Menschenkunde*, 2 (1927/1928), 276-81.
/MORPHOLOGY/RESEARCH: OSTEOLOGY

1927-8 **Boos-Hamburger**, Hilde. "Philipp Otto Runge." *Das Goetheanum*, 6 (1927), 134-6.
/RUNGE, P/CHROMATICS/RESEARCH: CHROMATICS/FINE ARTS

1927-9 **Carus**, C[arl]. G[ustav]. *Goethe: zu dessen näherem Verständnis.* Dresden: Wolfgang Jess[, 1927]. 284 pp.
Rpt. of 1843-5.
Rpt. 2nd edn. 1949.
/NATURPHILOSOPHIE

1927-10 **Carus**, C[arl]. G[ustav]. *Neun Briefe über Landschaftsmalerei: Geschrieben in den Jahren 1815 bis 1824: Zuvor ein Brief von Goethe als Einleitung.* Dresden: Wolfgang Jess[, 1927]. 229 pp.
Rpt. of No. 1831-3.
/RESEARCH: FINE ARTS/NATURPHILOSOPHIE

1927-11 **Dahl**, Maria. "Goethes mikroskopische Studien an niederen Tieren und Pflanzen im Hinblick auf seine Morphologie." *Goethe*, 13 (1927), 172-83.
/BIOLOGY/MORPHOLOGY

1927-12 **Dennert**, Friedrich. *Goethe im Harz: Goethes Harzreisen in seinen Tagebüchern, Briefen, Dichtungen.* 2nd rev. and exp. edn.

Quedlinburg: Verlag Hermann Schwanecke[, 1927]. 212 pp.
2nd rev. and exp. edn. of No. 1920-4.
/GEOLOGY/PLACES: HARZ

1927-13 **Diergart**, Paul. "Auf unbeachteten Pfaden Goethes in Straßburg. Der Chemiker und Arzt Jakob Reinbold Spielmann." *Chemiker-Zeitung*, 51, No. 30 (1927), 281-3.
Rpt. of No. 1922-10.
/PLACES: STRAßBURG/SPIELMANN, J

1927-14 **Dietert**, Friedrich. *Goethe im Harz: Goethes Harzreisen in seinen Tagebüchern, Briefen, Dichtungen.* 2nd rev. and exp. edn. Wernigerode and Chorin: Deutscher Kultur- und Heimatverlag[, 1927]. 120 pp.
2nd rev. and exp. edn of No. 1920-5.
/GEOLOGY/PLACES: HARZ

1927-15 [**Goethe**, J. W. von.] *Goethes Naturwissenschaftliche Schriften.* Ed. M. Masson. Deutsche Schulausgaben, 225. Bielfeld und Leipzig: Velhagen u. Klasing, 1927. 102 pp.
/EDITION: SELECTIONS

1927-16 [**Goethe**, J. W. von.] "Goethes naturwissenschaftliche Weltanschauung: Auswahl aus seinen naturwissenschaftlichen Schriften." Ed. H. Wohlbold. Belhagen & Klasings Lesebogen: Materialien zum Arbeitsunterricht an höheren Schulen. Bielefeld n. Leipzig: Verlag von Belhagen & Klasing, 1927. 44 pp.
/EDITION: SELECTIONS

1927-17 *[**Goethe**, J. W. von.] *Materialien zur Geschichte der Farbenlehre.* Vol. 3 of *Goethes Schriften zur Naturwissenschaft.* Ed. and intro. Richard Müller-Freienfels. Berlin: Volksverband der Bücherfreunde Wegweiser-Verlag, 1927.
Cf. No. 1927-42.
/EDITION

1927-18 *[**Goethe**, J. W. von.] *Zur Geologie, Mineralogie und Meteorologie.* Vol. 4 of *Goethes Schriften zur Naturwissenschaft.* Ed. Richard Müller-Freienfels. Berlin: Volksverband der Bücherfreunde Wegweiser-Verlag, 1927.
Cf. No. 1927-43.
/GEOLOGY/MINERALOGY/METEOROLOGY

1927-19 **Grünewald**, Max. "Wie kam Goethe zur Entdeckung des

menschlichen Zwischenkiefers?" *Der Naturforscher*, 4, No. 6
(1927/1928), 297-8.
Rpt. of No. 1926-12.
/OSTEOLOGY

1927-20 **Haeberlin**, Carl. "Der Arzt Carl Gustav Carus und Goethe. Mit
Ausblicken auf die Psychologie des Unbewußten." *Goethe*, 13
(1927), 184-204.
/CARUS, C/RESEARCH: PSYCHOLOGY

1927-21 **Haecker**, Valentin. *Goethes morphologische Arbeiten und die
neuere Forschung*. Jena: Verlag von Gustav Fischer, 1927. iv, 98
pp.
Rev. H. M. Elster, *Horen*, 5 (1929), 1088.
/MORPHOLOGY/RECEPTION/OSTEOLOGY/BOTANY
/BIOLOGY: EVOLUTION/DARWIN, C

1927-22 ***Headstrom**, Birger R. "Scientism of Goethe." *The Open
Court*, 41 (1927), 488-92.
/GENERAL INTRODUCTION

1927-23 **Hemmeter**, John C. "Goethe as a Naturalist." In his *Master
Minds in Medicine: An Analysis of Human Genius as the Instrument in
the Evolution of Great Constructive Ideas in the History of Medicine
together with a System of Historic Methodology*. Intro. Karl Sudhoff.
New York: Medical Life Press, 1927, pp. 575-608.
/GENERAL INTRODUCTION/DARWIN, C

1927-24 **Hennig**, Richard. "Goethe und der Panamakanal." *Die Pro-
pyläen*, 24 (1927), 195.
/TECHNOLOGY

1927-25 **Hering**, Robert. "Der Prosahymnus 'Die Natur' und sein Verfasser." *Goethe*, 13 (1927), 138-56.
/WORKS: DIE NATUR

1927-26 **Heß von Wichdorff**, Hans. "Goethe und seine Vorliebe für die
Höhle am Gr. Hermannstein bei Ilmenau." *Die Thüringer Höhlen:
Zeitschrift des Thüringer Höhlenvereins*, 1 (1927-1930), 11-12.
/GEOLOGY/PLACES: ILMENAU

1927-27 **Heß von Wichdorff**, Hans. "Thüringer Höhlenforschung vor
nahezu 150 Jahren auf Goethe's Anregung: Die Zinselhöhle bei
Meschenbach-Rauenstein." *Die Thüringer Höhlen: Zeitschrift des*

Thüringer Höhlenvereins, 1 (1927-1930), 6-9.
/GEOLOGY/PLACES: MESCHENBACH-RAUENSTEIN

1927-28 **Jablonski**, Walter. *Vom Sinn der Goetheschen Naturforschung.*
Berlin: Verlag Reuß & Pollack, 1927. 63 pp.
/NATURPHILOSOPHIE/GENERAL INTRODUCTION

1927-29 **Karutz**, Richard. *Von Goethe zur Völkerkunde der Zukunft.*
Stuttgart: Verlag Ernst Suhrkamp[, 1927]. 169 pp.
Rpt. No. 1929-27; partial rpt. No. 1929-26.
/ANTHROPOLOGY/RESEARCH: ANTHROPOLOGY

1927-30 **Leser**, Hermann. "Zu Goethes Naturansicht." *Beiträge zur
Philosophie des deutschen Idealismus*, 4, No. 2 (1927), 1-19.
/NATURPHILOSOPHIE/PHILOSOPHY

1927-31 **Lohmeyer**, Karl. "Das Meer und die Wolken in den beiden
letzten Akten des 'Faust'." *Goethe*, 13 (1927), 106-33.
/METEOROLOGY/WORKS: FAUST

1927-32 **Macco**, Herm[ann]. Friedr[ich]. "Der Chemiker Johann Caspar
Staudt und seine Beziehungen zu Goethe." *Der deutsche Herold:
Zeitschrift für Wappen-, Siegel- und Familienkunde*, 58, No. 1-2
(1927), 6-7.
/STAUD[T], J/CHEMISTRY

1927-33 **Martell**, Paul. "Goethes Farbenlehre." *Natur und Kultur:
Monatsschrift für Naturwissenschaft und ihre Grenzgebiete*, 24
(1927), 43-7.
/CHROMATICS

1927-34 **Martell**, Paul. "Goethe und die Chemie." *Welt und Wissen:
Unterhaltende und belehrende illustrierte Zeitschrift*, 16 (1927), 148-
51.
/CHEMISTRY

1927-35 **Martell**, Paul. "Goethe und die Technik." *Unsere Welt:
Illustrierte Zeitschrift für Naturwissenschaft und Weltanschauung*, 19
(1927), 8-11.
Rpt. of No. 1921-18.
/TECHNOLOGY

1927-36 **Masson**, M[?]. "Einleitung." In [Goethe, J. W. von.] *Goethes
Naturwissenschaftliche Schriften.* Sel. M. Masson. Deutsche

Schulausgaben 225. Bielefeld/Leipzig: Velhagen u. Klasing, 1927, pp. 6-16.
/GENERAL INTRODUCTION

1927-37 *Meißner, Otto. "Goethe als Entomologe." *Entomologische Zeitschrift*, 41 (1927/1928), 270-71.
/ENTOMOLOGY

1927-38 Michel, Ernst. "Goethes Naturbetrachten." *Das deutsche Gesicht: Vierteljahresberichte aus dem Verlage Eugen Diederichs in Jena*, 1 (1927), 66-70.
Partial rpt. of No. 1920-15.
/METHOD/EPISTEMOLOGY

1927-39 Mirbs, C[?]. A. "Bibliographie der innerhalb der anthroposophischen Bewegung erschienenen naturwissenschaftlichen Arbeiten." *Gäa-Sophia: Jahrbuch der naturwissenschaftlichen Sektion der Freien Hochschule für Geisteswissenschaft am Goetheanum*, 2 (1927), 431-41.
/RESEARCH: VARIOUS/BIBLIOGRAPHY

1927-40 Möbius, M[artin]. "Eine Pflanzenmißbildung und Goethes Beobachtungen darüber." *Natur und Museum: Senckenbergische Naturforschende Gesellschaft*, 57 (1927), 241-7.
/BOTANY/PATHOLOGY

1927-41 Müller, Johannes. *Über die phantastischen Gesichtserscheinungen*. Ed. and intro. Martin Müller. Klassiker der Medizin herausgegeben von Karl Sudhoff, 32. Leipzig: Verlag von Johann Ambrosius Barth, 1927. 101 pp.
Rpt. of No. 1826-9.
Rpt. No. 1968-29.
/RESEARCH: CHROMATICS/RESEARCH: PHYSIOLOGY

1927-42 Müller-Freienfels, Richard. "Einleitung." *Materialien zur Geschichte der Farbenlehre*. Vol. 3 of *Goethes Schriften zur Naturwissenschaft*. Ed. Richard Müller-Freienfels. Berlin: Volksverband der Bücherfreunde Wegweiser-Verlag, 1927, pp. v-xxv.
/CHROMATICS/HISTORY OF SCIENCE

1927-43 Müller-Freienfels, Richard. "Einleitung." *Zur Geologie, Mineralogie und Meteorologie*. Vol. 4 of *Goethes Schriften zur Naturwissenschaft*. Ed. Richard Müller-Freienfels. Berlin: Volksverband der Bücherfreunde Wegweiser-Verlag, 1927, pp. v-xxiii.

/GEOLOGY/MINERALOGY/METEOROLOGY

1927-44 *Muthesius, Karl. "Goethes Anschauungsbegriff und seine pädagogische Bedeutung." *Erziehung*, 2 (1927), 497-516; 576-94; 660-90.
/EPISTEMOLOGY/PEDAGOGY

1927-45 Nordenskiöld, Erik. "Goethe." In his *Biologan historia. Yleiskatsauksellisesti esitettyna. II. 1700 -- luvun alusta: Darwinin aikoihin.* Trans. T. J. Hinstikka. Powoo, 1927, pp. 162-72. Finnish trans. of No. 1920-17.
/BIOLOGY/HISTORY OF SCIENCE

1927-46 *Ovio, G[?]. "Teoria di Goethe [Goethe's Theory]." In *La Scienza dei colori. Visione dei colori.* Milano, 1927. In Italian.
/CHROMATICS

1927-47 Philippson, Robert. "Hat Goethe die Eiszeit entdeckt?" *Goethe*, 13 (1927), 157-71.
/GEOLOGY

1927-48 Picht, C[?]. S. "Rudolf Steiner zu Goethe's Fragment 'An die Natur'." *Gäa-Sophia: Jahrbuch der naturwissenschaftlichen Sektion der Freien Hochschule für Geisteswissenschaft am Goetheanum*, 2 (1927), 61-2.
/STEINER, R

1927-49 Pöhlmann, Tobias. *Goethes Naturauffassung in neutestamentlicher Beleuchtung.* Berlin: Furche-Verlag, 1927. 189 pp.
/NATURPHILOSOPHIE/THEOLOGY

1927-50 Poppelbaum, Hermann. "Neue Strömungen in der Naturdeutung." *Die Drei*, 6 (1927), 845-53. Cf. No. 1927-63.
/EDITIONS/STEINER, R

1927-51 Poppelbaum, Hermann. "Zum Wesensunterschied zwischen Mensch und Tier." *Das Goetheanum*, 6 (1927), 35-7.
/RESEARCH: ANTHROPOLOGY/RESEARCH: ZOOLOGY

1927-52 Rabel, Gabriele. "Naturwissenschaft." In *Goethe und Kant.* 2 vols. Wien: Paul Gerin, 1927. xv, 400 pp.
/KANT, I/NATURPHILOSOPHIE/PHILOSOPHY

1927-53 *Remes, M[?]. "Jan Ev. Purkyne v Goethove prirodovedecke korespondenci [Purkyne's Scientific Correspondence with Goethe]." *Vesmir*, 6 (1927/1928), 66-8.
In Czech.
/PURKYNE, J

1927-54 Schiff, Julius. "Goethe und die Astrologie." *Preußische Jahrbücher*, 210 (1927), 86-96.
/ASTROLOGY

1927-55 Schoepf, Hermann. "Ein Naturdenkmal im Fichtelgebirge." *Naturschutz: Monatsschrift für alle Freunde der deutschen Heimat*, 9 (1927/1928), 61-2.
/GEOLOGY/PLACES: LUISENBURG

1927-56 Schubert, Richard. "Die Kabiren vom Gesichtspunkt der Anatomie." *Gäa-Sophia: Jahrbuch der naturwissenschaftlichen Sektion der Freien Hochschule für Geisteswissenschaft am Goetheanum*, 2 (1927), 243-53.
/RESEARCH: ANATOMY/WORKS: FAUST

1927-57 Schuster, Julius. "Wege zu Goethes Naturwissenschaft." *Archiv für Geschichte der Mathematik, der Naturwissenschaften und der Technik*, 10 [NF 1], No. 3 (1927/1928), 365-6.
/GENERAL INTRODUCTION

1927-58 Selle, Friedrich. "Goethe als Sinndeuter der heutigen Naturwissenschaft." *Zeitwende [München]*, 3, No. 3 (1927), 282-3.
/NATURPHILOSOPHIE/GENERAL INTRODUCTION

1927-59 Splechtner, F[?]. J. N. "Die Metamorphose der Pflanzen, der Grund einer Physiologie und Biologie derselben." *Gäa-Sophia: Jahrbuch der naturwissenschaftlichen Sektion der Freien Hochschule für Geisteswissenschaft am Goetheanum*, 2 (1927), 145-56.
/RESEARCH: MORPHOLOGY/RESEARCH: BOTANY

1927-60 Steffen, Albert. "Erster Entwurf zur Metamorphose der Tiere im Sinne Goethes." *Das Goetheanum*, 6 (1927), 89-91.
/RESEARCH: ZOOLOGY

1927-61 Steffen, Albert. "Über Schopenhauers Lebensverhältnis zu Goethes Farbenlehre." *Das Goetheanum*, 6 (1927), 169-71.
/SCHOPENHAUER, A/NEWTON, I/CHROMATICS

1927-62 **Strakosch-Giesler**, Maria. "Über Farbenperspektive." *Das Goetheanum*, 6 (1927), 6-7.
/RESEARCH: CHROMATICS

1927-63 [**Troll**, Wilhelm.] "Ein anthroposophischer Angriff gegen die Trollsche Ausgabe von Goethes morphologischen Schriften." *Das deutsche Gesicht: Vierteljahresberichte aus dem Verlage Eugen Diederichs in Jena*, 1 (1927), 76-83.
Response to No. 1927-50.
/EDITIONS/MORPHOLOGY/STEINER, R/POPPELBAUM, H

1927-64 **Troll**, Wilhelm. "Magnetes Geheimnis." *Das deutsche Gesicht: Vierteljahresberichte aus dem Verlage Eugen Diederichs in Jena*, 1 (1927), 70-75.
Partial rpt. of No. 1926-41.
/NATURPHILOSOPHIE

1927-65 **Wohlbold**, Hans. "Die Naturerkenntnis im Weltbild Goethes." *Goethe*, 13 (1927), 1-46.
/NATURPHILOSOPHIE/GENERAL INTRODUCTION

1928-1 [**anon.**] "Goethes Farbentafeln gefunden." *Farbe und Lack*, 1928, Anzeigen-S. 1421.
Rpt. No. 1929-4.
/CHROMATICS

1928-2 [**anon.**] "Goethes Naturauffassung [und das Christentum]." *Die Religionsstunde. Zweimonatschrift für evangel[ische]. Religionsunterricht. Beilage zum Evangelischen Schulblatt*, 7, No. 3 (1928), 19-20; No. 4 (1928), 25-8.
Longer title in the continuation.
/GENERAL INTRODUCTION/THEOLOGY

1928-3 **Barthel**, Ernst. "Goethe und die Naturwissenschaft." *Zeitschrift für deutsche Bildung*, 4, No. 11 (1928), 589-97.
/GENERAL INTRODUCTION

1928-4 **Barthel**, Ernst. "Der Streit Goethes gegen die Newtonsche Optik und die Gegenwart." *Die Auslese: Internationale Zeitschriftenschau*, 2 (1928), 551-3.
Rpt. of No. 1928-5.
/CHROMATICS/NEWTON, I/RESEARCH: CHROMATICS

1928-5 **Barthel**, Ernst. "Der Streit Goethes gegen die Newtonsche Optik und die Gegenwart." *Natur und Kultur: Monatsschrift für Naturwissenschaft und ihre Grenzgebiete*, 25 (1928), 296-8.
Rpt. No. 1928-4.
/CHROMATICS/NEWTON, I/RESEARCH: CHROMATICS

1928-6 **Barthel**, Ernst. *Die Welt als Spannung und Rhythmus: Erkenntnistheorie, Ästhetik, Naturphilosophie, Ethik.* Leipzig: Universitätsverlag von Robert Noske, 1928. xviii, 411 pp.
/RESEARCH: PHILOSOPHY

1928-7 **Bürger**, K[?]. "Goethe und die Baumannshöhle." In *Goethe und der Brocken*. Quedlinburg: H. C. Huch, 1928, pp. 45-55.
Rpt. of No. 1928-8.
/GEOLOGY

1928-8 **Bürger**, K[?]. "Goethe und die Baumannshöhle." *Zeitschrift des Harz-Vereins für Geschichte und Altertumskunde*, 61 (1928), 45-55.
Rpt. No. 1928-7.
/GEOLOGY

1928-9 **Döbling**, Hugo. "Anhang: Nachtrag zum Schriftverkehr zwischen Döbereiner und Goethe." In his *Die Chemie in Jena zur Goethezeit.* Zeitschrift des Vereins für Thüringische Geschichte und Altertumskunde, NF, Beiheft 13. Beiträge zur Geschichte der Universität Jena, 2. Jena: Verlag von Gustav Fischer, 1928, pp. 156-212.
/CHEMISTRY/DÖBEREINER, J/PLACES: JENA

1928-10 **Döbling**, Hugo. "Aus der Schaffenszeit Johann Wolfgang Döbereiners." In his *Die Chemie in Jena zur Goethezeit.* Zeitschrift des Vereins für Thüringische Geschichte und Altertumskunde, NF, Beiheft 13. Beiträge zur Geschichte der Universität Jena, 2. Jena: Verlag von Gustav Fischer, 1928, pp. 52-155.
/CHEMISTRY/DÖBEREINER, J/WORKS: CORRESPONDENCE

1928-11 **Fischer**, Hugo. "Der Begriff der Pflanzen-Metamorphose einst und jetzt." *Der Naturforscher: Illustrierte Zeitschrift für das gesamte Gebiet der Naturwissenschaften*, 5 (1928), 122-7.
/BOTANY/MORPHOLOGY

1928-12 **[Goethe**, J. W. von.] "Aus Goethes morphologischen Schriften. Aus 'Bildung und Umbildung organischer Naturen'." *Deutsches*

Volkstum: Monatsschrift für das deutsche Geistesleben, 1 (1928), 389-91.
/EDITION: SELECTIONS

1928-13 **Goethe**, J. W. von. *Beyträge zur Optik. Erstes Stück; Beyträge zur Optik. Zweites Stück.* [Berlin: W. Junk, 1928]. 62 + 30 pp.
   Rpt. No. 1964-9.
   Cf. No. 1928-42.
   "Vereinsgabe des Berliner Bibliophilen Abends für 1927."
   /EDITION

1928-14 **[Goethe**, J. W. von.] "Durchgewachsene Rosen und Nelken." *Monatsblatt: das Heimatblatt Mitteldeutschlands: Wissenschaftliche Beilage der Megdeburgischen Zeitung*, 70, No. 5 (1928), 38-9.
   /EDITION

1928-15 **[Goethe**, J. W. von.] *Goethes Farbenlehre.* Gott-Natur: Schriftenreihe zur Neubegründung der Naturphilosophie. Ed. and intro. Hans Wohlbold. Jena: Eugen Diederichs Verlag, 1928. 557 pp.
   Rpt. 1932.
   Cf. No. 1928-60.
   Rev. [anon.], "Goethes Farbenlehre," n.p., 3 January 1929 [In Mappe III E 21/C91: "Goethe und die Farbenlehre 1913-. Sammelmappe Zeitungsausschnitte" at the Frankfurter Goethe-Museum.]
   Rev. Herbert Nette [No. 1929-48].
   Rev. Hans Zint [No. 1932-385].
   Rev. Walter Benjamin [No. 1972-1].
   /EDITION

1928-16 **[Goethe**, J. W. von]. *Goethes Naturwissenschaftliche Schriften: Eine Auswahl: 1. Band.* Vol. 15 of *Goethes Werke.* Ed. Chr. Christiansen, Hans Schimank, Julius Schuster, and Hermann Tiemann. 32 vols. Hamburg: Gutenberg Verlag, 1928. xxxi, 294 pp.
   Cf. No. 1928-40.
   /EDITION: SELECTIONS

1928-17 **Goethe**, J. W. von. *Goethes Naturwissenschaftliche Schriften: Eine Auswahl: 2. Band.* Ed. Julius Schuster. Vol. 16 of *Goethes Werke.* Ed. Chr. Christiansen, Hans Schimank, Julius Schuster, and Hermann Tiemann. 32 vols. Hamburg: Gutenberg Verlag, 1928. 340 pp.

Cf. No. 1928-43.
/EDITION: SELECTIONS

1928-18 **Goethe**[, J. W. von.] *Grosse Tafel zu der Beyträge zur Optik Zweytem Stück 1792.* Ed. Julius Schuster. Berlin: W. Junk, 1928. 7 pp.
    Cf. No. 1928-13.
    /OPTICS

1928-19 **Goethe**[, J. W. von] [Tobler, Friedrich]. "Die Natur. Ein Hymnus von Goethe." [Charlottenburg:] privately printed[, 1928]. [16 pp.]
    /EDITION

1928-20 **Goethe**[, J. W. von]. *Schriften über die Natur.* Ed. and intro. Gunther Ipsen. Leipzig: Alfred Kröner Verlag[, 1928]. 343 pp.
    Rpt. (Kröners Taschenausgabe, 62) 1949.
    /EDITION: SELECTIONS

1928-21 [**Göttling**, Johann Friedrich August.] "Johann Friedrich August Göttlings Briefe an Goethe: Nach den Handschriften des Goethe- und Schiller-Archivs mitgeteilt von Julius Schiff." *Goethe*, 14 (1928), 130-46.
    /GÖTTLING, J

1928-22 **Günther**, Gerhard. "Goethes Farbenlehre, eine Brücke zur Intuition." *Die Drei*, 8 (1928), 442-50.
    /CHROMATICS/EPISTEMOLOGY/STEINER, R

1928-23 **Günther**, Gerhard. "Goethes Farbenlehre und Rudolf Steiners Vorträge 'Über das Wesen der Farben' im Lichte des 'Hüters der Schwelle'." *Die Drei: Monatsschrift für Anthroposophie, Dreigliederung und Goetheanismus*, 8 (1928), 139-55.
    /STEINER, R/RESEARCH: CHROMATICS

1928-24 **Haas**, Albert. "Goethes Weltanschauung als System der Natur- und Gesellschafts-Wissenschaften." *Phoenix: Zeitschrift für deutsche Geistesarbeit in Südamerika*, 14 (1928), 418-53.
    Cf. continuation, No. 1929-15.
    /NATURPHILOSOPHIE/SOCIOLOGY

1928-25 **Hegelmann**, Emil. *Grundfragen der Physik im Lichte Goethe'scher Erkenntnisart. Mit dem Versuch einer neuen Darstellung der Hauptsätze der Wärmelehre.* Mannheim: Reischmann, 1928.

xiv, 124 pp.
/METHOD/RESEARCH: PHYSICS/RESEARCH:
THERMODYNAMICS

1928-26 **Hegelmann**, Emil. "Zur Methodik in der Physik insbesondere der Wärmelehre auf der Grundlage Goethe'scher Erkenntnisart." Diss. Technische Hochschule Darmstadt, 1928. xiv, 125 pp.
/METHOD/RESEARCH: PHYSICS/RESEARCH:
THERMODYNAMICS

1928-27 **Klages**, Ludwig. "Goethe als Seelenforscher." *Jahrbuch des freien deutschen Hochstifts*, 1928, 3-44.
/PSYCHOLOGY

1928-28 **König**, Karl. "Beiträge zu einer reinen Anatomie des menschlichen Knochengerüsts." *Natura: Zeitschrift zur Erweiterung der Heilkunst nach geisteswissenschaftlicher Menschenkunde*, 3 (1928/1929), 218-43.
Cf. continuation, No. 1931-24.
/RESEARCH: OSTEOLOGY

1928-29 **König**, Karl. "Betrachtungen über den Zusammenhang des Verdauungssystems mit der Gehirnorganisation bei Mensch und Tier." *Natura: Zeitschrift zur Erweiterung der Heilkunst nach geisteswissenschaftlicher Menschenkunde*, 3 (1928/1929), 289-307.
/RESEARCH: ANATOMY

1928-30 **Linden**, Walther. "Goethe als Naturforscher." In Bielschowsky, Albert. *Goethe: Sein Leben und seine Werke*. Revised by Walther Linden. 2 vols. München: C. H. Beck'sche Verlagsbuchhandlung[, 1928], pp. 385-432.
Entirely new.
/GENERAL INTRODUCTION

1928-31 **Loew**, Wilhelm. "Goethes Naturauffassung in neutestamentlicher Beleuchtung." *Die Furche*, 14 (1928), 86-91.
/NATURPHILOSOPHIE/THEOLOGY

1928-32 **Meißner**, Otto. "Goethe als Entomologe." *Entomologische Zeitschrift*, 41 (1927/1928), 270-71.
/ENTOMOLOGY

1928-33 *****Michel**, M[?]. "Kuriose und historische Stücke aus den Sammlungen der mineralogisch-petrograph. Abt. d. Naturhistor.

Museums [Wien]." *Mitteilung der Wiener mineralogischen Gesellschaft*, No. 90, 1928, 16-19.
"(Beil. zu Tschermaks mineralog. u. petrograph. Mitt. 39, 1928.)"
/GOETHE'S COLLECTIONS/GEOLOGY/MINERALOGY

1928-34 **Muthesius**, Karl. "Goethe und die spezifische Sinnesenergie." *Thüringische Allgemeine Zeitung [Erfurt]*, 13 June 1928.
/CHROMATICS

1928-35 **Nordenskiöld**, Erik. "Goethe." In his *The History of Biology. A Survey.* New York/London: Alfred Knopf, 1928, pp. 279-85.
English trans. of No. 1920-17.
/BIOLOGY/HISTORY OF SCIENCE

1928-36 **Obst**, Walter. "Klopstock wider Goethes Farbenlehre." *Technische Mitteilungen für Malerei*, 44, No. 2 (1928), 21.
/CHROMATICS/MARAT, J

1928-37 **Poppelbaum**, Hermann. *Mensch und Tier: Fünf Einblicke in ihren Wesensunterschied: Gestalt: Abkunft: Seele: Erlebnis: Schicksal.* Basel: Rudolf Geering Verlag, 1928. 158 pp.
Rpt. Nos. 1956-21 and 1981-70.
Partial trans. into French, No. 1958-29.
Trans. into English, No. 1960-38.
Trans. into Dutch, No. 1973-34.
"Herausgegeben von der Naturwissenschaftlichen Sektion der Freien Hochschule für Geisteswissenschaft am Goetheanum in Dornach (Schweiz)."
/RESEARCH: ZOOLOGY

1928-38 **Schoenichen**, Walther. "Goethe als Biologe." In his *Deutschkunde im naturgeschichtlichen Unterricht.* Handbuch der Deutschkunde: Führer zu deutscher Schulerziehung, 7. Frankfurt am Main: Verlag Moritz Diesterweg, 1928, pp. 174-83.
/BIOLOGY

1928-39 **Schreyer**, Lothar. "Goethe und die Metamorphosenlehre." *Deutsches Volkstum: Monatsschrift für das deutsche Geistesleben*, 1 (1928), 383-8.
/BOTANY/MORPHOLOGY

1928-40 **Schuster**, Julius. "Camarupa oder Goethes organismische Sendung. Eine Einleitung in Goethes Naturwissenschaft." In

[Goethe, J. W. von]. *Goethes Naturwissenschaftliche Schriften: Eine Auswahl: 1. Band.* Vol. 15 of *Goethes Werke.* Ed. Chr. Christiansen, Hans Schimank, Julius Schuster, and Hermann Tiemann. 32 vols. Hamburg: Gutenberg Verlag, 1928, pp. vii-xxxi.
/NATURPHILOSOPHIE/GENERAL INTRODUCTION

1928-41 **Schuster**, Julius. "Goethe als anatomischer Zeichner." *Der Kunstwanderer: Halbmonatsschrift für Alte und Neue Kunst für Kunstmarkt und Sammelwesen,* 10 (1928), 58-62.
/ANATOMY: ILLUSTRATION

1928-42 **Schuster**, Julius. "Nachwort." In *Beyträge zur Optik. Erstes Stück; Beyträge zur Optik. Zweites Stück.* [Berlin:] n.p.[, 1928], pp. i-xx.
/OPTICS

1928-43 **Schuster**, Julius. "Nachwort des Herausgebers. Nachweis zum Bildwerk." In Goethe, J. W. von. *Goethes Naturwissenschaftliche Schriften: Eine Auswahl: 2. Band.* Ed. Julius Schuster. Vol. 16 of *Goethes Werke.* Ed. Chr. Christiansen, Hans Schimank, Julius Schuster, and Hermann Tiemann. 32 vols. Hamburg: Gutenberg Verlag, 1928, pp. 327-33.
/GENERAL INTRODUCTION

1928-44 **Spiegel**, Gustav. "'Goetheanismus': Die Psychologie des Karl Gustav Carus: Eine Würdigung." *Die Drei: Monatsschrift für Anthroposophie, Dreigliederung und Goetheanismus,* 8 (1929), 217-38.
/CARUS, C/RESEARCH: PSYCHOLOGY/NATUR-PHILOSOPHIE

1928-45 **Steffen**, Albert. "Das Farbenspektrum und der Gang der Geschichte." In his *Der Künstler und die Erfüllung der Mysterien.* Dornach/Stuttgart: Verlag für schöne Wissenschaften, 1928, pp. 100-21.
/RESEARCH: CHROMATICS/CHROMATICS

1928-46 **Steffen**, Albert. "Metamorphose der Tiere." In his *Der Künstler und die Erfüllung der Mysterien.* Dornach/Stuttgart: Verlag für schöne Wissenschaften, 1928, 225-33.
/RESEARCH: MORHPOLOGY/RESEARCH: ZOOLOGY

1928-47 **Steffen**, Albert. "Metamorphose des Irdischen." In his *Der Künstler und die Erfüllung der Mysterien.* Dornach/Stuttgart: Verlag

für schöne Wissenschaften, 1928, pp. 212-19.
/RESEARCH: MORPHOLOGY

1928-48 **Steffen**, Albert. "Metamorphose des Pflanzlichen." In his *Der Künstler und die Erfüllung der Mysterien.* Dornach/ Stuttgart: Verlag für schöne Wissenschaften, 1928, pp. 220-24.
/RESEARCH: MORPHOLOGY/RESEARCH: BOTANY

1928-49 **Steffen**, Albert. "Über Schopenhauers Lebensverhältnis zu Goethes Farbenlehre." In his *Der Künstler und die Erfüllung der Mysterien.* Dornach/Stuttgart: Verlag für schöne Wissenschaften, 1928, pp. 155-68.
/SCHOPENHAUER, A/CHROMATICS

1928-50 **Steiner**, Rudolf. *Goethe's Conception of the World.* Tr. H. Collison. London: Anthroposophical Publishing Co./New York: Anthroposophic Press, 1928. xvi, 193 pp.
English trans. of No. 1897-12.
Rpt. No. 1973-47.
/GENERAL INTRODUCTION/HEGEL, G/NATUR-PHILOSOPHIE

1928-51 **Steiner**, Rudolf. *Das Wesen der Farben. (R. Steiners Farbenlehre 1.): 3 Vorträge.* Ed. Marie Steiner. Kunst im Lichte der Mysterienweisheit, 7. Dornach: Philosophisch-Anthroposophischer Verlag am Goetheanum, 1928. xiv, 88 pp.
Rpt. No. 1929-63.
Trans. into English, Nos. 1935-33 and 1970-40.
Trans. into Dutch, No. 1981-93.
Trans. into Japanese, No. 1986-91.
/CHROMATICS/RESEARCH: CHROMATICS

1928-52 **Trentini**, Albert. "Goethes 'Farbenlehre'." *Die Kunstwart: Monatshefte für Kunst, Literatur und Leben*, 42, No. 4 (1928/1929), 253-7.
/CHROMATICS

1928-53 **Trillich**, Heinrich. "Die Systeme der Farbenlehre." *Technische Mitteilungen für Malerei*, 44 (1928), 161-3; 195-9; 219-21; 231-3; 283-6.
Continuation of No. 1928-54.
/RESEARCH: CHROMATICS

1928-54 **Trillich**, Heinrich. "Urheber und Ursachen von Irrtümern in der

Farbenlehre. V. Newton." *Technische Mitteilungen für Malerei*, 44, No. 10 (1928), 123-6.
Cf. continuation, No. 1928-53.
/CHROMATICS/NEWTON, I

1928-55 **Troll**, Wilhelm. *Organisation und Gestalt im Bereich der Blüte.* Monographien aus dem Gesamtgebiet der wissenschaftlichen Botanik, 1. Berlin: Verlag von Julius Springer, 1928. xiii, 413 pp.
Rev. Hans André, "Eine Erbe der Naturanschauung Goethes," *Hochland*, 26, No. 2 (1929), 213-4.
/RESEARCH: BOTANY/RESEARCH: MORPHOLOGY

1928-56 **Trommsdorff**, Hermann. "Friedrich Wilhelm Heinrich von Trebra. Geb. am 5. April 1740. Gest. den 16. Juli 1819." *Zeitschrift des Harz-Vereins für Geschichte und Altertumskunde*, 61 (1928), 17-45.
/TREBRA, F VON/GEOLOGY

1928-57 *****Vogel**, Richard. "Goethe als Naturwissenschaftler." *Dresdner Anzeiger*, Wissenschaftliche Beilage, 25 December 1928.
/GENERAL INTRODUCTION

1928-58 **Wahle**, Julius. "Ein Brief Herders an Goethe." *Goethe*, 14 (1928), 97-9.
Part of a longer article [pp. 93-100] entitled "Aus dem Goethe- und Schiller-Archiv."
/CHROMATICS

1928-59 **Weitemeyer**, Max. "Goethe und Kant." *Jahrbücher der Akademie gemeinnütziger Wissenschaften zu Erfurt*, NS 47 (1928), 31-75.
"Nach einem am 28. September 1927 in der Akademie gemeinnütziger Wissenschaften zu Erfurt gehaltenen Vortrage."
/KANT, I/NATURPHILOSOPHIE

1928-60 **Wohlbold**, Hans. "Einführung des Herausgebers." In *Goethes Farbenlehre*. Ed. and intro. Hans Wohlbold. Jena: Eugen Diederichs Verlag, 1928, pp. 13-123.
/CHROMATICS

1928-61 **Wohlbold**, H[ans]. *III: Führer durch Goethes Sammlung optischer Apparate: zugleich als Einführung in die Farbenlehre.* Amtliche Ausgabe. [Weimar:] Das Goethe-Nationalmuseum in

Weimar[, 1928]. 103 pp.
/GOETHE'S COLLECTIONS/CHROMATICS

1928-62 *Zschacke, F[?]. H. "Goethes Anschauungen über das Glas."
Glastechnische Berichte, 6 (1928/1929), 89-96.
/TECHNOLOGY

1929-1 André, Hans. "Vom Wesen und Gegenwartswert christlich-
mittelalterlicher und Goethescher Naturanschauung." *Der Kunstwart:
Monatshefte für Kunst, Literatur und Leben*, 43, No. 3 (1929), 158-
76; No. 4 (1930), 242-51; No. 5 (1930), 313-23.
/NATURPHILOSOPHIE/THEOLOGY/PHILOSOPHY

1929-2 [anon.] "Goethe als Naturforscher: Festsitzung der Akademie der
naturforscher: Universitätsaula." *Hallesche Zeitung*, 226, No. 54, 4
March 1929.
  Account of session on Goethe, 2 March 1929.
  /GENERAL INTRODUCTION/INSTITUTIONS:
  LEOPOLDINA

1929-3 [anon.] "Goethe als Naturforscher: Festsitzung der Leopoldina."
Hallische Nachrichten, 41, No. 54, 5 March 1929.
  Account of session on Goethe, 2 March 1929.
  /GENERAL INTRODUCTION/INSTITUTIONS:
  LEOPOLDINA

1929-4 *[anon.]. "Goethes Farbentafeln gefunden." *Technische Mit-
teilungen für Malerei*, 45 (1929), 179.
  Rpt. of No. 1928-1.
  /CHROMATICS

1929-5 Berthelot, René. "Lamarck et Goethe: L'Evolutionnisme de la
continuité au début du XIXe siècle." *Revue de métaphysique et de
morale*, 36 (1929), 285-341.
  Rpt. No. 1932-26.
  /LAMARCK, J DE/BIOLOGY: EVOLUTION

1929-6 *Beutler, Ernst. "Goethe und die Natur." *Natur und Museum*, 59
(1929), 129-43.
  /GENERAL INTRODUCTION

1929-7 Chemnitius, Fritz. "Die Chemie an der Universität zur Zeit
Goethes." In his *Die Chemie in Jena von Rolfinck bis Knorr (1629-
1921)*. Jena: Verlag der Frommannschen Buchhandlung Walter

Biedermann, 1929, pp. 24-31.
/CHEMISTRY/INSTITUTIONS: UNIVERSITÄT JENA

1929-8 **Crow**, William Bernard. *Contributions to the Principles of Morphology.* Diss. Univ. of London. London: Kegan Paul, Trench, Trubner a. Co., 1929. viii, 94 pp.
/MORPHOLOGY/BIOLOGY

1929-9 **Düren**, Wilhelm. "Über Goethe und Spengler: Aphoristisch." Bonn: Verlag Gebr. Scheur/Bonner Universitäts-Buchdruckerei, 1929. 48 pp.
/SPENGLER, O/MORPHOLOGY/RESEARCH: HISTORIOGRAPHY

1929-10 **Feldmann**, Rich[ard]. "Goethes 'Farbe' als geistiges Eigentum." *Form und Farbe: Fachblatt für das Malerhandwerk*, 18 (1929), 103-6.
/CHROMATICS/RAEHLMANN, E

1929-11 **Feldmann**, Rich[ard]. "Goethes Farbenlehre und die moderne Naturwissenschaft." *Form und Farbe: Fachblatt für das Malerhandwerk*, 18 (1929), 149-54.
/CHROMATICS/RESEARCH: CHROMATICS/METHOD

1929-12 **Franz**, Viktor. "Der Zwischenkiefer und Goethe." *Der Naturforscher vereint mit Natur und Technik*, 6, No. 11 (1929 /1930), 404-11.
/OSTEOLOGY/ANATOMY: COMPARATIVE

1929-13 **Grohmann**, Gerbert. *Die Pflanze als dreigliedriges Wesen in ihren Wechselbeziehungen zur Erde und Mensch.* Stuttgart/ Den Haag/London: Orient-Occident Verlag, 1929. 202 pp.
/RESEARCH: BOTANY/BOTANY/STEINER, R

1929-14 **Günther**, Gerhard. "Goethes Farbenlehre, eine Brücke zur Intuition." *Die Drei: Monatsschrift für Anthroposophie, Dreigliederung und Goetheanismus*, 8 (1929), 442-50.
/CHROMATICS/METHOD

1929-15 **Haas**, Albert. "Goethes Weltanschauung als System der Natur- und Gesellschafts-Wissenschaften. II. (Fortsetzung und Schluß.)" *Phoenix: Zeitschrift für deutsche Geistesarbeit in Südamerika*, 14 [15] (1929), 23-49.
Continuation of No. 1928-24.
/NATURPHILOSOPHIE/SOCIOLOGY

1929-16 **Hegel**, Georg Wilhelm Friedrich. *Encyklopädie der philosophischen Wissenschaften im Grundrisse.* Vol. 6 of his *Sämtliche Werke. Jubiläumsausgabe in zwanzig Bänden.* Ed. Hermann Glockner. Stuttgart: Fr. Fromanns Verlag (H. Kurtz), 1929. Rpt. of No. 1817-7.
/CHROMATICS/NATURPHILOSOPHIE/NEWTON, I

1929-17 ***Hemleben**, Johannes. "Goethes Kampf für und gegen die Naturwissenschaften." *Kieler Neueste Nachrichten*, 26 October 1929.
/GENERAL INTRODUCTION

1929-18 **Ipsen**, Gunther. "Einleitung." In Goethe[, J. W. von]. *Schriften über die Natur.* Leipzig: Alfred Kröner Verlag[, 1929], pp. 1-11.
/GENERAL INTRODUCTION

1929-19 **Ipsen**, Gunther. "Nachwort." In Goethe[, J. W. von]. *Schriften über die Natur.* Leipzig: Alfred Kröner Verlag[, 1929], pp. 333-4.
/GENERAL INTRODUCTION

1929-20 **Jablonski**, Walter. "Die geistesgeschichtliche Stellung der Naturforschung Goethes." *Goethe*, 15 (1929), 22-61.
/PHILOSOPHY/NATURPHILOSOPHIE

1929-21 **Jablonski**, Walter. "Goethes Farbenlehre." *Hippokrates*, 1 (1928/1929), 422-33.
/CHROMATICS

1929-22 **Jablonski**, Walter. "Goethe und die Abstammungslehre." *Hippokrates*, 2 (1929/1930), 74-85.
/BIOLOGY: EVOLUTION

1929-23 **Junk**, Wilhelm. "Das Mißgeschick Goethes. Zu dem Stuttgarter Goethefund." *Berliner Tageblatt*, 12 September 1929, Morgenausgabe.
/OPTICS

1929-24 **Kaemmerer**, Paul. *Auge und Sehkraft: Ihre geistige, kosmische und physiologische Bedeutung.* Geiselgasteig bei München: Selbstverlag, 1929. vi, 185 pp.
/CHROMATICS/NEWTON, I/RESEARCH: CHROMATICS/RESEARCH: PHYSIOLOGY

1929-25 **Kaemmerer**, Paul. "Zur Nachprüfung des Problems Goethe-Newton." *Technische Mitteilungen für Malerei*, 45 (1929), 178-9.
/CHROMATICS/NEWTON, I

1929-26 **Karutz**, Richard. "Aus 'Von Goethe zur Völkerkunde der Zukunft." *Gäa-Sophia: Jahrbuch der naturwissenschaftlichen Sektion der Freien Hochschule für Geisteswissenschaft am Goetheanum*, 3 (1929), 8-18.
Partial rpt. of No. 1927-29.
/ANTHROPOLOGY/RESEARCH: ANTHROPOLOGY

1929-27 **Karutz**, Richard. *Von Goethe zur Völkerkunde der Zukunft.* 2nd imp. and exp. edn. Stuttgart: Verlag Ernst Suhrkamp[, 1927]. 159 pp.
Rpt. of No. 1927-29.
/ANTHROPOLOGY/RESEARCH: ANTHROPOLOGY

1929-28 *****Kaubisch**, Martin. "Vom Sinn und Wesen Goetheschen Erkennens." *Neue Jahrbücher für Wissenschaft und Jugendbildung*, 5 (1929), 204-8.
/EPISTEMOLOGY

1929-29 *****Kern**, H[ans]. "Goethe als Naturforscher." *Das deutsche Buch*, 9, No. 7/8 (1929), 193-6.
/GENERAL INTRODUCTION

1929-30 **Li[?]**. "Dem Gedenken Goethes. Festsitzung der Leopoldinischen deutschen Akademie der Naturforscher." *Volksblatt Sozialdemokratische Tageszeitung für Halle und den Bezirk Merseburg*, 4 March 1929.
Account of session on Goethe, 2 March 1929.
/GENERAL INTRODUCTION/INSTITUTIONS: LEOPOLDINA

1929-31 **Linden**, Walther. "Goethes Farbenlehre im Zusammenhange seiner Weltanschauung." *Zeitschrift für Deutschkunde*, 43 (1929), 449-69.
"Vortrag in der Goethe-Gesellschaft in Leipzig und Magdeburg 1928, in der Kant-Gesellschaft in Halle 1929 und in der Deutschen Welle: Berlin 1929."
/CHROMATICS/PHILOSOPHY

1929-32 **Lohmann[, W]**. "Goethes anatomische Arbeiten und seine Ansichten über das Verhältnis von Tier und Mensch." *Natur und*

Heimat: Blätter für Naturerhaltung und Heimatliebe [Schwelm i. Westfalen], July 1929, 97-100.
/ZOOLOGY/MORPHOLOGY/COMPARATIVE ANATOMY

1929-33 **Lohmann**[, W]. "Goethes Geologie." *Natur und Heimat: Blätter für Naturerhaltung und Heimatliebe [Schwelm i. Westfalen]*, September 1929, 129-32.
/GEOLOGY

1929-34 **Lohmann**[, W]. "Goethes Metamorphose der Pflanze." *Natur und Heimat: Blätter für Naturerhaltung und Heimatliebe [Schwelm i. Westfalen]*, May 1929, 66-8.
/BOTANY/MORPHOLOGY

1929-35 **Lohmann**[, W]. "Goethes Meteorologie." *Natur und Heimat: Blätter für Naturerhaltung und Heimatliebe [Schwelm i. Westfalen]*, November 1929, 162-4.
METEOROLOGY

1929-36 **Lohmann**[, W]. "Goethes 'Urpflanze'." *Natur und Heimat: Blätter für Naturerhaltung und Heimatliebe [Schwelm i. Westfalen]*, June 1929, 80-83.
/BOTANY/MORPHOLOGY

1929-37 **Lohmann**[, W]. "Ueber die Bedeutung von Goethes naturwissenschaftlichen Schriften." *Natur und Heimat: Blätter für Naturerhaltung und Heimatliebe [Schwelm i. Westfalen]*, 4 (1929), 46-8.
/GENERAL INTRODUCTION

1929-38 **Lohmann**[, W]. "Über den volklichen Anteil bei der Ausgestaltung der neuzeitlichen Entwicklungslehre. -- Über das Verhältnis von Goethes Ansichten zum Darwinismus." *Natur und Heimat: Blätter für Naturerhaltung und Heimatliebe [Schwelm i. Westfalen]*, 4 (1929), 113-15.
/BIOLOGY: EVOLUTION/DARWIN, C

1929-39 **Mamlock**, G[?]. "Arion IV. Goethe-Tag der Hallenser Akademie." *Berliner Tageblatt und Handels-Zeitung [Abendzeitung]*, 58, No. 107, 4 March 1929.
/INSTITUTIONS: AKADEMIE DER NATURFORSCHER ZU HALLE

1929-40 **Martell**, Paul. "Goethe und die Technik." *Peine-Ilseder Werkszeitung*, 25 (1929), 10-11; No. 26 (1929), 9.

Rpt. of No. 1921-18.
/TECHNOLOGY

1929-41 *Matthaei, Rupprecht. "Das Gestaltproblem." *Ergebnisse der Physiologie*, 29 (1929), 1-82.
 Rpt. No. 1929-42.
 /RESEARCH: MORPHOLOGY/RESEARCH: PHYSIOLOGY

1929-42 *Matthaei, Rupprecht. "Das Gestaltproblem." München: Bergmann, 1929. iv, 103 pp.
 Rpt. of No. 1929-41.
 /RESEARCH: MORPHOLOGY/RESEARCH: PHYSIOLOGY

1929-43 Meyer, Adolf. "Goethes Naturerkenntnis: Ihre Voraussetzung in der Antike: ihre Krönung durch Carus." *Jahrbuch des Freien Deutschen Hochstifts Frankfurt am Main*, 1929, pp. 196-233.
 /NATURPHILOSOPHIE/PHILOSOPHY/CARUS, C

1929-44 Meyer, Adolf. "Das Wesen der idealistischen Biologie und ihre Beziehungen zur modernen Biologie." *Archiv für Geschichte der Mathematik, der Naturwissenschaften und der Technik*, 11 [NS 2] (1928/1929), 149-78.
 /BIOLOGY/RESEARCH: BIOLOGY

1929-45 Michel, Ernst. "Goethes Naturanschauung im Blickfeld unsrer Zeit." *Kunstwart*, 42, 2 (1929), 1-10.
 /NATURPHILOSOPHIE

1929-46 Migliorato, Garavini E. "La teratologia vegetale fino alla metamorfosi di Wolfgang Goethe (1790) [Botanical Teratology up to Goethe's *Metamorphosis*]." *Bollettino dell'Orto Botanico dell'Università di Napoli*, 10 (1929), 29-31.
 In Italian.
 /BOTANY/PATHOLOGY/MORPHOLOGY

1929-47 *Morin, Georges. "Gall et Goethe, Goethe disciple de Gall." *Paris médicale*, 19 (1929), 425.
 /GALL, F/ANATOMY

1929-48 Nette, Herbert. "Goethes Farbenlehre." *Darmstädter Tagblatt*, 12 February 1929.
 Cf. No. 1928-15.
 /CHROMATICS/REVIEW

1929-49 **Nussberger [Nusbergers]**, Max [Maksis]. "Goethes Urpflanze. Eine biographische Untersuchung von Max Nussberger." *Latvijas Universitates Raksti Filologijas un Filosofijas Fakultates Serija: Acta Universitatis Latviensis Series nova secundum ordines divisa: Philologorum et Philosophorum Ordinis Series I. Sejemus Tomus*, 1929/1931, 1-16.
Cf. Latvian synopsis, p. 16.
/BOTANY/MORPHOLOGY

1929-50 **Rauther**, Max. "Vom Wesen der Morphologie." In *Festschrift der Technischen Hochschule Stuttgart zur Vollendung ihres ersten Jahrhunderts 1829-1929*. Berlin: Verlag von Julius Springer, 1929, pp. 309-30.
/RESEARCH: MORPHOLOGY

1929-51 **Reiff**, Hermann J. "Goethe und die Optik." *Deutsche Optiker-Zeitung*, 5 (1929), 151-3; 169-71; 220-23; 239-40.
Cf. continuation, No. 1930-33.
/CHROMATICS/OPTICS

1929-52 **Reuther**, Hermann. "Platons und Goethes Naturanschauung." *Neue Jahrbücher für Wissenschaft und Jugendbildung*, 5, No. 6 (1929), 688-707.
/PLATO/NATURPHILOSOPHIE

1929-53 **S[?]., W[?].** "Goethe als Naturforscher." *Vossische Zeitung Berlin: Das Unterhaltungsblatt der Vossischen Zeitung*, No. 54, 5 March 1929.
Account of session on Goethe, 2 March 1929.
/GENERAL INTRODUCTION/INSTITUTIONS: LEOPOLDINA

1929-54 **Schiff**, Julius. "Chemie und Pharmazie an der Universität Jena zur Goethezeit." *Pharmazeutische Zeitung*, 74 (1929), 588-92.
/CHEMISTRY/INSTITUTIONS: UNIVERSITÄT JENA

1929-55 **Schmid[, Günther]**. "Goethe als Naturforscher." *Zeitschrift für Naturwissenschaften: Organ des Naturwissenschaftlichen Vereins für Sachsen und Thüringen zu Halle a. S.*, 89 (1929), 60-64.
/GENERAL INTRODUCTION

1929-56 **Schreyer**, Lothar. "Anmerkungen zu Goethes Farbenlehre." *Deutsches Volkstum: Monatsschrift für das deutsche Geistesleben [Hamburg]*, 1 (1929), 274-9.

/CHROMATICS/EPISTEMOLOGY

1929-57 **Schuster**, Julius. "Goethe." In his "Die Anfänge der wissen-
schaftlichen Erforschung der Geschichte des Lebens durch Cuvier und
Geoffroy Saint-Hilaire. Eine historisch-kritische Untersuchung."
*Archiv für Geschichte der Mathematik, der Naturwissenschaften und
der Technik*, 12 [NS 3] (1929), 341-9.
/BIOLOGY: EVOLUTION/ANATOMY/OSTEOLOGY/VICQ
D'AZYR, F

1929-58 **Schuster**, J[ulius]. "Idealistische Morphologie als Gegen-
wartsproblem." *Sitzungsberichte der Gesellschaft Naturforschender
Freunde zu Berlin*, 1928, 189-212.
/MORPHOLOGY/RESEARCH: MORPHOLOGY

1929-59 **Schuster**, Julius. "Ein Linnésches Dichtungsmotiv und Goethes
Metamorphosen-Elegie." *Forschungen und Fortschritte*, 5, No. 9
(1929), 99-100.
/WORKS: LYRICS/LINNAEUS [LINNÉ], C

1929-60 **Soret**, Frédéric. *Zehn Jahre bei Goethe: Erinnerungen an
Weimars klassische Zeit 1822-1832: Aus Sorets handschriftlichem
Nachlaß, seinen Tagebüchern und seinem Briefwechsel.* Sel., trans.
and comm. H[einrich]. H[ubert]. Houben. Leipzig: F. A. Brockhaus,
1929. 799 pp.
/SORET, F/PLACES: WEIMAR

1929-61 **Spiegel**, Gustav. "'Goetheanismus': 'Die Hauptmotive der Geschichte der Seele' von Gotthilf Heinrich Schubert." *Die Drei:
Monatsschrift für Anthroposophie, Dreigliederung und Goetheanismus*, 8 (1929), 217-38.
/SCHUBERT, G/RESEARCH: PSYCHOLOGY

1929-62 **Stein**, Robert. "Ein Irrtum in Goethes 'Naturwissenschaftlichem
Entwicklungsgang'. Kritische Bemerkungen zu Goethe-Ausgaben."
*Archiv für die Geschichte der Mathematik, der Naturwissenschaften
und der Technik*, 12 [NS 3], No. 1 (1929), 100-104.
/EDITIONS

1929-63 **Steiner**, Rudolf. *Das Wesen der Farben: Drei Vorträge.* Ed.
Marie Steiner. Kunst im Lichte der Mysterienweisheit: Rudolf
Steiners Farbenlehre I, 7. Dornach/Schweiz: Philosophisch-
Anthroposophischer Verlag am Goetheanum, 1929. xiv, 88 pp.
Rpt. of No. 1928-51.

/RESEARCH: CHROMATICS

1929-64 **Stettner**, Thomas. "Goethe und die Münchner Lithographie." In his *Gefundenes und Erlauschtes*. Ansbach: Verlag von C. Brügel & Sohn, 1929, 81-95.
Rpt. of No. 1902-20.
/TECHNOLOGY

1929-65 **Strohl**, Jean. *Mißbildungen im Tier- und Pflanzenreich: Versuch einer vergleichenden Betrachtung.* Jena: Verlag von Gustav Fischer, 1929. viii, 62 pp.
/RESEARCH: PATHOLOGY

1929-66 **Trillich**, Heinrich. "Die Farbenforscher bis zu Goethes Tod." *Technische Mitteilungen für Malerei*, 45, No. 19 (1929), 243-4.
/CHROMATICS/HISTORY OF SCIENCE

1929-67 **Trillich**, Heinrich. "Die Farbensysteme und ihre Lehrer. Goethe." *Technische Mitteilungen für Malerei*, 45, No. 14 (1929), 173-8.
/CHROMATICS

1929-68 **Troll**, Wilhelm. "Grundprobleme der Pflanzenmorphologie und der Biologie überhaupt." *Biologisches Zentralblatt*, 49 (1929), 43-60.
/RESEARCH: BOTANY

1929-69 *****Trümpner**, Egon. "Goethe als Naturforscher und Natur- philosoph." *Neue Preußische Zeitung (Kreuz-Zeitung)*, Beiblatt: Zeitenspiegel, 26 May 1929.
/GENERAL INTRODUCTION/NATURPHILOSOPHIE

1929-70 **tz[?]**. "Goethe als Naturforscher. Festsitzung der Kaiserlich Leopoldinischen Akademie der Naturforscher in Halle." *Saale- Zeitung: Hallesche Neueste Nachrichten*, 64, No. 54 (1929).
Account of session on Goethe, 2 March 1929.
/GENERAL INTRODUCTION/INSTITUTIONS: LEOPOLDINA

1929-71 **Vulpius**, Walther. "Goethe und die Medizin." *Zeitschrift für ärztliche Fortbildung*, 26 (1929), 673-5.
/MEDICINE

1929-72 **Walther**, Johannes. "Goethe als Mitglied der Akademie der Naturforscher zu Halle." *Forschungen und Fortschritte*, 5 (1929),

137-8.
  /INSTITUTIONS: AKADEMIE DER NATURFORSCHER ZU
  HALLE

1929-73 **Weber**, Erich C. H. "Wie Goethe als Geologe den Harz sah."
*Montagsblatt: das Heimatblatt Mitteldeutschlands: Wissenschaftliche
Beilage der Magdeburgischen Zeitung*, 71 (1929), 393-6.
  /GEOLOGY/PLACES: HARZ

1930-1 **Barthel**, Ernst. "Einheitliche Theorie des Sehvorgangs." *Hippokrates: Zeitschrift für Einheitsbestrebungen der Gegenwartsmedizin*, 3 (1930/1931), 635-7.
/CHROMATICS/RESEARCH: CHROMATICS/NEWTON, I

1930-2 **Barthel**, Ernst. "Goethe redivivus contra Newton-Huyghens." *Antäus: Blätter für neues Wirklichkeitsdenken*, No. 9 (1930), 125-42.
/CHROMATICS/RESEARCH: CHROMATICS/NEWTON, I/HUYGHENS, C

1930-3 **Barthel**, Ernst. *Goethe das Sinnbild deutscher Kultur.* Darmstadt/Leipzig: Hoffmann & Co., 1930. vii, 348 pp.
Contains five chapters on Goethe's scientific work.
/GENERAL INTRODUCTION/CHROMATICS /MORPHOLOGY

1930-4 **Beggerow**, Hans. "Der Wahrheitsgehalt von Goethes Farbenlehre." *Preußische Jahrbücher*, 221, No. 2 (1930), 184-92.
/CHROMATICS/EPISTEMOLOGY

1930-5 **Beils**, Willi. "Goethe in der Rhön." *Didaskalia: Wöchentliche Beilage der Frankfurter Nachrichten*, 108 (1930), 102.
/GEOLOGY

1930-6 **Biema**, Carry van. "Einige Hauptbegriffe aus Goethes Farbenlehre." In her *Farben und Formen als lebendige Kräfte.* Jena: Eugen Diederichs, 1930, pp. 67-127.
Rev. Hans Zint [No. 1932-385].
/CHROMATICS/FINE ARTS/HÖLZEL, A

1930-7 **Carus**, C[arl]. G[ustav]. "Goethes Verhältnis zur Natur und Naturwissenschaft." In *Goethe als Seher und Erforscher der Natur: Untersuchungen über Goethes Stellung zu den Problemen der Natur.* Ed. Johannes Walther. Halle: Kaiserlich Leopoldinische Deutsche Akademie der Naturforscher, 1930, pp. 17-33.
Originally 1832.
/GENERAL INTRODUCTION

1930-8 **Chemnitius**, Fritz. "Die Botaniker an der Universität Jena." Jena: Verlag der Fromannschen Buchhandlung Walter Biedermann, 1930. 22 pp.
/BOTANY/RECEPTION/INSTITUTIONS: UNIVERSITÄT JENA

1930-9 **Chemnitius**, Fritz. "Die Mineralogen an der Universität Jena (Ein Beitrag zur Jenaer Universitätsgeschichte)." *Altes und Neues aus der Heimat: Beilage zum Jenaer Volksblatt*, 41 (1930). 2 pp.
/GEOLOGY/RECEPTION/INSTITUTIONS: UNIVERSITÄT JENA/OKEN, L

1930-10 **Disselhorst**, Rudolf. "Goethes anatomische Studien." In *Goethe als Seher und Erforscher der Natur: Untersuchungen über Goethes Stellung zu den Problemen der Natur*. Ed. Johannes Walther. Halle: Kaiserlich Leopoldinische Deutsche Akademie der Naturforscher, 1930, pp. 227-51; 321-21.
/ANATOMY

1930-11 **Düren**. Wilhelm. "Die Metamorphose der Pflanze im Samen." Bonn: Verlag L. Neuendorff[, 1930]. 19 pp.
/RESEARCH: BOTANY/RESEARCH: MORPHOLOGY

1930-12 **Eckermann**[, J. P.]. *Conversations with Goethe*. Trans. John Oxenford. Ed. J. K. Moorhead. Intro. Havelock Ellis. Everyman's Library: Essays of Belles-Lettres, 851. London: J. M. Dent & Sons Ltd./New York: E. P. Dutton & Co. Inc., 1930. xxx, 448 pp.
Rpt. 1935.
Contains a comprehensive index, pp. 427-48.
/EDITION

1930-13 **Franz**, Viktor. "Vergleichende Anatomie vor hundert Jahren: Zur Erinnerung an Goethes Anteilnahme am Pariser Akademiestreit." *Süddeutsche Monatshefte*, 27, No. 8 (1930), 535-40.
/COMPARATIVE ANATOMY/SAINT-HILAIRE, G DE/CUVIER, G

1930-14 **Fuchs**, Fr[itz]. "Die Metamorphose der Insekten." *Gäa-Sophia: Jahrbuch der Naturwissenschaftlichen Sektion der Freien Hochschule für Geisteswissenschaft am Goetheanum Dornach*, 5 (1930), 133-52.
/RESEARCH: ENTOMOLOGY/RESEARCH: MORPHOLOGY

1930-15 **Gebhardt**, Martin. "Goethe und das umgekehrte Spektrum." *Psychologische Optik*, 6 (1930), 93-9.
/CHROMATICS/OPTICS

1930-16 **Gebhardt**, Martin. "Das umgekehrte Spektrum." *Unterrichtsblätter für Mathematik und Naturwissenschaften*, 36 (1930), 256-60.
/RESEARCH: CHROMATICS/CHROMATICS

1930-17 **[Goethe**, J. W. von.] "Geschichte meines botanischen Studiums." *Goethe-Kalender auf das Jahr 1930.* Leipzig: Dieterich'sche Verlagsbuchhandlung, 1930, pp. 216-54.
/EDITION

1930-18 **Graevenitz**, George von. "Goethe und das Luftfahrt-Problem." *Didaskalia: Wöchentliche Beilage der Frankfurter Nachrichten*, 108, No. 32, 10 August 1930, 132.
/TECHNOLOGY

1930-19 **Grohmann**, Gerbert. [Rev. of:] *Gäa-Sophia: Jahrbuch der Naturwissenschaftlichen Sektion der Freien Hochschule für Geisteswissenschaft am Goetheanum Dornach*, 5 (1930). *Anthroposophical Movement: News for English-speaking Members of the Anthroposophical Society*, 7 (1930), 395-7.
Cf. Nos. 1930-14, -30, -32, -41 and -47.
/RESEARCH: VARIOUS/REVIEW

1930-20 **Herting**, Johannes. "'Max' (Jacobi's) Studentenzeit und seine Beziehungen zu Goethe." In *Carl Wigand Maximilian Jacobi ein deutscher Arzt (1775-1858): Ein Lebensbild nach Briefen und anderen Quellen.* Görlitz: Verlag für Sippenforschung und Wappenkunde C. A. Starke, 1930, pp. 21-51.
/JACOBI, M/PSYCHIATRY/MEDICINE

1930-21 **Houben**, H[einrich]. H[ubert]. "Vor 100 Jahren: Nach Frédéric Soret: 'Zehn Jahre bei Goethe'." *Aus der Heimat: Naturwissenschaftliche Monatsschrift*, 43, No. 7 (1930), 210-11.
/SORET, F

1930-22 **Jablonski**, Walter. "Zum Einfluß der Goetheschen Farbenlehre auf die physiologische und psychologische Optik der Folgezeit." *Archiv für Geschichte der Mathematik, der Naturwissenschaften und der Technik*, 13 [NS 4] (1930/1931), 75-82.
/CHROMATICS/RECEPTION

1930-23 **Karsten**, George. "Über die Pflanzengattung Goetheana." In *Goethe als Seher und Erforscher der Natur: Untersuchungen über Goethes Stellung zu den Problemen der Natur.* Ed. Johannes Walther. Halle: Kaiserlich Leopoldinische Deutsche Akademie der Naturforscher, 1930, pp. 117-22.
/BOTANY

1930-24 **Katalog** *der Goethe-Beireis-Ausstellung im Juleum August --*
Septbr. 1930. 27 pp.
"Herausgegeben vom Universitätsbund Helmstedt."
/BEIREIS, G/TECHNOLOGY/EXHIBITION

1930-25 **Klemm**, Friedrich. "Ernst Gottfried Fischer und Goethe: Ein
Beitrag zu Goethes Farbenlehre." *Optische Rundschau*, 21, No. 5
(1930), 51-3; No. 6 (1930), 63-5.
/CHROMATICS/FISCHER, E

1930-26 **Loiseau**, H[ippolyte]. "De l'oeuvre scientifique de Goethe et en
particulier de sa grande erreur en optique." *Mémoires de l'Académie*
des Sciences Inscriptions et Belles-Lettres de Toulouse, Series 12, 8
(1930), 305-23.
/CHROMATICS/OPTICS/GENERAL INTRODUCTION

1930-27 **Lorentz**, Paul. "Goethes fromme Naturforschung." *Zeitschrift*
für den Evangelischen Religionsunterricht, 41 (1930), 337-50.
/GENERAL INTRODUCTION

1930-28 **Lorey**, Wilhelm. "Goethes Stellung zur Mathematik." In
Goethe als Seher und Erforscher der Natur: Untersuchungen über
Goethes Stellung zu den Problemen der Natur. Ed. Johannes
Walther. Halle: Kaiserlich Leopoldinische Deutsche Akademie der
Naturforscher, 1930, pp. 131-56; 309-12.
/MATHEMATICS

1930-29 ***Palcos**, Alberto. "La ciencia en Goethe [Goethe and Science]."
La Prensa, Buenos Aires, diciembre 21, 1930.
In Spanish.
/GENERAL INTRODUCTION

1930-30 **Pfeiffer**, Ehrenfried. "Metamorphose der niederen Tierreihen."
Gäa-Sophia: Jahrbuch der Naturwissenschaftlichen Sektion der Freien
Hochschule für Geisteswissenschaft am Goetheanum Dornach, 5
(1930), 82-90.
/RESEARCH: ZOOLOGY/RESEARCH: MORPHOLOGY

1930-31 **Pfeiffer**, Ehrenfried. "Wandlungen der naturwissenschaftlichen
Problemstellung." *Das Goetheanum*, 9 (1930), 85-6.
/BERTALANFFY, L/BUCHWALD, E

1930-32 **Poppelbaum**, Hermann. "Polaritäten im Tierreich: Polyp und
Meduse." *Gäa-Sophia: Jahrbuch der Naturwissenschaftlichen Sektion*

der Freien Hochschule für Geisteswissenschaft am Goetheanum Dornach, 5 (1930), 67-81.
/RESEARCH: ZOOLOGY/RESEARCH: MORPHOLOGY

1930-33 *Reiff, Hermann J. "Goethe und die Optik." *Deutsche Optiker-Zeitung*, 6 (1930), 5; 52; 73; 82.
Continuation of No. 1929-51.
/CHROMATICS/OPTICS

1930-34 **Rinkel**, Richard. "Newtons und Goethes Farbenlehre." *Zeitschrift für den Physikalischen und Chemischen Unterricht*, 43 (1930), 145-7.
/CHROMATICS/NEWTON, I

1930-35 **Schiff**, Julius. "Christian Gottfried Nees von Esenbeck und Goethe." *Schlesische Monatshefte: Blätter für Kultur und Schrifttum der Heimat [Breslau]*, 7, No. 11 (1930), 478-84.
/NEES VON ESENBECK, C/BOTANY/NATUR-PHILOSOPHIE

1930-36 **S[?].**, K. "Goethe und die Elektrizität." (Aus dem Goethe--Nationalmuseum.) *Forschungen und Fortschritte*, 6 (1930), 426-7.
/PHYSICS

1930-37 **Schmid**, Günther. "Goethes Metamorphose der Pflanzen." In *Goethe als Seher und Erforscher der Natur: Untersuchungen über Goethes Stellung zu den Problemen der Natur*. Ed. Johannes Walther. Halle: Kaiserlich- Leopoldinische Deutsche Akademie der Naturforscher, 1930, pp. 205-26; 313-19.
/BOTANY

1930-38 **Schmid**, Günther. "Goethe und die Nova acta der Leopoldinisch-Carolinischen Deutschen Akademie der Naturforscher." *Leopoldina: Berichte der Deutschen Akademie der Naturforscher zu Halle*, 6 (1930), 15-61.
/INSTITUTIONS: LEOPOLDINA

1930-39 **Schmid**, Günther. "Goethe und von Seelus." *Ekkehard: Mitteilungsblatt deutscher Genealogischer Abende*, 6/7 (1930/ 1931), 58-60.
/SEELUS, ? VON/BOTANY

1930-40 **Schröder[, ?].** "Goethe und die Medizin." *Medizinische Klinik*, 26 (1930), 30.

/MEDICINE

1930-41 **Splechtner**, F[?]. J. N. "Goethes Gesetz der Metamorphose und die Regel von der sogenannten homologen Variationen." *Gäa-Sophia: Jahrbuch der Naturwissenschaftlichen Sektion der Freien Hochschule für Geisteswissenschaft am Goetheanum Dornach*, 5 (1930), 118-32.
/MORPHOLOGY/COMPARATIVE ANATOMY

1930-42 **Steiner**, Rudolf. *Das Wesen der Farbe in Licht und Finsternis: Maß, Zahl und Gewicht: Drei Vorträge.* Rudolf Steiners Farbenlehre, 2. Ed. Maria Steiner. Kunst im Lichte der Mysterienweisheit, 8. Dornach (Schweiz): Philosophisch-Anthroposophischer Verlag am Goetheanum, 1930. 80 pp.
/RESEARCH: CHROMATICS/RESEARCH: PHYSICS/CHROMATICS

1930-43 **Trojan**, Felix. "Zur Psychologie der Farben bei Goethe." *Zeitschrift für Ästhetik und allgemeine Kunstwissenschaft*, 24 (1930), 232-8.
/CHROMATICS

1930-45 **Usteri**, Alfred. "Lorenz Oken und Goethe." *Das Goetheanum*, 9 (1930), 293; 299-300.
   Includes numerous aphorisms from Oken's *Lehrbuch des Systems der Naturphilsophie*.
/OKEN, L/MORPHOLOGY/RESEARCH: MORPHOLOGY

1930-46 **Veh**, Robert von. "Untersuchungen und Betrachtungen zum Blattstellungsproblem." *Flora oder Allgemeine Botanische Zeitung*, 125, NS 25 (1930), 83-154.
   Cf. esp. "Goethes Vertikal- und Spiraltendenz," pp. 132-3.
/BOTANY/RESEARCH: BOTANY

1930-47 **Wachsmuth**, Guenther. "The Animal World: *The Gäa Sophia*, 1930. The Annual Report of the Natural Science Section at the Goetheanum. Foreword by the Editor." *Anthroposophical Movement: News for English-speaking Members of the Anthroposophical Society*, 7 (1930), 265-6.
/RESEARCH: VARIOUS/ANTHROPOSOPHY

1930-48 **Walden**, Paul. "Goethe und die Chemie." *Berliner Tageblatt und Handelszeitung*, 59, No. 275 (1930), Abend-Ausgabe.
/CHEMISTRY

1930-49 **Walden**, Paul. "Goethe und die Chemie." *Zeitschrift für angewandte Chemie*, 43 (1930), 523-96; 792-7; 847-59; 864-8.
Cf. No. 1930-50.
Rev. "Dr. O. S." *Das Goetheanum*, 9 (1930), 367.
/CHEMISTRY

1930-50 **Walther**, Johannes. "Eine Alraune aus Goethes Hand." In *Goethe als Seher und Erforscher der Natur: Untersuchungen über Goethes Stellung zu den Problemen der Natur*. Ed. Johannes Walther. Halle: Kaiserlich Leopoldinische Deutsche Akademie der Naturforscher, 1930, pp. 123-30; 309.
/CHEMISTRY

1930-51 **Walther**, Johannes, ed. "Goethe als Seher und Erforscher der Natur." In *Goethe als Seher und Erforscher der Natur: Untersuchungen über Goethes Stellung zu den Problemen der Natur*. Halle: Kaiserlich Leopoldinische Akademie der Naturforscher zu Halle, 1930, pp. 59-99; 306-7.
/GENERAL INTRODUCTION

1930-52 **Walther**, Johannes, ed. *Goethe als Seher und Erforscher der Natur: Untersuchungen über Goethes Stellung zu den Problemen der Natur*. Halle: Kaiserlich Leopoldinische Akademie der Naturforscher zu Halle, 1930. viii, 323 pp.
Cf. Nos. 1930-7,-10, -23, -28, -37, -50, -51, -53, -54, -56, -59 and -62.
Rev. Wilhelm Westphal, "Der Naturwissenschaftler Goethe," 1931. [In Mappe III E 61/C20: "Goethe und die Naturwissenschaften. Zeitungsausschnitte 1913 -" at the Frankfurter Goethe-Museum.]
/COLLECTION

1930-53 **Walther**, Johannes. "Goethe und die Leopoldina." In *Goethe als Seher und Erforscher der Natur: Untersuchungen über Goethes Stellung zu den Problemen der Natur*. Ed. Johannes Walther. Halle: Kaiserlich Leopoldinische Deutsche Akademie der Naturforscher, 1930, pp. 1-12; 301-2.
/INSTITUTIONS: LEOPOLDINA

1930-54 **Walther**, Johannes. "Goethe und das Reich der Steine." In *Goethe als Seher und Erforscher der Natur: Untersuchungen über Goethes Stellung zu den Problemen der Natur*. Ed. Johannes Walther. Halle: Kaiserlich Leopoldinische Deutsche Akademie der

Naturforscher, 1930, pp. 253-300; 321-2.
/GEOLOGY

1930-55 **Weiß**, Otto. "Goethes Farbenlehre." *Schriften der Königsberger Gelehrten Gesellschaft [Naturwissenschaftliche Klasse]*, 7, No. 4 (1930), 163-75.
/CHROMATICS

1930-56 **Wessely**, Karl. "Welche Wege führen noch heute zu Goethes Farbenlehre?" In *Goethe als Seher und Erforscher der Natur: Untersuchungen über Goethes Stellung zu den Problemen der Natur.* Ed. Johannes Walther. Halle: Kaiserlich Leopoldinische Deutsche Akademie der Naturforscher, 1930, pp. 157-84; 313.
/CHROMATICS/RESEARCH: CHROMATICS

1930-57 **Wien**, Wilhelm. "Goethe und die Physik." In *Wilhelm Wien: Aus dem Leben und Wirken eines Physikers.* Leipzig: Verlag von Johann Ambrosius Barth, 79-102.
Rpt. of No. 1923-30.
"Vortrag gehalten in der Münchner Universität am 9. Mai 1923."
/CHROMATICS

1930-58 **Wittels**, Fritz. "Goethe und Freud." *Die psychoanalytische Bewegung*, 2 (1930), 431-66.
/FREUD, S/RESEARCH: PSYCHOLOGY/RESEARCH: PSYCHIATRY

1930-59 **Wolff**, Ferdinand von. "Über den Goethit." In *Goethe als Seher und Erforscher der Natur: Untersuchungen über Goethes Stellung zu den Problemen der Natur.* Ed. Johannes Walther. Halle: Kaiserlich Leopoldinische Deutsche Akademie der Naturforscher, 1930, pp. 111-16; 307-8.
/GEOLOGY

1930-60 **Zaunick**, Rudolph. "Carl Gustav Carus und sein Kreis." In *Ausstellung Freistaat Sachsen Dresden 1930 Internationale Hygiene-Ausstellung*, pp. 64-100.
/CARUS, C/BIOLOGY/NATURPHILOSOPHIE

1930-61 **Zaunick**, Rudolph. "Oken, Carus, Goethe. Zur Geschichte des Gedankens der Wirbel-Metamorphose." In *Historische Studien und Skizzen zu Natur- und Heilwissenschaft.* Festschrift Georg Sticker. Berlin: Springer Verlag, 1930, pp. 118-29.

/OSTEOLOGY/COMPARATIVE ANATOMY/OKEN, L/CARUS, C

1930-62 **Ziehen**, Theodor. "Goethes naturphilosophische Anschauungen." In *Goethe als Seher und Erforscher der Natur: Untersuchungen über Goethes Stellung zu den Problemen der Natur.* Ed. Johannes Walther. Halle: Kaiserlich Leopoldinische Deutsche Akademie der Naturforscher, 1930, pp. 35-57; 303-6.
/NATURPHILOSOPHIE

1931-1 **André**, Hans. "Wiederherstellung des bildbedingten Denkens in der Biologie durch Goethe und K. Chr. Planck." In his *Urbild und Ursache in der Biologie.* München/Berlin: Verlag von R. Oldenbourg, 1931, pp. 85-145.
/EPISTEMOLOGY/BIOLOGY/PLANCK, K

1931-2 [anon.] "Goethe-Zimmer in Marktredwitz." *Deutsche Museums-Nachrichten: Korrespondenz- und Nachrichtenblatt für das gesamte Museumswesen*, 2, No. 2 (1931), 2.
/PLACES: MARKTREDWITZ

1931-3 *****Aragon**, Augustin. "Goethe y la fisica. (Teoria de los colores) [Goethe and Physics. (Theory of Colors)]." *Universidad de Mexico*, 8 (1931/1932), 463-8.
In Spanish.
/CHROMATICS/PHYSICS

1931-4 **Baron**, Walter. "Die idealistische Morphologie Al. Brauns and A. P. de Candolles und ihr Verhältnis zur Deszendenzlehre." *Beihefte zum Botanischen Centralblatt*, 48, No. 3 (1931), 314-34.
/BRAUN, A/CANDOLLE, A DE

1931-5 **Barthel**, Ernst. "Wesen und Wert des Goetheschen Physik. (Die Farbe als Spannungsphänomen)." In his *Vorstellung und Denken: Eine Kritik des pragmatischen Verstandes.* Schriften der Elsass-Lothringischen Wissenschaftlichen Gesellschaft zu Strassburg, Reihe B, Theologie und Philosophie, 4. [Straßburg?:] Selbstverlag der Elsaß-Lothringischen Gesellschaft zu Straßburg, 1931, pp. 188-207.
Rev. S. Friedländer, "Über Goethes Farbenlehre," *Berliner Tageblatt*, 6 February 1931. [In Mappe III E 21/C91: "Goethe und die Farbenlehre 1913-. Sammelmappe Zeitungsausschnitte" at the Frankfurter Goethe-Museum.]
/CHROMATICS

1931-6 **Bauer**, Adolf. "Goethes psychiatrische Intuition und intuitive Psychiatrie." *Medizinische Klinik*, 27 (1931), 267-8.
/PSYCHIATRY/RESEARCH: PSYCHIATRY

1931-7 **Boehm**, Albert. "Goethe und der Bergbau." *Zeitschrift für das Berg-, Hütten- und Salinenwesen im Preußischen Staate*, 79 (1931), B507-B555.
/GEOLOGY

1931-8 **Bölsche**, Wilhelm. "Der naturwissenschaftliche Entwicklungsgedanke bei Goethe." In *Deutscher Almanach für das Jahr 1932*. Leipzig: Verlag von Philipp Reclam jun.[, 1931], pp. 149-57.
/BIOLOGY: EVOLUTION

1931-9 **Brett**, G[?]. S. "Goethe's Place in the History of Science." *University of Toronto Quarterly*, 1 (1931/1932), 279-99.
/GENERAL INTRODUCTION

1931-10 **Carus**, Carl Gustav. *Goethe: zu dessen näherem Verständnis.* Ed. and afterword Rudolf Marx. Kröners Taschenausgabe, 97. Leipzig: Alfred Kröner Verlag[, 1931]. 164 pp.
Rpt. of No. 1843-5.
/GENERAL INTRODUCTION

1931-11 **Deetjen**, Werner. "Goethe und die Ausgrabungen um Weimar." *Thüringisch-Sächsische Zeitschrift für Geschichte und Kunst*, 20 (1931), 62-7.
/GEOLOGY/ARCHAEOLOGY/EDITION/VULPIUS, C

1931-12 **Fischer**, Paul. "Natur und Naturwissenschaft (Allgemeines. Botanik. Optik, Farbenlehre. Geologie. Zoologie.)" In his *Goethes letztes Lebensjahr*. Weimar: Hermann Böhlaus Nachfolger, 1931. viii, 171 pp.
/GENERAL INTRODUCTION

1931-13 *****Flaum**, M[?]. "Goethe przyrodnikiem [Goethe as a Scientist]." *Kurjer Warszawski*, No. 135, 1931, 4-5.
In Polish.
/GENERAL INTRODUCTION

1931-14 **Franz**, Viktor. "Die sogennante Vervollkommnung in der Stammesgeschichte und Goethes Aeußerungen zu diesem Problem." *Der Naturforscher vereint mit Natur und Technik*, 8 (1931/ 1932), 142-51.

/BIOLOGY: EVOLUTION

1931-15 **Franz**, Viktor. "Systematik und Phylogenie der Wirbeltiere." In *Handbuch der vergleichenden Anatomie der Wirbeltheorie*. Ed. Louis Bolk et al. 6 vols. Berlin: Urban & Schwarzenberg, 1931, I, 185-268.
/TAXONOMY/COMPARATIVE ANATOMY /OSTEOL-OGY/VICQ D'AZYR, F

1931-16 **Gebhardt**, Martin. "Forschung und Schule. Goethe und unsere Wissenschaften." *Unterrichtsblätter für Mathematik und Naturwissenschaften*, 37 (1931), 385-90.
/GENERAL INTRODUCTION/RECEPTION

1931-17 [**Goethe**, Johann Wolfgang von.] *Die schönsten Essays von Goethe*. Ed. Y. Yokonama. 3rd edn. Tokyo: Verlag von Daigaku shorin, 1931. 114 pp.
Rpt. of No. 1924-13.
Contains several sections on science.
/EDITION: SELECTIONS

1931-18 **Grassi**, Leonardo. "Filosofia e scienza in Goethe attraverso l'episodio delle Madri nel II Faust [Philosophy and Science in Goethe through the Episode of the Mothers in *Faust II*]." *Archivio di Filosofia*, 1, No. 4 (1931), 52-69.
In Italian.
/METHOD/WORKS: FAUST

1931-19 *****Grohmann**, Gerbert. "Goethes botanische Ideen." *Anthroposophie*, 14 (1931/1932), 265-9.
/BOTANY

1931-20 *****Hoffmann**, A[?]. "Die Ausbeute Goethes an Mineralien auf der Glatzer Reise 1790." *Die Grafschaft Glatz*, 26, No. 1 (1931), 12-13.
/GOETHE'S COLLECTIONS/MINERALOGY/PLACES: GLATZ

1931-21 **Keudell**, Elise von. *Goethe als Benutzer der Weimarer Bibliothek. Ein Verzeichnis der von ihm entliehenen Werke*. Ed. and intro. Werner Deetjen. Weimar: Hermann Böhlaus Nachfolger, 1931. xiv, 391 pp.
/INFLUENCES

1931-22 **Kleinschmidt**, Otto. "Die Entdeckung des Zwischenkiefers."

Falco, 27 (1931), 8-10.
/OSTEOLOGY

1931-23 **Knauer**, Helmut. "Über die Entstehung der Farben beim Prisma." *Das Goetheanum*, 10 (1931), 117-8.
/CHROMATICS/RESEARCH: CHROMATICS

1931-24 **König**, Karl. "Beiträge zu einer reinen Anatomie des menschlichen Knochengerüstes. II. Teil." *Natura: Eine Zeitschrift zur Erweiterung der Heilkunst nach geisteswissenschaftlichen Menschenkunde*, 5 (1931/1932), 1-23.
Continuation of No. 1928-28.
Cf. continuation, No. 1931-25.
RESEARCH: OSTEOLOGY

1931-25 **König**, Karl. "Beiträge zu einer reinen Anatomie des menschlichen Knochengerüstes. III. Teil." *Natura: Eine Zeitschrift zur Erweiterung der Heilkunst nach geisteswissenschaftlichen Menschenkunde*, 5 (1931/1932), 316-42.
Continuation of No. 1931-24.
Cf. continuation, No. 1932-188.
/RESEARCH: OSTEOLOGY

1931-26 **Kretschmer**, Max. "Lehrgestalt eines Goethevierteljahrs in der Einklassigen." *Erziehung und Bildung: Wissenschaftliche und schulpraktische Beilage der Preuß. Lehrerzeitung*, 12, No. 23 (1931), 177-81.
/PEDAGOGY/GENERAL INTRODUCTION

1931-27 **Krumbiegel**, Ingo. "Das sogennante Kompensationsgesetz Goethes betreffs Korrelation von Kopfwaffen und Oberzähnen. Zu Goethes 100. Todestag am 22. 3. 1932." *Zeitschrift für Säugetierkunde*, 6 (1931), 186-202.
/COMPARATIVE ANATOMY/MORPHOLOGY/OSTEOLOGY

1931-28 **Maring**, Albert. "Goethe als Physiker." *Gral*, 26 (1931/1932), 503-8.
/CHROMATICS

1931-29 *****Müllerried**, Federico K. G. "Goethe, geologo y paleontologo [Goethe, Geologist and Paleontologist]." *Universidad de Mexico*, 3 (1931/1932), 449-62.
In Spanish.
/GEOLOGY/PALEONTOLOGY

1931-30 **Rassy**, Gustav Christian. "Goethe als Naturwissenschaftler." *Der Brocken: Heimatliche Monatsblätter der Harzer Landschaft*, 3, No. 4 (1931), 107-9.
/GENERAL INTRODUCTION

1931-31 **Rösch**, Siegfried. "Notiz über Optimalfarben." *Die Naturwissenschaften*, 19 (1931), 615-17.
/CHROMATICS

1931-32 ***Santos**, Verginia. "Goethe e a anatomia [Goethe and Anatomy]." *Arquivo de Anatomia e Antropologia [Instituto de Anatomia da Faculdade de Medecina de Universidad e de Lisboa]*, 14 (1931), 781-94.
In Portuguese.
/ANATOMY

1931-33 **Schuster**, Julius. "Goethe als Plagiator? Historisch-kritischer Send-Brief an Dr. Dr. h. c. Wilhelm Junk: Ein Intermezzo zum Fest-Essen der Gesellschaft der Bibliophilen am 15. November 1931." [Berlin:] Gustav Feller, 1931. 14 pp.
/BOTANY/KOSMELI, M/SEIDEL, J

1931-34 ***Skowronnek**, K[?]. "Goethe und die Elektrizität." *Ingenieur-Zeitschrift*, 2 (1931), 51.
/PHYSICS

1931-35 **Steiner**, Rudolf. *Die schöpferische Welt der Farbe: Drei Vorträge*. Rudolf Steiners Farbenlehre, 3. Ed. Marie Steiner. Dornach (Schweiz): Philosophisch-Anthroposophischer Verlag am Goetheanum, 1931. 82 pp.
Actually four lectures: 26 July 1914; 1 January 1915; 18 and 20 May 1923; and 4 January 1924.
/RESEARCH: CHROMATICS/CHROMATICS/RESEARCH: AESTHETICS

1931-36 **Stober**, K[?]. W. "Goethe als Naturforscher." *Der Naturforscher*, 8 (1931/1932), 409-11.
/GENERAL INTRODUCTION

1931-37 **Stück**, Reinhold. "Goethe und Ilmenau." In *Festschrift zur Goethe-Hundertjahrfeier in Ilmenau 1931*. Ilmenau: Ausschuß für die Goethe-Hundertjahrfeier, 1931, pp. 7-27.
/GEOLOGY/INSTITUTIONS: ILMENAUER BERGBAU

1931-38 ***Urdizil**, Johannes. "Goethe, Graf J. B. Paar und Hahnemann."
Germanoslavica, 1 (1931/1932), 491-7.
Rpt. No. 1932-343.
/PAAR, J/HAHNEMANN, C

1931-39 **Vogt[, ?]**. "Die Veterinärschule zu Jena. Ein Briefwechsel zwischen dem Großherzog Karl August von Weimar und Goethe über die Jenaer Veterinärschule." *Berliner Tierärztliche Wochenschrift*, 47 (1931), 126.
/VETERINARY MEDICINE/INSTITUTIONS: TIERARZNEI-
SCHULE JENA

1931-40 **Wildermann**, Hans. "Von der Farbe und dem Licht auf der Bühne im Hinblick auf Goethes Farbenlehre." In *Farbe-Ton-Forschungen*. Ed. Georg Anschütz. Vol. 3 of *Bericht über den II. Kongreß für Farbe-Ton-Forschung (Hamburg, 1.-5. Oktober 1930)*. Hamburg: Psychologisch-ästhetische Forschungsgesellschaft (Vertrieb für den Buchhandel durch Otto Meißners Verlag), 1931, pp. 1-64; 4-13.
/RESEARCH: CHROMATICS/CHROMATICS

1931-41 **Wildermann**, Hans. "Von der Farbe und dem Licht auf der Bühne im Hinblick auf Goethes Farbenlehre unter besonderer Berücksichtigung von Richard Wagners 'Parsifal'." *Zeitschrift für Musik*, 98, No. 7 (1931), 556-8.
/CHROMATICS/WAGNER, R

1931-42 **Witkop**, Philipp. "Die Farbenlehre." In his *Goethe: Leben und Werk*. Stuttgart/Berlin: J. G. Cotta'sche Buchhandlung, 1931, pp. 323-34.
/CHROMATICS

1931-43 **Wohlbold**, H[ans]. "The Archetypal Plant and the Blue Flower." *Anthroposophical Movement: News for English-speaking Members of the Anthroposophical Society*, 8 (1931), 141-4.
English trans. of ?.
/BOTANY/NOVALIS [HARDENBERG, F VON]

1932-1 **[anon.]** "Goetheana über den Arzt und die Heilkunst." *Fortschritte der Medizin*, 50 (1932), 227-8.
/MEDICINE

1932-2 **[anon.]** "Goethe et la science." In *Bibliothèque Nationale:*

Goethe 1749-1832: Exposition organisée pour commémorer le centenaire de la mort de Goethe. Éditions des Bibliothèques Nationales de France, 1932, pp. 152-9.
/EXHIBITION

1932-3 [anon.] "Goethe. Medici e medicine nella vita di un grande poeta [Goethe. Physicians and Medicine in the Life of a Great Poet]." *Il Giardino di Esculapio*, 5 (1932), 5-32.
In Italian.
/MEDICINE

1932-4 [anon.] "Goethe -- der Psychotherapeut." *Fortschritte der Medizin*, 50 (1932), 229.
/PSYCHOLOGY

1932-5 [anon.] "Goethe scienziato [Goethe the Scientist]." *Minerva*, 42, No. 1 (1932), 7-9.
In Italian.
Review of an article by P. Mauriac in *Revue Hebdomadaire*.
/GENERAL INTRODUCTION

1932-6 [anon.] "Goethe und der Arzt Johann Franz Wenzel Krimer." *Fortschritte der Medizin: Die Zeitschrift des praktischen Arztes*, 50 (1932), 217-19.
/KRIMER, J/MEDICINE

1932-7 [anon.] "Goethe und der englische Quäker Luke Howard." *Der Quäker: Monatshefte der Deutschen Freunde*, 9 (1932), 248.
/HOWARD, L/METEOROLOGY

1932-8 [anon.] *Illustrierte für Ärzte.* 22 March 1932. 4 pp.
Special issue devoted to Goethe.
/COLLECTION

1932-9 [anon.] "Palma di Goethe [Goethe's Palm]." *Wiener Medizinische Wochenschrift*, 82 (1932), opposite p. 36.
/BOTANY

1932-10 [anon.] "Raum 6: Darstellung von Goethes Farbenlehre." In *Wunder und Wissen: Kurzes Verzeichnis der Ausstellung von Bildern und Büchern aus 6 Jahrhunderten der Natur- und Heilkunde zur 92. Tagung der Gesellschaft Naturforscher und Ärzte.* Wiesbaden: Nassauischer Kunstverein und die Städtische Kunstsammlung im Museum zu Wiesbaden, 1932.

/EXHIBITION/CHROMATICS

1932-11 **Abel**, Othenio. "Goethe als Biologe." *Forschungen und Fortschritte*, 8 (1932), 98-9.
Rpt. No. 1932-12.
/BIOLOGY

1932-12 **Abel**, Othenio. "Goethe als Biologe." In *Forschungen und Fortschritte: Goethe*. Ed. Karl Kerkhof. Leipzig: Kommissionsverlag von Johann Ambrosius Barth[, 1932], pp. 12-13.
Rpt. of No. 1932-11.
/BIOLOGY

1932-13 **Abel**, Othenio. "Goethe und die Biologie." *Biologia generalis*, 9 (1932), 1-24.
Rpt. No. 1932-14.
/BIOLOGY

1932-14 **Abel**, Othenio. "Goethe und die Biologie." In *Goethe im Spiegel der Lebensforschung*. Intro. Otto Porsch. Wien/Leipzig: Emil Heim & Co., 1932, pp. 1-24.
Rpt. of No. 1932-13.
/BIOLOGY

1932-15 **André**, Hans. "Goethes Naturanschauung in ihrer Bedeutung für die moderne Biologie." *Literaturwissenschaftliches Jahrbuch der Görres-Gesellschaft*, 7 (1932), 65-104.
/BIOLOGY

1932-16 **André**, Hans. "Stilgesetze pflanzlicher Formgestaltung im Lichte Goethescher Naturanschauung." *Der Kunstwart: Monatshefte für Kunst, Literatur und Leben*, 45 (1932), 292-9.
/BOTANY/MORPHOLOGY

1932-17 **Arx**, Max von. "Goethe, ein Vorläufer der Ballontheorie." *Oltner Tagblatt*, No. 98, 26 and 27 April 1932.
/ANATOMY/ZOOLOGY

1932-18 **Baravalle**, Hermann von. "Goethes naturwissenschaftliche Methode und die Forderungen im Leben der Gegenwart." *"Gäa-Sophia": Jahrbuch der naturwissenschaftlichen Sektion der Freien Hochschule für Geisteswissenschaft am Goetheanum Dornach*, 6 (1932), 104-11.
/METHOD/GENERAL INTRODUCTION

1932-19 **Barthel**, Ernst. "Goethes Farbenlehre -- eine Frage der Ehrlich-keit." *Die Sonne: Monatsschrift für Nordische Weltanschauung und Lebensgestaltung*, 9 (1932), 494-6.
/CHROMATICS

1932-20 **Barthel**, Ernst. "Goethes Farbenlehre in ihrer wissenschaftlich-weltanschaulichen Bedeutung." *Bayreuther Blätter*, 55 (1932), 66-74.
/CHROMATICS/NEWTON, I

1932-21 **Bazzicalupo**, Carlo. "Goethe naturalista [Goethe the Nat-uralist]." *Gazzetta internazionale di medicina*, 40, No. 19 (1932), 628-35.
In Italian.
/GENERAL INTRODUCTION

1932-22 **Beneke**, Rudolf. "Goethe als pathologischer Anatom." *Die Medizinische Welt*, 6 (1932), 432-4.
/PATHOLOGY/ANATOMY

1932-23 **Beneke**, Rudolf. "Goethe und die medizinische Fakultät in Halle." *Heimatkalender für Halle und den Saalkreis 1932*, 13 (1932), 29-36.
/MEDICINE/INSTITUTIONS: UNIVERSITÄT HALLE /LODER, J [VON] /REIL, J

1932-24 **Benn**, Gottfried. "Goethe und die Naturwissenschaften." *Die Neue Rundschau*, 43 (1932), 463-90.
Rpt. Nos. 1932-25, 1933-6, 1949-14, 1949-15, 1959-1, 1962-1, 1967-3, 1968-2, 1973-4, 1975-1 and 1987-15.
/GENERAL INTRODUCTION

1932-25 **Benn**, Gottfried. "Goethe und die Naturwissenschaften." In his *Nach dem Nihilismus*. Berlin: Gustav Kiepenhauer Verlag, 1932, pp. 25-85.
Rpt. of No. 1932-24.
Rev. W. Klau, *Tat*, 26 (1934/1935), 877-9.
/GENERAL INTRODUCTION

1932-26 **Berthelot**, René. *Science et philosophie chez Goethe*. Bibliothèque de la philosophie contemporaine. Paris: F. Alcan, 1932. 190 pp.
Rpt. of No. 1929-5.
Rev. Geneviève Bianquis, *Revue Philosophique de la France et*

de l'Étranger, 57, No. 113 (1932), 468-9.
/BIOLOGY: EVOLUTION/MORPHOLOGY/LAMARCK, J
DE

1932-27 **Bianquis**, Geneviève. "L'Urphaenomen dans la pensée et dans l'oeuvre de Goethe." *Revue Philosophique de la France et de l'Étranger*, 57, No. 113 (1932), 207-44.
Rpt. No. 1951-5.
/METHOD/EPISTEMOLOGY

1932-28 **Biema**, Carry van. "Goethes Farbenlehre." *Graphische Jahrbücher*, 53 (1932), 59-61.
/CHROMATICS/NEWTON, I/FINE ARTS

1932-29 **Biema**, Carry van. "Goethes Farbenlehre in der Praxis des Kunsterziehers." *Kunst und Jugend*, 12 (1932), 51-2.
/CHROMATICS/RESEARCH: FINE ARTS/PEDAGOGY

1932-30 **Biema**, Carry van. "Die weltanschaulichen Grundbegriffe in Goethes Farbenlehre." *Deutsche Lehrerinnen-Zeitung (ADLV)*, 49 (1932), 105-6.
/CHROMATICS/PHILOSOPHY/NEWTON, I

1932-31 **Birnbaum**, Max. "Goethe als Naturforscher." *Blätter für Volksgesundheitspflege: Gemeinverständliche Zeitschrift des Landesausschusses für hygienische Volksbelehrung in Preußen des Deutschen Vereins für Volkshygiene*, 32 (1932), 33-4.
/GENERAL INTRODUCTION

1932-32 **Blaustein**, Leopold. "Goethe jako psycholog [Goethe as a Psychologist]." *Przeglad humanistyczny*, 7 (1932), 349-64.
In Polish.
/PSYCHOLOGY

1932-33 **Boehm**, Albert. "Der Anteil des Bergbaus an Goethes naturwissenschaftlicher Forschungsarbeit." *Zeitschrift für das Berg-, Hütten- und Salinenwesen im preussischen Staate*, 80 (1932), B257-70.
/TECHNOLOGY/GEOLOGY/MINERALOGY

1932-34 **Böker**, Hans. "Goethe und die Anatomie." *Münchener Medizinische Wochenschrift*, 79 (1932), 457-61.
/ANATOMY

1932-35 **Bölsche**, Wilhelm. "Der naturwissenschaftliche Entwick-

lungsgedanke bei Goethe." *Deutscher Almanach für das Jahr 1932.* Leipzig: Verlag von Philipp Reclam jun., 1932., pp. 149-57.
/BIOLOGY: EVOLUTION

1932-36 **Bonne**, Georg Heinrich. "Goethe als Volkshygieniker und Führer aus der Weltkrisis." *Blätter für Volksgesundheitspflege: Gemeinverständliche Zeitschrift des Landesausschusses für hygienische Volksbelehrung in Preußen des Deutschen Vereins für Volkshygiene*, 32 (1932), 34-7.
/MEDICINE

1932-37 **Bonnet**, L[?]. "Goethe et la couleur." *Revue génerale teinture, impression, blanchiment, apprêt*, 10 (1932), 291.
/CHROMATICS/FINE ARTS

1932-38 **Brown**, M[?]. Webster. "Medicine and Goethe." *Medical Journal and Record*, 135 (1932), 349-50.
/MEDICINE

1932-39 **Brunelli**, Gustavo. "Goethe naturalista. Rapporti della scienza coll'arte nel pensiero goethiano [Goethe the Naturalist. Relations between Science and Art in Goethe's Thought]." *Rivista di Biologia*, 14 (1932), 1-13.
In Italian.
/METHOD/GENERAL INTRODUCTION

1932-40 **Burzio**, Filippo. "Goethe e Helmholtz [Goethe and Helmholtz]." *Risanamentio medico*, 3 (1932), fasc. 21, 6ff.
Rpt. Nos. 1932-41 and 1933-12.
In Italian.
/HELMHOLTZ, H

1932-41 **Burzio**, Filippo. "Goethe e Helmholtz [Goethe and Helmholtz]." *La Stampa*, 20 October 1932.
Rpt. of No. 1932-40.
In Italian.
/HELMHOLTZ, H

1932-42 ***Buytendijk**, Frederik Jacobus J. "De beteekenis van Goethe voor de natuurwetenschap van onzen tijd [Goethe's Significance for the Contemporary Sciences]." In his *Twee redevoeringen.* Gröningen: Rijksuniv., 1932, pp. 20-45.
Rpt. No. 1961-5.
"Redevoering gehouden . . . 16. Maart 1932 ter herdenking van

Goethe's sterfjaar."
/GENERAL INTRODUCTION

1932-43 *Cassirer, C[?]. "Der Naturforscher Goethe." *Hamburger Fremdenblatt*, 19 March 1932, Goethe-Beilage.
/CHROMATICS

1932-44 Castiglioni, Arturo. "Volfango Goethe biologo [Goethe the Biologist]." *Realtà*, 11 (1932), 341-9.
In Italian.
/BIOLOGY

1932-45 Castle, Eduard. "Zur Geschichte der Ausgaben der naturwissenschaftlichen Schriften Goethes." *Archiv für das Studium neuerer Sprachen*, 163 (1932), 172-86.
/EDITIONS

1932-46 Chance, Burton. "Goethe and his theory of colors." *Annals of Medical History*, NS 5 (1932), 360-75.
"Read at the Meeting of the Section on Medical History, College of Physicians, Philadelphia, April 11, 1932."
/CHROMATICS

1932-47 *Chandler, Asa C. "Goethe and Science." *Rice Institute Pamphlet*, 19 (1932), 129-47.
"Goethe Centenary Lectures, 1932."
/GENERAL INTRODUCTION

1932-48 Chandler, Stéphanie. "Goethe et la Science." *Revue germanique*, 23 (1932), 333-42.
/GENERAL INTRODUCTION

1932-49 Chemnitius, Fritz. "IV. Der Einfluss Goethes auf den Ausbau der Naturwissenschaften (Von Johann Georg Lenz bis zur vollständig durchgeführten Teilung aller Wissenszweige)." In *Geschichte der naturwissenschaftlichen und mathematischen Studien an der Universität Jena von ihrer Gründung bis zur Gegenwart. Altes und Neues aus der Heimat: Beilage zur Jenaer Volksblatt*, 43, No. 162 (13 July 1932)ff.
Published in ten different installments through 11 July 1933.
/HISTORY OF SCIENCE/RECEPTION/LENZ, J

1932-50 Cohn, Jonas. "Goethes Denkweise." *Archiv für die Geschichte der Philosophie*, 41 (1932), 1-56.

/PHILOSOPHY

1932-51 **Cole**, F[?]. J. "Goethe as Biologist." *Nature: A Weekly Journal of Science*, 124 (1932), 423-5.
/BIOLOGY

1932-52 **Colosi**, Giuseppe. "Goethe filosofo della natura [Goethe as a Philosopher of Nature]." *Bollettino di Zoologia*, 3, No. 4 (1932), 145-52.
Rpt. No. 1932-53.
In Italian.
"Solenne celebrazione del centenario della morte di Volfango Goethe, presso la R. Università di Napoli (25 Aprile 1932)."
/GENERAL INTRODUCTION

1932-53 **Colosi**, Giuseppe. "Goethe filosofo della natura [Goethe as a Philosopher of Nature]." Napoli: N. Jovene, 1932. 8 pp.
Rpt. of No. 1932-52.
In Italian.
/GENERAL INTRODUCTION

1932-54 **Cortesi**, Fabrizio. "Volfango Goethe naturalista [Goethe the Naturalist]." *Il Messaggero*, 31 January 1932.
In Italian.
/GENERAL INTRODUCTION

1932-55 **Croce**, B[enedetto]. "Goethe ou la métamorphose poétique." *Europe. Numéro spécial*, 28, No. 112 (1932), 143-60.
In Italian.
/LITERARY THEORY/MORPHOLOGY

1932-56 **Dacqué**, Edgar. "Goethes Wesen und das Urbild im Dasein." In his *Natur und Erlösung*. München/Berlin/Zürich: R. Oldenbourg[1933], pp. 59-108.
/MORPHOLOGY/GENERAL INTRODUCTION

1932-57 **Dainelli**, Giotto. "Goethe naturalista [Goethe the Naturalist]." *Il Marzocco*, 37, No. 26 (1932), p. 1.
In Italian.
/GENERAL INTRODUCTION

1932-58 **Darmstaedter**, Ernst. "Goethe und die Alchymisten." *Forschungen und Fortschritte*, 8 (1932), 90-92.
Rpt. No. 1932-59.

/ALCHEMY

1932-59 **Darmstaedter**, Ernst. "Goethe und die Alchymisten." In *Forschungen und Fortschritte: Goethe*. Ed. Karl Kerkhof. Leipzig: Kommissionsverlag von Johann Ambrosius Barth[, 1932], pp. 14-16. Rpt. of No. 1932-58.
/ALCHEMY

1932-60 *****Deinhardt**, E[?]. M. "Die Art wie Goethe beobachtet." *Gymnastik*, 7, No. 5/6 (1932), 71-80.
/METHOD/METEOROLOGY

1932-61 **Del Lungo**, Carlo. "Scienza e poesia in Goethe [Science and Poetry in Goethe]." *Minerva*, 42, No. 10 (1932), 361-3.
In Italian.
/GENERAL INTRODUCTION

1932-62 **De Lorenzo**, Giuseppe. "Goethe scienziato [Goethe the Scientist]." *L'Avvisatore librario settimanale*, 5, No. 14 (1932), 343-4.
In Italian.
/GENERAL INTRODUCTION

1932-63 **Dennert**, Wolfgang. "Der Naturforscher Goethe und die Gegenwart." In *Festschrift zur 75-Jahrfeier der Klinger-Oberrealschule Frankfurt a. M.* Frankfurt am Main: Gebrüder Knauer, 1932, pp. 136-51.
/GENERAL INTRODUCTION

1932-64 *****Deutsch**, Adolf. "Goethe und kein Ende." *Westdeutsche Ärztezeitung*, 23 (1932), 345-8; 368-70; 381-3.
Rpt. No. 1933-17.
"Vortrag im Ärztlichen Verein Frankfurt zu Goethes Todestag 1932."
/GENERAL INTRODUCTION

1932-65 *****Derganz**, France. "Goethe in medicina [Goethe and Medicine]." *Zdravniski vestnik*, 1 (1932), 1-4.
In Slovenian.
/MEDICINE

1932-66 **Diepgen**, Paul. "Goethe und die Medizin." *Klinische Wochenschrift: Organ der Gesellschaft Deutscher Naturforscher und Ärzte*, 11 (1932), 1611-16.

Rpt. No. 1932-67.
/MEDICINE

1932-67 **Diepgen**, Paul. "Goethe und die Medizin." *Mitteilungen aus dem Institut für Geschichte der Medizin und der Naturwissenschaften in Berlin: Sonderdruck aus Klinische Wochenschrift: Organ der Gesellschaft Deutscher Naturforscher und Ärzte.* Berlin: Verlag von Julius Springer/München: J. F. Bergmann, 1932. 16 pp.
Rpt. of No. 1932-66.
/MEDICINE

1932-68 **Dietrich**, Alfred. "Goethe im Egerlande: unter Berücksichtigung des einschlägigen Schrifttums neudargestellt im Goethe-Gedenkjahr 1932." Veröffentlichung des Vereines "Unser Egerland", Verein für Heimaterkundung und Heimatpflege in Eger. Eger: Verlag Buchhandlung Helm[, 1932]. 24 pp.
/PLACES: EGER/GEOLOGY

1932-69 *****Dimmer**, G[?]. "Goethe als Naturforscher und Techniker." *Elektrotechnik und Maschinenbau*, 50 (1932), 187-8.
/GENERAL INTRODUCTION

1932-70 **Disse**, A[?]. "Goethes Farbenlehre im Physikunterricht." *Zeitschrift für mathematischen und naturwissenschaftlichen Unterricht*, 63 (1932), 49-53.
/CHROMATICS/PEDAGOGY

1932-71 **Dörr**, Walter. "Goethe und Apotheker Spielmann." *Süddeutsche Apotheker-Zeitung*, 72, No. 55 (1932), 377-8.
/SPIELMANN, J

1932-72 **Dohrn**, Max. "Goethe über seine naturwissenschaftliche Denk- und Arbeitsweise." In *Goethes naturwissenschaftliches Denken und Wirken: Drei Aufsätze.* Ed. Schriftleitung der Zeitschrift *Die Naturwissenschaften.* Berlin: Springer, 1932, pp. 28-59.
"Vortrag, am 21. Januar 1932 gehalten in Colloquium des Hauptlaboratoriums der Schering-Kahlbaum A. G. und am 11. März 1932 in der Kaiser Wilhelm-Gesellschaft zur Förderung der Wissenschaften und der Physiologischen Gesellschaft."
/GENERAL INTRODUCTION/METHOD

1932-73 *****Domin**, Karel. "Goethe a priroda [Goethe and Nature]." *Narodni Politika*, 12 March 1932.
Trans. into French in *L'Europe Centrale*, 7, Nr. 12/13.

In Czech.
/GENERAL INTRODUCTION

1932-74 **Domin**, Karel. "Goethova nauka o metamorfose rostlin [Goethe's Scientific Studies of the Metamorphosis of Plants]." In *Goethuv sbornik: Pamatce 100. vyroci basnikovy smrti vydali cesti germaniste.* Prague: Statni nakladatelstvi, 1932, pp. 199-201. In Czech.
/BOTANY/MORPHOLOGY

1932-75 **Eisenschmied**, Hans. "Die Verleugnung Goetheschen Geistes in der Physik." *Anthroposophie*, 15 (1932), 35-40.
/CHROMATICS

1932-76 **Enke**, Elisabeth. "Goethes Bedeutung für die modernen Naturwissenschaften." *Neue Jahrbücher für Wissenschaft und Jugendbildung*, 8 (1932), 385-400.
/GENERAL INTRODUCTION/CHROMATICS

1932-77 **Enzinger**, Moriz. "Goethe und Tirol." Innsbruck: Wagner'sche Universitäts-Buchhandlung, 1932. vii, 168 pp.
/PLACES: TIROL

1932-78 **Epstein**, Paul. "Goethes Stellung zur Mathematik." *Forschungen und Fortschritte*, 8 (1932), 86-8.
Rpt. No. 1932-79.
/MATHEMATICS/ALCHEMY/PARACELSUS

1932-79 **Epstein**, Paul. "Goethes Stellung zur Mathematik." In *Forschungen und Fortschritte: Goethe.* Ed. Karl Kerkhof. Leipzig: Kommissionsverlag von Johann Ambrosius Barth[, 1932], pp. 10-12.
Rpt. of No. 1932-78.
/MATHEMATICS/ALCHEMY/PARACELSUS

1932-80 **Erhard**, Hubert. "Goethe und die Naturwissenschaften." In *Universität Freiburg, Schweiz: Vorträge gehalten am 29. Februar 1932 bei der Goethefeier.* Freiburg, Schweiz: St. Paulus-Druckerei, 1932, pp. 32-46.
/GENERAL INTRODUCTION

1932-81 **Ermatinger**, Emil. "Goethe und die Natur." Wege zur Dichtung: Zürcher Schriften zur Literaturwissenschaft, 13. Horgen-Zürich/Leipzig: Verlag der Münster-Presse, 1932. 33 pp.
"Rede zur Goethe-Feier der Universität Zürich am 22. Februar

1932."
/GENERAL INTRODUCTION

1932-82 **Ferrari**, Giuseppe Michele. "Goethe naturalista: Nel centenario della morte [Goethe the Scientist: On the Centenary of his Death]." In *Anno accademico CXXX: Commentari dell'Ateneo di Brescia per l'anno 1931*. Brescia: Stab. Tipografici Ditta F. Apollonio & C., 1932, pp. 301-30.
Partial rpts. Nos. 1932-83 and 1932-84.
In Italian.
/GENERAL INTRODUCTION

1932-83 **Ferrari**, Giuseppe Michele. "Goethe naturalista: Nel centenario della morte [Goethe the Scientist: On the Centenary of his Death]: Estratto dai 'Commentari dell'Ateneo di Brescia' per il 1931." Brescia: Stabilimenti Tipografici F. Apollonio e C., 1932. 30 pp.
Partial rpt. of No. 1932-82.
In Italian.
/GENERAL INTRODUCTION

1932-84 **Ferrari**, Giuseppe Michele. "Goethe naturalista [Goethe the Naturalist]." *La Nuova Antologia*, 67, No. 682 [360] (1932), fasc. 1442, 478-90.
Partial rpt. of No. 1932-82.
In Italian.
/GENERAL INTRODUCTION

1932-85 **Ferrari**, Giuseppe Michele. "Goethe pensatore e naturalista [Goethe the Thinker and Naturalist]." *Giornale d'Oriente, Alessandria d'Egitto*, 25 and 26 March 1932.
In Italian.
/GENERAL INTRODUCTION

1932-86 **Ficker**, Heinrich von. "Bemerkungen über Goethes 'Versuch einer Witterungslehre'." *Sitzungsberichte der preussischen Akademie der Wissenschaften: Physikalisch-mathematische Klasse*, 18 and 25 Feb. 1932, pp. 47-52.
Rpt. Nos. 1932-87 and 1934-10.
/METEOROLOGY

1932-87 **Ficker**, Heinrich von. "Bemerkungen über Goethes 'Versuch einer Witterungslehre': Sonderausgabe aus den Sitzungsberichten der preussischen Akademie der Wissenschaften Phys.-math. Klasse." Berlin: Verlag der Akademie der Wissenschaften: In Kommission bei

Walter de Gruyter u. Co., 1932.
Rpt. of No. 1932-86.
/METEOROLOGY

1932-88 **Ficker**, Heinrich von. "Goethe und die Meteorologie." *Forschungen und Fortschritte*, 8 (1932), 95-6.
Rpt. No. 1932-89.
/METEOROLOGY/HOWARD, L

1932-89 **Ficker**, Heinrich von. "Goethe und die Meteorologie." In *Forschungen und Fortschritte: Goethe*. Ed. Karl Kerkhof. Leipzig: Kommissionsverlag von Johann Ambrosius Barth[, 1932], pp. 19-20.
Rpt. of No. 1932-88.
/METEOROLOGY/HOWARD, L

1932-90 **Fischer**, Paul. *Gott-Natur: Goethes Naturanschauung im Lichte seiner Frömmigkeit*. Weimar: Verlag von Hermann Böhlaus Nachfolger, 1932. 66 pp.
/METHOD

1932-91 *****Fischer**, Walter. "Beziehungen der sächsischen Naturforscher zu Goethe." *Dresdner Nachrichten*, No. 376, 11 August 1932, 3-4.
/PLACES: SACHSEN/LUDWIG, C/TREBRA, F/WERNER, A/RACKNITZ, J VON/TITIUS, K/CARUS, C/SEIDEL, J/REICHENBACH, G

1932-92 **Fischer**, Walther. "Goethes Geologie und wir." *Sitzungsberichte und Abhandlungen der Naturwissenschaftlichen Gesellschaft Isis in Dresden*, 1932, 41-2.
Synopsis of No. 1932-93.
/GEOLOGY

1932-93 *****Fischer**, Walther. "Goethes Geologie und wir." *Wissenschaftliche Beilage des Dresdener Anzeigers*, 9, No. 22 (1932), 85-7.
Cf. synopsis, No. 1932-92.
/GEOLOGY

1932-94 **Fischer**, Walther. "Goethes geologische Beziehungen zu Sachsen." In *Sächsischer Kunstverein zu Dresden Juni--Juli 1932: Brühlsche Terasse: Goethe Ausstellung*. Dresden: Verlag Buchdruckerei der Wilhelm und Bertha v. Baensch Stiftung, 1932, pp. 32-45.
/GEOLOGY/PLACES: SACHSEN

1932-95 **Fischl**, Friedrich. "Goethe und Graf Kaspar Sternberg." In *Aus*

Goethes Marienbader Tagen. Leipzig: J. J. Weber, 1932.
"Herausgegeben von der Kurstadt Marienbad."
/STERNBERG, K VON

1932-96 **Flander**, Heinz. "Goethe und die Psychoanalyse: Auch ein Buchkritik." In *Deutscher Almanach für das Jahr 1932.* Leipzig: Verlag von Philipp Reclam jun., 1932, pp. 135-9.
/PSYCHOANALYSIS/FREUD, S

1932-97 **Foà**, Carlo. "Goethe naturalista [Goethe the Naturalist]." *Gerarchia*, 13 (1932), 515-20.
In Italian.
/GENERAL INTRODUCTION

1932-98 *****Fokker**, A[?]. D. "Goethe in de natuurwetenschappen [Goethe in the Sciences]." *De Gids*, 96, No. 2 (1932), 68-76.
In Dutch.
/GENERAL INTRODUCTION/CHROMATICS

1932-99 *****Fraenkel**, Alexander. "Goethe und Darwin als Naturforscher." *Wiener Klinische Wochenschrift*, 45 (1932), 449-54.
/BIOLOGY: EVOLUTION/DARWIN, C

1932-100 **Frank**, Ernst. *Goethe im Elbogener Ländchen.* Elbogen: Verlag Egerlandhaus für Buch und Kunst Karl H. Frank, 1932. 83 pp.
/PLACES: ELBOGEN

1932-101 **Franz**, Victor. "Goethes anatomisch-zoologische Studien." *Forschungen und Fortschritte*, 8 (1932), 99-100.
Rpt. No. 1932-102.
/ANATOMY/ZOOLOGY

1932-102 **Franz**, Victor. "Goethes anatomisch-zoologische Studien." In *Forschungen und Fortschritte: Goethe.* Ed. Karl Kerkhof. Leipzig: Kommissionsverlag von Johann Ambrosius Barth[, 1932], pp. 23-4.
Rpt. of No. 1932-101.
/ANATOMY/ZOOLOGY

1932-103 **Franz**, Victor. "Zum Ausgleich zwischen verschiedenen phyletischen Forschungswegen." *Biologisches Zentralblatt*, 52 (1932), 584-98.
/BIOLOGY/METHOD

1932-104 **Freundlich**, Herbert. "Einige Bemerkungen zu Goethes Auf-

satz 'Der Versuch als Vermittler von Objekt und Subjekt'." *Scientia (Rivista di scienza)*, 52 (1932), 374-80.
Trans. into French, No. 1932-105.
/METHOD

1932-105 **Freundlich**, Herbert. "Quelques remarques sur le mémoire de Goethe: L'expérience considerée comme l'intermédiaire entre le sujet et l'objet'." *Scientia (Rivista di scienza)*, 52 (1932), 196-202.
French trans. of No. 1932-104.
/METHOD

1932-106 **Freydank**, Hanns. "Goethe besucht das Braunkohlenbergwerk zu Langenbogen (19. Juli 1802)." *Heimatkalender für Halle und den Saalkreis*, 13 (1932), 49-52.
/TECHNOLOGY/PLACES: LANGENBOGEN/GEOLOGY

1932-107 **[Freydank**, Hanns.] "Goethe als Bergmann in der Goethe-Ausstellung der Stadt Halle." *Hallische Nachrichten*, 44, No. 124 (30 May 1932), 3.
/TECHNOLOGY/EXHIBITION/PLACES: HALLE

1932-108 **Friedlaender**, Salomo. "Warum verwarf der Farbenlehrer Goethe die Farbenlehre des Goetheaners Schopenhauer?" *Jahrbuch der Schopenhauer-Gesellschaft*, 19 (1932), 287-90.
/CHROMATICS/SCHOPENHAUER, A

1932-109 **Friedrich**, Arthur. "Goethe und die Salzsieder." *Mitteldeutsche Illustrierte*, No. 30, 24 July 1932, 11.
/TECHNOLOGY

1932-110 **Fudjinami**, K[?]. ["Goethe als Naturforscher."] *Goethe-Jahrbuch: Die Goethe-Gesellschaft in Japan*, 1 (1932), 20-37.
Cf. synopsis, No. 1938-5.
In Japanese.
/GENERAL INTRODUCTION

1932-111 **Gebhardt**, Martin. *Goethe als Physiker: Ein Weg zum unbekannten Goethe*. Berlin: G. Grote'sche Verlagsbuchhandlung, 1932. viii, 163 pp.
Rev. Richard Wolf [No. 1932-375].
Rev. Hans Zint [No. 1932-385].
/CHROMATICS/NEWTON, I/METHOD

1932-112 *****Gebhardt**, Martin. "Goethe und das umgekehrte Spektrum."

Neue psychologische Studien, 6 (1932), 95-9.
/CHROMATICS/KIRSCHMANN, J

1932-113 **Goethe**, J. W. von. "Aus der Einleitung zur Farbenlehre." In
Insel-Almanach auf das Goethejahr 1932. Leipzig: Insel-Verlag,
1932, pp. 171-2.
/EDITION

1932-114 *__Goethe__, J. W. von. "Experiment as Mediator between Object
and Subject." *Anthroposophy*, Easter 1932.
English Trans. by George Adams.
Rpt. No. 1952-14.
/TRANSLATION: ENGLISH

1932-115 [**Goethe**, J. W. von.] "Druzheskii prizyv [Freundlicher
Zuruf]." Trans. V. O. Likhtenshtadta. In *Gete. Sobrannye sochen-
neniie.* Iubileinoe izdannie. Moskva/Leningrad, 1932, I, lxxviii-
lxxix.
[Zhitomirskaia 2187]
Contained within the article "Vol'fgang Gete [Wolfgang
Goethe]" by A. Lunacharskii.
/TRANSLATION: RUSSIAN

1932-116 [**Goethe**, J. W. von.] "From the Scientific Writings of Goethe."
Anthroposophy: A Quarterly Review of Spiritual Science, 7 (1932), 1-
25.
"Translation and introductory notes by George Adams Kauf-
mann, M. A. Cantab."
/TRANSLATION: ENGLISH

1932-117 **Goethe**, Johann Wolfgang von. "Der Granit." [Burg
Giebichenstein: Werkstätten der Stadt Halle/Staatl. Städt.
Kunstgewerbeschule, 1935.] [16] pp.
/EDITION

1932-118 [**Goethe**, J. W. von.] "Der Kammerberg bei Eger 1808." In
*Goethe-Festschrift der Kurstadt Franzensbad aus Anlaß der Feier des
100. Todestages J. W. Goethes*. Ed. Alois John. Franzensbad: Verlag der Kurverwaltung Franzensbad/Prag: A. Haase, 1932. 75 pp.
/EDITION

1932-119 **Goethe**, Johann Wolfgang. "Natur." Illustr. Hans Orlowski.
[Berlin: Kunstgewerbeschule Berlin-West, 1932]. [2] pp.
"Goethe/Natur mit Holzschnitten von Hans Orlowski wurde als

Privatdruck im Jahre 1932 in 50 Exemplaren auf der Presse der Kunstgewerbeschule Berlin-West gedruckt."
/EDITION

1932-120 **[Goethe**, J. W. von.] "Natur! Wir sind von ihr umgeben und umschlungen, . . . [Die Natur: Ein Fragment]." [Illustr. J. L. Gampp. Hamburg: Gustav Petermann Druckerei-Gesellschaft, 1932.] [1] p.
/EDITION

1932-121 **[Goethe**, J. W. von.] "Natur! Wir sind von ihr umgeben und umschlungen, . . . [Die Natur: Ein Fragment]." [Illustr. J. L. Gampp. Hamburg: Gustav Petermann Druckerei-Gesellschaft, 1932.] [2] pp.
/EDITION

1932-122 **Goethe**[, J. W. von]. "Om graniten [Über den Granit]." In *Essäer och annat: Brev: Maximer och Reflexioner*. Vol. 9 of his *Skrifter i urval*. Ed. Allan Bergstrand. Stockholm: Albert Bonnieis Förlag, 1932, pp. 114-18.
/TRANSLATION: SWEDISH

1932-123 **Goethe**, J. W. von. "Über den Granit." In *Insel-Almanach auf das Goethejahr 1932*. Leipzig: Insel-Verlag, 1932, pp. 63-8.
/EDITION

1932-124 **Goethe**, J. W. von. "Der Versuch als Vermittler von Objekt und Subjekt." In *Insel-Almanach auf das Goethejahr 1932*. Leipzig: Insel-Verlag, 1932, pp. 179-88.
/EDITION

1932-125 **Goethe**, J. W. von. "Der Versuch als Vermittler von Objekt und Subjekt." Offenbach am Main: Buchdruckwerkstatt der Kunstgewerbeschule zu Offenbach am Main/Wilhelm Kumm, 1932. 12 pp.
/EDITION

1932-126 **Goethe**, J. W. von. "Versuch einer allgemeinen Vergleich-ungslehre." In *Insel-Almanach auf das Goethejahr 1932*. Leipzig: Insel-Verlag, 1932, pp. 164-9.
/EDITION

1932-127 **Goethe** *im Spiegel der Lebensforschung*. Intro. Otto Porsch. Wien/Leipzig: Haim, 1932. 150 pp.

Cf. Nos. 1932-14, -176 and -252.
= Sonderausgabe of *Biologia generalis*, 9 (1932)
/COLLECTION/BIOLOGY

1932-128 **Goethes** *naturwissenschaftliches Denken und Wirken: Drei Aufsätze.* Ed. Schriftleitung der Zeitschrift *Die Naturwissenschaften: Wochenschrift für die Fortschritte der reinen und der angewandten Naturwissenschaften.* Berlin: Springer, 1932. 99 pp.
Cf. Nos. 1932-72, -150 and -266.
Rev. Adolf Hess, *Schweizerische Rundschau*, 32 (1932/ 1933), 475-6.
Rev. Pierre Schmit, "Ein Schlager des Goethejahres." *Weltbühne*, 28, No. 2 (1932), 174-5.
/GENERAL INTRODUCTION

1932-129 *****Goldberg**, Josip. "Gete kao prirodoslovac [Goethe as a Natural Scientist]." *Priroda*, 22 March 1932, 80-86.
In Serbo-Croatian.
/GENERAL INTRODUCTION

1932-130 *****Goldztaub**, S[?]. "Structure cristalline de la goethite." *Comptes rendus hebd. des séances de l'Académie des sciences*, 195 (1932), 964-7.
/MINERALOGY

1932-131 **Gräntz**, Fritz. "Goethes Metamorphosen-Gedichte." In *Festschrift zur 75-Jahrfeier der Klinger-Oberrealschule Frankfurt a. M.* Frankfurt a. M.: Gebrüder Knauer, 1932, pp. 123-35.
/WORKS: LYRICS

1932-132 **Graffi**, Elsa. "Della teoria goethiana del cranio [Goethe's Theory of the Skull]." *Ateneo Veneto*, 110, No. 123 (1932), 299-300.
In Italian.
/OSTEOLOGY

1932-133 **Greef**, Richard. "Goethe, sein Verhältnis zu den Brillen und seine Kurzsichtigkeit." *Optische Rundschau und Photo-Optiker*, 23 (1932), 178-82.
/OPTICS

1932-134 *****Grosser**, Otto. "Einige Bemerkungen über Goethes Stellung zu den Naturwissenschaften." In *Im Zeichen Goethes: Sonderheft d. Urania (Prag)*, 1932, pp. 5-6.
/GENERAL INTRODUCTION

1932-135 **Grünewald**, Max. "Goethe, der Entdecker des menschlichen Zwischenkiefers." *Fortschritte der Medizin*, 50 (1932), 223-4.
/OSTEOLOGY

1932-136 *****Guyot van der Ham**, A[?]. "Goethes geologische en mineralogische onderzoekingen in Bohemen [Goethe's Geological and Mineralogical Investigations in Bohemia]." *Geologie en Mijnbouw*, 11 (1932), 2-4.
In Dutch.
/GEOLOGY/MINERALOGY/PLACES: BÖHMEN

1932-137 **Haberlandt**, Gottlieb. "Goethe als Naturforscher." In *Johann Wolfgang Goethe 1832-1932: Ein Gedenkblatt der Hallischen Nachrichten zum hundertsten Todestage des Dichters am 22. März*. *Hallische Nachrichten*, No. 67, 19 March 1932, p. 15.
/GENERAL INTRODUCTION

1932-138 *****Haberling**, Wilhelm. "Johann Wolfgang Goethes Beziehungen zur Heilkunde." *Deutsches Ärzteblatt*, 61 (1932), 125-9.
/MEDICINE

1932-139 **Hamburger**, Carl. "Zwei Versuche zur Farbenlehre Goethes." *Medizinische Klinik: Wochenschrift für praktische Ärzte*, 28 (1932), 417.
Rpt. No. 1932-141.
Cf. synopsis, No. 1932-141.
/CHROMATICS/RESEARCH: CHROMATICS

1932-140 **Hamburger**, Carl. "Zwei Versuche zur Farbenlehre Goethes." *Klinische Wochenschrift: Organ der Gesellschaft Deutscher Naturforscher und Ärzte*, 11 (1932), 1084-5.
Synopsis of No. 1932-140.
/CHROMATICS/RESEARCH: CHROMATICS

1932-141 **Hamburger**, Carl. "Zwei Versuche zur Farbenlehre Goethes." *Deutsche medizinische Wochenschrift*, 58 (1932), 658.
Rpt. of No. 1932-139.
/CHROMATICS/RESEARCH: CHROMATICS

1932-142 *****Hansen**, Albert. "Goethes Interesse for kemien [Goethe's Interest in Chemistry]." *Naturens verden*, 16 (1932), 175-82.
In Dutch.
/CHEMISTRY

338

1932-143 **Hanssen**[, ?]. "Aerztliches von Goethe." *Fortschritte der Medizin*, 50 (1932), 226-7.
/MEDICINE

1932-144 **Hara**, H[?]. ["Goethe und die Pflanzen."] *Goethe-Jahrbuch: Die Goethe-Gesellschaft in Japan*, 1 (1932), 60-75.
In Japanese.
/BOTANY

1932-145 *****Hartwig**, R[?]. "Was bleibt von Goethes Naturforschung übrig?" *Leipziger Neueste Nachrichten*, 19 March 1932. Sonderbeilage "Lebendiges Wissen."
/RECEPTION

1932-146 *****Haupt**, Heinz. "Um Goethes naturwissenschaftliche Leistungen." *Vorstoß [Berlin]*, 2 (1932), 264-6.
/CHROMATICS/GEBHARDT, M/OSTWALD, W

1932-147 **Heim**, Walter. "Goethes Farbenlehre mit Experimenten." *Angewandte Chemie*, 45 (1932), 651.
Synopsis of No. 1932-148.
/CHROMATICS

1932-148 **Heim**, Walter. "Goethes Farbenlehre mit Experimenten." *Verhandlungen der Schweizerischen Naturforschenden Gesellschaft*, 113 (1932), 310-11.
Cf. synopsis, No. 1932-147.
/CHROMATICS/NEWTON, I

1932-149 **Helmholtz**, Hermann von. "Goethes Vorahnungen kommender naturwissenschaftlicher Ideen." *Die Naturwissenschaften: Wochenschrift für die Fortschritte der reinen und der angewandten Naturwissenschaften*. Sonderheft z. Goethe-Jahrhundertfeier, 20 (1932), 213-23.
Rpt. of No. 1892-10.
Rpt. No. 1932-150.
Rev. [No. 1932-375].
/GENERAL INTRODUCTION

1932-150 **Helmholtz**, Hermann von. "Goethes Vorahnungen kommender naturwissenschaftlicher Ideen." In *Goethes naturwissenschaftliches Denken und Wirken: Drei Aufsätze*. Ed. Schriftleitung der Zeitschrift *Die Naturwissenschaften: Wochenschrift für die Fortschritte der*

reinen und der angewandten Naturwissenschaften. Berlin: Verlag von Julius Springer, 1932, pp. 1-27.
  Rpt. of No. 1932-149.
  /GENERAL INTRODUCTION

1932-151 *Henckel, K[?]. O. "Los trabajos de Goethe sobre morfología animal y las investigaciones modernas [Goethe's Works on Animal Morphology and Modern Research]." *Atenea [Universidad de Concepción, Santiago de Chile]*, 63 (1932). 13 pp.
  In Spanish.
  /MORPHOLOGY/RECEPTION

1932-152 **Henriet**, Jacques. "Goethe et l'anatomie." *Strasbourg Médical*, 92, No. 33 (1932), 721-32.
  Rpt. (extract) No. 1934-19.
  /ANATOMY

1932-153 **Hesse**, Otto. "Zu Goethes Farbenlehre." In *Br[uder]. Johann Wolfgang von Goethe: Zum 100. Todestag 1932. Allgemeine Logen-Zeitung.* Würzburg: Verlag Paul Scheiner, 1932, pp. 110-16.
  /CHROMATICS

1932-154 **Hildebrandt**, Kurt. "Goethe und Darwin: Eine Hundertjahrbetrachtung zum Siege der Naturwissenschaft über die Philosophie." *Archiv für Geschichte der Philosophie*, 41, No. 1/2 (1932), 57-79.
  /DARWIN, C/BIOLOGY: EVOLUTION/NATUR-PHILOSOPHIE

1932-155 *Himmelbaur**, Wolfgang. "Goethe als Naturbetrachter." *Deutsche Akademiker-Zeitung*, 23, No. 7/9 (1932), 7-9.
  Cf. No. 1932-156.
  /GENERAL INTRODUCTION

1932-156 **Himmelbaur**, Wolfgang. "Goethe als Naturbetrachter." In *Goethe: Festgabe zum hundertsten Todestage des Dichters.* Ed. Karl Wache. Wien: Verlag der "Sudetendeutschen Akademiker-Zeitung," 1932, pp. 63-80.
  Cf. No. 1932-155.
  /GENERAL INTRODUCTION

1932-157 *Hochreutiner**, B[?]. P. G. "Goethe et la science." *Revue Générale des Sciences Pures et Appliquées*, 43 (1932), 407-10.
  /GENERAL INTRODUCTION

1932-158 **Hochstetter**[, A(?). D.]. "Der Arzt in Goethes Werken."
Deutsche Medizinische Wochenschrift, 58 (1932), 743-4; 784-5.
/MEDICINE

1932-159 **Hochstetter**[, A(?). D.]. "Goethe und die Ärzte." *Deutsche
Medizinische Wochenschrift*, 58 (1932), 223-5; 261-3.
/MEDICINE

1932-160 **Houllevigue**, L[ouis]. "Goethe, naturaliste et physicien." *La
Revue de Paris*, 39 (1932), 688-95.
/GENERAL INTRODUCTION

1932-161 ***Howard**, Elizabeth Fox. "Goethe and Luke Howard F. R. S."
The Friends' Quarterly Examiner, July 1932.
Rpt. No. 1932-162.
Trans. into German, No. 1932-163.
/HOWARD, L/METEOROLOGY

1932-162 **Howard**, Elizabeth Fox. "Goethe and Luke Howard F. R. S."
Leominster: The Orphans' Printing Press, 1932. 7 pp.
Rpt. of No. 1932-161.
/HOWARD, L/METEOROLOGY

1932-163 **Howard**, Elizabeth Fox. "Goethe und Luke Howard." *Der
Quäker: Monatshefte der Deutschen Freunde*, 9 (1932), 207-11.
German trans. of No. 1932-161.
/HOWARD, L/METEOROLOGY

1932-164 **Hucke**, Kurt. "Goethe und die Geschiebeforschung." *Zeitschrift für Geschiebeforschung*, 8 (1932), 87-95.
/GEOLOGY

1932-165 **Huxley**, T[homas]. H[enry]. "Goethe's Reflections on Nature."
Nature, 129 (1932), 425-6.
Rpt. of No. 1869-3.
/TRANSLATION: ENGLISH

1932-166 **Hykes**, O[?]. V. and D[?]. E. **Hykesová**. "Goethe a Purkyne
[Goethe and Purkyne]." In *Goethuv sborník: Památce 100. vyroci
básníkovy smrti vydali cestí germanisté*. Praha: Státní nakladatelství,
1932, pp. 13-32.
/PURKYNE, J/CHROMATICS/RESEARCH: CHROMATICS

1932-167 **Ipsen**, Gunther. "Goethes Naturwissenschaft und die philosophische Anthropologie." *Insel-Almanach auf das Goethejahr 1932*. Leipzig: Insel-Verlag, 1932, pp. 151-63.
/GENERAL INTRODUCTION/ANTHROPOLOGY/PHILOSOPHY

1932-168 **Jablonski**, Walter. "Goethes Farbenlehre vom physiologischen und augenärztlichen Standpunkt betrachtet." *Optische Rundschau und Photo-Optiker*, 23 (1932), 75-7.
/CHROMATICS/HERING, E

1932-169 **John**, Alois. "Goethe und der Kammerbühl." In *Goethe-Festschrift der Kurstadt Franzenbad aus Anlaß der Feier des 100. Todestages J. W. Goethes*. Ed. Alois John. Franzensbad: Verlag der Kurverwaltung, 1932, pp. 36-48.
/GEOLOGY/PLACES: KAMMERBÜHL

1932-170 **John**, Alois. "Goethe und Rat Grüner." In *Aus Goethes Marienbader Tagen: Zwanzig Beiträge mit fünfzehn Bildbeigaben*. Leipzig: Verlag von J. J. Weber, 1932, pp. 31-5.
"Herausgegeben von der Kurstadt Marienbad."
/GRÜNER, J/MINERALOGY

1932-171 **Juliusburger**, Otto. "Goethe, Spinoza und Giordano Bruno." *Fortschritte der Medizin*, 50 (1932), 927-9.
/SPINOZA, B/BRUNO, G

1932-172 **Kahn**, R[ichard]. H. "Aus Goethes Purkinje Zeit." *Naturwissenschaftliche Zeitschrift Lotos*, 80 (1932), 38-64.
Rpt. of No. 1932-173.
/PURKYNE, J/CHROMATICS/RESEARCH: CHROMATICS

1932-173 *****Kahn**, R[ichard]. H. "Aus Goethes Purkinje Zeit." Prag: privately printed, 1932. 27 pp.
Rpt. No. 1932-172.
/PURKYNE, J/CHROMATICS/RESEARCH: CHROMATICS

1932-174 **Kahn**, R[ichard]. H. "Goethes Augen." *Beiträge zur ärztlichen Fortbildung*, 10, No. 6 (1932), 113-4.
Abstract of No. 1932-176.
/CHROMATICS/OPTICS

1932-175 **Kahn**, R[ichard]. H. "Goethes Augen." *Klinische Wochenschrift*, 11 (1932), 1207.

Abstract of No. 1932-176.
Rpt. of No. 1932-174.
/CHROMATICS/OPTICS

1932-176 **Kahn**, R[ichard]. H. "Goethes Augen. Deren Beschaffenheit und Sehvermögen." In *Goethe im Spiegel der Lebensforschung*. Intro. Otto Porsch. Wien/Leipzig: Emil Haim & Co., 1932, pp. 25-106.
Rpt. No. 1933-32.
Cf. abstract, No. 1932-175.
/CHROMATICS/OPTICS

1932-177 **Karrig**, Otto. "Waldhistorik nach Goethe." *Badische Forstzeitung: Fachorgan der Staats- und Gemeindeförster Badens*, 10 (1932), 67-70; 80-81; 92.
/FORESTRY

1932-178 **Karutz**, Richard. "Goethe und die Völkerkunde." *"Gäa-Sophia": Jahrbuch der naturwissenschaftlichen Sektion der Freien Hochschule für Geisteswissenschaft am Goetheanum Dornach*, 6 (1932), 32-46.
/ANTHROPOLOGY/STEINER, R

1932-179 *****Kaßner**, C[?]. "Goethe als Wetter-Forscher." *Allgemeine Thüringische Landeszeitung*, No. 235, 24 August 1932, 5.
/METEOROLOGY

1932-180 *****Klages**, Ludwig. *Goethe als Seelenforscher*. Leipzig: Barth?, 1932. 94 pp.
Rpt. No. 1949-94.
/PSYCHOLOGY/RESEARCH: PSYCHOLOGY

1932-181 **Klein**, Edmond J. "Centenaire de la mort de Goethe." *Societé des Naturalistes Luxembourgeois*, NF 26 (1932), 71.
/GENERAL INTRODUCTION

1932-182 *****Klemm**, Friedrich. "Goethes Naturforschung." *Dresdener Anzeiger*, 3 June 1932.
/GENERAL INTRODUCTION

1932-183 **Klemm**, Friedrich. "Naturforschung." In *Sächsischer Kunstverein zu Dresden Juni--Juli 1932: Brühlsche Terasse: Goethe Ausstellung*. Dresden: Verlag Buchdruckerei der Wilhelm und Bertha v. Baensch Stiftung, 1932, pp. 191-210.

343

/GENERAL INTRODUCTION

1932-184 Klughardt, August and Manfred **Richter**. "Darstellung von Goethes Farbenlehre." In *Wunder und Wissen: Kurzes Verzeichnis der Ausstellung von Bildern und Büchern aus 6 Jahrhunderten der Natur- und Heilkunde zur 92. Tagung der Gesellschaft Naturforscher und Ärzte.* Wiesbaden: Nassauischer Kunstverein und die Städtische Kunstsammlung im Museum zu Wiesbaden, 1932, pp. 17-19.
"In Erweiterung des auf der Dresdner Goethe-Ausstellung Gezeigten zusammengestellt von der Abteilung Farbforschung am D. Forsch.- Inst. f. Textil-Industrie in Dresden."
/EXHIBITION/CHROMATICS

1932-185 Knauer, Helmut. "Über die Entstehung der Farben im Spektrum im Sinne der Goetheschen Farbenlehre." *Gäa-Sophia: Jahrbuch der naturwissenschaftlichen Sektion der Freien Hochschule Dornach*, "Goethe-Jahrbuch," 6 (1932), 119-34.
/CHROMATICS/RESEARCH: CHROMATICS

1932-186 Koberg, Fritz. "Goethe und die Landwirtschaft." Schriften für das deutsche Landvolk. Prag: Verlag der Geschäftsstelle der deutschen Land- und Forstwirschaft in Prag-Weinberge, 1932. 24 pp.
/AGRONOMY

1932-188 König, Karl. "Beiträge zu einer reinen Anatomie des menschlichen Knochengerüstes. IV. Über die intimere Gestalt von Atlas, Epistrophens, Kreuz- und Steißbein." *Natura: Eine Zeitschrift zur Erweiterung der Heilkunst nach geisteswissenschaftlichen Menschenkunde*, 6 (1932/1933), 37-46.
Continuation of No. 1931-25.
/RESEARCH: OSTEOLOGY/RESEARCH: ANATOMY

1932-189 Kohut, A[dolf]. "Goethe als 'Anatom'." *Fortschritte der Medizin*, 50 (1932), 222-3.
/ANATOMY

1932-190 Kolisko, L[ili]. "Von Goethes Naturanschauung zur Anthroposophie." Stuttgart: n.p., 1932. 24 pp.
"Vortrag, gehalten in Stuttgart am 18. März 1932."
/ANTHROPOSOPHY/EPISTEMOLOGY

1932-191 Komarov, V[?]. L. "Gete kak botanik [Goethe as a Botanist]." In *Gete. 1832-1932. Doklady, prochitannye na torzhestvennykh zasedaniiakh v pamiat' Gete 26 i 30 marta 1932 g.* Leningrad: Uzd.

AN SSSR, 1932.
In Russian.
[Zhitomirskaiia 4411]
/BOTANY

1932-192 **Koniëtzko**, C[?]. L. G. "Goethe und Batavia einst und jetzt." *Deutsche Wacht: Niederländisch-Indische Halbmonatsschrift*, 18, No. 6 (1932), 50-52.
/INSTITUTIONS: BATAVIAASCH GENOOTSCHAP VAN KUNSTEN EN WETENSCHAPEN

1932-193 **Kretschmer**, Ernst. "Goethe und die Biologie." *Mitteilungen Universitätsbund Marburg*, No. 3 (1932), 43-9.
/BIOLOGY

1932-194 **Krusch**, Paul. "Goethe als Geologe." In *Johann Wolfgang Goethe 1832-1932: Ein Gedenkblatt der Hallischen Nachrichten zum hundertsten Todestage des Dichters am 22. März, Hallische Nachrichten*, 19 March 1932, 15.
/GEOLOGY

1932-195 **Kühn**, Alfred. "Goethe und die Naturforschung." *Nachrichten von der Gesellschaft der Wissenschaften zu Göttingen: Geschäftliche Mitteilungen*, 1932/1933, pp. 47-69.
Rpt. No. 1932-196.
"Vortrag gehalten in der öffentlichen Sitzung der Gesellschaft der Wissenschaften am 12. November 1932."
/GENERAL INTRODUCTION

1932-196 **Kühn**, Alfred. "Goethe und die Naturforschung." Nachrichten von der Gesellschaft der Wissenschaften zu Göttingen: Geschäftliche Mitteilungen. Sonderdruck Fachgruppe VI (Biologie), 8. Berlin: Weidmannsche Buchhandlung, 1932/1933. 23 pp.
Rpt. of No. 1932-195.
/GENERAL INTRODUCTION

1932-197 **Kühnemann**, Eugen. "Goethe und die Natur." In *Insel-Almanach auf das Goethejahr 1932*. Leipzig: Insel-Verlag, 1932, pp. 52-62.
/GENERAL INTRODUCTION

1932-198 **Lacroix**, Wilhelm. "Goethes Naturanschauung." *Die Sonne: Monatsschrift für Nordische Weltanschauung und Lebensgestaltung*, 9 (1932), 486-92; 558-64.

/GENERAL INTRODUCTION

1932-199 ***Lakowitz**, Konrad. "Goethe als Seher und Erforscher der belebten Natur." *Bericht des westpreussischen botanischen-zoologischen Vereins*, 54 (1932), 119-31.
/BIOLOGY

1932-200 **Le Gendre**, Paul. "Goethe et les sciences médicales, ses opinions en médecine, et ses maladies." *Bulletin de la Societé français d'Histoire de la Médecine*, 26 (1932), 249-95.
/MEDICINE

1932-201 **Leisegang**, Hans. *Goethes Denken*. Leipzig: Verlag von Felix Meiner, 1932. xii, 182 pp.
/PHILOSOPHY

1932-202 **Leschke**, Erich. "Goethe als Lebensforscher." *Fortschritte der Medizin*, 50 (1932), 829-35.
Cf. exp. edn., No. 1932-203.
/GENERAL INTRODUCTION/BIOLOGY

1932-203 **Leschke**, Erich. *Goethe als Lebensforscher*. Leipzig: Verlag von Johann Ambrosius Barth, 1932. 80 pp.
Exp. edn. of No. 1932-202.
Rev. [No. 1932-375].
/GENERAL INTRODUCTION/BIOLOGY

1932-204 **Liebert**, Arthur. "Goethes Platonismus: Zur Metaphysik der Morphologie." *Kant-Studien*, 37 (1932), 1-48.
/EPISTEMOLOGY/PLATO/PHILOSOPHY/MORPHOLOGY

1932-205 **Liebert**, Arthur. "Goethe und die Natur." *Deutsche Medizinische Wochenschrift*, 58 (1932), 1, 437-9.
/GENERAL INTRODUCTION

1932-206 **Linck**, Gottlob. "Goethes mineralogisch-geologische Grundideen." *Forschungen und Fortschritte*, 8 (1932), 92-3.
Rpt. No. 1932-207.
/GEOLOGY

1932-207 **Linck**, Gottlob. "Goethes mineralogisch-geologische Grundideen." In *Forschungen und Fortschritte: Goethe*. Ed. Karl Kerkhof. Leipzig: Kommissionsverlag von Johann Ambrosius Barth[, 1932], pp. 15-17.

Rpt. of No. 1932-206.
/GEOLOGY

1932-208 **Linden**, Walther. "Goethe als Naturforscher." In *Zum 100. Todestage Goethes. Illustrierte Zeitung*, 178, No. 4539 (10 March 1932), 274.
/GENERAL INTRODUCTION

1932-209 **Linden**, Walther. "Naturwissenschaft der lebendigen Kräfte." In his *Goethe und die deutsche Gegenwart*. Berlin: Deutsches Verlagshaus Bong & Co.[, 1932]. 71 pp.
/BIOLOGY

1932-210 *****Link**, Eugen. "Ueber Goethes Naturwissenschaft." *Ponta Grossa Paraná: Deutsche Vereinigung für Evangelisation und Volksmission*, 1932. 12 pp.
Lecture.
/GENERAL INTRODUCTION

1932-211 *****Lippmann**, Edmund O. von. "Zum hundertjährigen Todestage Goethes." *Deutsche Zuckerindustrie*, 32 (1932), 247-8.
/GENERAL INTRODUCTION

1932-212 **Lisbôa**, Achilles. "Homenagem do Jardim Botanico à memoria de Goethe [Commemoration of Goethe by the Botanical Garden]." Rio de Janiero: Tip. do Ministerio da Agricultura Rio de Janiero, 1932. viii, 16 pp.
In Portuguese.
/GENERAL INTRODUCTION/BOTANY

1932-213 **Lockemann**, Georg. "Goethes Beziehungen zur Chemie. Zur hundertsten Wiederkehr von Goethes Todestage am 22. März 1832." *Chemiker-Zeitung*, 56 (1932), 225-8.
/CHEMISTRY

1932-214 **Lockemann**, Georg. "Des jungen Goethe Beziehungen zur Heilkunde." *Fortschritte der Medizin*, 50 (1932), 210-13.
"Aus einem in der Berliner Gesellschaft für Geschichte der Naturwissenschaft, Medizin und Technik am 4. März 1932 gehaltenen Vortrage."
/MEDICINE

1932-215 **Lorentz**, Paul. "Goethes fromme Naturforschung." *Zeitschrift für den Evangelischen Religionsunterricht*, 41 (1932), 337-50.

/GENERAL INTRODUCTION/THEOLOGY

1932-216 *Luetge, Guillermo [Wilhelm]. "Goethe y las disciplinas cien-
tificas [Goethe and the Scientific Disciplines]." *La Nación*, Buenos
Aires, mayo 31, 1932.
 In Spanish.
 /GENERAL INTRODUCTION

1932-217 Lütge, Wilhelm. "Goethe als Wissenschaftler." *Phoenix:
Zeitschrift für deutsche Geistesarbeit Südamerika*, 18 (1932), 5-43.
 /CHROMATICS

1932-218 *Lukas, Josef. "Goethe und die Textil-Industrie." Zürich:
Juchli-Beck, 1932. 16 pp.
 /TECHNOLOGY

1932-219 *Luppol, J[?]. "Estestvenno-nauchnye vzgliadi Gete [Goethe's
Scientific Views]. *Izvestiia*, 23 March 1932.
 In Russian.
 /GENERAL INTRODUCTION

1932-220 Mainx, Felix. "Christian Reichels Dissertation über die Saft-
bewegung in den Pflanzen (1758)." *Naturwissenschaftliche Zeitschrift
Lotos*, 80 (1932), 31-7.
 /REICHEL, G/BOTANY

1932-221 Martell, Paul. "Goethes Farbenlehre." *Kunsthandel*, 24
(1932), 11-15.
 /CHROMATICS/RECEPTION/RESEARCH: FINE ARTS

1932-222 *Martinovsky, J[?]. O. "Goethe biolog [Goethe as a
Biologist]." *Priroda [Brno]*, 25, No. 3 (1932).
 In Czech.
 /BIOLOGY

1932-223 Martius, Alexander von. *Goethe und Martius*. Mittenwald:
Arthur Nemayer Verlag[, 1932]. 110 pp.
 /MARTIUS, K VON/BOTANY

1932-224 Mastrostefano, Raffaele. "La concezione goethiana del mondo
[The Goethean Conception of the World]." *La Stirpe*, 10, No. 4
(1932), 164-6.
 In Italian.
 /GENERAL INTRODUCTION/STEINER, R

1932-225 **Matschoß**, Conrad. "Goethe und die Technik." *Forschungen und Fortschritte*, 8 (1932), 104-5.
Rpt. No. 1932-226.
/TECHNOLOGY

1932-226 **Matschoß**, Conrad. "Goethe und die Technik." In *Forschungen und Fortschritte: Goethe*. Ed. Karl Kerkhof. Leipzig: Kommissionsverlag von Johann Ambrosius Barth[, 1932], pp. 28-9.
Rpt. of No. 1932-225.
/TECHNOLOGY

1932-227 **Matthaei**, Rupprecht. "Goethes Spektren und sein Farbenkreis. Darin der erste Rekonstruktionsversuch des Goetheschen Farbenkreises auf einer bunten Tafel." *Ergebnisse der Physiologie*, 34 (1932), 191-219.
/CHROMATICS

1932-228 **Mayerhofer**, Ernst. "Goethes Naturanschauung und Biologie." *Biologische Heilkunst*, 13 (1932), 1-4; 24-6; 39-42; 58-9; 73-5; 91-2; 104-6.
/GENERAL INTRODUCTION/BIOLOGY

1932-229 **Mayerhofer**, Ernst. "Goethe, Naturwissenschaft und Medizin." *Wiener Medizinische Wochenschrift*, 82 (1932), 295-301.
/GENERAL INTRODUCTION/MEDICINE

1932-230 **Mayerhofer**, Ernst. "Goethe und die Naturwissenschaften." *Die Umschau: Vereinigt mit "Naturwissenschaftliche Wochenschrift", "Prometheus" und "Natur": Illustrierte Wochenschrift über die Fortschritte in Wissenschaft und Technik*, 36 (1932), 201-4.
/GENERAL INTRODUCTION

1932-231 *****Menninger-Lerchenthal**, E[?]. "Eine Halluzination Goethes." *Zeitschrift für die Geschichte der Neurologie und Psychiatrie*, 140 (1932), 486-95.
/?

1932-232 **Menzbir**, M[?]. A. "Znacheniie Gete v istorii morfologii zhivotnykh [Goethe's Significance in the History of Animal Morphology]." In *Gete. 1832-1932. Doklady, prochitannye na torzhestvennykh zasedaniiakh v pamiat' Gete 26 i 30 marta 1932*. Leningrad: Izdaniia AN SSSR, 1932.
In Russian.

[Zhitomirskaiia 4411]
/MORPHOLOGY

1932-233 **Meyer**, Christian. "Goethes Mißtrauen gegen das physikalische Experiment." *Unsere Welt*, 24 (1932), 65-9.
/METHOD/CHROMATICS

1932-234 **Meyer-Eckhardt**, Victor. "Goethes Farbenlehre." *Preussische Jahrbücher*, 227 (1932), 206-28.
/CHROMATICS

1932-235 **Michaelis**, Edgar. "Goethe und C. G. Carus." *Die Medizinische Welt*, 6 (1932), 397-9.
/CARUS, C

1932-236 **Möbius**, Martin. "Zu Goethes botanischen Studien. Ausstellung in unserer Eingangshalle." *Natur und Museum: Senckenbergische Naturforschende Gesellschaft 1817-1932*, 62 (1932), 93.
/EXHIBITION

1932-237 **Mohr**, Werner. "Naturwissenschaft und Naturphilosophie bei Goethe." In *Br[uder]. Johann Wolfgang von Goethe: Zum 100. Todestag 1932. Allgemeine Logen-Zeitung*. Würzburg: Verlag Paul Scheiner, 1932, pp. 89-109.
Rpt. No. 1932-238.
/GENERAL INTRODUCTION/NATURPHILOSOPHIE

1932-238 **Mohr**, Werner. "Naturwissenschaft und Naturphilosophie bei Goethe. Mit besonderer Berücksichtigung von Goethes Wahlverwandtschaften." Würzburg: Paul Scheiner, 1932. 23 pp.
Rpt. of No. 1932-237.
/GENERAL INTRODUCTION/NATURPHILOSOPHIE

1932-239 **Müller**, Martin. "Goethes Stellung zur theoretischen und praktischen Medizin." *Fortschritte der Medizin*, 50 (1932), 218-22; 257-60.
/MEDICINE

1932-240 **Müller**, Martin. "Goethe und die Heilkunde." *Forschungen und Fortschritte*, 8 (1932), 1024.
Rpt. No. 1932-241.
/MEDICINE

1932-241 **Müller**, Martin. "Goethe und die Heilkunde." In *Forschungen*

350

und Fortschritte: Goethe. Ed. Karl Kerkhof. Leipzig: Kommissions-
verlag von Johann Ambrosius Barth[, 1932], pp. 26-8.
Rpt. of No. 1932-240.
/MEDICINE

1932-242 **Müllner**, Ludwig. *Goethes Faust im Lichte seiner Naturforschung.* Oedenburg: Verlag der Röttig-Romwalter Druckerei AG,
1932.
Rpt. No. 1981-59.
/WORKS: FAUST

1932-243 **Nemec**, Bohumil. "Goethe jako prirodozpytec [Goethe as
Scientist]" *Vesmir*, 10 (1932), 169-74.
In Czech.
/GENERAL INTRODUCTION

1932-244 ***Oberhauser**, F[?]. "Goethe, hombre de ciencia [Goethe, Man
of Science]." *Annales de la Universidad de Chile*, 2, No. 3 (1932),
85-93.
In Spanish.
/GENERAL INTRODUCTION

1932-245 **Olbert**, Theodor. "Goethe und die ärztliche Kunst." In *Aus
Goethes Marienbader Tagen.* Leipzig: J. J. Weber, 1932, pp. 20-
125.
/MEDICINE

1932-246 **Ostwald**, Wilhelm. "Goethe der Prophete." Leipzig: Oscar
Brandstetter, 1932. 37 pp.
"Zum Jahresessen des Leipziger Bibliophilen-Abends."
/CHROMATICS

1932-247 **Ostwald**, Wilhelm. "Goethe, Schopenhauer und die Farben-
lehre." *Jahrbuch der Schopenhauer-Gesellschaft*, 19 (1932), 341-4.
Rev. Hans Zint [No. 1932-385].
/SCHOPENHAUER, A/CHROMATICS

1932-248 **Petella**, G[?]. "Goethe filosofo naturalista e scienziato [Goethe
the Natural Scientist and Philosopher]." *Annali di medicana navale e
coloniale*, 38 (1932), 470-84.
In Italian.
/GENERAL INTRODUCTION

1932-249 **Pezold**, Hans von. "Goethe und das Problem der Verjüngung."

Deutsche Medizinische Wochenschrift, 58 (1932), 1099-1100.
/MEDICINE

1932-250 **Pezold**, Hans von. "Goethe und der Alkohol." *Deutsche Medizinische Wochenschrift*, 58 (1932), 2010.
/MEDICINE

1932-251 **Podach**, Erich F. "Goethes Wiederkehr." *Die Koralle: Monatshefte für alle Freunde von Natur und Technik*, 7 (1932), 424-7.
/GENERAL INTRODUCTION

1932-252 **Porsch**, Otto. "Goethe und die Pflanze." In *Goethe im Spiegel der Lebensforschung*. Intro. Otto Porsch. Wien/Leipzig: Emil Haim & Co., 1932, pp. 107-50.
Rpt. No. 1933-36.
/BOTANY

1932-253 **Purkyne**, Cyril. "Moje vymarská pout [My Pilgrimage to Weimar]." *Goethuv sbornik: Pamatce 100. vyroci basnikovy smrti vydali cesti germaniste*. Praha: Statni nakladatelstvi, 1932, pp. 33-7.
/PURKYNE, J/CHROMATICS/RESEARCH: CHROMATICS

1932-254 **Rakovskii**, Ivan. "[Goethe -- Naturhistoriker]." In *Zum hundertjährigen Todestage des Johann Wolfgang Goethe*. Lemberg, Sevcenko-Gesellschaft der Wissenschaften in Lemberg, 1932, pp. 68-75.
In Russian.
/GENERAL INTRODUCTION

1932-255 **Rauther**, Max. "Goethe und die Biologie." *Jahreshefte des Vereins für vaterländische Naturkunde in Württemberg*, 88 (1932), 1-18.
Rpt. No. 1932-256.
/BIOLOGY

1932-256 **Rauther**, Max. "Goethe und die Biologie." Stuttgart: Ernst Klett, Buchdruckerei Zu Gutenberg, 1932. 18 pp.
Rpt. of No. 1932-255.
/BIOLOGY

1932-257 **Reuter**, Robert. "Goethes Naturschau und unsere Natur- forschung." *Société des Naturalistes Luxembourgeois*, 26 (1932), 39-49.
/GENERAL INTRODUCTION

1932-258 **Reychler**, Lucien. "Goethe dans ses Rapports avec les Représentants de la Science tels qu'ils sont révélés par Eckermann dans ses Conversations avec Goethe." [n.p.]: Editions du Dauphin, 1932. 30 pp.
/CONTEMPORARIES/ECKERMANN, J

1932-259 **Richter**, Manfred. "Goethes Farbenlehre im Lichte unserer Zeit." *Deutsche Optische Wochenschrift*, 18 (1932), 177-81.
/CHROMATICS/RESEARCH: CHROMATICS

1932-260 **Robertson**, J[?]. G. "Goethe as Scientist and Critic." In *Goethe: A Symposium*. Ed. Dagobert D. Runes. Intro. Nicholas Roerich. New Era Library. New York: Roerich Museum Press, 1932, pp. 105-14.
/GENERAL INTRODUCTION

1932-261 **Robertson**, J[?]. G. "Goethe's Contributions to Science." In his *The Life and Work of Goethe 1749-1832*. London: George Routledge and Sons Ltd., 1932, pp. 302-12.
/GENERAL INTRODUCTION

1932-262 [**Rolleston**, J(?). D.] "Goethe's Medical History." *British medical Journal*, 9 April 1932, 670.
Mostly biographical.
/MEDICINE

1932-263 *S[?]. "Goethe und der Mond." *Die Umschau*, 36 (1932), 20.
/ASTRONOMY

1932-264 *Samsalovic**, Gustav. "Gete i more [Goethe and the Ocean]." *Jadranska straza*, June 1932.
In Serbo-Croatian.
/OCEANOGRAPHY

1932-265 **Schaeffer**, Albrecht. "Die Wand: Dramatische Mythe." In Albrecht Schaefer, Wolfgang Goetz, and Arnold Zweig. *Goethe in neuer Dichtung: Erinnerungsgabe zum 22. März 1932 für die Mitglieder der Ortsgruppe Berlin der Goethe-Gesellschaft*, pp. 5-71.
/BIOGRAPHY

1932-266 **Schiff**, Julius. "Naturwissenschaftliche Gleichnisse in Goethes Dichtungen, Briefen und literarischen Schriften." In *Goethes naturwissenschaftliches Denken und Wirken: Drei Aufsätze*. Ed. Schrift-

leitung der Zeitschrift *Die Naturwissenschaften: Wochenschrift für die Fortschritte der reinen und der angewandten Naturwissenschaften.* Berlin: Verlag von Julius Springer, 1932, pp. 60-99.
Rpt. of No. 1932-267.
/WORKS: VARIOUS

1932-267 **Schiff**, Julius. "Naturwissenschaftliche Gleichnisse in Goethes Dichtungen, Briefen und literarischen Schriften." *Die Naturwissenschaften*, 20 (1932), 223-40.
Rpt. No. 1932-266.
/WORKS: VARIOUS

1932-268 **Schirmer-Behrendt**, Elisabeth. "Zum 22. März." *Veterinärhistorische Mitteilungen*, 12, No. 4 (1932), 25-30.
/EDITION/INSTITUTIONS: TIERARZNEISCHULE JENA

1932-269 **Schmid**, Günther. "Goethe als Naturforscher in der Ausstellung 'Goethe und Halle'." *Saale-Zeitung*, 67, No. 133, 9 June 1932, 2.
Rpt. of No. 1932-270.
/EXHIBITION/INSTITUTIONS: UNIVERSITÄT HALLE

1932-270 **Schmid**, Günther. "Goethe als Naturforscher: Zu der Ausstellung 'Goethe und Halle' in der Garnisonskirche." *Hallische Nachrichten*, 44, No 133, 9 June 1932, 2-3.
Rpt. No. 1932-271.
/EXHIBITION/INSTITUTIONS: UNIVERSITÄT HALLE

1932-271 **Schmidt**, J[?]. Heinrich. "Zur Farbenlehre Goethes." *Zeitschrift für Kunstgeschichte: Neue Folge von Repertorium für Kunstwissenschaft*, 1 (1932), 109-24.
/CHROMATICS

1932-272 ***Schraennen**, Willem. "Goethe naturaliste [Goethe the Naturalist]." *Europe (Paris)*, 28 (1932), 704-19.
"Numéro spéciale consacrée à Goethe."
/CHROMATICS

1932-273 **Schultze-Galléra**, Siegmar Baron von. "Goethe über die Metamorphose der Pflanzen: Ein bisher unveröffentlichtes Gespräch." *Montagsblatt: Das Heimatblatt Mitteldeutschlands: Wissenschaftliche Beilage der Magdeburgischen Zeitung*, 74, No. 9, 29 February 1932, 70-71.
/EDITION/BOTANY/MORPHOLOGY/FALK, J

1932-274 **Schuster**, Julius. "Der anatomische Gedanke bei Goethe."
Klinische Wochenschrift, 11 (1932), 1084.
    Rpt. No. 1932-275.
    /ANATOMY

1932-275 **Schuster**, Julius. "Der anatomische Gedanke bei Goethe."
Medizinische Klinik, 28 (1932), 417.
    Rpt. of No. 1932-274.
    /ANATOMY

1932-276 **Schuster**, Julius. "Die biologische Weltorientierung Goethes
als Vermächtnis und Erhellung." *Fortschritte der Medizin*, 50 (1932),
213-18.
    Rpt. No. 1932-277.
    /BIOLOGY/PHILOSOPHY

1932-277 **Schuster**, Julius. "Die biologische Weltorientierung Goethes
als Vermächtnis und Erhellung." *Fortschritte der Medizin*, 50 (1932).
Sonder-Abdruck. 10 pp.
    Rpt. of No. 1932-276.
    /BIOLOGY/PHILOSOPHY

1932-278 **Schuster**, Julius. "Goethes Botanik als Gestaltlehre."
Forschungen und Fortschritte, 8 (1932), 96-8.
    Rpt. No. 1932-279.
    /BOTANY/MORPHOLOGY

1932-279 **Schuster**, Julius. "Goethes Botanik als Gestaltlehre." In
Forschungen und Fortschritte: Goethe. Ed. Karl Kerkhof. Leipzig:
Kommissionsverlag von Johann Ambrosius Barth[, 1932], pp. 20-27.
    Rpt. of No. 1932-278.
    /BOTANY/MORPHOLOGY

1932-280 **Schuster**, Julius. "Goethe und die Biologie." *Sitzungsberichte
der Gesellschaft Naturforschender Freunde zu Berlin*, 1932, pp. 295-
322.
    Rpt. No. 1932-281.
    /BIOLOGY

1932-281 **Schuster**, Julius. "Goethe und die Biologie." Sonderabdruck
aus *Sitzungsberichte der Gesellschaft Naturforschender Freunde zu
Berlin*, 1932. 28 [295-322] pp.
    Rpt. No. 1932-280.

/BIOLOGY

1932-282 **Schuster**, Julius. "Die Spirale: Ein Tag aus dem Leben des naturforschenden Goethe." *Reclams Universum die große illustrierte Wochenschrift*, 48 (1932), 1627-8.
/BOTANY?

1932-283 **Schuster**, Julius. "Wie stellt sich die heutige Wissenschaft zur Naturforschung Goethes?" *Deutsche Adelsblatt: Zeitschrift der Deutschen Adelsgenossenschaft für die Aufgaben des christlichen Adels*, 50 (1932), 166-7.
/RECEPTION/CHROMATICS

1932-284 *****Schwartz**, Philipp. "Goethe und die Statistik." *Allgemeines statistisches Archiv*, 22 (1932), 257-79.
Rpt. (rev. edn.) of No. 1932-285.
/STATISTICS

1932-285 *****Schwartz**, Philipp. "Goethe und die Statistik." *Zeitschrift des Bayrischen Statistischen Landesamts*, 64 (1932), 1-13.
Rpt. rev. edn. No. 1932-284.
/STATISTICS

1932-286 **Seidlitz**, W[?]. von. "Füchsel -- Goethe -- Hoff." *Zeitschrift der deutschen geologischen Gesellschaft*, 84 (1932), 663-73.
"Eröffnungsansprache zur Hauptversammlung der Deutschen Geologischen Gesellschaft in Jena am 5. August 1932."
/GEOLOGY/PLACES: THÜRINGEN/FÜCHSEL, G/HOFF, K

1932-287 **Senn**, Gustav. "Antike Elemente in Goethes Biologie." *Verhandlungen der Schweizerischen Naturforschenden Gesellschaft*, 113 (1932), 453-4.
/BIOLOGY/INFLUENCES

1932-288 **Senn**, Gustav. "Goethe als Botaniker." In Andreas Heusler, Gustav Senn, and Karl Spiro. *Drei Basler Goethereden*. Schriften der "Freunde der Universität Basel," 2. Basel: Verlag von Helbing & Lichtenhahn, 1932, pp. 23-40.
/BOTANY

1932-289 **Serlo**, Walter. "Auf den Spuren Goethes im Bergbau an der Lahn." *Zeitschrift für das Berg-, Hütten und Salinenwesen im preussischen Staate*, 80 (1932), B 270-74.
/TECHNOLOGY

1932-290 **Simmel**, H[?]. "Goethe und 'Dr. Gift'. *Die medizinische Welt*, 6, 27 February 1932, 323-4.
/RUNGE, F

1932-291 **Snellen**. J[?]. H. "Zur Morphologie der Naturwissenschaft." *Deutsche Rundschau*, 233 (1932), 32-40.
/HISTORY OF SCIENCE

1932-292 **Sonnefeld**, A[?]. "Die optischen Studien von Goethe: 'Zur Farbenlehre'." *Optische Rundschau und Photo-Optiker*, 23 (1932), 170-78.
/OPTICS/CHROMATICS

1932-293 **Sonnefeld**, A[?]. "Über Goethes Arbeiten 'Zur Farbenlehre'." *Centralzeitung für Optik und Mechanik*, 53 (1932), 95-7.
/CHROMATICS

1932-294 **Soret**, Frédéric. *Conversations avec Goethe: Documents*. Ed. A. Robinet de Cléry. Paris: Éditions Montaigne, 1932. xx, 261 pp.
/SORET, F/MINERALOGY

1932-295 **Speiser**, Andreas. "Goethes Farbenlehre." In his *Die mathematische Denkweise*. Zürich/Leipzig/Stuttgart: Rascher & Co. A.-G. Verlag[, 1932], pp. 88-97.
Rpt. Nos. 1937-58, 1945-8 and 1951-46.
/CHROMATICS

1932-296 **Speiser**, Andreas. "Goethes Farbenlehre und die Gegenwart." *Kölnische Zeitung*, 19, 10 March 1932.
/CHROMATICS

1932-297 **Spiro**, Karl. "Goethe und die Biologie." In Andreas Heusler, Gustav Senn, and Karl Spiro. *Drei Basler Goethereden*. Schriften der "Freunde der Universität Basel," 2. Basel: Verlag von Helbing & Lichtenhahn, 1932, pp. 41-71.
Rpt. of No. 1932-298.
/BIOLOGY

1932-298 **Spiro**, Karl. "Goethe und die Biologie." *Schweizerische Medizinische Wochenschrift*, 13 (1932), 273-80.
Rpt. No. 1932-297.
"Vortrag, gehalten aus Anlaß der Feier von Goethes hundertstem Sterbetag in der Festsitzung der Naturforschenden Gesellschaft

Basel am 29. Februar 1932."
/BIOLOGY

1932-299 **Srbik**, Robert Ritter von. "Goethe und die Geologie: Gedenkworte anläßlich des 100. Todestages." *Geologische Rundschau: Zeitschrift für allgemeine Geologie*, 23 (1932), 1-12.
/GEOLOGY

1932-300 *****Stäglich**, Hans. *Goethe-Schopenhauer*. Leipzig, 1932.
Rpt. No. 1949-170.
Cf. exp. edn. No. 1960-44.
/SCHOPENHAUER, A/BIBLIOGRAPHY/CHROMATICS

1932-301 **Starkenstein**, Emil. "Arznei und Gift im Leben Goethes." *Beiträge zur ärztlichen Fortbildung*, 10 (1932), 95-112.
Rpt. Nos. 1932-302 and 1932-303.
Abbreviated rpt. No. 1932-304.
/PHARMACOLOGY/MEDICINE

1932-302 **Starkenstein**, Emil. "Arznei und Gift im Leben Goethes." *Forschungen und Fortschritte*, 8 (1932), 100-102.
Rpt. of No. 1932-301.
/PHARMACOLOGY/MEDICINE

1932-303 **Starkenstein**, Emil. "Arznei und Gift im Leben Goethes." In *Forschungen und Fortschritte: Goethe*. Ed. Karl Kerkhof. Leipzig: Kommissionsverlag von Johann Ambrosius Barth[, 1932], pp. 24-6.
Rpt. of No. 1932-301.
/PHARMACOLOGY/MEDICINE

1932-304 **Starkenstein**, Emil. "Arznei und Gift im Leben Goethes." *Klinische Wochenschrift*, 11 (1932), 1207.
Abbreviated rpt. of No. 1932-301.
/PHARMACOLOGY/MEDICINE

1932-305 **Stavenhagen**, G[?]. "Die Bedeutung der Erziehung zur Farbe. I. Teil." *Natura: Eine Zeitschrift zur Erweiterung der Heilkunst nach geisteswissenschaftlicher Menschenkunde*, 6 (1932-1933), 358-63.
/RESEARCH: CHROMATICS/PEDAGOGY

1932-306 **Steiner**, Rudolf. *Der Baugedanke des Goetheanum. Einleitender Vortrag mit Erklärungen zu den Bildern des Baus*. Dornach: Philosophisch-Anthroposophischer Verlag am Goetheanum, 1932. 161 pp.

Rpt. Nos. 1977-51 and 1986-100.
/RESEARCH: ARCHITECTURE/RESEARCH: MORPHOL-
OGY

1932-307 **Steiner**, Rudolf. "Goethe, Haeckel und Swedenborg." *Gäa-Sophia: Jahrbuch der naturwissenschaftlichen Sektion der Freien Hochschule Dornach*, "Goethe-Jahrbuch," 6 (1932), 15-22.
/HAECKEL, E/SWEDENBORG, E

1932-308 **Steiner**, Rudolf. *Goethe-Studien und Goetheanistische Denkmethoden: Der Goetheanumgedanke inmitten der Kulturkrisis der Gegenwart: Gesammelte Aufsätze.* Dornach/Schweiz: Philosophisch-Anthroposophischer Verlag am Goetheanum, 1932. xx, 265 pp.
Cf. Nos. 1932-309, -310 and -311.
"Ein Goethejahrbuch herausgegeben von der Leitung der Sektion für Redende und Musische Künste am Goetheanum 1932."
Contains selection of lectures and essays on Goethe from the years 1899-1923.
/COLLECTION/RESEARCH: VARIOUS

1932-309 **Steiner**, Rudolf. "Goethe und die Medizin." In his *Goethe-Studien und Goetheanistische Denkmethoden: Der Goetheanumgedanke inmitten der Kulturkrisis der Gegenwart: Gesammelte Aufsätze.* Dornach/Schweiz: Philosophisch-Anthroposophischer Verlag am Goetheanum, 1932, pp. 57-66.
Rpt. of No. 1901-19.
/MEDICINE/RESEARCH: MEDICINE

1932-310 **Steiner**, Rudolf. "Goethe und die Mathematik." In his *Goethe-Studien und Goetheanistische Denkmethoden: Der Goetheanumgedanke inmitten der Kulturkrisis der Gegenwart: Gesammelte Aufsätze.* Dornach/Schweiz: Philosophisch-Anthroposophischer Verlag am Goetheanum, 1932, pp. 198-201.
Rpt. of No. 1921-28.
/MATHEMATICS

1932-311 **Steiner**, Rudolf. "Goethe und Goetheanum." In his *Goethe-Studien und Goetheanistische Denkmethoden: Der Goetheanumgedanke inmitten der Kulturkrisis der Gegenwart: Gesammelte Aufsätze.* Dornach/Schweiz: Philosophisch-Anthroposophischer Verlag am Goetheanum, 1932, pp. 202-6.
Rpt. of No. 1923-28.
/ANTHROPOSOPHY/MORPHOLOGY/EPISTEMOLOGY

1932-312 **Steinhauer**, Walter. "Der unbekannte Goethe: Leicht faßliche Darstellung von Goethes Naturlehre." 2 pp.
"[D]er von der Goethe-Gesellschaft, Weimar, autorisierte Jubiläums-Vortrag zum 100. Todestage Goethes"; "Bearbeitet von Dr. Edgar Beyfuß."
/GENERAL INTRODUCTION

1932-313 **Stewart**, Charles D[avid]. "Two Men of Mark." *Atlantic Monthly*, 150 (1932), 201-5.
Rpt. No. 1935-34.
/CUVIER, G/BIOLOGY

1932-314 ***Stoklasa**, Julius. ["Goethes Beziehungen zur Landwirtschaft und zu Böhmen."] *Vestnik CS Akad. zemed. VIII*, No. 5, 1932, 465ff.
In Czech.
/AGRONOMY/PLACES: BÖHMEN

1932-315 ***Stransky**, Max. "Goethe -- prirodozpytec [Goethe -- the Scientist]." *Dunaj [Vienna]*, 9, No. 2/3 (1932), 113-15.
In Czech.
/GENERAL INTRODUCTION

1932-316 ***Strecker**, Reinhard. "Goethes Denkmethode. Ein Beitrag zur Forstphilosophie." *Forstwissenschaftliches Centralblatt*, 54 (1932).
/METHOD/FORESTRY/PHILOSOPHY

1932-317 **Strecker**, Reinhard. "Goethes Stellung zur Natur." In his *Um den Sinn des Lebens*. Berlin: Neuland-Verlag G. m. b. H., 1932, pp. 39-60.
Exp. rpt. of No. 1932-318.
/GENERAL INTRODUCTION/FORESTRY

1932-318 **Strecker**, Reinhard. "Goethes Stellung zur Natur." *Zeitschrift für Forst- und Jagdwesen*, 64 (1932), 129-45.
Exp. rpt. No. 1932-317.
"Akademische Festrede zur Reichgründungsfeier der Forstlichen Hochschule Eberswalde am 18. Januar 1932."
/GENERAL INTRODUCTION/FORESTRY

1932-319 **Strohl**, Jean. "Goethe, savant naturaliste." *Nouvelle Revue Française*, Numéro spécial, 20, No. 222, 1er mars 1932, 495-505.
/GENERAL INTRODUCTION

1932-320 **Strunz**, Franz. "Goethes Beziehungen zur Technologie und

Technik." *Oesterreichische Chemiker-Zeitung*, 35 (1932), 88-9.
/TECHNOLOGY

1932-321 **Stüve**, Rudolf. "Goethe und die Naturwissenschaft." *Veröffentlichungen des Naturwissenschaftlichen Vereins zu Osnabrück*, 23 (1932-1935), 21-53.
Rpt. No. 1936-29.
"Rede gehalten bei der Goethe-Feier im Naturwissenschaftlichen Verein in Osnabrück am 13. April des Goethe-Jahres 1932."
/GENERAL INTRODUCTION

1932-322 **Sudhoff**, Karl. "Paracelsus und Goethe." *Die Medizinische Welt*, 6 (1932), 1409-12.
/PARACELSUS

1932-323 **Suk**, V[?]. "Basnik a prirodozpytec [Poet and Scientist]." In *Goethuv sbornik: Pamatce 100. vyroci asnikovy smrti vydali cesti germaniste*. Praha: Statni nakladatelstvi v Praze, 1932, pp. 202-13.
In Czech.
/GENERAL INTRODUCTION

1932-324 *****Suklje**, Fran[?]. "Gete kao geolog [Goethe as a Geologist]." *Priroda*, April-May 1932, pp. 115-8.
In Serbo-Croatian.
/GEOLOGY

1932-325 *****Teige**, Karel. "Goethe prirodozpytec [Goethe as a Scientist]." *Rozhledy po literature a umeni*, 1 (1932), No. 5
In Czech.
/GENERAL INTRODUCTION

1932-326 *****Theus**, Richard. "Goethe über die Mathematik und deren Mißbrauch." *Aufstieg. Zeitschrift des Berliner Abend-Gymnasiums*, No. 9, 1932, 15-18.
/MATHEMATICS/CHROMATICS

1932-327 **Timpanaro**, Sebastiano. "Goethe e la scienza [Goethe and Science]." *L'Italia letteraria*, 4, No. 16 (1932).
In Italian.
/GENERAL INTRODUCTION

1932-328 **Tischner**, Rudolf. "Goethe und die Homöopathie. Auch ein Beitrag zum Goethejahr." *Allgemeine Homöopathische Zeitung*, 180 (1932), 160-67.

361

/HOMEOPATHY

1932-329 **Totzauer**, Robert. "Goethe als Geologe in Marienbad: Die Entstehungsgeschichte seiner geologischen Sammlungen von Marienbad und Umgebung." In *Aus Goethes Marienbader Tagen*. Leipzig: J. J. Weber, 1932, pp. 47-68.
    Rpt. of No. 1925-32.
    "Herausgegeben von der Kurstadt Marienbad."
    /GOETHE'S COLLECTIONS/GEOLOGY

1932-330 **Trappen**, A[?]. von der. "Lichtbilder zu Goethes Farbenlehre." Privately printed[, 1932]. 4 pp.
    Cf. No. 1932-331.
    "Ergänzungsreihe nach Prof. Dr. Matthaei, Tübingen."
    /CHROMATICS

1932-331 **Trappen**, A[?]. von der. "Zehn Lichtbilder zu Goethes Farbenlehre." Privately printed[, 1932]. 4 pp.
    Cf. No. 1932-330.
    "nach Prof. Dr. Matthaei, Tübingen"
    /CHROMATICS

1932-332 **Troll**, Wilhelm. "Goethes botanische Studien." *Münchener Medizinische Wochenschriften*, 79 (1932), 461-6.
    /BOTANY

1932-333 **Tschermak-Seysenegg**, Armin [von]. "Goethes Bedeutung für die physiologische Optik." *Bericht über die neunundvierzigste Zusammenkunft der Deutschen Opthalmologischen Gesellschaft in Leipzig 1932*. Ed. A. Wagenmann. München: Verlag von J. F. Bergmann, 1932, pp. 3-16.
    Rpt. Nos. 1932-334, -335, -338 and -339.
    Cf. synopses, No. 1932-336, -337, -338 and -339.
    /PHYSIOLOGY/OPTICS

1932-334 **Tschermak-Seysenegg**, Armin [von]. "Goethes Farbenlehre in ihrer Bedeutung für die physiologische Optik der Gegenwart." *Beiträge zur ärztlichen Fortbildung*, 10, No. 6 (1932), 87-94.
    Rpt. of No. 1932-333.
    Rpt. No. 1932-340.
    /PHYSIOLOGY/OPTICS

1932-335 *****Tschermak-Seynsegg**, Armin von. "Goethes Farbenlehre in ihrer Bedeutung für die physiologische Optik der Gegenwart."

Bohemia [Prag], 14 May 1932.
Rpt. of No. 1932-333.
/PHYSIOLOGY/OPTICS

1932-336 **Tschermak-Seysenegg**, Armin[von]. "Goethes Farbenlehre in ihrer Bedeutung für die physiologische Optik der Gegenwart." *Forschungen und Fortschritte*, 8 (1932), 88-9.
Synopsis of No. 1932-333.
Rpt. Nos. 1932-337, -338 and -339.
/PHYSIOLOGY/OPTICS

1932-337 **Tschermak-Seysenegg**, Armin[von]. "Goethes Farbenlehre in ihrer Bedeutung für die physiologische Optik der Gegenwart." In *Forschungen und Fortschritte: Goethe*. Ed. Karl Kerkhof. Leipzig: Kommissionsverlag von Johann Ambrosius Barth[, 1932], pp. 12-13.
Rpt. of No. 1932-336.
/PHYSIOLOGY/OPTICS

1932-338 **Tschermak-Seysenegg**, Armin[von]. "Goethes Farbenlehre in ihrer Bedeutung für die physiologische Optik der Gegenwart." *Klinische Wochenschrift*, 11 (1932), 1207.
Rpt. of No. 1932-336.
/PHYSIOLOGY/OPTICS

1932-339 *****Tschermak-Seysenegg**, Armin[von]. "Goethes Farbenlehre in ihrer Bedeutung für die physiologische Optik der Gegenwart." *München-Augsburger Abend-Zeitung*, 15 March 1932.
Rpt. of No. 1932-336.
/PHYSIOLOGY/OPTICS

1932-340 **Tschermak-Seysenegg**, Armin[von]. "Goethes Farbenlehre in ihrer Bedeutung für die physiologische Optik der Gegenwart." Sonderabdruck aus der Goethenummer der "Beiträge zur ärztlichen Fortbildung." 8 pp.
Rpt. of No. 1932-334.
/PHYSIOLOGY/OPTICS

1932-341 **Urdang**, Georg. "Goethe und die Pharmazie." *Pharmazeutische Zeitung*, 77 (1932), 333-9.
"Vortrag, gehalten am 22. März 1932 in der Arbeitsgruppe Berlin-Brandenburg der Gesellschaft für Geschichte der Pharmacie."
/PHARMACOLOGY

1932-342 **Urdizil**, Johannes. *Goethe in Böhmen.* Wien/Leipzig: Verlag Dr. Hans Epstein, 1932. 273 pp.
/GEOLOGY/PLACES: BÖHMEN

1932-343 **Urdizil**, Johannes. "Goethe, Graf J. B. Paar und Hahnemann." *Die Medizinische Welt,* 6 (1932), 865-6.
Rpt. of No. 1931-38.
/PAAR, J/HAHNEMANN, C

1932-344 **Velenovsky**, Josef. "Goethe jako botanik [Goethe as a Botanist]." In *Goethuv sbornik: Pamatce 100. vyroci basnikovy smrti vydali cesti germaniste.* Praha: Statni nakladatelstvi v Praze, 1932, pp. 185-98.
In Czech.
/BOTANY/CELAKOVSKY, L

1932-345 **Venzmer**, Gerhard. "Was die Naturwissenschaften Goethe verdanken." *Kosmos,* 29 (1932), 77-83; 111-115.
/RECEPTION

1932-346 **Virchow**, Rudolf. "Goethes Erziehung zur Medizin." *Fortschritte der Medizin,* 50 (1932), 224-5.
Rpt. from No. 1861-10.
/MEDICINE

1932-347 **Visser**, S[?]. W. "Goethes Farbenlehre." *Deutsche Wacht: Niederländisch-Indische Halbmonatsschrift,* 18, No. 6 (1932), 18-22.
"Nach einem Vortrag in der Königlichen Naturwissenschaftlichen Vereinigung zu Batavia am Montag, den 21. März 1932"; "Aus dem Holländischen übersetzt von C. L. G. Koniëtzko."
/CHROMATICS

1932-348 *****Volkringer**, P[?]. and H. "Goethe et la science." *Les Nouvelles Littéraires (Hommage à Goethe),* 1932.
/GENERAL INTRODUCTION

1932-349 *****Vreede**, Elizabeth. "Goethes Verhältnis zur Astronomie." *Kalender 1932/1933.* Hrsg. v. d. math.-astronom. Sektion am Goetheanum, pp. 38-40.
/ASTRONOMY

1932-350 *****Vulf**, E[?]. "Gete kak botanik i evoliucinist [Goethe as Botanist and Evolutionist]." *Priroda,* No. 5 (1932).

In Russian.
/BOTANY/BIOLOGY: EVOLUTION

1932-351 **Vulpius**, Walther. "Goethe und die Medizin." *Korrespondenz-Blätter des Allgemeinen ärztlichen Vereins von Thüringen zugleich amtliches Organ der Thüringer Ärztekammer*, 61 (1932), 42-7.
Rpt. No. 1932-352.
/MEDICINE

1932-352 **Vulpius**, Walther. "Goethe und die Medizin." *Die medizinische Welt*, 6 (1932), 1226-8.
Rpt. of No. 1932-351.
/MEDICINE

1932-353 **Waaser**, Friedrich. "Goethe als Naturforscher!" *Aus der Heimat: Naturwissenschaftliche Monatsschrift*, 45 (1932), 1-23.
/GENERAL INTRODUCTION/EPISTEMOLOGY

1932-354 **Waaser**, Studienrat[Friedrich]. "Goethe und die Naturwissenschaften." In *Johann Wolfgang Goethe 1832-1932: Sonntags-Beilage zum Schwäbischen Merkur*, No. 67, 20 March 1932, 13-14.
/GENERAL INTRODUCTION

1932-355 **Wachsmuth**, Guenther. "Goethe's Doctrine of Metamorphosis and the Repeated Earthly Lives of Man." *Anthroposophy: A Quarterly Review of Spiritual Science*, 7 (1932), 103-19.
English trans. of No. 1932-356.
/MORPHOLOGY/RESEARCH: MORPHOLOGY

1932-356 **Wachsmuth**, Günther. "Goethes Metamorphosenlehre und die wiederholten Erdenleben des Menschen." *Gäa-Sophia: Jahrbuch der naturwissenschaftlichen Sektion der Freien Hochschule Dornach*, "Goethe-Jahrbuch," 6 (1932), 23-31.
Trans. into English, No. 1932-355.
/MORPHOLOGY/RESEARCH: MORPHOLOGY

1932-357 **Wachsmuth**, Gunther. "The Goethe Number of the Gaia-Sophia: (Yearbook of the Natural Science Section of the Goetheanum): Preface by the Editor." *Anthroposophical Movement: News for English-speaking Members of the Anthroposophical Society*, 9 (1932), 63-4.
/RESEARCH: VARIOUS/ANTHROPOSOPHY

1932-358 **Wagner**, George. "Goethe as a Scientist." In *The Goethe

Centenary at the University of Wisconsin: A memorial volume of addresses and some other contributions. Ed. A. R. Hohlfeld. University of Wisconsin Studies in Language and Literature, 34. Madison: University of Wisconsin, 1932, pp. 63-83.
/GENERAL INTRODUCTION

1932-359 **Walden**, Paul. *Goethe als Chemiker und Techniker.* Berlin: Verlag Chemie, G. m. b. H., 1932. 87 pp.
/CHEMISTRY/TECHNOLOGY

1932-360 *****Walden**, Paul. "Goethe und die Chemie." *Zeitschrift für angewandte Chemie*, 45 (1932), T.A., 792-7; 847-50; 864-8.
/CHEMISTRY

1932-361 **Walden**, Paul. "Goethe und seine Stellung zur reinen und angewandten Chemie." *Forschungen und Fortschritte*, 8 (1932), 89-90.
Rpt. No. 1932-362.
/CHEMISTRY

1932-362 **Walden**, Paul. "Goethe und seine Stellung zur reinen und angewandten Chemie." In *Forschungen und Fortschritte: Goethe.* Ed. Karl Kerkhof. Leipzig: Kommissionsverlag von Johann Ambrosius Barth[, 1932], pp. 13-14.
Rpt. of No. 1932-361.
/CHEMISTRY

1932-363 **Walther**, Johannes. "Goethe und das Steinreich." *Forschungen und Fortschritte*, 8 (1932), 93-5.
Rpt. No. 1932-364.
/GEOLOGY

1932-364 **Walther**, Johannes. "Goethe und das Steinreich." In *Forschungen und Fortschritte: Goethe.* Ed. Karl Kerkhof. Leipzig: Kommissionsverlag von Johann Ambrosius Barth[, 1932], pp. 17-19.
Rpt. of No. 1932-363.
/GEOLOGY

1932-365 **Walther**, Johannes. *Die Natur in Goethes Weltbild.* Leipzig: Akademische Verlagsgesellschaft m. b. H., 1932. viii, 104 pp.
/GENERAL INTRODUCTION

1932-366 **Wanscher**, Vilhelm. "H. C. Oersteds und Gotlieb Bindesboells Besuch bei Goethe im Jahre 1822: Aus einem unveröffentlichten

Briefe H. C. Oersteds an seine Gattin Inger Birgitte Oersted." In his *Gotlieb Bindesboell 1800-1856 der Erbauer von Thorvaldsens Museum.* Vol. 1 of *Artes: Monuments et mémoires publiés sous la direction de Vilhelm Wanscher professeur de l'histoire de l'art à l'Académie Royale des Beaux-Arts de Copenhague.* Copenhague: P. Haase & Fils H. H. Thiele imprimeur, 1932, pp. 135-6.
/OERSTEDT, G/BINDESBOELL, G

1932-367 **Weinhandl**, Ferdinand. *Die Metaphysik Goethes.* Berlin: Junker und Dünnhaupt Verlag, 1932. xv, 400 pp.
    Rpt. No. 1965-40.
    /EPISTEMOLOGY/METHOD

1932-368 **Weiss**, Julius. "Goethe im Spiegel der Medizin." *Wiener Medizinische Wochenschrift*, 82 (1932), 678-81.
    /MEDICINE

1932-369 **Werner**, Hugo. "Goethes Verhältnis zur Natur und zu den Naturwissenschaften." *Jahreshefte des Vereins für vaterländische Naturkunde in Württemberg*, 88 (1932), lvii-lviii.
    /GENERAL INTRODUCTION

1932-370 *****Wester**, D[?]. H. "Goethes betrekkingen tot de scheikunde (ter herdenking van zijn 100 sterfdag) [Goethe's Relationship to Chemistry (In Commemoration of the Centenary of his Death]. *Chemisch Weekblad [Amsterdam]*, 29 (1932), 178-82.
    In Dutch.
    /CHEMISTRY

1932-371 **Will**, Robert. "Le génie visuel de Goethe." In *Goethe. Etudes publiées pour la centenaire de sa mort.* Publications de la Faculté des Lettres de l'Université de Strasbourg, 57. Paris, 1932, pp. 229-47.
    /GENERAL INTRODUCTION

1932-372 **Willige**, Wilhelm. "Der Seher." In his *Goethe: Umrisse seiner geistigen Gestalt.* Weimar: Verlag von Hermann Böhlaus Nachfolger, 1932, pp. 44-70.
    /GENERAL INTRODUCTION

1932-373 **Wohlbold**, Hans. "Goethe und die moderne Biologie." *Gäa-Sophia: Jahrbuch der naturwissenschaftlichen Sektion der Freien Hochschule Dornach*, "Goethe-Jahrbuch," 6 (1932), 89-103.
    /BIOLOGY

1932-374 **Wohlbold**, Hans. "Goethe und die Naturwissenschaft." In *Katalog der Goethe-Ausstellung München 1932.* München: Verein Ausstellungspark, 1932, pp. 108-23.
/GENERAL INTRODUCTION

1932-375 **Wolf**, Richard. "Goethe, der Naturforscher." *Deutsche Allgemeine Zeitung*, 14 December 1932.
Rev. of Nos. 1932-111, -149 and -203.
In Mappe III E 61/C20: "Goethe und die Naturwissenschaften. Zeitungsausschnitte 1913 -" at the Frankfurter Goethe-Museum.
/GENERAL INTRODUCTION

1932-376 **Wroblewski**, Viktor Augustin and Heinz **Amelung**. "Briefwechsel Goethe-Jakowlew: Zum erstenmal veröffentlicht." *Die Gartenlaube*, No. 12 (1932) 224-6.
/EDITION/JAKOWLEW, L/GEOLOGY/GOETHE'S COLLECTIONS

1932-377 **Würtz**, Hans. "Goethes Wesen und Umwelt im Speigel der Krüppelpsychologie." Leipzig: Verlag von Leopold Voß, 1932. 31 pp.
/MEDICINE/PSYCHOLOGY

1932-378 **Wundt**, Max. "Goethe und die Philosophie." *Forschungen und Fortschritte*, 8 (1932), 85-6.
Rpt. No. 1932-379.
/PHILOSOPHY

1932-379 **Wundt**, Max. "Goethe und die Philosophie." In *Forschungen und Fortschritte: Goethe.* Ed. Karl Kerkhof. Leipzig: Kommissionsverlag von Johann Ambrosius Barth[, 1932].
Rpt. of No. 1932-378.
/PHILOSOPHY

1932-380 *****Zapletal**, K[?]. "Goethe geolog a paleontolog [Goethe as a Geologist and Paleontologist]." *Priroda [Brno]*, 25 (1932), No. 3.
In Czech.
/GEOLOGY/PALEONTOLOGY

1932-381 *****Zarnik**, Boris. "Goethe als Biologe." *Morgenblatt [Zagreb]*, No. 20, 20 March 1932, Beil.
/BIOLOGY

1932-382 ***Zarnik**, Boris. "Goethe i biologiia [Goethe and Biology]."
Priroda, April-May 1932, pp. 97-115.
 In Serbo-Croatian.
 /BIOLOGY

1932-383 **Zeylmans van Emmichoven**, F[?]. W. "Goethe's beteekenis
voor de natuurwetenschappen, in het bijzonder voor de leer van het
licht [Goethe's Significance for the Sciences, Especially for the
Theory of Light]." Den Haag: Goetheanum Uitgeverij, 1932. 28 pp.
 In Dutch.
 /CHROMATICS/METHOD

1932-384 **Zint**, Hans. "Schopenhauers Goethe-Bild." *Jahrbuch der
Schopenhauer-Gesellschaft*, 19 (1932), 3-31.
 /SCHOPENHAUER, A/CHROMATICS

1932-385 **Zint**, Hans. "Zur Farbenlehre." *Jahrbuch der Schopenhauer-
Gesellschaft*, 19 (1932), 341-4.
 Rev. of Nos. 1928-15, 1930-6, 1932-111 and 1932-247.
 /REVIEW/SCHOPENHAUER, A/CHROMA-
 TICS/RESEARCH: CHROMATICS

1933-1 **Abel**, Othenio. "Goethe und die Biologie." *Biologia Generalis*, 9
(1933), 1-24.
 /BIOLOGY

1933-2 **André**, Hans. "Goethes Metamorphosenlehre, ihr Sinn und ihre
Bedeutung für die heutige Biologie." *Medizinische Klinik*, 29 (1933),
1411-13.
 Rpt. No. 1933-3.
 /BIOLOGY/MORPHOLOGY

1933-3 **André**, Hans. "Goethes Metamorphosenlehre, ihr Sinn und ihre
Bedeutung für die heutige Biologie." Sonderdruck aus *Medizinische
Klinik*. Berlin: Urban & Schwarzenberg, 1933. 8 pp.
 Rpt. of No. 1933-2.
 /BIOLOGY/MORPHOLOGY

1933-4 **[B(?)., Dr. von.]** "Museum Darwinianum." *Der Biologe:
Monatsschrift zur Wahrung der Belange der Biologie und der
deutschen Biologen*, 2 (1933), 120-21.
 /EXHIBITION/INSTITUTIONS: DARWIN MUSEUM, MOS-
 COW

1933-5 **Barthel**, Ernst. "Die heutige wissenschaftliche Bedeutung von Goethes Farbenlehre." *Geisteskultur*, 42 (1933), 15-20.
/CHROMATICS

1933-6 **Benn**, Gottfried. "Goethe und die Naturwissenschaften." In his *Der neue Staat und die Intellektuellen*. Stuttgart/ Berlin: Deutsche Verlags-Anstalt, 1933, pp. 77-128.
Rpt. of No. 1932-24.
/GENERAL INTRODUCTION

1933-7 *****Beutler**, E[rnst]. "Goethe und die Heilkunst." *Deutsches Ärzteblatt*, 63 (1933), 778-80.
/MEDICINE

1933-8 **Bluntschli**, Hans. "Goethe als Begründer der Morphologie." *Schweizerische Medizinische Monatsschrift*, 14, No. 1, (1933), 2-9.
"Vortrag auf dem Medizinisch-biologischen Abend der Universität Frankfurt a.M., gehalten am 25. Juli 1932."
/MORPHOLOGY

1933-9 **Brown**, Irene. "Goethe's Theory of Colours in its bearing on a new Creative Impulse." *Anthroposophy: A Quarterly Review of Spiritual Science*, 8 (1933), 73-89.
/RESEARCH: CHROMATICS

1933-10 *****Bürgi**, Emil. "Die Medizin in der Dichtkunst. Nach e. akad. Vortr. Bern 1933. Pochor Jent. 30 pp. Aus: Kleiner Bund. 1933.
/MEDICINE

1933-11 **Bürgin**, Hans. *Der Minister Goethe vor der römischen Reise: Seine Tätigkeit in der Wegbau- und Kriegskommission*. Weimar: Verlag Hermann Böhlaus Nachf., 1933. xiii, 228 pp.
/TECHNOLOGY

1933-12 **Burzio**, Filippo. "Goethe e Helmholtz [Goethe and Helmholtz]." In his *Ritratti. II: Aspetti del Demiurgo*. Genova: Degli Orfini, 1933, pp. 167-76.
Rpt. of No. 1932-40.
In Italian.
/HELMHOLTZ, H

1933-13 **Carus**, Carl Gustav. *Goethe. Zu dessen näherem Verständnis.* Leipzig 1843. Afterword Rudolf Marx. Kröners Taschenausgabe, 97. Leipzig: Alfred Kröner Verlag, 1933. 164 pp.

Rpt. of No. 1843-5.
/GENERAL INTRODUCTION

1933-14 **Castle**, Eduard. "Zur Geschichte der Ausgaben der naturwissenschaftlichen Schriften Goethes." *Archiv für das Studium der neueren Sprachen*, 163 [NS 63] (1933), 172-186.
/EDITIONS/ECKERMANN, J

1933-15 **Chance**, Burton. "Goethe and his Theory of Colors." *Annals of Medical History*, 5 (1933), 360-75.
"Read at the Meeting of the Section on Medical History, College of Physicians, Philadelphia, April 11, 1932."
/CHROMATICS

1933-16 **Collard**, Auguste. "Goethe et Quetelet. Leurs relations de 1829 à 1832." *Isis*, 20 (1933), 426-35.
/QUETELET, A/ASTRONOMY

1933-17 **Deutsch**, Adolf. "Goethe und kein Ende." Leipzig: Verlag von Johann Ambrosius Barth, 1933. 24 pp.
Rpt. of No. 1932-64.
/GENERAL INTRODUCTION

1933-18 **Fischer**, Walther. "Dann hält Herr Fischer seinen Vortrag über Goethe's Geologie und wir." *Sitzungsberichte und Abhandlungen der Naturwissenschaftlichen Gesellschaft Isis in Dresden Jahrgang 1932.* Dresden: In Kommission der Hofbuchhandlung H. Burdach, 1933, pp. 41-2.
Synopsis of a lecture.
/GEOLOGY

1933-19 **Franz**, Victor. "Goethes Zwischenkieferpublikation nach Anlaß, Inhalt und Wirkung. Mit Ausblicken auf Goethes Morphologie überhaupt." *Ergebnisse der Anatomie und Entwicklungsgeschichte*, 30 (1933), 469-543.
Rpt. No. 1933-20.
/OSTEOLOGY/MORPHOLOGY

1933-20 **Franz**, Victor. *Goethes Zwischenkieferpublikation nach Anlaß, Inhalt und Wirkung. Mit Ausblicken auf Goethes Morphologie überhaupt.* Berlin: Verlag von Julius Springer, 1933. iv, 75 pp.
Rpt. of No. 1933-19.
/OSTEOLOGY/MORPHOLOGY

1933-21 **Haase**, Karl. "Goethe als Geschichtsforscher mit besonderer Berücksichtigung der Vor- und Zukunftsgeschichte der Menschheit." *Jahrbücher der Akademie gemeinnütziger Wissenschaften zu Erfurt*, NS 51 (1933), 105-6.
/HISTORIOGRAPHY/HISTORY OF SCIENCE

1933-22 **Kahn**, R[ichard]. H. "Goethes Augen. Deren Beschaffenheit und Sehvermögen." *Biologia generalis*, 9 (1933), 25-106.
Rpt. of No. 1932-176.
/CHROMATICS/OPTICS

1933-23 *****Kaulbersz**, Jerzy. "Goethe i medycyna [Goethe and Medicine]." *Polska Gazeta Lekarska*, 12/13 (1933), 1-13.
In Polish.
/MEDICINE/GENERAL INTRODUCTION

1933-24 **Knauer**, Helmut. "Goethes Weg als Naturforscher." *Das Goetheanum*, 12 (1933), 83-6.
/GENERAL INTRODUCTION

1933-25 **Knoll**, Fritz. "Goethes Naturbetrachtung." *Natur und Heimat: Sudetendeutsche Vierteljahrsschrift für Pflanzen- und Tierkunde*, 4 (1933), 33-5.
/GENERAL INTRODUCTION

1933-26 **Knoll**, Fritz. "Goethe und die Pflanzenwelt." *Natur und Heimat: Sudetendeutsche Vierteljahrsschrift für Pflanzen- und Tierkunde*, 4 (1933), 102-5.
/BOTANY

1933-27 **Löwy**, Max. "Psychologische Anmerkungen zu Goethes Farbenlehre." *Medizinische Klinik: Wochenschrift für praktische Ärzte*, 29 (1933), 1113-16.
/CHROMATICS/RESEARCH: CHROMATICS/RESEARCH: PSYCHOLOGY

1933-28 **Matthaei**, R[upprecht]. "Farbenlehre." *Handwörterbuch der Naturwissenschaften*. 2nd edn. Jena: G. Fischer, 1933, III, 979-89.
/RESEARCH: CHROMATICS/CHROMATICS

1933-29 **Matthaei**, Rupprecht. "Goethes Farbenkreis. Die quellenmässige Begründung einer Rekonstruktion." *Euphorion*, 34 (1933), 195-211.
/CHROMATICS/INFLUENCES

1933-30 **Nicholas**, J[?]. S. "Goethe, The Layman in Science." Transactions of the Connecticut Academy of Arts and Sciences, 32. New Haven: Connecticut Academy of Arts and Sciences/ Yale University Press, 1933. 19 pp.
/GENERAL INTRODUCTION

1933-31 ***Pajiedaitè**, B[?]. "Goethe -- biologas [Goethe as a Biologist]." *Kosmos*, 14 (1933), 147-51.
In Lithuanian.
/BIOLOGY

1933-32 ***Pelikan**, W[?]. "Natürliche Düfte und ihre Wirkung. Ein Versuch im Sinne goethescher Naturbetrachtung." *Weleda-Nachrichten: Hausmitteilungen der Weleda-Werke*, Stuttgart, 1933, H. 5.
/RESEARCH: PHARMACOLOGY

1933-33 **Petella**, G[?]. "Piante e colori negli scritti scientifici di Goethe [Plants and Colors in Goethe's Scientific Writings]." *Annali di medicina navale e coloniale*, 39 (1933), vol. 1, fasc. 5-6, pp. 347-64.
In Italian.
/BOTANY/CHROMATICS

1933-34 **Pezold**, Hans von. "Goethe und die Prostitution." *Mitteilungen der Deutschen Gesellschaft zur Bekämpfung der Geschlechtskrankheiten*, 31 (1933), 197-99.
/MEDICINE

1933-35 **Podestà**, Hans. "Rückblick auf Goethes Anschauungen über die Farbenblindheit." *Zeitschrift für Bahnärzte*, 28 (1933), 13-18.
/COLORBLINDNESS

1933-36 **Porsch**, Otto. "Goethe und die Pflanze." *Biologia Generalis*, 9 (1933), 107-50.
Rpt. of No. 1932-252.
/BOTANY

1933-37 ***Prochazka**, J[?]. S. "Goethe a ceska prirodeveda" [Goethe and Czech Science]. *Casopis Musea Kralovstvi ceskeho [Prag]*, 107 (1933), 14-24.
In Czech.
/INFLUENCES/RECEPTION/PLACES: CZECHOSLOVAKIA

1933-38 ***Reiffen**, Kurt. "Wissenschaftliches und ästhetisches Weltbild."

Diss. Bonn 1933. 72 pp.
/CHROMATICS

1933-39 **Schiff**, Julius. "Goethe als Gärtner und Botaniker." *105. Jahres-Bericht der Schlesischen Gesellschaft für vaterländische Cultur: 1932.* Breslau: M. & H. Marcus Verlagsbuchhandlung, 1933, pp. 180-83.
/BOTANY

1933-40 **Schmid**, Günther. "Goethes Metamorphosen-Elegie und Neuenhahn der jüngere von Nordhausen." *Sonderdruck aus der Thür.-Sächs. Zeitschrift für Geschichte und Kunst*, 22 (1933). 14 pp.
Rpt. of No. 1933-41.
/WORKS: LYRICS/NEUENHAHN, C/BOTANY

1933-41 **Schmid**, Günther. "Goethes Metamorphosen-Elegie und Neuenhahn der jüngere von Nordhausen." *Thüringisch-Sächsische Zeitschrift für Geschichte und Kunst*, 22 (1933), 92-105.
Rpt. No. 1933-40.
/WORKS: LYRICS/NEUENHAHN, C/BOTANY

1933-42 **Sieglbauer**, Felix. "Goethes Begriff der Morphologie." *Wiener klinische Wochenschrift*, 46 (1933), 129-32.
Rpt. No. 1949-167.
/MORPHOLOGY

1933-43 **Spinner**, Heinrich. "Goethes Typusbegriff." Diss. Zürich, 1933. Horgen-Zürich/Leipzig: Verlag der Münster-Presse, 1933. 130 pp.
Partial rpt. No. 1933-44.
/METHOD/EPISTEMOLOGY

1933-44 **Spinner**, Heinrich. "Goethes Typusbegriff." Horgen-Zürich/Leipzig: Verlag der Münster-Presse, 1933. 273 pp.
Partial rpt. of No. 1933-43.
/METHOD/EPISTEMOLOGY

1933-45 **Sureda Blanes**, José. "Goethe i la química [Goethe and Chemistry]." Ciutat de Mallorca: La Nostra terra, 1933. 21 pp.
Excerpt from No. 1933-46.
In Catalan.
"Conferència organitzada per l'"Ateneo de Oviedo," llegida en el paranimf de la Universidad d'aquella ciutat, el 10 de desembre de 1932."

L of C PT 2208.C4S8
/CHEMISTRY

1933-46 *__Sureda Blanes__, José. "Goethe i la química [Goethe and Chemistry]." *La Nostra terra*, 6, No. 63 (1933).
Excerpt rpt. No. 1933-45.
In Catalan.
"Conferència organitzada per l'"Ateneo de Oviedo," llegida en el paranimf de la Universidad d'aquella ciutat, el 10 de desembre de 1932."
/CHEMISTRY

1933-47 __Tobler__, Friedrich. "Goethe als Botaniker." *Der Biologe: Monatsschrift zur Wahrung der Belange der Biologie und der deutschen Biologen*, 2, No. 7 (1933), 169.
/BOTANY

1933-48 __Trappen__, A[?]. von der. "Lichtbilder zu Goethes Farbenlehre. Ergänzungsreihe nach Prof. Dr. Matthaei, Tübingen." Stuttgart: Neckarstraße 140A[, 1933]. 4 pp.
/CHROMATICS

1933-49 __Twardowski__, Julius von. "Goethe und Polen, Polen und Goethe." *Goethe*, 19 (1933), 142-66.
/RECEPTION/PLACES: POLAND

1933-50 __Walden__, Paul. "Goethe und die Naturwissenschaften." *Bremer Beiträge zur Naturwissenschaft*, 1 (1933), 3-53.
Rpt. No. 1933-51.
/CHROMATICS/GENERAL INTRODUCTION

1933-51 __Walden__, Paul. *Goethe und die Naturwissenschaften*. Bremer Beiträge zur Naturwissenschaft, 1. Bremen-Leipzig: G. A. v. Halem Export- und Verlagsbuchhandlung A.-G., 1933. 53 pp.
Rpt. of No. 1933-50.
/GENERAL INTRODUCTION

1933-52 __Zekert__, Otto. "Goethe und die Chemie." *Pharmazeutische Monatshefte*, 14 (1933), 131-7.
"Vortrag, gehalten in der Jahres-Vollversammlung des Wiener Goethe-Vereines am 29. April 1933."
/CHEMISTRY

1934-1 __Bahr__, G[?]. "Einiges über Blatt-Signaturen." *Natura: Eine*

Zeitschrift zur Erweiterung der Heilkunst nach geisteswissenschaftlicher Menschenkunde, 7 (1934/1935/1936/1937), 209-32.
/RESEARCH: BOTANY

1934-2 **Berthold**, Eugen. "Merkuriale Pflanzen." *Natura: Eine Zeitschrift zur Erweiterung der Heilkunst nach geisteswissenschaftlicher Menschenkunde*, 7 (1934/1935/1936/1937), 241-68.
/RESEARCH: BOTANY

1934-3 **Brenke**, Else. "Ein bislang unbekannter Bericht über den Phrenologen Gall." *Thüringisch-Sächsische Zeitschrift für Geschichte und Kunst*, 23 (1934/1935), 67-70.
/PHRENOLOGY/EICHENDORFF, J/GALL, F

1934-4 **Cuénot**, Claude. "Une application de la morphologie goethéénne à l'histoire littéraire en Allemagne." *Revue de littérature comparée*, 14 (1934), 241-52.
/RESEARCH: HISTORIOGRAPHY/RESEARCH: MORPHOLOGY

1934-5 ***Dietmar**, H[?]. "Goethe und das Physikum." *Ärzteblatt für Sachsen, Prov. Sachsen, Anhalt u. Thüringen*, 1 March 1932, Nr. 5, pp. 47-9.
/MEDICINE

1934-6 **Donat**, Walter. "Zur Auffassung Goethes von der Wissenschaft." *Goethe-Jahrbuch: Die Goethe-Gesellschaft in Japan*, 3 (1934), 30-46.
In German.
/METHOD

1934-7 **Düren**, Wilhelm. "Goethe widerlegt Spengler." Bonn: Ludwig Röhrscheid Verlag, 1934. 42, ii pp.
/SPENGLER, O

1934-8 ***Eckstein**, Friedrich. "Goethes magische Farbenlehre und die Dampfmaschine." *Neue Freie Presse [Wien]*, 14 June 1934.
/CHROMATICS/TECHNOLOGY

1934-9 ***Eiff**, W[?]. "Die Farbenlehre Newtons, Goethes und Ostwalds in der Auffassung des Künstlers." *Glastechnische Berichte*, 12 (1934), 77-84.
/AESTHETICS/CHROMATICS/NEWTON, I/OSTWALD, W

1934-10 **Ficker**, Heinrich von. "Bemerkungen über Goethes 'Versuch

einer Witterungslehre'." *Die Naturwissenschaften: Wochenschrift für die Fortschritte der reinen und der angewandten Naturwissenschaften*, 22 (1934), 81-4.
    Rpt. of No. 1932-86.
    Cf. response, No. 1934-11.
    /METEOROLOGY

1934-11 **Fricke**, Hermann. "Goethe als Entdecker einer neuen Meteorologie." *Deutsche Optische Wochenschrift und Centralzeitung für Optik und Mechanik*[, 1934], 347-9.
    Cf. exp. version No. 1934-12.
    Response to No. 1934-10.
    /METEOROLOGY

1934-12 **Fricke**, Hermann. "Goethe als Entdecker einer neuen Meteorologie." In his *Die im Innern erdähnliche Sonne: Eine neue Anschauung von Aether, Schwerkraft und Sonne*. Weimar: Verlag R. Borkmann, 1934, pp. 65-71.
    Exp. version of No. 1934-11.
    /METEOROLOGY

1934-13 **Froehner**, Reinhard. "Goethe und die Tierarzneischule in Jena. Der Bremer Goethefund." *Veterinärhistorische Mitteilungen*, 14 (1934), 42-3.
    /VETERINARY MEDICINE/INSTITUTIONS: JENAER VETERINÄRSCHULE

1934-14 **Gehrt**, Albert John. "Goethe, the Chemist." *Journal of Chemical Education*, 11 (1934), 543-5.
    /CHEMISTRY

1934-15 **Goethe**, Johann Wolfgang von. "Der Granit." Halle/Burg Giebichenstein: Werkstätten der Stadt Halle[, 1934.] [16] pp.
    /EDITION

1934-16 **Hauschka**, Rudolf. "Pflanzenbilder." *Natura: Eine Zeitschrift zur Erweiterung der Heilkunst nach geisteswissenschaftlicher Menschenkunde*, 7 (1934/1935/1936/1937), 102-6.
    /RESEARCH: BOTANY/RESEARCH: CHROMATICS

1934-17 **Heinemann**, Fritz. "Goethe's Phenomenological Method." *Philosophy*, 9 (1934), 67-81.
    Trans. into French, No. 1935-13.
    /EPISTEMOLOGY/PHENOMENOLOGY

1934-18 **Hellfritsch**, Otto. "Über einiges Pathologische bei Goethe." *Goethe-Jahrbuch: Die Goethe-Gesellschaft in Japan*, 3 (1934), 18-29.
/PATHOLOGY

1934-19 ***Henriet**, Jacques. "Goethe et l'anatomie." *Strasb. Ed. Univ.*, 1934. 30 pp.
Rpt. (extract) of No. 1932-152.
/ANATOMY

1934-20 **Hochstetter**, A[?]. D. "Goethe und die Versammlungen der deutschen Naturforscher und Ärzte." *Deutsche Medizinische Wochenschrift*, 60 (1934), 1395-8.
/INSTITUTIONS: SCIENTIFIC SOCIETIES/INSTITUTIONS: MEDICAL SOCIETIES

1934-21 **Kein**, Otto. *Die Universalität des Geistes im Lebenswerk Goethes und Schellings im Zusammenhang mit der organisch-synthetischen Geistesrichtung der Goethezeit*. Berlin: Junker und Dünnhaupt Verlag, 1934. 520 pp.
/GENERAL INTRODUCTION

1934-22 ***Knauer**, Helmut. "Der Kampf Goethes gegen Newton." *Das Goetheanum*, 13 (1934), 354-6.
/CHROMATICS/NEWTON, I

1934-23 ***Knoll**, Fritz. "Goethes Naturbetrachtung." *Heimatbildung [Reichenberg]*, 15 (1934), 150-52.
/GENERAL INTRODUCTION

1934-24 ***Knoll**, Fritz. "Goethe und die Pflanzenwelt." *Heimatbildung [Reichenberg]*, 15 (1934), 332-4.
/BOTANY

1934-25 ***Maurer**, Th[?]. "Goethe im Lichte der Eidetik." *Das Goetheanum*, 13 (1934), 106-8.
/EPISTEMOLOGY/MÜLLER, J/JAENSCH, E

1934-26 **Plathow**, Gerhard. *Das Wahrheitsproblem in Goethes Wissenschaft*. Germanische Studien unter Mitwirkung der Herren [etc.] herausgegeben von Dr. Emil Ebering. Berlin: Verlag Dr. Emil Ebering, 1934. 150 pp.
/EPISTEMOLOGY/SPINOZA, B/NEOPLATONISM

1934-27 ***Rick**, A[?]. "Der Goethesche Zwischenkiefer und die Gaumenspalten." *Korrespondenzblätter für Zahnärzte*, 58, No. 1 (1934), 1-7.
/OSTEOLOGY

1934-28 **Schmid**, Günther. "Pietra fungaja. Ein mykologischer Briefwechsel Goethes: Mit einer Tafel." *Zeitschrift für Pilzkunde: Organ der Deutschen Gesellschaft für Pilzkunde*, NS 13, Nos. 3-5 (1934), 71-81; 110-18; 140-51.
/BIOLOGY

1934-29 ***Schneider**, A[?]. and W[?]. **Deckert**. "Goethes und Ostwalds Farben im Unterricht." *Die deutsche Berufsschule*, 43 (1934), 265-70.
/CHROMATICS/OSTWALD, W

1934-30 **Schuster**, Julius. "Nostoch, Paracelsus und Goethe. Aus deutscher Volksmedizin und Naturphilosophie." *Medizinische Mitteilungen*, 6 (1934), 194-99.
/NOSTOCH, ?/PARACELSUS/MEDICINE

1934-31 **Sparr**, Leopold. "Vom Wesen der Bäume und ihren Hölzern." *Natura: Eine Zeitschrift zur Erweiterung der Heilkunst nach geisteswissenschaftlicher Menschenkunde*, 7 (1934 /1935/1936/1937), 280-306.
/RESEARCH: BOTANY

1934-32 **Wadepuhl**, Walter. *Goethes Interest in the New World*. Jena: Frommannsche Buchhandlung Walter Biedermann, 1934. 85 pp.
/GEOLOGY/PLACES: NORTH AMERICA

1934-33 ***Wegener**, Ernst. "Goethe und die 'Erdstrahlen'." *Vossische Zeitung*, 18 February 1934.
/GEOLOGY

1935-1 **Berger**, Hermann. "Berührungspunkte zwischen dem Studenten Goethe und der Medizin. Ein Streifzug durch 'Dichtung und Wahrheit'." *Münchener Medizinische Wochenschrift*, 82 (1935), 1452-3.
/MEDICINE/WORKS: DICHTUNG UND WAHRHEIT

1935-2 **Beurlen**, Karl. "Das Gestaltproblem in der organischen Natur." *Zeitschrift für die gesamte Naturwissenschaft einschließlich Naturphilosophie und Geschichte der Naturwissenschaft und Medizin*, 1

(1935/1936), 445-57.
/RESEARCH: MORPHOLOGY

1935-3 **Dacqué**, Edgar. *Organische Morphologie und Paläontologie.*
Berlin: Verlag von Gebrüder Bornträger, 1935. viii, 476 pp.
/MORPHOLOGY/RESEARCH: MORPHOLOGY/RESEARCH:
BIOLOGY

1935-4 **Donat**, Walter. "Umbruch des wissenschaftlichen Denkens."
Goethe-Jahrbuch: Die Goethe-Gesellschaft in Japan, 4 (1935), 32-46.
/METHOD

1935-5 **Düren**, Wilhelm. "Die Urphänomene der Vertikal- und Spiral-
tendenz im Vegetativen." In his *Die Umwertung aller Werte.* Bonn:
Ludwig Röhrscheid Verlag, 1935, pp. 11-26.
/RESEARCH: BOTANY/BOTANY

1935-6 **Düren**, Wilhelm. "Die Urphänomene in der Kunst." In his *Die
Umwertung aller Werte.* Bonn: Ludwig Röhrscheid Verlag, 1935,
pp. 27-53.
/RESEARCH: AESTHETICS

1935-7 ***Eberhard**, Lilli Elisabeth. "Goethes Farbenforschung als Funda-
ment." *Sonderheft des Süddeutschen graphischen Anzeigers*, 10
(1935), H. 11, pp. 1-4.
Rpt. No. 1935-8.
/CHROMATICS

1935-8 ***Eberhard**, Lilli Elisabeth. "Goethes Farbenforschung als Funda-
ment und Wegweiser zu Eberhards 'Neue Farbenlehre'." *Sonderheft
des Süddeutschen graphischen Anzeigers*, 10 (1935), H. 12. 24 pp.
Rpt. of Nos. 1935-7 and 1935-9.
/CHROMATICS

1935-9 ***Eberhard**, Lilli Elisabeth. "Wertvolle Aufschlüsse durch die
Goetheschen Farbenforschungen." *Sonderheft des Süddeutschen
graphischen Anzeigers*, 10 (1935), H. 10, pp. 3-5.
Rpt. No. 1935-8.
/CHROMATICS

1935-10 **Goethe**[, J. W. von]. "Botanischer Vortrag 8. April 1807."
[Burg Giebichenstein: Werkstätten der Stadt Halle, 1935.] [4] pp.
/EDITION

1935-11 **Goethe**[, J. W. von]. "Goethe und der Enzian." [Burg Giebichenstein: Werkstätten der Stadt Halle, 1935.] [1] p.
/EDITION

1935-12 **Götting**, Franz. "Die Tragödie des Ilmenauer Bergbaus." *Goethe-Kalender auf das Jahr 1935.* Leipzig: Dieterich'sche Verlagsbuchhandlung[, 1935], pp. 154-90.
/TECHNOLOGY/PLACES: ILMENAU

1935-13 **Heinemann**, Fritz. "Phénoménologie de la Nature chez Goethe." *Revue Philosophique de la France et de l'Étranger*, 119 (1935), 93-120.
French trans. by Henry Corbin of No. 1934-17.
/EPISTEMOLOGY/PHENOMENOLOGY

1935-14 **Husemann**, Friedrich. *Goethe und die Heilkunst: Betrachtungen zur Krise in der Medizin.* Dornach: Philosophisch-Anthroposophischer Verlag am Goetheanum, 1935. 176 pp.
Rpt. Nos. 1936-12 and 1957-24.
Trans. into English No. 1938-9.
/MEDICINE/RESEARCH: MEDICINE/STEINER, R

1935-15 *****Kern**, Hans. "Vulkan besiegt Neptun." *Münchener Neueste Nachrichten*, 26 May 1935, No. 144.
Rpt. No. 1936-14.
/GEOLOGY

1935-16 **Kikuchi**, E[iichi]. ["Einige naturwissenschaftliche Grundbegriffe bei Goethe."] *Goethe-Jahrbuch: Die Goethe-Gesellschaft in Japan*, 4 (1935), 61-82.
In Japanese.
/METHOD

1935-17 **Kippenberg**, Anton. "Goethe, Dittmar und Lavater." *Jahrbuch der Sammlung Kippenberg*, 10 (1935), 132-54.
/DITTMAR [DIETMAR], J/METEOROLOGY/LAVATER, J

1935-18 **Knittermeyer**, Hinrich, ed. "Unbekannte Briefe und Urkunden aus dem Goethekreis. Aus dem Nachlaß Johann Michael Färbers." *Abhandlungen und Vorträge herausgegeben von der Bremer Wissenschaftlichen Gesellschaft*, 7, No. 3/4 (1935). cvi, 152 pp.
/FÄRBER, J/PLACES: JENA

1935-19 **Lippmann**, Edmund O. "F. F. Runge und Goethe." *Der*

deutsche Chemiker (Beilage zur Angewandten Chemie), 1 (1935), 10-11.
/RUNGE, F/CHEMISTRY

1935-20 ***Martell**, P[aul]. "Goethe und die Medizin." *Ärzteblatt für das Rheinland*, 1935, 189-90.
/MEDICINE

1935-21 ***Martell**, P[aul]. "Goethe und die Medizin." *Zahnärztliche Fortbildung*, 29 (1935), 187-9.
/MEDICINE

1935-22 **Michel**, Ernst. "Goethes Naturbetrachtung in religiöser Bedeutung." *Frankfurter Zeitung*, 31 October 1935.
/THEOLOGY/CHROMATICS

1935-23 **Müllner**, Ludwig. *Goethes Faust im Lichte seiner Naturforschung: Billige Neu-Ausgabe.* Basel: Verlag von Rudolf Geering, 1935. 402 pp.
/WORKS: FAUST/STEINER, R/ANTHROPOSOPHY

1935-24 ***Nette**, Herbert. "Goethes Forschungsweise in der Naturwissenschaft." *Stuttgarter Neues Tageblatt*, 3 August 1935, Nr. 29.
/METHOD

1935-25 **Obenauer**, Karl Justus. "Goethe als Naturforscher." *Das deutsche Wort*, 11 [= NS 3], No. 34 (1935), 8-10.
/GENERAL INTRODUCTION

1935-26 **Richter**, Rudolf. "Natur-Museum 'Senckenberg': Unsere Volksgründung streift auch äußerlich ihre Abschließung ab." *Natur und Volk: Bericht der Senckenbergischen Naturforschenden Gesellschaft*, 65 (1935), 570-72.
/INSTITUTIONS: MUSEUM SENCKENBERG /INSTITUTIONS: SENCKENBERGISCHE NATURFORSCHENDE GESELLSCHAFT

1935-27 **Rüchardt**, Eduard. "Eine Entdeckung von Goethes Kammerdiener." *Münchener Neueste Nachrichten*, 283 (1935), 3-4.
/CHROMATICS/STADELMANN, J

1935-28 ***Schirmer-Behrendt**, Elisabet. "Goethe und die Tierarzneischule in Jena." *Veterinärhistorische Mitteilungen*, 15 (1935), 73-8.
/INSTITUTIONS: TIERARZNEISCHULE JENA

/VETERINARY MEDICINE

1935-29 **Schmid**, Günther. "Goethe. Botan. Vortr. 8 April 1807."
Halle-Giebichenstein: privately printed, 1935. 4 pp.
/EDITION/BOTANY

1935-30 **Schmid**, Günther. "Goethe und die Mühlsteine." *Hallische
Nachrichten*, 47, No. 268 (1935) 15 November 1935, 5.
/TECHNOLOGY/GEOLOGY

1935-31 **Schmid**, Günther. "Physisch-chemisch-mechanisches Problem.
Entstehungsgeschichte des Goetheschen Aufsatzes." *Archiv für das
Studium der neueren Sprachen*, 168 [NS 68] (1935), 161-9.
/EDITIONS

1935-32 **Schmid**, Günther. "Über die Herkunft der Ausdrücke Mor-
phologie und Biologie. Geschichtliche Zusammenhänge." *Nova Acta
Leopoldina: Abhandlungen der Leopoldinisch-Carolinisch Deutschen
Akademie der Naturforscher*, 2 (1935), 597-620.
/MORPHOLOGY/BIOLOGY/LANGUAGE

1935-33 **Steiner**, Rudolf. *Colour*. Intro. Marie Steiner. London: Rudolf
Steiner Publishing Co./New York, Anthroposophic Press, 1935. 176
pp.
English trans. of No. 1928-51.
Cf. No. 1970-40.
/RESEARCH: CHROMATICS

1935-34 **Stewart**, Charles David. "Two Men of Mark." In his *Fellow
Creatures*. Boston: Little, Brown, and Company, 1935, pp. 237-43.
Rpt. of No. 1932-313.
/CUVIER, G/BOTANY

1935-35 **Troll**, Wilhelm. "Die Wiedergeburt der Morphologie aus dem
Geiste deutscher Wissenschaft." *Zeitschrift für die gesamte Naturwis-
senschaft einschließlich Naturphilosophie und Geschichte der Natur-
wissenschaft und Medizin*, 1 (1935/1936), 349-56.
Rpt. Nos. 1937-61, 1941-32 and 1967-51.
/METHOD/RESEARCH: BOTANY/RESEARCH: MORPHOL-
OGY

1935-36 **Wagner**, Karl. "Goethes Farbenlehre und Schopenhauers Farbentheorie." *Jahrbuch der Schopenhauer-Gesellschaft*, 1935, pp. 92-
176.

Rev. Kurt Hildebrandt, *Zeitschrift für d. ges. Naturwissensch. (Braunschweig)*, 2 (1936/1937), 329-31.
/CHROMATICS/SCHOPENHAUER, A/NEWTON, I

1935-37 **Wolf**, K[arl]. Lothar, and H[?]. G. **Trieschmann.** "Kepler, Newton und Goethe: Aus der Abteilung für Geschichte der Naturwissenschaften des Instituts für Physikalische Chemie und Elektrochemie der Universität Kiel." *Zeitschrift für die gesamte Naturwissenschaft einschließlich Naturphilosophie und Geschichte der Naturwissenschaft und Medizin*, 1 (1935/1936), 71-3.
/CHROMATICS/NEWTON, I/KEPLER, J

1935-38 **Zambonini**, Ferruccio. "Schopenhauer und die modernen Naturwissenschaften. Schopenhauer und Goethe." *Jahrbuch der Schopenhauer-Gesellschaft*, 1935, pp. 51-91.
/SCHOPENHAUER, A/CHROMATICS

1936-1 **Böker**, Hans. "Goethes Beziehungen zur Anatomie und zum Anatomischen Institut zu Jena." *Sudhoffs Archiv für Geschichte der Medizin und der Naturwissenschaften*, 29 (1936), 123-35.
/ANATOMY/INSTITUTIONS: ANATOMISCHES INSTITUT JENA

1936-2 **Böker**, Hans. "Was ist Ganzheitsdenken in der Morphologie?" *Zeitschrift für die gesamte Naturwissenschaft einschließlich Naturphilosophie und Geschichte der Naturwissenschaft und Medizin*, 2 (1936/1937), 253-76.
/RESEARCH: MORPHOLOGY/MORPHOLOGY

1936-3 **Broekman**, R[?]. W. "Goethe als Wissenschaftler und seine besondere Beschäftigung mit dem 'Os intermaxillare'." *Zahnärztliche Rundschau: Wochenblatt für die gesamte Zahnheilkunde* [etc.], 45 (1936), cols. 1297-1304; 1499-1504.
/OSTEOLOGY

1936-4 **Deichgräber**, Karl. "Goethe und Hippokrates." *Sudhoffs Archiv für Geschichte der Medizin und der Naturwissenschaften*, 29 (1936), 27-56.
/HIPPOCRATES/MEDICINE

1936-5 **Fairley**, Barker. "Goethe's Attitude to Science." *Bulletin of the John Rylands Library Manchester*, 20 (1936), 297-311.
Rpt. No. 1984-19.
"A lecture delivered in the John Rylands Library on the 11th

March, 1936."
/GENERAL INTRODUCTION

1936-6 **Gausewitz**, Walter. "Optic and Acoustic Phenomena in the Poetic Works of Goethe and Schiller." Diss. The University of Wisconsin 1936. [W 1936, 92]
    Abstract in *Summaries of Doctoral Dissertations: University of Wisconsin*, vol. 1, pp. 323-4.
    /CHROMATICS/SENSORY PHYSIOLOGY/SCHILLER, F

1936-7 **Grohmann**, Gerbert. "Studien am Oberarmknochen." *Das Goetheanum*, 15 (1936), 332.
    /RESEARCH: OSTEOLOGY

1936-8 **Haupt**, Hans. "Das Homologieprinzip bei Richard Owen." *Sudhoffs Archiv für Geschichte der Medizin und der Naturwissenschaften*, 28 (1936), 143-228.
    /OSTEOLOGY/OWEN, R

1936-9 **Hecker**, Max. "Ein neu gefundenes Goethe-Gedicht." *Goethe*, 1 (1936), 62-5.
    "So wie ich weiß,/Hieß es Granit-Gneis. . ."
    /EDITION/GEOLOGY

1936-10 *****Heinemann**, F[ritz]. "La méthode phénoménologique de Goethe." Privately printed. Lille, 1936.
    Rpt. No. 1936-11.
    /METHOD/EPISTEMOLOGY/PHENOMENOLOGY

1936-11 **Heinemann**, F[ritz]. "La méthode phénoménologique de Goethe." *Revue d'Histoire de la Philosophie et d'Histoire Générale de la Civilisation*, NS 16 (1936), 326-50.
    Rpt. of No. 1936-10.
    /METHOD/EPISTEMOLOGY/PHENOMENOLOGY

1936-12 **Husemann**, Friedrich. *Goethe und die Heilkunst: Betrachtungen zur Krise in der Medizin*. Dresden: Verlag Emil Weises Buchhandlung (Karl Eymann)[, 1936]. 176 pp.
    Rpt. of No. 1935-14.
    Rev. R. Schubert, *Das Goetheanum*, 15 (1936), 206.
    /MEDICINE/RESEARCH: MEDICINE/STEINER, R

1936-13 **Julius**, F[rits]. H[endrik]. *Goetheanistische chemie: Een bijdrage tot een niet-atomistische natuurbeschouwing*. Vrije opvoed-

kunst serie, 4. Delft: G. Niessen, 1936. 112 pp.
Trans. into German, No. 1965-16.
In Dutch.
/RESEARCH: CHEMISTRY

1936-14 *Kern, Hans. "Vulkan besiegt Neptun." *Berliner Börsen-Zeitung*, No. 140, 17 June 1936.
Rpt. of No. 1935-15.
/GEOLOGY

1936-15 Krause, Franz. "Eine Differenz zwischen Goethe und Purkynê." *Das Goetheanum*, 15 (1936), 348-50; 362-4.
/PURKYNE, J/CHROMATICS

1936-16 Krause, Franz. "Johann Evangelista Purkynês Weg zu Goethe: *(Ein Nachtrag)*." *Das Goetheanum*, 15 (1936), 30-31.
Cf. No. 1936-17.
/PURKYNE, J/CHROMATICS

1936-17 Krause, Franz. *Weg und Welt des Goetheanisten Johannes Evangelista Purkyne*. Basel: Rudolf Geering Verlag, 1936. 148 pp.
Cf. No. 1936-16.
Trans. into Czech, No. 1937-37.
/PURKYNE, J/CHROMATICS

1936-18 Lipps, Hans. "Goethes Farbenlehre: Ansätze zu einer Interpretation." *Jahrbuch des Freien Deutschen Hochstifts*, 1936/1940, pp. 123-38.
"Der Aufsatz ist die Ausarbeitung eines Vortrags, den ich im Februar 1939 in Rom in der Kulturabteilung des Kaiser-Wilhelm-Instituts für Kunst- und Kulturwissenschaft gehalten habe."
/CHROMATICS

1936-19 Locher, Louis. "Goethes Verhältnis zur Mathematik." *Das Goetheanum*, 15 (1936), 227-30.
"Nach einem Sektionsvortrag am Internationalen Mathematiker-Kongress in Oslo (Juli 1936)."
/MATHEMATICS

1936-20 Matthaei, Rupprecht. "Goethes biologische Farbenlehre." *Goethe*, 1 (1936), 42-54.
/CHROMATICS

1936-21 **Moser**, Otto. "Die goetheanistischen Maler." *Das Goetheanum*, 15 (1936), 130-31.
/FINE ARTS/RESEARCH: CHROMATICS

1936-22 **Ostwald**, Wilhelm. *Er und ich*. Leipzig: Theodor Martins Textilverlag, 1936. 112 pp. 13 figures.
/RESEARCH: CHROMATICS/CHROMATICS

1936-23 **Proskauer**, H[einrich]. O. "Versuch einer Verarbeitung grundlegender Hinweise Rudolf Steiners in seinen naturwissenschaftlichen Arbeiten." *Das Goetheanum*, 15 (1936), 188-90.
/RESEARCH: CHROMATICS/STEINER, R

1936-24 **Richter**, Manfred. "Das Schrifttum über Goethes Farbenlehre mit besonderer Berücksichtigung der naturwissenschaftlichen Probleme." Diss. Technische Hochschule Dresden 1936. 110 pp.
Rpt. No. 1938-18.
/BIBLIOGRAPHY/CHROMATICS/RECEPTION

1936-25 **Rüchardt**, Eduard. "Eine Entdeckung von Goethes Kammerdiener Stadelmann." *Die Naturwissenschaften: Wochenschrift für die Fortschritte der reinen und der angewandten Naturwissenschaften*, 24 (1936), 353-6.
/CHROMATICS/STADELMANN, J

1936-26 **Ruska**, Julius. "Nachlese zum Briefwechsel Goethe-Nees von Esenbeck." *Sudhoffs Archiv für Geschichte der Medizin und der Naturwissenschaften*, 28 (1936), 365-80.
/NEES VON ESENBECK, C/BOTANY/NATUR-PHILOSOPHIE

1936-27 **Scherer**, Christoph. *Zum Briefwechsel zwischen Goethe und Johannes Müller: Eine wissenschaftsgeschichtliche Untersuchung*. Bamberg: C. C. Buchners Verlag, 1936. vi, 70 pp.
/EDITION/MÜLLER, J/SENSORY PHYSIOLOGY /CHROMATICS

1936-28 **Steffen**, Albert. "Gladstones Verhältnis zu Goethes Farbenlehre." *Das Goetheanum*, 15 (1936), 10-11.
/GLADSTONE, W/CHROMATICS

1936-29 **Stüve**, Rudolf. "Goethe und die Naturwissenschaft." Osnabrück: Carl Prelle, 1936. 33 pp.
Rpt. of No. 1932-321.

/GENERAL INTRODUCTION

1936-30 **Takeda**, T[?]. ["Goethes Naturanschauung, betrachtet vom Standpunkt der neuen Sachlichkeit."] *Goethe-Jahrbuch: Die Goethe-Gesellschaft in Japan*, 5 (1936), 124ff.
In Japanese.
/GENERAL INTRODUCTION

1936-31 **Tischner**, Rudolf. "Goethe als Mitentdecker der biologischen Reizregel. (Biologisches Grundgesetz.)" *Zeitschrift für Deutsche Philologie*, 61 (1936), 55-8.
/BIOLOGY/PHYSIOLOGY

1936-32 *****Tischner**, Rudolf. "Goethe und das 'Biologische Grundgesetz'." *Allgemeine homöopathische Zeitung*, 1936, pp. 402-10.
/BIOLOGY

1936-33 *****Trapp**, Marianne. *Goethes naturwissenschaftliches Denken*. Giessen: n.p. 1936.
/GENERAL INTRODUCTION

1936-34 **Vogel**, Werner. "Goethe und Loder." *Goethe-Kalender auf das Jahr 1936*. Leipzig: Dieterich'sche Verlagsbuchhandlung, pp. 211-19.
/LODER, J [VON]/MEDICINE

1936-35 **Wilhelmsmeyer**, Hans. *Carl Gustav Carus als Erbe und Deuter Goethes*. Neue Deutsche Forschungen, Abteilung Neuere Deutsche Literaturgeschichte, 8. Inaug.-Diss., Kiel. Berlin: Junker und Dünnhaupt Verlag, 1936. 102 pp.
/CARUS, C/RECEPTION/MEDICINE/NATURPHILOSOPHIE

1936-36 **Winderlich**, Rudolf. "Goethe und die Leuchtsteine." *Chemiker-Zeitung*, 60 (1936), 188.
/CHEMISTRY

1937-1 **[anon.]** "'Am farb'gen Abglanz haben wir das Leben!' Naturforscher Goethe zwischen seinem Rüstzeug -- Eine faustische Welt." *Hallische Nachrichten*, No. 97, 27 April 1937.
/CHROMATICS/EXHIBITION/INSTITUTIONS: GOETHE-NATIONALMUSEUM WEIMAR

1937-2 **[anon.]** "Goethes Farbenkreis auf der Glasscheibe." *Hamburger Tageblatt*, No. 138, 25 May 1937.

/CHROMATICS/EXHIBITION/INSTITUTIONS: GOETHE-
NATIONALMUSEUM WEIMAR

1937-3 [anon.] "Goethes Farbenkreis auf der Glasscheibe." *Kurhess-
ische Landes-Zeitung*, No. 120, 27 May 1937.
/CHROMATICS

1937-4 [anon.] "Goethes Farbenkreis auf der Glasscheibe." *Schlesische
Tages-Zeitung (Breslau)*, No. 143, 27 May 1937.
/CHROMATICS/EXHIBITION/INSTITUTIONS: GOETHE-
NATIONALMUSEUM WEIMAR

1937-5 [anon.] "Goethes Farbenkreis leuchtet auf." *Thüringische Gau-
Zeitung*, No. 113, 19 May 1937.
/CHROMATICS/EXHIBITION/INSTITUTIONS: GOETHE-
NATIONALMUSEUM WEIMAR

1937-6 [anon.] "Goethes Farbenlehre demonstriert." *Berliner Tageblatt*,
No. 239, 23 May 1937.
/CHROMATICS/EXHIBITION/INSTITUTIONS: GOETHE-
NATIONALMUSEUM WEIMAR

1937-7 [anon.] "Goethes Farbenlehre experimentell dargestellt." *Dres-
dener Neueste Nachrichten*, No. 114, 19 May 1937.
/CHROMATICS/EXHIBITION/INSTITUTIONS: GOETHE-
NATIONALMUSEUM WEIMAR

1937-8 [anon.] "Goethes Farbenlehre in zeitnaher Darstellung."
Hakenkreuzbanner (Mannheim), No. 232, 24 May 1937.
/CHROMATICS/EXHIBITION/INSTITUTIONS: GOETHE-
NATIONALMUSEUM WEIMAR

1937-9 [anon.] "Goethes Farbenlehre wird demonstriert." *Allgemeine
Thüringische Landes-Zeitung*, No. 132, 19 May 1937.
/CHROMATICS/EXHIBITION/INSTITUTIONS: GOETHE-
NATIONALMUSEUM WEIMAR

1937-10 [anon.] "Goethes Farbenlehre wird demonstriert." *Eisenacher
Tagespost*, No. 114, 19 May 1937.
/CHROMATICS/EXHIBITION/INSTITUTIONS: GOETHE-
NATIONALMUSEUM WEIMAR

1937-11 **Böttcher**, Otto. "Runge und Goethe." In *Philipp Otto Runge:
Sein Leben, Wirken und Schaffen*. Friedrichsen, de Gruyter & Co.,

1937, pp. 107-119.
/RUNGE, P/FINE ARTS/RESEARCH: CHROMATICS

1937-12 **Bonte**, Hans Georg. "Goethes Farbenlehre in Weimar jetzt volkstümlich dargestellt." *Stettiner General-Anzeiger*, No. 140, 22 May 1937.
/CHROMATICS/EXHIBITION/INSTITUTIONS: GOETHE-NATIONALMUSEUM WEIMAR

1937-13 **Bonte**, Hans Georg. "Im Weimarer Museum: Goethes Farbenlehre." *Braunschweiger Neueste Nachrichten*, No. 115, 21 May 1937.
/CHROMATICS/EXHIBITION/INSTITUTIONS: GOETHE-NATIONALMUSEUM WEIMAR

1937-14 **Bonte**, Hans Georg. "Die neue Darstellung der Farbenlehre im Goethe-National-Museum." *Berliner Börsen-Zeitung*, No. 232, 21 May 1937.
/CHROMATICS/EXHIBITION/INSTITUTIONS: GOETHE-NATIONALMUSEUM WEIMAR

1937-15 **Englert-Faye**, C. "Beiträge zu einer Goetheanistischen Geschichtswissenschaft: Entstehen und Vergehen, Werden und Wandel im Geschichtlichen Leben." *Das Goetheanum*, 16 (1937), 182-3; 198-9; 206-8; 215-16.
"Vorgelegt in einem Vortrag an der Ostertagung am Goetheanum in Dornach 1937."
/RESEARCH: HISTORIOGRAPHY

1937-16 **Feldkeller**, Paul. "'Am farbigen Abglanz haben wir das Leben.'" *Hamburger Anzeiger*, No. 115, 21 May 1937.
/CHROMATICS/EXHIBITION/INSTITUTIONS: GOETHE-NATIONALMUSEUM WEIMAR

1937-17 **Feldkeller**, Paul. "Der gerechtfertigte Goethe." *Deutsche Allgemeine Zeitung*, No. 233, 23 May 1937.
/CHROMATICS/EXHIBITION/INSTITUTIONS: GOETHE-NATIONALMUSEUM WEIMAR

1937-18 **Feldkeller**, Paul. "Goethe wird entdeckt." *General-Anzeiger [Frankfurt a. M.]*, No. 117, 24 May 1937.
/CHROMATICS/EXHIBITION/INSTITUTIONS: GOETHE-NATIONALMUSEUM WEIMAR

1937-19 **Feldkeller**, Paul. "Goethe wird entdeckt." *Westfälischer Kurier (Hamm)*, No. 120, 26 May 1937.
/CHROMATICS/EXHIBITION/INSTITUTIONS: GOETHE-NATIONALMUSEUM WEIMAR

1937-20 **Feldkeller**, Paul. "Goethe wird gerechtfertigt." *Die Zeit (Prag)*, No. 124, 28 May 1937.
/CHROMATICS/EXHIBITION/INSTITUTIONS: GOETHE-NATIONALMUSEUM WEIMAR

1937-21 **Feldkeller**, Paul. "Tagung der Goethe-Gesellschaft -- Erste exakte Darstellung der 'Farbenlehre'." *Danziger Neueste Nachrichten*, No. 249, 23 May 1937.
/CHROMATICS/EXHIBITION/INSTITUTIONS: GOETHE-NATIONALMUSEUM WEIMAR

1937-22 **Feldkeller**, Paul. "Tagung der Goethe-Gesellschaft -- Erste exakte Darstellung der 'Farbenlehre'." *Magdeburgische Zeitung*, No. 249, 20 May 1937.
/CHROMATICS/EXHIBITION/INSTITUTIONS: GOETHE-NATIONALMUSEUM WEIMAR

1937-23 **Ferrannini**, Andrea. "Volfango Goethe scienziato [Goethe as a Scientist]." *Riforma medica*, 53 (1937), 804.
In Italian.
/GENERAL INTRODUCTION

1937-24 **Fricke**, Hermann. "Goethes Schwerkrafttheorie der Meteorologie in neuer Begründung." *Natur und Geist: Monatshefte für Wissenschaft, Weltanschauung und Lebensgestaltung*, 5 (1937), 336-42.
/METEOROLOGY

1937-25 **Fuchs**, Fr[itz]. "Grün und Pfirsichblüt." *Das Goetheanum*, 16 (1937), 174-5.
Cf. continuation, No. 1939-7.
/CHROMATICS/WORKS: FAUST

1937-26 [**Goethe**, J. W. von.] "Aus Goethes Einführung in seine *Farbenlehre*." *Goethe*, NS 2 (1937), 82-3.
/EDITION: SELECTIONS

1937-27 **Goethe**, Johann Wolfgang von. "Über den Bologneser Spat." Ed. and comm. Günther Schmid. Burg Giebichenstein: Werkstätten

der Stadt Halle, 1937. 45 pp.
/EDITION/GEOLOGY

1937-28 [**Goethe**, J. W. von.] "Weisheit aus der *Farbenlehre*." *Goethe*, NS 2 (1937), 81.
/EDITION: SELECTIONS

1937-29 **Goethe** *und Rudolf Steiner: Auferstehungskräfte in Kunst und Wissenschaft*. Bühnenkunst am Goetheanum, 4. Dornach: Sektion für redende und musikalische Künste am Goetheanum, 1937. 55 pp.
/STEINER, R/ANTHROPOSOPHY/RESEARCH: FINE ARTS

1937-30 **Grohmann**, Gerbert. *Blüten-Metamorphosen: Metamorphosen im Pflanzenreich. Band 2.* Dresden: Verlag Emil Weises Buchhandlung (Karl Eymann), 1937. 165 pp.
Rev. Hermann Poppelbaum, "'Blüten-Metamorphosen', ein Schulungsbuch," *Das Goetheanum*, 16 (1937), 144-5.
/RESEARCH: BOTANY

1937-31 **Hug**, Willy. "Die Metamorphose der Schmetterlinge: (Ein Beitrag zur Neugestaltung der Insektenkunde)." *Das Goetheanum*, 16 (1937), 303-5.
/RESEARCH: ENTOMOLOGY

1937-32 **Jäckle**, Erwin. "Goethes Morphologie und Schellings Weltseele." *Deutsche Vierteljahresschrift für Literaturwissenschaft und Geistesgeschichte*, 15 (1937), 295-330.
/MORPHOLOGY/SCHELLING, F VON/NATUR-PHILOSOPHIE

1937-33 **Jaensch**, Erich. "Gefühl und Empfindung: Untersuchungen ihres Verhältnisses am Beispiel des Lichtsinns." *Forschungen und Fortschritte*, 13 (1937), 44-6.
/RESEARCH: CHROMATICS

1937-34 **Jakob**, Christfried. "Goethe in der Biologie." *Lasso: Deutschsüdamerikanische Monatsschrift*, 4 (1937), 509-14.
/BIOLOGY

1937-35 **Jost**, H[?]. E. "Das Ergebnis der Goethe-Tagung in Weimar." *Schlesische Zeitung*, No. 247, 20 May 1937.
/CHROMATICS/EXHIBITION/INSTITUTIONS: GOETHE-NATIONALMUSEUM WEIMAR

1937-36 **Knopf**, Otto. "Von der Gründung der Herzoglichen Sternwarte [1811] bis zu Ludwig Schröns Tod." In his *Die Astronomie an der Universität Jena von der Gründung der Universität im Jahre 1558 bis zur Entpflichtung des Verfassers im Jahre 1927.* Zeitschrift des Vereins für Thuringische Geschichte und Altertumskunde, Beiheft 19: Beiträge zur Geschichte der Universität Jena, 7. Jena: Verlag von Gustav Fischer, 1937, pp. 116-81.
/ASTRONOMY/METEOROLOGY/INSTITUTIONS: HER-ZOGLICHE STERNWARTE, WEIMAR

1937-37 *****Krause**, Franz. *Goethovec Jan Evangelista Purkyne [J. E. Purkyne, Goethean].* Trans. Bozena Jirankova. Brno, 1937.
Czech trans. of No. 1936-17.
/PURKYNE, J/RESEARCH: MEDICINE/RESEARCH: CHROMATICS

1937-38 **Krause**, Franz. "Medizinische Anschauungen J. E. Purkynes im Zusammenhang mit Goethes Farbenlehre." *Das Goetheanum*, 16 (1937), 350-52; 358-9.
/PURKYNE, J/RESEARCH: MEDICINE/RESEARCH: CHROMATICS

1937-39 *****Krause**, Franz. *Purkyne. Fünf Bilder aus dem Leben eines Goetheanisten.* 1937.
/PURKYNE, J/RESEARCH: MEDICINE/RESEARCH: CHROMATICS

1937-40 **Lobeck**, Fritz. "Aus: 'Erfahrungen mit Goethes Farbenlehre'." *Das Goetheanum*, 16 (1937), 400-401.
Partial rpt. of No. 1937-41.
/RESEARCH: CHROMATICS

1937-41 **Lobeck**, Fritz. *Erfahrungen mit Goethes Farbenlehre an Iris, Halo, Hof.* Leipzig/Straßburg/Zürich: Heitz & Co., 1937. ii, 147 pp.
Rpt. (partial) No. 1937-40.
Rev. Hermann Hiltsbrunner, *Neue Zürcher Zeitung*, 19 October 1937 (rpt. *Das Goetheanum*, 16 (1937), 362-3).
/RESEARCH: CHROMATICS

1937-42 **Locher-Ernst**, Louis. *Urphänomene der Geometrie Erster Teil.* Zürich: Orell Füssli Verlag, 1937.
Rpt. No. 1980-40.
Rev. Georg Unger, *Das Goetheanum*, 16 (1937), 393-4.

/RESEARCH: MATHEMATICS

1937-43 **Matthaei**, Rupprecht. "Die neue Darbietung der Farbenlehre im Goethe-Nationalmuseum." *Goethe*, NF 2 (1937), 84-108.
/CHROMATICS/EXHIBITION/INSTITUTIONS: GOETHE-NATIONALMUSEUM WEIMAR

1937-44 *****Meesen**, Hubert J[oseph]. "Beiträge zur Frage der Beziehungen zwischen Goethes polarem Denken und dichterischem Schaffen." Diss. Univ. of Wisconsin 1937. [W 1937, 94].
Abstract in *Summaries of Doctoral Dissertations: University of Wisconsin*, vol. 2, pp. 327-9.
/METHOD/EPISTEMOLOGY/WORKS: VARIOUS

1937-45 **Möbius**, Martin. *Geschichte der Botanik: Von den ersten Anfängen bis zur Gegenwart*. Jena: Verlag von Gustav Fischer, 1937. vi, 458 pp.
Goethe *passim*.
/BOTANY/RECEPTION/HISTORY OF SCIENCE

1937-46 *****Möbius**, Martin. "Goethes Stellung in der Botanik." *Proteus*, 2 (1937), 218-9.
Apparently a report on a lecture.
/BOTANY/RECEPTION/HISTORY OF SCIENCE

1937-47 *****Pastor**, E[?]. "Die Wolken, Howard und Goethe." *Wacht im Osten*, 4, No. 8/9 (1937), 345-54.
/METEOROLOGY/HOWARD, L

1937-48 **Poppelbaum**, Hermann. *Tier-Wesenskunde*. Dresden: Verlag Emil Weises, Buchhandlung (Karl Eymann), 1937. 264 pp.
Rpt. No. 1954-33.
Rev. Gerbert Grohmann, *Das Goetheanum*, 16 (1937), 118-20.
/RESEARCH: ZOOLOGY

1937-49 **Poppelbaum**, Hermann. "Vögel und Fische." *Das Goetheanum*, 16 (1937), 241.
"Aus dem hervorragenden Werke von Hermann Poppelbaum: Tier-Wesenskunde, Verlag Emil Weises Buchhandlung, Dresden." [see No. 1937-48.]
/RESEARCH: ZOOLOGY

1937-50 *****Rozbroj**, Hugo. "Jean-Paul Marat (1743-93), ein Naturforscher und Revolutionär, sein Zusammentreffen in der Geisteswelt mit

Goethe, Lamarck, Rousseau, u.a." Diss. Berlin 1937.
Cf. No. 1937-51.
/MARAT, J/CHROMATICS/METHOD

1937-51 **Rozbroj**, Hugo. *Jean-Paul Marat (1743-93): Ein Naturforscher und Revolutionär, sein Zusammentreffen in der Geisteswelt mit Goethe, Lamarck, Rousseau, u.a.* Historische Studien, 315. Berlin: Verlag Dr. Emil Ebering, 1937. 136 pp.
Cf. No. 1937-50.
/MARAT, J/CHROMATICS/METHOD

1937-52 **Schiller**, Paul Eugen. "Die farbigen Schatten." *Das Goetheanum*, 16 (1937), 296-8.
/RESEARCH: CHROMATICS/CHROMATICS

1937-53 **Schiller**, Paul Eugen. "Phänomene, die den farbigen Schatten zugrunde liegen." *Das Goetheanum*, 16 (1937), 254-6.
/RESEARCH: CHROMATICS

1937-54 **Schiller**, Paul Eugen. "Zur Frage der farbigen Schatten." *Das Goetheanum*, 16 (1937), 238-41.
/RESEARCH: CHROMATICS

1937-55 **Schmid**, Günther. *Goethe, Thüringer Laboranten und ein Faustsagenfragment.* Halle (Saale): Max Niemeyer Verlag, 1937. 67 pp.
/PLACES: THÜRINGEN/PHARMACOLOGY/WORKS: FAUST

1937-56 **Schmid**, Günther. "Schicksal einer Goetheschrift: Druckge-schichtliche Funde zur Farbenlehre." Burg Giebichenstein: Werk-stätten der Stadt Halle[, 1937]. 36 pp.
Rev. R. Matthaei, *Goethe*, 3 (1938), 220-23.
Rev. Friedrich Kreis, *Zentralblatt für Bibliothekswesen*, 56 (1939), 499-500.
Rev. Hubert Butterwege, *Germania*, 23 July 1938, No. 201.
/CHROMATICS/EDITIONS

1937-57 **Schmitthenner**, Heinrich. "Carl Ritter und Goethe." *Geographische Zeitschrift*, 43 (1937), 161-75.
/RITTER, C

1937-58 **Speiser**, A[ndreas]. "Goethes Farbenlehre." In his *Die mathematische Denkweise.* Zürich/Leipzig/Stuttgart: Rascher & Co. AG,

1937, pp. 78-85.
Rpt. of No. 1932-295.
/CHROMATICS

1937-59 **Stettner**, Thomas. "Goethe und die Botanik." In his *Von Blumen, Bäumen, Botanikern: Plaudereien*. Ansbach: Verlag C. Brügel & Sohn, 1937, pp. 49-58.
/BOTANY/ROUSSEAU, J

1937-60 **Troll**, Wilhelm. "Die Urpflanze." In his *Vegetationsorgane Erster Teil*. Vol. I. of *Vergleichende Morphologie der höheren Pflanzen*. Berlin: Verlag von Gebrüder Borntraeger, 1937, pp. 53-9.
Rpt. No. 1967-50.
/RESEARCH: BOTANY/BOTANY

1937-61 **Troll**, Wilhelm. "Die Wiedergeburt der Morphologie aus dem Geiste deutscher Wissenschaft." In his *Vegetationsorgane Erster Teil*. Vol. I. of *Vergleichende Morphologie der höheren Pflanzen*. Berlin: Verlag von Gebrüder Borntraeger, 1937, pp. 1-8.
Rpt. of No. 1935-35.
/METHOD/RESEARCH: BOTANY/RESEARCH: MORPHOLOGY

1937-62 **Tunell**, G. and E. **Posnjak**. "The Stability Relations of Goethite and Hematite." *Economic Geology and the Bulletin of the Society of Economic Geology [Lancaster, Pa.]*, 26 (1937), 337-43; 894-8.
/GEOLOGY

1937-63 **Urzidil**, Johannes. "Goethe und J. E. Purkyne." *Prager Rundschau*, 7 (1937), 432-43.
/PURKYNE, J/CHROMATICS/RESEARCH: CHROMATICS

1937-64 *****Urzidil**, Johannes. "Goethe und J. E. Purkyne." Prag: priv. printed, 1937. 12 pp.
/PURKYNE, J/CHROMATICS/RESEARCH: CHROMATICS

1937-65 **Vincent**, Ernst. *J. W. Goethe: Auge und Ahnung: Über die Natur*. Deutsche Reihe, 51. Jena: Eugen Diedrichs Verlag[, 1937]. 77, i pp.
/GENERAL INTRODUCTION

1938-1 **Barthel**, Ernst. "Komplementarische Wellenmechanik: Rechtfertigung der Goetheschen Farbenlehre." *Jahrbuch der Elsass-Lothringischen Wissenschaftlichen Gesellschaft zu Strassburg*, 11

(1938), 240-51.
/CHROMATICS/RESEARCH: CHROMATICS

1938-2 **Brandt**, Walter. "Goethes Typusbegriff und die moderne Entwicklungsmechanik. Naturwissenschaftlicher Bericht [32]." *Frankfurter Zeitung*, 17 February 1938.
    In Mappe III E 61/C20: "Goethe und die Naturwissenschaften. Zeitungsausschnitte 1913 -" at the Frankfurter Goethe-Museum.
    /BIOLOGY: EVOLUTION/MORPHOLOGY

1938-3 **Carus**, Carl Gustav. "Goethe und seine Bedeutung für diese und die künftige Zeit." In *Carl Gustav Carus 1789 bis 1869*. Vol. 6.1 of his *Gesammelte Schriften*. Ed. W. Keiper. Berlin: W. Keiper Verlag, 1938, pp. 4-32.
    Rpt. of No. 1849-2.
    /GENERAL INTRODUCTION

1938-4 **Freelance**, Pandora [Kathleen Mary **Housden**]. *Fool's Paradise or from Crooked Spectrum to Crooked Cross: A Short Study of Goethe's Theory of Colours and His Struggle Against Unreason being a Challenge to the Brains Trust*. Girton, Cambs.: The Shuttle Press, 1938. 108 pp.
    L of C PT 2208.C7H6.1938
    /CHROMATICS/NEWTON, I

1938-5 **Fudjinami**, K[?]. ["Goethe als Naturforscher."] *Goethe*, NF 3 (1938), 104.
    Synopsis of No. 1932-100.
    /GENERAL INTRODUCTION

1938-6 **Goethe**, J. W. *Auge und Ahnung: Über die Natur*. Sel. Ernst Vincent. Deutsche Reihe, 51. Jena: Eugen Diederichs Verlag, 1938. 77 pp.
    /EDITION: SELECTIONS

1938-7 **Goethe**[, J. W. von]. "Hallisches Salz." [Burg Giebichenstein: Werkstätten der Stadt Halle, 1938.] [1] p.
    /GEOLOGY

1938-8 **Haga**, M[?]. ["Goethes naturwissenschaftliche Methode."] *Goethe-Jahrbuch: Die Goethe-Gesellschaft in Japan*, 7 (1938), 99-118.
    In Japanese.

/METHOD

1938-9 **Husemann**, Friedrich. *Goethe and the Art of Healing: A Commentary on the Crisis in Medicine.* Trans. R. K. MacKaye and A. Goudschaal. London: The Rudolf Steiner Publishing Co./New York: Anthroposophic Press[, 1938]. viii, 165 pp.
Partial rpt., No. 1976-30.
English trans. of No. 1935-14.
/MEDICINE/RESEARCH: MEDICINE

1938-10 **Jablonski**, Walter. *Goethe e le scienze naturali: Saggi [Goethe and the Natural Sciences].* Biblioteca di cultura moderna, 315. Bari: Guis. Laterza & Figli, 1938. 289 pp.
In Italian.
Rev. G. V. Amoretti, *L'Italia che scrive*, 21, No. 4 (1938), 126.
Rev. R. Lange, *Il Loto*, 9 (1938), 39-41.
Rev. C. Luporini, *La Nuova Italia*, 9 (1938), 375-6.
/GENERAL INTRODUCTION

1938-11 **Julius**, F[rits]. H[endrik]. *Op de zoek naar den vorborgenen tuin: Een reeks natuurstudies op Goetheanistischen Grondslag [In Search of the Hidden Garden: A Series of Goethean Studies of Nature].* den Haag: priv. printed[, 1938].
Partial rpt., Nos. 1971-25, and 1971-26.
Partial trans. into German, Nos. 1985-53, 1985-54, 1985-55, 1985-56 and 1985-57.
In Dutch.
/RESEARCH: VARIOUS

1938-12 **Krause**, Franz. "Goethes Beziehungen zum Grafen Kaspar von Sternberg gestorben am 20. Dezember 1838." *Das Goetheanum*, 17 (1938), 228-30; 235-7.
/STERNBERG, K

1938-13 **Maurer**, Th[?]. "Eine Goetherede." *Das Goetheanum*, 17 (1938), 133-4.
/GENERAL INTRODUCTION

1938-14 **Morando**, F. Ernesto. "Wolfango Goethe e Leonardo da Vinci nella scienza e nell'amore [Goethe and da Vinci in Science and in Love]." *Le Opere e i Giorni*, 17, No. 5 (1938), 18-27.
Cf. continuation, No. 1938-15.
In Italian.
/DA VINCI, L

1938-15 **Morando**, F. Ernesto. "Wolfango Goethe e Leonardo da Vinci nella scienza e nell'amore [Goethe and da Vinci in Science and in Love]." *Le Opere e i Giorni*, 17, No. 6 (1938), 26-34.
Continuation of No. 1938-14.
In Italian.
/DA VINCI, L

1938-16 **[Puchtinger**, Franz.] "Goethes mineralogische Studien und der Steinschneider Müller." *Karlsbader Mitteilungen für die ärztliche Praxis*, 1 (1938), 14-17.
/MINERALOGY/MÜLLER, C

1938-17 **Purin**, C[?]. M. "Goethe und Russland." *Monatshefte*, 30 (1938), 110-19.
Cf. esp. pp. 118-19, "Wissenschaft."
/RECEPTION

1938-18 **Richter**, Manfred. *Das Schrifttum über Goethes Farbenlehre mit besonderer Berücksichtigung der naturwissenschaftlichen Probleme.* Berlin: Verlag Rudolph Pfau, 1938. ii, 110 pp.
Rpt. of No. 1936-24.
Cf. No. 1938-19.
Rev. Rupprecht Matthaei, *Goethe*, 3 (1938), 223.
Rev. Friedrich Kreis, *Zentralblatt für Bibliothekswesen*, 57 (1940), 178.
/BIBLIOGRAPHY/CHROMATICS/RECEPTION

1938-19 **Richter**, Manfred. "Überblick über die Schrifttumsgruppen über Goethes Farbenlehre." In his *Das Schrifttum über Goethes Farbenlehre mit besonderer Berücksichtigung der naturwissenschaftlichen Probleme.* Berlin: Verlag Rudolph Pfau, 1938, pp. 4-21.
/BIBLIOGRAPHY/CHROMATICS/RECEPTION

1938-20 *****Schierbeek**, A[?]. *Grote schrijvers als biologen. Een onbekende zijde van bekende mannen [Great Writers as Biologists. An Unknown Aspect of Well-known Men].* 's-Gravenhage: De Hofstad, 1938. 96 pp.
In Dutch.
/BIOLOGY/HISTORY OF SCIENCE

1938-21 **Schirmer-Behrendt**, Elisabet. "Noch einmal Goethe und die Veterinäranstalt in Jena." *Beiträge zur Geschichte der Veterinärmedizin*, 1 (1938), 153-63.

/INSTITUTIONS: TIERARZNEISCHULE JENA
/VETERINARY MEDICINE

1938-22 **Schlechta**, Karl. "Goethe in seinem Verhältnis zu Aristoteles."
Goethe, 3 (1938), 251-6.
/ARISTOTLE/INFLUENCES/PHILOSOPHY

1938-23 **Schlechta**, Karl. *Goethe in seinem Verhältnis zu Aristoteles: Ein*
Versuch. Frankfurter Studien zur Religion und Kultur der Antike, 16.
Frankfurt a. M.: Vittorio Klostermann, 1938. 136 pp.
Rev. C. G. Hardie, *J. Hellenic Stud.*, 59 (1939), 312-13.
/ARISTOTLE/INFLUENCES/PHILOSOPHY

1938-24 **Schmid**, Günther. "Aus der Frühgeschichte des botanischen
Gartens in München." *Sudhoffs Archiv für Geschichte der Medizin*
und der Naturwissenschaften, 31 (1938), 148-64.
/INSTITUTIONS: BOTANISCHER GARTEN, MÜNCHEN
/RIEMER, F

1938-25 **Schmid**, Günther. "Blumistik im klassischen Weimar." *Garten-*
flora, NS April-December 1938, pp. 57-60.
/BOTANY

1938-26 **Schnabel**, Franz. "Technik in Goethes Werk und Leben."
Frankfurter Zeitung, No. 411-12, 11 August 1938, 9.
/TECHNOLOGY

1938-27 **Steffens**, Henrik. "Goethe: Galls Demonstrationsobjekt. Nach
einem Bericht von Heinrich Steffens." *Frankfurter Zeitung*, 17 Feb-
ruary 1938.
"Aus Heinrich Steffens' 'Was ich erlebte', nach der Ausgabe im
Fritz-Eckhardt-Verlag, Leipzig, 1913."
In Mappe III E 61/C20: "Goethe und die Naturwissenschaften.
Zeitungsausschnitte 1913 -" at the Frankfurter Goethe-
Museum.
/GALL, F/NEUROLOGY

1938-28 **Steiner**, Rudolf. "Goetheanismus und Darwinismus." *Das*
Goetheanum, 17 (1938), 65-6.
"Aus einem Vortrag vom 26. Obtober 1917."
/BIOLOGY: EVOLUTION/DARWIN, C

1938-29 *"**Vorführung** entoptischer Gläser aus Goethes Nachlaß." *Sitz-*
ungsberichte der Physikalischen-medizinischen Sozietät zu Erlangen,

1938, pp. 27-31.
/OPTICS/GOETHE'S COLLECTIONS

1938-30 **Weyland**, Hermann. "Goethes Urpflanze vom stammesge-
schichtlichen Standpunkt gesehen." *Goethe*, NS 3 (1938), 181-93.
/BOTANY

1939-1 *__*Arndt**, Walther. "Goethe und die Schwämme." *Sitzungsberichte
der Gesellschaft Naturforschender Freunde.* Berlin: n.p., 1939
[1940], pp. 1-9.
/BIOLOGY

1939-2 *__*Bader**, Wilhelm. *Goethes Farbenlehre als Ausdruck seiner
Metaphysik.* Hamburg: Hansischer Gildenverlag, 1939. Diss. Ham-
burg. 66 pp.
Rev. Paul Schlager, *Goethe*, 6 (1941), 220.
/CHROMATICS/PHILOSOPHY

1939-3 **Baravalle**, Hermann von. "Feste Körper, Flüssigkeiten und
Gase." *Das Goetheanum*, 18 (1939), 26-7.
/RESEARCH: PHYSICS

1939-4 *__*Börnsen**, Hans. "Leibniz' Substanzbegriff und Goethes Gedanke
der Metamorphose." Diss. Hamburg 1939. iv, 115 pp.
/MORPHOLOGY/LEIBNIZ, G

1939-5 **Fricke**, Hermann. "Weltäther und Welträtsel: Goethe als
Physiker." In his *Weltätherforschung: Ein Aufbauprogramm nach
dem Umsturz in der Physik.* Weimar: Verlag Rudolf Borkmann,
1939, pp. 98-101.
/RESEARCH: PHYSICS/METEOROLOGY

1939-6 **Frieling**, Heinrich. *Die Sprache der Farben. Vom Wesen des
Lichts u. der Farben in Natur und Kunst.* München: Oldenbourg,
1939. 193 pp.
/CHROMATICS

1939-7 **Fuchs**, Fr[itz]. "Grün und Pfirsichblüt." *Das Goetheanum*, 18
(1939), 70-71.
Continuation of No. 1937-25.
/CHROMATICS/WORKS: FAUST

1939-8 **Fuchs**, Fr[itz]. "Pfirsichblüt." *Das Goetheanum*, 18 (1939), 85-
6.

/CHROMATICS

1939-9 **Fuchs**, Fr[itz]. "Physiologische Entstehung des Pfirsichblüt." *Das Goetheanum*, 18 (1939), 140.
/CHROMATICS

1939-10 [**Goethe**, J. W. von.] [**Tobler**, Georg Christoph?]. "Fragment über die Natur." Halle: privately printed, 1939. [12] pp.
Cf. No. 1939-27.
/EDITION

1939-11 ***Hartenstein**, Johannes Georg. "Auch als Naturforscher verdankt Goethe unserer Stadt wertvolle Anregungen." *Leipziger Beobachter*, 26 Aug. 1939.
/PLACES: LEIPZIG

1939-12 **Karell**, Victor. "Die Anfänge der Zettlitzer Kaolingewinnung." *Karlsbader historisches Jahrbuch für das Jahr 1939*, 1939, pp. 148-56.
/TECHNOLOGY

1939-13 **Kolbenheyer**, Erwin Guido. "Goethes Denkprinzipien und der biologische Naturalismus." In his *Der Einzelne und die Gemeinschaft: Goethes Denkprinzipien und der biologische Naturalismus: Zwei Reden*. München: Albert Langen/Georg Müller, 1939, pp. 13-25.
Rpt. No. 1982-99.
"Festansprache im Frankfurter Freien Deutschen Hochstift."
/EPISTEMOLOGY/BIOLOGY

1939-14 **Leiste**, Heinrich. "Goetheanistische Philosophie." *Das Goetheanum*, 18 (1939), 283-5.
/PHILOSOPHY/RESEARCH: PHILOSOPHY

1939-15 **Leiste**, Heinrich. "Neue Wege der Philosophie." *Das Goetheanum*, 18 (1939), 236-8.
/PHILOSOPHY/RESEARCH: PHILOSOPHY

1939-16 ***Lichtenberger**, Henri. "La valeur de la science d'après Goethe." In *Mélanges en l'honneur de Jules Legras*. Travaux publiés par l'Institut d'études slaves, 19. Paris: Librairie Droz, 1939, pp. 15-30.
/GENERAL INTRODUCTION

1939-17 **Lipps**, Hans. "Goethes Farbenlehre." Kaiser-Wilhelm-Institut für Kunst- und Kulturwissenschaft im Palazzo Zuccari, Rom: Veröffentlichungen der Abteilung für Kulturwissenschaft, erste Reihe, 16. Leipzig: Verlag Heinrich Keller, 1939. 14 pp.

> "Der Vortrag wurde in deutscher Sprach am 7. Februar 1939 in Rom gehalten."
> Rev. B. Croce, *La Critica*, 38 (1940), 255-6.
> /CHROMATICS

1939-18 **Matthaei**, Rupprecht. *Die Farbenlehre im Goethe-National- museum: Führer durch die neue Darbietung der Farbenlehre im Museum und das nachgelassene Gerät in Goethes Wohnhaus.* Jena: Verlag von Gustav Fischer, 1939. xii, 116 pp.

> Rpt. exp. edn. No. 1941-20.
> /CHROMATICS/EXHIBITION

1939-19 **Matthaei**, R[upprecht]. "Farbpapiere in besonderer Zusam- menstellung als Zubehör zu dem im Verlage Gustav Fischer, Jena, erschienenen Buch: Versuche zu Goethes Farbenlehre mit einfachen Mitteln." Jena: Verlag von Gustav Fischer[, 1939]. [30] pp.

> Accompaniment to No. 1939-21.
> /CHROMATICS

1939-20 **Matthaei**, Rupprecht. "Die ungeschriebenen Urkunden zu Goethes Farbenlehre." *Goethe*, 4 (1939), 312-15.

> /CHROMATICS

1939-21 **Matthaei**, R[upprecht]. *Versuche zu Goethes Farbenlehre mit einfachen Mitteln: Ein Aufreiß der Farbenlehre mit 32 Abbildungen im Text.* Jena: Verlag von Gustav Fischer, 1939. xvi, 130 pp.

> Cf. Nos. 1939-22 and 1939-19.
> /CHROMATICS

1939-22 **Matthaei**, R[upprecht]. "Zubehör für die im Verlage Gustav Fischer, Jena, erschienen Versuche zu Goethes Farbenlehre mit ein- fachen Mitteln." Jena: Verlag von Gustav Fischer[, 1939].

> Accompaniment to No. 1939-21.
> /CHROMATICS

1939-23 [**Mollweide**, Karl Brandan.] "Mollweide gegen Goethe." pri- vately printed[, 1939]. [4] pp.

> /CHROMATICS/MOLLWEIDE, K

1939-24 **Schierbeek**, A[?]. "Camper en Goethe over het tusschen-

kaaksbeen [Camper and Goethe on the Intermaxillary Bone]." *Neder-landsch Tijdschrift voor Geneeskunde*, 83 (1939), 2128-33.
In Dutch.
/OSTEOLOGY/CAMPER, P

1939-25 **Schmid**, Günther. "Ein Blumengedicht von Goethes 'wackerem Spiritus'." *Goethe*, NS 4 (1939), 91-7.
/GEIST, L/BOTANY

1939-26 **Schmid**, Günther. "Goethe und Mollweide in Halle." [Halle:], privately printed[, 1939].
/MOLLWEIDE, K/CHROMATICS/PLACES: HALLE

1939-27 **S[chmid]**., G[ünther]. "Nachwort." In [Goethe, J. W. von.] [Tobler, Georg Christoph?] "Fragment über die Natur." Halle: privately printed, 1939, p. [9].
/GENERAL INTRODUCTION

1939-28 **Schmid**, Günther. "Sammlung zur Erläuterung von Goethes Aufsatz 'Geschichte meines botanischen Studiums'." In *Jahres-versammlung der Gesellschaft der Bibliophilen (Weimar) gegr. 1899 in Halle (Saale) vom 30. Juni 1939: 400 Jahre Hallisches Büchersammeln: Katalog der von Hallischen Bibliophilen gemeinsam mit der Marienbibliothek, dem Städtischen Museum, der Ratsbücherei und dem Universitätsbibliothek veranstalteten Ausstellung im Rundturm der Moritzburg.* Ed. Bernhard Weissenborn. Halle: n.p., 1939, pp. 11-12.
/EXHIBITION

1939-29 **Schmidt**, Peter Heinrich. "Goethe als Geograph." Veröffentlichungen der Handels-Hochschule St. Gallen, Reihe B, 4. St. Gallen: Verlag der Fehr'schen Buchhandlung, 1939. 49 pp.
/GEOGRAPHY

1939-30 **Schoepf**, Hermann. "Der Geologe Goethe im Fichtelgebirge." *Das Raumbild*, 5, No. 9 (1939), 209-11.
/GEOLOGY/PLACES: FICHTELGEBIRGE

1939-31 **Strakosch**, Alexander. "Wie gewinnt der heutige Mensch ein rechtes Verhältnis zur Umwelt? Gedanken zu Dr. Hermann von Baravalle's Buch, 'Physik. I. Buch: Mechanik'." *Das Goetheanum*, 18 (1939), 277-8.
/RESEARCH: PHYSICS

1939-32 *Troll, W[ilhelm]. *Vergleichende Morphologie der höheren -
Pflanzen*. Bd 1/3. Berlin: 1939.
  Rpt. No. 1967-50.
  /RESEARCH: BOTANY/RESEARCH: MORPHOLOGY

1939-33 Uschmann, Georg. *Der morphobiologische Vervollkommnungs-
begriff bei Goethe und seine problemgeschichtlichen Zusammenhänge*.
Jena: Verlag von Gustav Fischer, 1939. vi, 103 pp.
  Partial rpt. No. 1939-34.
  "Aus dem Ernst-Haeckel-Haus, Anstalt für Geschichte der
    Zoologie, insbesondere der Entwicklungslehre, der Universität
    Jena (Leiter: Prof. Dr. V. Franz)."
  Review: Paul Schlager, *Goethe*, NS 6 (1941), 220-21.
  /BIOLOGY/MORPHOLOGY

1939-34 *Uschmann, Georg. *Der morphobiologische Vervollkomm-
nungsbegriff bei Goethe und seine problemgeschichtlichen Zusammenhänge*. Jena: Math.-naturw. Diss. Jena, 1939. vi, 103 pp.
  Partial rpt. of No. 1939-33.
  /BIOLOGY/MORPHOLOGY

1940-1 **Frieling**, Heinrich. "Goethe und Newton, zwei Pole nationalen Wesens." *Natur und Kultur: Monatsschrift für Naturforschung und Kulturpflege*, 37 (1940), 57-8.
/NEWTON, I/CHROMATICS

1940-2 **Gerhard**, Melitta. "Verlauf und Bedeutung von Schillers und Goethes Begegnung im Juli 1794." *The Journal of English and Germanic Philology*, 39 (1940), 115-23.
/SCHILLER, F/EPISTEMOLOGY

1940-3 ***Gröper**[, ?]. "Goethe über den Granit." *Der Bau-Kurier [Berlin]*, 12, No. 35 (1940), 35.
/GEOLOGY

1940-4 ***Halbe**, Georg. "Goethes Naturanschauung und lebensge-setzlicher Landbau." *Demeter*, 15, No. 12 (1940), 116-18.
/AGRONOMY/RESEARCH: AGRONOMY

1940-5 **Heinsius**, Ernst. "Goethes Farbenlehre in ihrer Bedeutung für die Sinnes-Physiologie." *Medizinische Welt*, 14, No. 1 (1940), 16-19.
/CHROMATICS/SENSORY PHYSIOLOGY

1940-6 **Koegel**, A[?]. "Mit Goethe zu deutscher Wissenschaft." *Natur und Kultur*, 37 (1940), 174-6.
/GENERAL INTRODUCTION

1940-7 **Lipps**, Hans. "Goethes Farbenlehre: Ansätze zu einer Inter-pretation." *Jahrbuch des Freien Deutschen Hochstifts*, 1940, pp. 123-38.
"Vortrag in Rom in der Kulturabteilung des Kaiser-Wilhelm-Instituts für Kunst- und Kulturwissenschaft, Febr. 1939."
/CHROMATICS

1940-8 **Matthaei**, Rupprecht. "Neues von Goethes Entoptischen Studien: (Mit zwei Tafeln nach Aquarellen des Verfassers und fünf Abbildungen im Text)." *Goethe*, NF 5 (1940), 71-96.
Includes a short note of 1820, "Glimmerplättchen und deren Wirkung."
/CHROMATICS/EDITION

1940-9 **Runge**, P[hilipp]. O[tto]. *Briefwechsel mit Goethe*. Ed. Hellmuth Freiherr von Maltzahn. Schriften der Goethe-Gesellschaft, 51. Weimar: Verlag der Goethe-Gesellschaft, 1940. 119 pp.
/WORKS: CORRESPONDENCE/RUNGE, P/FINE ARTS

1940-10 *Schatter, K[?]. "Goethe und der Naturschutz." *Naturschutz*, 21, No. 6 (1940), 65-7.
/ECOLOGY

1940-11 *Schlodtmann, W[?]. "Goethes Bedeutung für die heutige Sinnesphysiologie." In his *Aufsätze*. Lübeck: Rahtgens, 1940, pp. 3-7.
/PHYSIOLOGY/RECEPTION

1940-12 **Schmid**, Günther. *Goethe und die Naturwissenschaften: Eine Bibliographie*. Ed. Emil Abderhalden. Halle (Saale): Kaiserlich Leopoldinisch-Carolinisch Deutsche Akademie der Naturforscher, 1940. xv, 620 pp.
Rev. Ernst Beutler, No. 1941-6.
Rev. Sten Lindroth, *Lynchnos*, 1942, p. 390.
/BIBLIOGRAPHY/RECEPTION

1940-13 **Schmid**, Günther. "Die Goethe und seinem Andenken gewidmeten Bücher aus dem Gebiet der Naturwissenschaft und der Medizin. Eine Bibligraphie." *Philobiblon: Die Zeitschrift der Bücherfreunde*, 12 (1940), 244-53.
Rev. Rudolph Zaunick, *Mitt. Gesch. Med.*, 40 (1941/1942), 35.
/BIBLIOGRAPHY/RECEPTION

1940-14 **Schmid**, Günter. "Der Windenberg bei Lauchstädt. Eine unbekannt gebliebene Goethestätte." *Das Merseburger Land*, 40 (1940), 145-57.
/PLACES: WINDBERG BEI LAUCHSTÄTT/GEOLOGY

1940-15 **Schonewille**, Otto. "Die Bedeutung von Goethe's Versuch über die Metamorphose der Pflanzen (1790) für den Fortgang in der botanischen Morphologie." Diss. Halle 1940.
Rpt. No. 1941-24.
/BOTANY/RECEPTION

1940-16 *[Steiner, Rudolf.] "Goethe -- der Naturforscher." *Demeter*, 15, No. 5 (1940), 41-2.
Excerpt from Steiner's autobiography, *Mein Lebensgang* (1925).
/GENERAL INTRODUCTION/EDITIONS

1940-17 **Steiner**, Rudolf. *A Theory of Knowledge Based on Goethe's World Conception: Fundamental Outlines with Special Reference to Schiller*. Tr. Olin D. Wannamaker. New York: Anthroposophic

Press, 1940. 131 pp.
English trans. of No. 1886-9.
Rpt. 3rd edn. No. 1978-39.
/EPISTEMOLOGY

1940-18 *Stier[, ?]. "Goethe als Pilzkenner." *Zeitschrift für Pilzkunde*, 24 [NF 19] (1940), 112.
/BOTANY

1940-19 **Troll**, Wilhelm and K[arl]. Lothar **Wolf**. "Goethes morphologischer Auftrag: Zum 150. Jahr des Erscheinens von Goethes Versuch über die Metamorphose der Pflanzen." *Botanisches Archiv: Zeitschrift für die gesamte Botanik und ihre Grenzgebiete*, 41 (1940), 1-71.
Rpt. Nos. 1940-23, 1942-36 and 1950-75.
/MORPHOLOGY/RESEARCH: MORPHOLOGY

1940-20 **Waaser**, Friedrich. "Goethes Typus-Idee und das Problem der organischen Form." *Zeitschrift für die gesamte Naturwissenschaft einschließlich Naturphilosophie und Geschichte der Naturwissenschaft und Medizin*, 6 (1940), 6-16.
/MORPHOLOGY

1940-21 **Weber**, Hans H. "Goethes oder Herings Farbenkreis?" *Forschungen und Fortschritte*, 16 (1940), 65-8.
/CHROMATICS/HERING, E

1940-22 **Weber**, Hans H. "Über die allgemeinere psychologische Bedeutung des Totalitätsgesetzes Goethes, insbesondere für die Tonpsychologie." *Forschungen und Fortschritte*, 16 (1940), 146-7.
/PSYCHOLOGY/ACOUSTICS/RESEARCH: PSYCHOLOGY/RESEARCH: ACOUSTICS

1940-23 **Wolf**, K[arl]. Lothar and Wilhelm **Troll**. *Goethes morphologischer Auftrag: Versuch einer naturwissenschaftlichen Morphologie*. Leipzig: Akademische Verlagsgesellschaft m. b. H., 1940. vi, 71 pp.
Rpt. of No. 1940-19.
/MORPHOLOGY/RESEARCH: MORPHOLOGY

1940-24 *Zúquete, Alfonso Eduardo M. "Goethe naturalista [Goethe the Naturalist]." *Arquivo de Anatomia e Antropologia [Instituto de Anatomia da Faculdade de Medicina da Universidad e de Lisboa]*, 20 (1940), 55-74.

In Portuguese.
/GENERAL INTRODUCTION

1941-1 **Aeppli**, Willi. "Goethe und Troxler." *Das Goetheanum*, 20 (1941), 384-5; 392-4.
/TROXLER, I

1941-2 **[anon.]** "Vor 150 Jahren erschien Goethes erste natur-wissenschaftliche Schrift, die 'Beiträge zur Optik', aus der wir die schönen Einleitungssätze in Erinnerung bringen." *Goethe*, NF 6 (1941), 231-2.
/OPTICS

1941-3 **Arber**, Agnes. "The Interpretation of Leaf and Root in the Angiosperms." *Biological Reviews of the Cambridge Philosophical Society*, 16 (1941), 81-105.
/RESEARCH: BOTANY

1941-4 **Augustin**, Hermann. *Goethe und Stifters Nausikaa-Tragödie: Über die Urphänomene.* Basel: Benno Schwabe & Co., 1941. 91 pp.
Library of Congress PT 1958.N3A8
/STIFTER, A/RESEARCH: LITERARY CRITI-CISM/RESEARCH: LITERARY THEORY

1941-5 **Baravalle**, Hermann von. "'Der Mensch begreift niemals, wie anthropomorphisch er ist' (Goethe)." *Das Goetheanum*, 20 (1941), 126-7.
/RESEARCH: ANTHROPOLOGY

1941-6 **Beutler**, Ernst. "Goethe und die Naturwissenschaftler." *Frankfurter Zeitung*, 30 March 1941.
Review of No. 1940-12.
In Mappe III E 61/C20: "Goethe und die Naturwissenschaften. Zeitungsausschnitte 1913 -" at the Frankfurter Goethe-Museum.
/REVIEW/BIBLIOGRAPHY/RECEPTION

1941-7 **Bier**, D[?]. "Die Pellagra, vor 155 Jahren von Goethe be-schrieben." *Münchener medizinische Wochenschrift*, 88, No. 50 (1941), p. 1339.
/MEDICINE

1941-8 ***Glockner**, Hermann. "Das Malerische. Ein ästhetisches Kapitel." *Zeitschrift für Kulturphilosophie*, 7 (1941), 96-192.

/CHROMATICS

1941-9 **Gode-von Aesch**, Friedrich. *Natural Science in German Romanticism*. Diss. Columbia. Columbia University Germanic Studies, NS 11. New York: Columbia University Press, 1941. xiii, 302 pp.
On Goethe *passim*.
/RECEPTION/RESEARCH: VARIOUS

1941-10 **Hebing**, Julius. "Briefe zur Farbenlehre: II: Beiträge zur Geschichte der Farbenlehre: Heft 1." Typescript. Berlin: privately printed, 1941. 35 pp. + 4 loose plates.
/RESEARCH: CHROMATICS/HISTORY OF SCIENCE/CHROMATICS

1941-11 **Hebing**, Julius. "Briefe zur Farbenlehre: II: Beiträge zur Geschichte der Farbenlehre: Heft 2." Typescript. Berlin: privately printed, 1941. 32 pp. + 6 loose plates.
/RESEARCH: CHROMATICS/HISTORY OF SCIENCE/CHROMATICS

1941-12 **Heisenberg**, Werner. "Die Goethesche und die Newtonsche Farbenlehre im Lichte der modernen Physik." *Geist der Zeit*, 19 (1941), 261-75.
Rpt. Nos. 1942-12, 1942-13, 1947-15, 1959-15, 1967-26 and 1973-17.
Trans. into Hungarian, No. 1941-13.
Trans. into English, Nos. 1952-35 and 1987-60.
Trans. into Russian, No. 1953-4.
/CHROMATICS/NEWTON, I/METHOD/RESEARCH: PHYSICS

1941-13 *****Heisenberg**, Werner. ["Die Goethesche und die Newtonsche Farbenlehre im Lichte der modernen Physik."] Trans. Faragó Péter. Budapest: Franklin, 1941.
Hungarian trans. of No. 1941-12.
/CHROMATICS/NEWTON, I/METHOD/RESEARCH: PHYSICS

1941-14 **Hölder**, Helmut. "Grenzfragen naturwissenschaftlicher Forschung. Zum Problem der Grenzüberschreitung empirischer Methodik, gestützt auf Goethesche Naturforschung und einige Beispiele aus der Gegenwart." Tübinger naturwissenschaftliche Abhandlungen, 16. Stuttgart: Enke, 1941. 46 pp.

Rpt. rev. edn. No. 1947-19.
Cf. esp. "Goethes Forschung und ihre Grenzen," pp. 15-33.
/METHOD/EPISTEMOLOGY

1941-15 **Kikuti**, Eiiti. ["Die Historik der Naturerscheinungen. Ein Problem der Naturwissenschaft bei Goethe."] *Goethe-Jahrbuch: Die Goethe-Gesellschaft in Japan*, 10 (1941), 66-85.
In Japanese.
/METHOD

1941-16 **Kipp**, Friedrich A. "Über die Pfahlstellung der Rohrdommeln und verwandte Erscheinungen." *Beiträge zur Fortpflanzungsbiologie der Vögel*, 17 (1941), 101-5.
Rpt. No. 1983-54.
/RESEARCH: ORNITHOLOGY

1941-17 ***Kuan**, Ch'i-t'ung. "I ko hsin ti shih-chieh ying-hsiang chih Chien-li chieh-Ko-te [Goethe as the Founder of a New World-View]." *Chung Te hsueh-chih*, 3, No. 3 (1941), 349-403.
In Chinese.
/PHILOSOPHY

1941-18 **Lievegoed**, B[ernhard]. C. J. "Hippocrates, Paracelsus, Goethe." In R. A. B. Oosterhuis and B. C. J. Lievegoed. *Paracelsus herdacht 1493-1543*. den Haag: W. P. van Stockum & Zoon, 1941, pp. 32-55.
/HIPPOCRATES/PARACELSUS/MEDICINE

1941-19 ***Mägdefrau**, Karl. "Die Erforscher der Jenaer Trias." *Beiträge zur Geologie von Thüringen*, 5, No. 2, 88.
/GEOLOGY

1941-20 **Matthaei**, Rupprecht. *Die Farbenlehre im Goethe-Nationalmuseum: Eine Darstellung auf Grund des gesamten Nachlasses in Weimar mit der ersten völligen Bestandsaufnahme*. 2nd edn. Jena: Verlag von Gustav Fischer, 1941. xix, 216 pp.
Rpt. of No. 1939-18.
Rev. Erich Mollwo, *Göttingische gelehrte Anzeigen*, 204 (1942),429-32.
/CHROMATICS/EXHIBITION

1941-21 **Nette**, Herbert. "Typus und Metamorphose: Zwei Grundbegriffe Goethescher Naturlehre." *Kölnische Zeitung*, 3 November 1941.
Rpt. No. 1975-39.

In Mappe III E 61/C20: "Goethe und die Naturwissenschaften. Zeitungsausschnitte 1913 -" at the Frankfurter Goethe-Museum.
/MORPHOLOGY

1941-22 **Pfannenstiel**, Max and Rudolph **Zaunick**. *Lorenz Oken und J. W. von Goethe: dargestellt auf Grund neu erschlossener Quellenzeugnisse.* Pt. II of *Aus Leben und Werk von Lorenz Oken, dem Begründer der deutschen Naturforschungsversammlungen. Eine Quellensammlung.* Ed. Rudolph Zaunick. Leipzig: Johann Ambrosius Barth Verlag, 1941. 63 pp.
> Rev. Paul Diepgen, *Mitt. Ges. Med.*, 40 (1941/1942), 32-4.
> Rev. Nils von Hofsten, *Lychnos*, 1943, 382.
> /OKEN, L/OSTEOLOGY/MORPHOLOGY

1941-23 **Schaeppi**, Hansjakob. "Über das Wesen der vergleichenden Morphologie. Zur Erinnerung an die vor 150 Jahren zum ersten mal erschienen Abhandlung Goethes: 'Versuch die Metamorphose der Pflanzen zu erklären'." *Sudhoffs Archiv für Geschichte der Medizin und der Naturwissenschaften*, 33 (1941), 173-86.
> /MORPHOLOGY/BOTANY

1941-24 **Schonewille**, Otto. "Die Bedeutung von Gothes Versuch über die Metamorphose der Pflanze für den Fortgang der botanischen Morphologie." *Botanisches Archiv*, 42 (1941), 421-60.
> Rpt. of No. 1940-15.
> Rev. Rudolph Zaunick, *Mitt. Ges. Med.*, 40 (1941/1942), 164.
> /BOTANY/RECEPTION/MORPHOLOGY/INFLUENCES

1941-25 **Sieckmann**, Hermann Eduard. "Hahnemann und Goethe, ein erkenntnistheoretischer Versuch." *Hippokrates*, 12 (1941), 865-8; 891-4.
> /HAHNEMANN, C/EPISTEMOLOGY/MEDICINE

1941-26 **Theile**, Harold. "Die Blume des Lichts: Zur Geistesgeschichte der Farbe." *Das Reich*, 14 Sept. 1941, 1-3.
> /RESEARCH: CHROMATICS

1941-27 **Trapp**, Marianne. "Goethes naturphilosophische Denkweise." *Zeitschrift für deutsche Kulturphilsophie*, 7 (1941), 240-74.
> /METHOD

1941-28 **Troll**, Wilhelm. "Aufgaben und Wege morphologischer Forschung in der Botanik." In his *Gestalt und Urbild: Gesammelte*

Aufsätze zu Grundfragen der organischen Morphologie. Die Gestalt: Abhandlungen zu einer allgemeinen Morphologie, 2. Leipzig: Akademische Verlags-Gesellschaft, 1941, pp. 91-147.
/RESEARCH: BOTANY/RESEARCH: MORPHOLOGY

1941-29 **Troll**, Wilhelm. "Gestalt und Gesetz. Versuch einer geistes-geschichtlichen Grundlegung der morphologischen und physiolo-gischen Forschung." In his *Gestalt und Urbild: Gesammelte Aufsätze zu Grundfragen der organischen Morphologie.* Die Gestalt: Abhand-lungen zu einer allgemeinen Morphologie, 2. Leipzig: Akademische Verlags-Gesellschaft, 1941, pp. 20-50.
Rpt. of No. 1925-33.
Rpt. 2nd edn. 1942.
RESEARCH: MORPHOLOGY/RESEARCH: PHYSIOLOGY
/NATURPHILOSOPHIE

1941-30 **Troll**, Wilhelm. *Gestalt und Urbild: Gesammelte Aufsätze zu Grundfragen der organischen Morphologie.* Die Gestalt: Abhand-lungen zu einer allgemeinen Morphologie, 2. Leipzig: Akademische Verlags-Gesellschaft, 1941. vi, 182 pp.
Rpt. 1942.
Cf. Nos. 1941-28, -29, -31 and -32.
/METHOD/RESEARCH: BOTANY/RESEARCH: MORPHOL-OGY

1941-31 **Troll**, Wilhelm. "Die urbildliche Denkweise." In his *Gestalt und Urbild: Gesammelte Aufsätze zu Grundfragen der organischen Morphologie.* Die Gestalt: Abhandlungen zu einer allgemeinen Mor-phologie, 2. Leipzig: Akademische Verlags-Gesellschaft, 1941, pp. 51-90.
Rpt. 1942.
/METHOD/RESEARCH: BOTANY/RESEARCH: MORPHOL-OGY

1941-32 **Troll**, Wilhelm. "Wiedergeburt der Morphologie aus dem Geiste deutscher Wissenschaft." In his *Gestalt und Urbild: Gesammelte Aufsätze zu Grundfragen der organischen Morphologie.* Die Gestalt: Abhandlungen zu einer allgemeinen Morphologie, 2. Leipzig: Akademische Verlags-Gesellschaft, 1941, pp. 148-57.
Rpt. of No. 1935-35.
/METHOD/RESEARCH: BOTANY/RESEARCH: MORPHOL-OGY

1941-33 **Wachsmuth**, Andreas B[runo]. "Die Entwickelung von Goethes

naturwissenschaftlicher Denkweise und Weltanschauung von den Anfängen bis zur Reife." *Goethe*, NF 6 (1941), 263-84.
Rpt. No. 1966-33.
Cf. No. 1941-34.
/GENERAL INTRODUCTION

1941-34 **Wachsmuth**, [Andreas] Bruno. "Die Entwicklung von Goethes naturwissenschaftlicher Denkweise und Weltanschauung von den Anfängen bis zur Reife." *Mitteilungen zur Geschichte der Medizin, der Naturwissenschaften und der Technik*, 40 (1941/1942), 305-6.
Summary of No. 1941-33.
Rpt. No. 1966-33.
/GENERAL INTRODUCTION

1941-35 **Zaunick**, Rudolph. "Aus Leben und Werk von Lorenz Oken, dem Begründer der deutschen Naturforschungsversammlungen. Eine Quellensammlung im Auftrage der Gesellschaft Deutscher Naturforscher und Ärzte bearbeitet und herausgegeben. 2. Lorenz Oken und J. W. Goethe, dargestellt auf Grund neu erschlossener Quellenzeugnisse von Max Pfannenstiel in Gemeinschaft mit Rudolph Zaunick." *Sudhoffs Archiv für Geschichte der Medizin und der Naturwissenschaften*, 33, Nos. 3 and 4 (1941), 113-73.
/OKEN, L/OSTEOLOGY/MORPHOLOGY/INSTITUTIONS: GESELLSCHAFT DEUTSCHER NATURFORSCHER UND ÄRZTE

1942-1 *****Barthel**, Ernst. "Goethes Farbenlehre." *Rhein-Westfälische Zeitung*, 10 Apr. 1942.
/CHROMATICS

1942-2 **Boos-Hamburger**, Hilde. *Die Schöpferische Kraft der Farbe: Der Impuls Rudolf Steiners zu einer neuen Kunst der Farbengestaltung.* Goetheanum, Dornach: Sektion für redende und musikalische Künste, 1942. 61 pp. + 8 plates.
Rpt. No. 1979-14.
Rev. Maria Strakosch-Giesler, *Das Goetheanum*, 21 (1942), 332-3.
/RESEARCH: CHROMATICS/STEINER, R

1942-3 **Chamberlain**, Stewart Houston. "Goethe indagatore della natura [Goethe as an Investigator of Nature]." *Minerva*, 52, No. 4 (1942), 71-2.
In Italian.
/GENERAL INTRODUCTION

1942-4 **Clara**, Max. "Goethes Begriff des Urbildes im Lichte der modernen Entwicklungsgeschichte." Typescript. Leipzig: Goethe-Gesellschaft, 1942. 35 pp.
   Cf. abstract, No. 1943-3.
   /BIOLOGY: EVOLUTION/MORPHOLOGY

1942-5 **Cysarz**, Herbert. "Goethe und Schopenhauer." *Jahrbuch der Schopenhauer-Gesellschaft*, 29 (1942), 3-22.
   /SCHOPENHAUER, A

1942-6 ***Feldkeller**, Paul. "Abermals die Urpflanze." *Deutsche Allgemeine Zeitung*, 18 March 1942, No. 132.
   /BOTANY

1942-7 ***Feldkeller**, Paul. "Goethe und die Mathematik." *Deutsche Allgemeine Zeitung*, 8 March 1942, No. 115.
   Rpt. No. 1942-8.
   /MATHEMATICS/LOREY, W

1942-8 ***Feldkeller**, Paul. "Goethe und die Mathematik." *Deutsche Bergwerkszeitung [Düsseldorf]*, 1942, No. 29.
   Rpt. of No. 1942-7.
   /MATHEMATICS/LOREY, W

1942-9 **Fels**, Alice. "Von einer Ausstellung goetheanistischer Kunst." *Das Goetheanum*, 21 (1942), 132-3; 150.
   /FINE ARTS/EXHIBITION

1942-10 **Goethe**, Johann Wolfgang von. "Die Natur. Ein Hymnus." 1942. 2 pp.
   "Den Bücherfreunden zum 5. Oktober 1942. Karl Silomon."
   Frankfurter Goethe-Museum, III E 60/5.
   /EDITION

1942-11 **Gyhr**, M[?]. "Wandel der Landschaft." *Das Goetheanum*, 21 (1942), 13-14.
   /RESEARCH: ECOLOGY

1942-12 **Heisenberg**, Werner. "Die Goethesche und die Newtonsche Farbenlehre im Lichte der modernen Physik." In his *Wandlungen in den Grundlagen der Naturwissenschaften: Sechs Vorträge*. 3rd exp. edn. Leipzig: S. Hirzel Verlag, 1942, pp. 58-76.
   Rpt. of No. 1941-12.

1st (1935) and 2nd (1936) edns. did not contain this essay.
/CHROMATICS/NEWTON, I/METHOD/RESEARCH:
METHOD

1942-13 **Heisenberg**, Werner. "Die Goethesche und die Newtonsche Far-
benlehre im Lichte der modernen Physik." *Schweizer Journal*, 8, No.
3 (1942), 41-3.
Rpt. of No. 1941-12.
/CHROMATICS/NEWTON, I/METHOD/RESEARCH:
PHYSICS

1942-14 **Kaßner**, C[?]. "Goethe und der Wetterdienst im Grossherzog-
tum Sachsen-Weimar-Eisenach." *Zeitschrift für angewandte Meteorologie*, 59 (1942), 277-8.
/METEOROLOGY/PLACES: WEIMAR

1942-15 **Kipp**, Friedrich A. "Das Kompensationsprinzip in der Brut-
biologie der Vögel." *Beiträge zur Fortpflanzungsbiologie der Vögel*,
18 (1942), 52-9.
Rpt. No. 1983-53.
/RESEARCH: ORNITHOLOGY

1942-16 **Klug**, Ernst. "'Die Phantasie' als neue musikalische Meta-
morphosenform verstanden." *Das Goetheanum*, 21 (1942), 364-6.
Continuation of No. 1942-17.
/RESEARCH: MUSICOLOGY/RESEARCH: MORPHOLOGY

1942-17 **Klug**, Ernst. "Über die Bedeutung der Metamorphosenlehre für
den Komponisten." *Das Goetheanum*, 21 (1942), 226-7; 243-5; 253-
5; 278-9.
Cf. continuation, No. 1942-16.
/RESEARCH: MUSICOLOGY/RESEARCH: MORPHOLOGY

1942-18 **Loesche**, Martin. "Typus und Metamorphose." *Zeitschrift für
Deutschkunde*, 56 (1942), 1-11.
"Festvortrag zur Feier von Goethes Geburtstag der
Ortsvereinigung Leipzig der Weimarer Goethegesellschaft am
28. August 1941 im Gewandhaus zu Leipzig."
/MORPHOLOGY

1942-19 ***Mader**, Anton. "Gestalt und Typus in der Biologie." *Frankfurter Zeitung*, No. 69, 7 February 1942.
/MORPHOLOGY/RESEARCH: MORPHOLOGY

1942-20 *__Marquardt__, Hans. "Goethe und die Botanik." *Pariser Zeitung*, 18 December 1942.
Rpt. No. 1943-24.
/BOTANY

1942-21 __Noggler__, Josef. "Goethe und die Alchimie." *Das Antiquariat [Wien]*, 5, No. 7/8 (1949), 112-17.
/ALCHEMY/INFLUENCES

1942-22 __Poppelbaum__, Hermann. *Menschengemässe Naturerkenntnis: Gesammelte Aufsätze*. Basel: Rudolf Geering Verlag, 1942. 53 pp.
/RESEARCH: VARIOUS

1942-23 __Rovereto__, Gaetano. "Wolfango Goethe geologo in Italia [Goethe the Geologist in Italy]." *Atti della reale accademia d'Italia: Memorie della classe di scienza fisiche, matematiche e naturali*, 13 (1942), 709-29. 10 figures.
In Italian.
"Presentata nell'Adunanza del 20 febbraio 1942-XX."
/GEOLOGY/PLACES: ITALY

1942-24 __Schmid__, Günther. "Der Enzian: Zur Frühgeschichte der Goeth-ischen Botanik." *Goethe*, NF 7 (1942), 16-41.
/BOTANY

1942-25 __Sherrington__, Sir Charles. "Goethe on Nature and Science: The Philip Maurice Deneke Lecture Delivered at Lady Margaret Hall, Oxford, on the 4th March 1942." Cambridge: Cambridge University Press, 1942. 32 pp.
Publ. simul. by Macmillan, New York.
Rpt. No. 1981-86.
Rpt. exp. edn. No. 1949-166.
Review: W. H. Bruford, *Modern Language Review*, 38 (1943), 75-6.
/GENERAL INTRODUCTION

1942-26 __Steiner__, Rudolf. "Galilei, Giordano Bruno und Goethe." *Das Goetheanum*, 21 (1942), 9-11; 17-19; 25-7; 33-4; 41-1.
"Vortrag von Dr. *Rudolf Steiner*, gehalten am 26. Januar 1911 in Berlin, Architektenhaus."
/GALILEI, G/BRUNO, G

1942-27 __Steiner__, Rudolf. *Der Goetheanismus, ein Menschen-Umwand-lungsimpuls und Auferstehungsgedanke. Sechs Vorträge, gehalten*

vom 3. bis 12. Januar 1919 in Dornach. Dornach/ Schweiz: Philosophisch-Anthroposophischer Verlag am Goetheanum, 1942. 137 pp.
  Rpt. 2nd exp. edn. No. 1967-49.
  3rd edn. 1982.
  /RESEARCH: VARIOUS

1942-28 ***Troll**, Wilhelm. "Bryophyllum calcinum. Goethes Idee von der Metamorphose der Pflanzen." *Krakauer Zeitung*, 4 (1942), Nos. 295 and 297.
  /BOTANY/EDITIONS

1942-29 **Vogg**[, ?]. "Die Welt der Farben. Zu Goethes naturwissenschaftlichen Studien." *Rhein-Westfälische Zeitung*, 29 December 1942, No. 659.
  In Mappe III E 21/C91: "Goethe und die Farbenlehre 1913-. Sammelmappe Zeitungsausschnitte" at the Frankfurter Goethe-Museum.
  /CHROMATICS

1942-30 **Waaser**, Friedrich. "Gestalt und Wirklichkeit im Lichte Goethescher Naturanschauung." Die Gestalt: Abhandlungen zu einer allgemeinen Morphologie, 8. Halle: Max Niemeyer Verlag, 1942. 35 pp.
  /MORPHOLOGY

1942-31 **Waaser**, Friedrich. "Natur und Geist: Gedanken zu einer Synthese vom Standpunkt Goethescher Naturbetrachtung." *Mitteilungen des Vereins für Naturwissenschaft und Mathematik in Ulm*, 23 (1942/1950), 12-36.
  Rpt. Nos. 1942-32 and 1951-51.
  /METHOD

1942-32 **Waaser**, Friedrich. "Neues zum Kampf um die wahre Gestalt der Abstammungs- und Entwicklungslehre." Sonderdruck aus *Mitteilungen des Vereins für Naturwissenschaft und Mathematik in Ulm*, 23. Ulm-Donau: Dr. Karl Höhn, 1942, pp. 13-35.
  Rpt. of No. 1942-31.
  "Nach einem im Verein für Naturwissenschaft und Mathematik am 24. 11. 1941 in Ulm gehaltenen Vortrag."
  /BIOLOGY: EVOLUTION

1942-33 ***Wachsmuth**, Andreas B[runo]. "Goethe und die Metamorphose." *Ärztin*, 18 (1942), 355-8.

/MORPHOLOGY

1942-34 **Walden**, Paul. "Goethe als Chemiker und Techniker." *Europäischer Wissenschaftsdienst*, 2 (1942), 9-11.
/CHEMISTRY/TECHNOLOGY

1942-35 **Weinhandl**, Ferdinand. "Die gestaltanalytische Philosophie in ihrem Verhältnis zur Morphologie Goethes und zur Transzendentalphilosophie Kants." *Kant-Studien*, 42 (1942/ 1943), 106-45.
/MORPHOLOGY/PSYCHOLOGY/KANT/EPISTEMOLOGY

1942-36 *****Wolf**, K[arl]. Lothar and Wilhelm **Troll**. *Goethes morphologischer Auftrag: Versuch einer naturwissenschaftlichen Morphologie*. Halle: Niemeyer, 1942. 72 pp.
   Rpt. of No. 1940-19.
   /MORPHOLOGY/RESEARCH: MORPHOLOGY

1943-1 *****Buschenhagen**[, ?]. "Goethe über Mond und Wetter." *Deutsche Allgemeine Zeitung*, No. 174 (1943).
   /ASTRONOMY/METEOROLOGY

1943-2 **Carus**, Carl Gustav. *Goethe und seine Bedeutung für diese und die künftige Zeit: eine Festrede gehalten zu Dresden 28. August 1849. Denkschrift zum hundertjährigen Geburtsfeste Goethes: über ungleiche Befähigung der verschiedenen Menschheitsstämme für höhere geistige Entwickelung*. Berlin: W. Keiper, 1943. 138 pp.
   Rpt. of No. 1849-2.
   /GENERAL INTRODUCTION

1943-3 *****Clara**, Max. "Goethes Begriff des Urbildes im Lichte der modernen Entwicklungsgeschichte." *Natur und Kultur*, 40 (1943), 27.
   Abstract of No. 1942-4.
   /BIOLOGY: EVOLUTION/MORPHOLOGY

1943-4 *****Eberhard-Reißner**, L[?]. E. "Entdeckung eines Farbphänomens." *Deutscher Drucker*, 49 (1943), No. 582, pp. 217-20.
   /RESEARCH: CHROMATICS/CHROMATICS

1943-5 **Ehrenstein**, Walter. "Theoretisch fruchtbare Gedanken in Goethes Farbenlehre." *Archiv für die gesamte Psychologie*, 112 (1943), 196-206.
   /RESEARCH: CHROMATICS/CHROMATICS

1943-6 *Fiebrandt, Werner. "Dichter als Naturforscher. *Allgemeiner Wegweiser*, April 1943, pp. 93-4.
    Rpt. No. 1943-7.
    /GENERAL INTRODUCTION

1943-7 *Fiebrandt, Werner. "Dichter als Naturforscher. *Donau-Zeitung [Belgrad]*, 1 October 1943.
    Rpt. of No. 1943-6.
    /GENERAL INTRODUCTION

1943-8 *Francé-Harrar, Annie. "Blumen werfen Funken." *Berliner Börsen-Zeitung*, 18 July 1943.
    /BOTANY/CHROMATICS

1943-9 Franz, Leonhard. "Ein vergessenes gesteinskundliches Gutachten Goethes." *Goethe*, 8 (1943), 299-306.
    /EDITIONS/GEOLOGY/VULPIUS, C

1943-10 *Freyh, Rike. "Die ästhetische Funktion der Farbe in Goethes Farbenlehre." Diss. Marburg 1943. 172 pp.
    /CHROMATICS/AESTHETICS

1943-11 Goethe[, J. W. von]. *Schriften über die Natur*. Ed. and sel. Gunther Ipsen. Kröners Taschenausgabe, 62. Stuttgart: Alfred Kröner Verlag, 1943. 343 pp.
    Cf. No. 1943-20.
    Rpt. 1949.
    /EDITION: SELECTIONS

1943-12 Goethe, J. W. von. *Über Natur und Naturbetrachtung: Eine Auswahl*. Sel. Wilhelm Troll and K. Lothar Wolf. Weimar: Böhlau, 1943. 128 pp.
    /EDITION: SELECTIONS

1943-13 Grünthal, E[rnst]. "Goethes Äußerungen zur Hirnanatomie." *Monatsschrift für Psychiatrie und Neurologie*, 107 (1943), 147-64.
    Cf. expanded version, No. 1949-64.
    /ANATOMY/NEUROLOGY

1943-14 Heinz, R[udolf]. "Goethe, die deutsche Geologie und Kopernikus." *Beiträge zur Geologie von Thüringen*, 7 (1943), 269-75.
    "Aus dem Vortrag: 'Goethes geologische Studien und seine Stellung in der Geologie', gehalten auf der 18. Mitgliederver-

sammlung des Thüringschen Geologischen Vereins zu Schleiz am 8. August 1943."
/GEOLOGY/COPERNICUS, N

1943-15 **Heinz**, Rudolf. "Zu Hermann Credners 100. Geburtstag: Mit Bemerkungen zur Stellung Goethes in der Geologie." *Mitteilungen der Gesellschaft für Erdkunde zu Leipzig*, 56 (1943), 5-16.
/CREDNER, H/GEOLOGY

1943-16 **Hesse**, Peter G. "Goethe." *Der Lebensbegriff bei den Klassikern der Naturforschung: Seine Entwicklung bei 60 Denkern und Forschern bis zur Goethezeit.* Jena: Verlag von Gustav Fischer, 1943, pp. 80-100.
/GENERAL INTRODUCTION

1943-17 ***Hundt**, Rudolf. "Der Geraer Schaumkalk, ein Mineral, mit dem sich Goethe beschäftigte." *Geraer Zeitung*, 1 October 1943, No. 230.
/GEOLOGY

1943-18 ***Hundt**, Rudolf. "Goethe als Mineraloge." *Deutsche Bergwerkzeitung*, 25 December 1943, No. 303.
/GEOLOGY

1943-19 ***Hundt**, Rudolf. "Goethes 'problematisches basaltähnliches Gestein, in welchem bei Schleiz der Amiant vorkommt'." *Geraer Zeitung*, 18 November 1943, No. 241.
/GEOLOGY

1943-20 **Ipsen**, Gunther. "Einleitung." In Goethe[, J. W. von]. *Schriften über die Natur.* Ed. and sel. Gunther Ipsen. Stuttgart: Alfred Kröner Verlag, 1943, pp. 1-11.
/GENERAL INTRODUCTION

1943-21 ***Kaiser**, E[?]. "Zu Goethes Himmelsbeobachtungen." *Weltall*, 43 (1943), 161.
/METEOROLOGY

1943-22 ***Loesche**, Martin. "Gestalt im Formlosen: Ein Beitrag zur Einführung in Goethes naturwissenschaftliches Denken." Leipzig: P. Schlager, 1943. 9 pp.
/MORPHOLOGY/GENERAL INTRODUCTION

1943-23 **Löwicke**, Fritz. "Goethe und die Meteorologie: Auf Grund

421

seiner Veröffentlichungen dargestellt." *Zeitschrift für angewandte Meteorologie*, 60 (1943), 392-6.
/METEOROLOGY

1943-24 ***Marquardt**, Hans. "Goethe und die Botanik." *Kolmarer Kurier*, 20 October 1943.
Rpt. of No. 1942-20.
/BOTANY

1943-25 **Michéa**, René. *Les travaux scientifiques de Goethe*. Cahiers de l'Institut d'études germaniques, 5. Paris: Aubier, 1943. 191 pp.
Rev. Heinrich Meyer, *Germanic Review*, 24 (1949), 229-31.
/GENERAL INTRODUCTION

1943-26 **Müller**, Günther. "Goethes Elegie 'Die Metamorphose der Pflanzen': Versuch einer morphologischen Interpretation." *Deutsche Vierteljahresschrift für Literaturwissenschaft und Geistesgeschichte*, 21, No. 1 (1943), 67-98.
Rpt. Nos. 1956-18 and 1968-25.
/WORKS: LYRICS/RESEARCH: LITERARY CRITICISM

1943-27 ***Rudolf**, Anton. "Das Urwunder der Farbe Alt-Karlsbader Gläser. Die Erfindung eines Alt-Karlsbader Glasschneiders in Goethes Farbenlehre." *Karlsbader Tageszeitung*, 2 March 1943, No. 51.
/CHROMATICS/PLACES: KARLSBAD

1943-28 ***Savelli**, Giovanni. "Metodo di Goethe [Goethe's Method]." *Il Regime fascista*, 8 July 1943.
In Italian.
/METHOD

1943-29 **Strakosch-Giesler**, Maria. "Rudolf Steiner: 'Das Wesen der Farben': Zum Erscheinen der zweiten Auflage." *Das Goetheanum*, 22 (1943), 46.
/REVIEW/STEINER, R/RESEARCH: CHROMATICS

1943-30 **Wachsmuth**, Andreas B[runo]. "Goethe und die Magie: Eduard Spranger zum 60. Geburtstag." *Goethe*, NF 8 (1943), 98-115; 215-31.
Rpt. Nos. 1957-33 and 1966-41.
/MAGIC/SPRANGER, E

1943-31 ***Walden**, Paul. *Goethe als Chemiker und Techniker*. Berlin:

Verlag Chemie, 1943. 87 pp. [Privately printed].
Trans. into Italian, No. 1943-32.
"Vortrag z. Goethe-Gedenkfeier 1932 im Verein dt. Chemiker,
Berlin."
/CHEMISTRY/TECHNOLOGY

1943-32 **Walden**, Paul. "Goethe chimico e tecnico." *Minerva*, 53, No. 3
(1943), 52-3.
Italian trans. of No. 1943-31.
/CHEMISTRY/TECHNOLOGY

1943-33 **Wehnelt**, B[runo]. *Die Pflanzenpathologie der deutschen
Romantik als Lehre vom kranken Leben und Bilder der Pflanzen: Ihre
Ideenwelt und ihre Beziehungen zu Medizin, Biologie und Natur-
philosophie historisch-romantischer Zeit*. Bonn: Bonner Universitäts-
Buchdrückerei Gebr. Scheur, 1943. 236 pp.
Partial rpt., No. 1944-19.
/RECEPTION/RESEARCH: BOTANY

1943-34 *****Weickmann**, Ludwig. "Witterungslehre zu Goethes Zeit und
heute. Nach einem Vortrag." Leipzig: Goethe-Gesellschaft,
Ortsvereinigung Leipzig der Goethe-Gesellschaft Weimar, 1943. [8]
pp.
2nd edn. 1944. 18 pp.
/METEOROLOGY

1944-1 *****Barthel**, E[rnst]. *Goethes Farbenlehre*. Deutscher Wissenschaftlicher Dienst, 41. 1944.
/CHROMATICS

1944-2 *****Brinkmann**, Donald. Introduction to Goethe, J. W. von. *Die
Metamorphose der Pflanzen*. Hofmann-Bibliothek, 21. Zürich: Hof-
mann, 1944.
/BOTANY

1944-3 **Frieling**, Heinrich. "Vom Sinn der Farben in der Natur." *Das
XX. Jahrhundert*, 6, No. 1 (1944), Febr., pp. 32-7.
/RESEARCH: CHROMATICS

1944-4 *****Goethe**, J. W. von. *Die Metamorphose der Pflanzen*. Intro.
Donald Brinkmann. Hofmann-Bibliothek, 21. Zürich: Hofmann,
1944. iv, 60 pp.
Cf. No. 1944-2.
/EDITION

1944-5 **Hübscher**, Arthur. "Um Schopenhauers Farbenlehre. Ein Brief und ein Bericht." *Jahrbuch der Schopenhauer-Gesellschaft*, 31 (1944), 83-90.
/SCHOPENHAUER, A/RESEARCH: CHROMA-TICS/VOLGER, O

1944-6 ***Hundt**, Rudolf. "Die Entstehung der Tafelberge im Orlagau. Goethes Ansichten über die Bryozeonriffe zwischen Neustadt und Pößneck." *Geraer Zeitung*, 23 March 1944, No. 70.
/GEOLOGY/PLACES: TAFELBERGE

1944-7 ***Hundt**, Rudolf. "Goethes Interesse an dem Geraer Steinsalz." *Geraer Zeitung*, 7 June 1944, No. 131.
/GEOLOGY/PLACES: GERA

1944-8 **Loesche**, Martin. *Grundbegriffe in Goethes Naturwissenschaft (und ihr Niederschlag im Faust)*. Kleine Bücherei zur Geistesge-schichte, 12. Leipzig: Verlag E. A. Seemann, 1944. 131 pp.
/GENERAL INTRODUCTION/WORKS: FAUST

1944-10 **Müller**, Günther. *Die Gestaltfrage in der Literaturwissenschaft und Goethes Morphologie*. Die Gestalt: Abhandlungen zu einer allgemeinen Morphologie, 13. Halle (Saale): Max Niemeyer Verlag, 1944. 84 pp.
Rpt. Nos. 1968-23 and -27.
/RESEARCH: LITERARY THEORY/RESEARCH: MOR-PHOLOGY

1944-11 ***Neumann**, Ernst Wilhelm. "Goethe und Schopenhauer." *Deut-sche Wissenschaftsdienst*, 5, No. 3/4 (1944), 8-9.
/SCHOPENHAUER, A/RESEARCH: CHROMA-TICS/RECEPTION

1944-12 ***Niebelschütz**, Ernst v[on]. "Goethes 'symbolische Pflanze'." *Pariser Zeitung*, 20 July 1944.
/BOTANY/EPISTEMOLOGY/SCHILLER, F

1944-13 **Schierbeek**, A[braham]. *Goethe als Natuuronderzoeker [Goethe as a Scientist]*. Amsterdam: H. Meulenhoff, 1944. 184 pp.
In Dutch.
/GENERAL INTRODUCTION

1944-14 ***Schmidt**, Armin. "Gibt es ausgezeichnete Komplimentär-

farbenpaare?" Diss. Erlangen 1944. 21 pp.
/CHROMATICS/RESEARCH: CHROMATICS

1944-15 **Skramlik**, Emil von. "'Ein Kästchen mit Glasbrocken' in Goethes Nachlass.9" *Goethe*, 9 (1944), 187-93.
/CHROMATICS/PURKYNE, J

1944-16 **Steiner**, Rudolf. *Le opere scientifice di Goethe*. Biblioteca scientifico-spirituale, diretta da Rinaldo Küfferle, Ser. II, 2. Milano: Fratelli Bocca, 1944. 246 pp.
Italian trans. of No. 1926-37.
Library of Congress PT 2206.S854
/GENERAL INTRODUCTION

1944-17 **Tomaselli**, Ruggero. "La teoria della metamorfosi e dell'evoluzione in Goethe [The Theory of Morphology and Metamorphosis in Goethe]." In *Pragmateia. Annuario per l'anno scolastico 1943-44. Centro scolastico "Antonio Rosmini", Castelnuovi Valsugana*. Trento: Temi[, 1944].
In Italian.
/MORPHOLOGY/BIOLOGY: EVOLUTION

1944-18 **Wachsmuth**, Andreas Bruno. "Goethes naturwissenschaftliche Lehre von der Gestalt." *Goethe*, NF 9 (1944), 54-87.
Rpt. No. 1966-39.
/MORPHOLOGY

1944-19 *****Wehnelt**, Bruno. "Einleitung." *Deutsche Allgemeine Zeitung*, 24 October 1944.
Partial rpt. of No. 1943-33.
/RECEPTION/RESEARCH: BOTANY

1944-20 **Zeydel**, Edwin H. "An Unpublished Note of Goethe." *Journal of English and Germanic Philology*, 43 (1944), 380-83.
/EDITION/AMPERE, J/STAPFER, F

1945-1 **Bettica-Giovannini**, Renato. "Goethe, Benn, Carossa." In his *L'atto sessuale. Saggi di umanesimo medico*, 1945, pp. 153-64.
Rpt. of No. 1945-2.
In Italian.
/GENERAL INTRODUCTION/BENN, G/CAROSSA, H

1945-2 **Bettica-Giovannini**, Renato. "Goethe poeta e scienziato, Benn e Carossa medici poeti [Goethe as Poet and Scientist, Benn and Carossa

as Physician-Poets]." *Minerva medica*, 36, 10-14 July 1945, 2-10.
Rpt. No. 1945-1.
In Italian.
/GENERAL INTRODUCTION/BENN, G/CAROSSA, H

1945-3 **Cassirer**, Ernst. "Goethe and the Kantian Philosophy." In his
Rousseau, Kant, Goethe: Two Essays. The History of Ideas Series, 1.
Princeton: Princeton University Press, 1945, pp. 61-98.
/KANT, I/EPISTEMOLOGY

1945-4 *****Gittner**, Hermann. "Goethe als Förderer der wissenschaftlichen
Pharmazie." Halle: Druckerei Burg Giebichenstein, 1945. 8 pp.
/PHARMACOLOGY

1945-5 *****Goethe**, J. W. von. "Schneeberger Reiseblätter." Postscr.
Günther Schmid. Typescript. Giebichenstein: Werkstätten der Stadt
Halle, 1945. 3 pp.
/GEOLOGY/PLACES: SCHNEEBERG

1945-6 **Houdremont**, Eduard. "Über das Urphänomen: Gedanken zur
naturwissenschaftlichen Betrachtungsweise Goethes und der
Physiker." *Schriften der Ortsvereinigung Essen der Goethe-
Gesellschaft zu Weimar*, 2. Essen: n. p., 1945, pp. 5-28.
/EPISTEMOLOGY/METHOD/CHROMATICS

1945-7 *****Kaila**, Eino. "Goethe ja Newton. Kohtaus wlysiumissa [Goethe
and Newton. Encounter in Elysium]." In *Juhlakirja V. A. Kosken-
niemen täyttäessä 60 vuotta 8. 7. 1945*. Ed. Rafael Koskimies,
Mikko Saarenheimo, Lauri Viljanen, N. P. Virtanen, Sulo Haltsonen.
Kirjallisuudentutkijain seuran vuosikirja, 8. Helsinki: Suomalaisen
kirjallisuuden seura, 1945, pp. 161-175.
In Finnish.
/CHROMATICS/NEWTON, I

1945-8 **Speiser**, Andreas. "Goethes Farbenlehre." In his *Die mathe-
matische Denkweise*. 2nd edn. Wissenschaft und Kultur, 1. Basel:
Birkhauser Verlag, 1945, pp. 75-82.
Rpt. of No. 1932-295.
/CHROMATICS

1945-9 *****Vogel**, Lothar. "Das Bild der Krankheit in Natur und Geistesan-
schauung Goethes." Diss. Tübingen 1945. iv, 98 pp.
/PATHOLOGY/MEDICINE

1945-10 **Waaser**, Friedrich. "Mensch und Tier: Eine pädagogische Betrachtung auf urbildlicher Grundlage." Die Gestalt: Abhandlungen zu einer allgemeinen Morphologie, 18. Halle (Saale): Max Niemeyer Verlag, 1945. 58 pp.
>   "Nach einem am 23. Januar 1943 im Gestalt-Kolloquium in Halle gehaltenen Vortrag."
>   /RESEARCH: ANTHROPOLOGY/RESEARCH: ZOOLOGY

1945-11 *****Wittkowski**, Victor. "Um artigo de Goethe sobre palmeiras e paisagens do Brasil [An Article by Goethe on the Palms and Landscapes of Brazil]." *O Estado de Sâo Paulo*, 11 October 1945.
>   Rpt. No. 1947-34.
>   In Portuguese.
>   /BOTANY/PLACES: BRAZIL

1946-1 **Arber**, Agnes. "Goethe's Botany: The Metamorphosis of Plants (1790) and Tobler's Ode to Nature (1782): With an introduction and translations." *Chronica botanica*, 10 (1946), 63-124.
>   Rpt. in part, No. 1950-18.
>   Rev. H. Meyer, *Monatshefte*, 38 (1946), 504f.
>   Rev. Elizabeth M. Wilkinson, *Publications of the English Goethe Society*, NS 16 (1947), 120-24.
>   Rev. M. I. Jehle, *Journal of English and Germanic Philology*, 47 (1948), 430f.
>   Rev. Elizabeth M. Wilkinson, *Modern Language Review*, 43 (1948), 556-8.
>   /TRANSLATION: ENGLISH/BOTANY

1946-2 *****Buhl**, Fritz. "Goethe und der Kuckuck. Ein naturwissenschaftliches Rätsel." *Südkurier* (Konstanz), 28 May 1946.
>   /ORNITHOLOGY

1946-3 **Fuchs**, Arthur. "Göttin Natura." *Das Goetheanum*, 25 (1946), 363-4; 372-4.
>   /PHILOSOPHY

1946-4 [**Goethe**, J. W. von.] "Extracts from Goethe's Scientific Work." Trans. Eleanor Merry. Pt. III of *Pure Colour*. Ed. Maria Schindler and Eleanor C. Merry. Towards a New Culture, 7. London: New Culture Publications, 1946, pp. 1-87.
>   "Contributions to Optics. Researches into the Elements of a Theory of Colour. Moral Effects of Colour. With 1 black and white plate."
>   /TRANSLATION: ENGLISH

1946-5 *Goethe, J. W. von. "Der Granit." Iserlohn: Silva-Verlag, 1946.
15 pp.
/EDITION

1946-6 *Goethe, J. W. von. "Der Granit. Ein Fragment vom 18 Jan.
1784." Halle: Isert, 1946. 2 pp.
/EDITION

1946-7 *Goethe, J. W. von. *Teoria de los colores*. Trans. Pablo Simón.
Collección Luz y Sombra. Buenos Aires: Edit. Poseidón, 1946. 486
pp.
/TRANSLATION: SPANISH

1946-8 Hocquette, Maurice. *Les Fantaisies botaniques de Goethe*. Lille:
Yves Demailly, 1946. 123 pp.
Rev. R. Michéa, *Études Germaniques*, 2 (1947), 466f.
/BOTANY

1946-9 Matthaei, Rupprecht. "Zu Goethe's Farbenaesthetik. Eine
mißverständliche Stelle, wie sie zu deuten ist und wie sie
veranschaulicht werden kann." *Natur und Volk*, 75/76 (1946), 38-43.
/CHROMATICS/AESTHETICS

1946-10 Merry, Eleanor C. "Painting and Imagination." Pt. II of *Pure
Colour*. Ed. Maria Schindler and Eleanor C. Merry. Towards a
New Culture, 6. London: New Culture Publications, 1946, pp. 1-66.
"With 2 black and white and 4 coloured reproductions of paint-
ings by the author."
/RESEARCH: CHROMATICS

1946-11 *Münz, Ludwig. "Wolkenstudien von Constable und Goethe."
Blick in die Welt [Hamburg], No. 5 (1946), 40-42.
/METEOROLOGY/CONSTABLE, J

1946-12 Schindler, Maria. "Goethe's Theory of Colour Applied." Pt. I
of *Pure Colour*. Ed. Maria Schindler and Eleanor C. Merry.
Towards a New Culture, 5. London: New Culture Publications,
1946, pp. 1-117.
/RESEARCH: CHROMATICS

1946-13 Schindler, Maria and Eleanor C. Merry. *Pure Colour*.
Towards a New Culture, 5-7. London: New Culture Publications,
1946. 117; 66; 87 pp.

Cf. Nos. 1946-4, 1946-10, 1946-12 and 1964-24.
Bound together, but paginated separately.
Rev. Elizabeth M. Wilkinson, *Publications of the English Goethe Society*, NS 16 (1947), 120-24.
/RESEARCH: CHROMATICS

1946-14 **Schmitt**, Paul. "Natur und Geist in Goethes Verhältnis zu den Naturwissenschaften." *Eranos-Jahrbuch*, 14 (1946), 332-84.
Rpt. No. 1959-31.
/EPISTEMOLOGY/METHOD

1946-15 *****Schottenloher**, H[?]. "Aus der Epoche der Grundlagen-schöpfung. Goethes Objektivität des Sinneserlebnisses." In his "Wie kann der Organismus auf verschiedene Einwirkungen hin verschieden ansprechen? Ein Beitrag zur Entwicklung unserer Vorstellungen über das Geschehen im Nervensystem." Diss. Erlangen 1946, pp. 30-53.
/NEUROLOGY

1946-16 **Steffen**, Albert. "Anschauende Urteilskraft und Ordnung des Schicksals als Grundlagen gegenwärtiger Dichtung." *Das Goetheanum*, 25 (1946), 132-3.
/RESEARCH: LITERARY THEORY

1946-17 **Steiner**, Rudolf. "Experiment und menschliches Interesse." *Das Goetheanum*, 25 (1946), 241-2.
/RESEARCH: METHOD/METHOD

1946-18 **Steiner**, Rudolf. "Von der Naturbeobachtung zum Experiment." *Das Goetheanum*, 25 (1946), 233-4.
/RESEARCH: METHOD/METHOD

1946-19 **Thone**, Frank. "A Poet's Botany." *Science News Letter*, 50 (1946), 318.
/BOTANY

1946-20 *****Vernadskii**, V[ladimir]. I[vanovich]. "Gete kak naturalist. Mysli i zamechaniia [Goethe as a Naturalist. Thoughts and Observations]." *Buileten' Moskovskogo obschestva ispytatelelei prirody, Novaia seriia*, 51 [odt. geologii], (1946), vyp. 1, 5-52.
Rpt. No. 1981-104 and 1988-77.
In Russian.
/GENERAL INTRODUCTION

1947-1 *****[anon.]** "Goethe im Reiche der Steine." *Der Naturstein [Ulm]*,

3 June 1947, 62-4.
/GEOLOGY

1947-2 **Bassermann**, Dieter. "Goethe als Naturforscher." In *Goethe als Naturforscher: Aus Goethes naturwissenschaftlichen Schriften, Briefen und Gesprächen.* Ed. and intro. Dieter Bassermann. Berlin: Minerva-Verlag, 1947, pp. 7-23.
   Rev. Helmut Gumtau, "Goethe als Naturforscher," *Aufbau: Kulturpolitisches Monatsschrift,* 5 (1949), 187-8.
   /GENERAL INTRODUCTION

1947-3 **Boller**, Ernst, Donald **Brinkmann** and Emil J. **Walter**. "Goethes Farbenlehre." In their *Einführung in die Farbenlehre.* Bern: A. Francke AG. Verlag, 1947, pp. 81-3.
   /CHROMATICS

1947-4 ***Bühler**, Walter. "Die Entdeckung der Urpflanze durch Goethe." Herford: Die Arche, 1947. 2 pp.
   /BOTANY

1947-5 ***Bühler**, Walter. "Nachwort" to Goethe, J. W. von. *Die Metamorphose der Pflanzen.* Postscr. Walter Bühler. Herford: Verlag Die Arche, 1947. 80 pp.
   /BOTANY

1947-6 **Federici**, Ajroldi Giovanna. "Metamorfosi degli animali [Die Metamorphose der Tiere]." *Dizionario Letterario Bompiani delle Opere e dei Personaggi di tutte le letterature.* Milano: Velantino Bompiani Editore, 1947, IV, 703.
   In Italian.
   /WORKS: LYRICS

1947-7 **Federici**, Ajroldi Giovanna. "Metamorfosi degli piante [Die Metamorphose der Pflanzen]." *Dizionario Letterario Bompiani delle Opere e dei Personaggi di tutte le letterature.* Milano: Velantino Bompiani Editore, 1947, IV, 1947, 703-4.
   In Italian.
   /WORKS: LYRICS

1947-8 **Goethe**, Johann Wolfgang von. "Die Metamorphose der Pflanzen." In *Die Arche: Zeitungsbände für jedermann.* Ed. Hans Wohlbold and Walther Bühler. Herford: Verlag Die Arche, 1947, pp. 9-31.
   /EDITION

1947-9 **Goethe**, J. W. von. *Die Metamorphose der Pflanzen*. Postscr. Walter Bühler. Herford: Verlag Die Arche, 1947. 80 pp.
   Cf. No. 1947-5.
   /EDITION

1947-10 **Goethe**, Johann Wolfgang von. "Die Natur (ein aphoristischer Aufsatz)." In *Die Arche: Zeitungsbände für jedermann*. Ed. Hans Wohlbold and Walther Bühler. Herford: Verlag Die Arche, 1947, pp. 1-2.
   /EDITION

1947-11 [**Goethe**, J. W. von.] *Naturwissenschaftliche Schriften*. 3 vols. Ed. Rudolf Steiner. 3rd edn. Bern: Troxler-Verlag, 1947-1949.
   Rpt. of Nos. 1882-10, 1884-5, and 1884-6.
   /EDITION

1947-12 **Goethe**, Johann Wolfgang von. *Schriften zur Geologie und Mineralogie 1770-1810*. Vol. I.1 of *Leopoldina-Ausgabe*. Ed. Günther Schmid. Weimar: Hermann Böhlaus Nachfolger, 1947. 393 pp., 20 plates.
   Rev. Paul Niggli, "Zur Neuausgabe der Naturwissenschaftlichen Schriften Goethes." *Neue Zürcher Zeitung*, 12 April 1948. [In Mappe III E 61/C20: "Goethe und die Naturwissenschaften. Zeitungsausschnitte 1913 -" at the Frankfurter Goethe-Museum.]
   Rev. H. Fischer, *Gesnerus*, 7 (1950), 91.
   Rev. J. Fränkel, *Erasmus*, 5 (1952), 98-104.
   /EDITION: SELECTIONS

1947-13 **Goethe**, Johann Wolfgang von. "Der Versuch als Vermittler von Objekt und Subjekt." In *Die Arche: Zeitungsbände für jedermann*. Ed. Hans Wohlbold and Walther Bühler. Herford: Verlag Die Arche, 1947, pp. 3-8.
   /EDITION

1947-14 **Goethe** *als Naturforscher: Aus Goethes naturwissenschaftlichen Schriften, Briefen und Gesprächen*. Ed. and intro. Dieter Bassermann. Berlin: Minerva-Verlag, 1947. 161 pp.
   Cf. No. 1947-2.
   /EDITION: SELECTIONS

1947-15 **Heisenberg**, Werner. "Die Goethesche und die Newtonsche Farbenlehre im Lichte der modernen Physik." In his *Wandlungen in den*

Grundlagen der Naturwissenschaft: Sieben Vorträge. 7th exp. edn.
Leipzig/Stuttgart/Zürich: S. Hirzel Verlag, 1947, pp. 54-70.
Rpt. of No. 1941-12.
/CHROMATICS/NEWTON, I/METHOD/RESEARCH:
PHYSICS

1947-16 **Hildebrandt**, Kurt. *Goethes Naturerkenntnis.* Hamburg-
Bergedorf: Strom-Verlag, 1947. 379 pp.
Rpt. 3rd edn. 1949.
Rev. H. J. Weigand, *Germanic Review*, 25 (1950), 232-3.
/GENERAL INTRODUCTION

1947-17 **Hirsch**, Ernst. "Georg Graf Buquoy, ein vergessener Goethe-
anist." *Das Goetheanum*, 26 (1947), 362-4.
/BUQUOY, G VON/NATURPHILOSOPHIE

1947-18 **Hodel**, Sebastian. *Die Mißbildungslehre und Goethes Metamor-
phosengedanke in historischer und erkenntnistheoretischer Darstel-
lung.* Basel: Zbinden, 1947. 54 pp.
Rpt. No. 1948-12.
/PATHOLOGY/MORPHOLOGY/EPISTEMOLOGY
/SÖMMERING, S

1947-19 **Hölder**, Helmut. "Grenzfragen naturwissenschaftlicher
Forschung. Zum Problem der Grenzüberschreitung empirischer
Methodik, gestützt auf Goethesche Naturforschung und einige
Beispiele aus der Gegenwart." Tübinger naturwissenschaftliche
Abhandlungen, 16. 2nd rev. edn. Stuttgart: Enke, 1947, pp. 12-26.
Rpt. (rev. edn.) of No. 1941-14.
Cf. esp. "Goethes Forschung und ihre Grenzen," pp. 15-33.
/METHOD/EPISTEMOLOGY

1947-20 **Hundt**, Rudolf. "Goethes 'Urpflanze' und die ältesten
Landpflanzen der Erde." *Natur und Technik*, 1 (1947), 156-7.
/BOTANY/BIOLOGY: EVOLUTION

1947-21 **Knauer**, Helmut. "Der Bau der Erde im Bewusstseinserleben
einer neuen Zeit." *Das Goetheanum*, 26 (1947), 389-91; 394.
/RESEARCH: GEOLOGY/GEOLOGY

1947-22 **Knauer**, Helmut. "Entstehung und Aufbau der Mineralien."
Das Goetheanum, 26 (1947), 178-81.
/RESEARCH: MINERALOGY/MINERALOGY

1947-23 **Locher-Ernst**, Louis. "Grundriss einer Metamorphosenlehre (Skizze zu einem Vortrag)." *Das Goetheanum*, 26 (1947), 322-5.
/RESEARCH: MORPHOLOGY

1947-24 **Matthaei**, Rupprecht. "Die Farbenlehre in Faust." *Goethe*, NF 10 (1947), 59-148.
/CHROMATICS/WORKS: FAUST

1947-25 **Matthaei**, Rupprecht. "Grundlagen der farbigen Gestaltung[: I-IV]." *Farben, Lacke, Anstrichstoffe [Stuttgart]*, 1 (1947), 40-46.
Cf. continuation, No. 1947-26.
/RESEARCH: CHROMATICS/CHROMATICS

1947-26 **Matthaei**, Rupprecht. "Grundlagen der farbigen Gestaltung: V. Wesen und Ursprung eines Grundgesetzes der farbigen Gestaltung (im Anschlusse an Goethe betrachtet)." *Farben, Lacke, Anstrichstoffe [Stuttgart]*, 1 (1947), 72-4.
Continuation of No. 1947-25.
Cf. continuation, No. 1948-18.
/RESEARCH: CHROMATICS/CHROMATICS

1947-27 **Oppel**, Horst. *Morphologische Literaturwissenschaft: Goethes Ansicht und Methode*. Mainz: Verlag Kirchheim, 1947. 120 pp.
Rpt. No. 1967-39.
/LITERARY THEORY/RESEARCH: LITERARY THEORY

1947-28 **Rebholz**, M[ax]. "Goethe und die Naturwissenschaft." *Die Kommenden*, 1, No. 22 (1947), 5-7.
/GENERAL INTRODUCTION

1947-29 **Rille**, J[?]. H. "Goethe und die Pellagra in Südtirol." *Wiener klinische Wochenschrift*, 59 (1947), 330-33; 347-9.
Cf. expanded version, No. 1949-126.
"Vortrag im Oesterreichischen Institut für Kultur und Wissenschaft, Innsbruck, 28. Mai 1946."
/MEDICINE/PLACES: TIROL

1947-30 **Steiner**, Rudolf. "Goetheanismus und Darwinismus." *Das Goetheanum*, 26 (1947), 329-30.
"Aus Rudolf Steiner: 'Der Sturz der Geister der Finsternis.' (Band II, Geistige Wesen und ihre Wirkungen.) Phil.-Anthrop. Verlag."
/BIOLOGY: EVOLUTION/DARWIN, C

1947-31 **Wachsmuth**, Andreas B[runo]. "Bildung und Wirkung: Die Polarität in Goethes Lebenskunst." *Goethe*, NF 10 (1947), 3-30.
  Rpt. No. 1966-32.
  /MORPHOLOGY

1947-32 **Willoughby**, L[eonard]. A[shley]. "Einheit und Zusammenhang bei Goethe." *Goethe*, 10 (1947), 149-67.
  German trans. of No. 1947-33.
  /PHILOSOPHY

1947-33 **Willoughby**, L[eonard]. A[shley]. "Unity and Continuity in Goethe." Oxford: Clarendon Press, 1947. 31 pp.
  Rpt. No. 1968-51.
  Trans. into German, No. 1947-32.
  The Taylorian Lecture for 1947.
  /PHILOSOPHY

1947-34 **Wittkowski**, Victor. "Um Artigo de Goethe, sôbre Palmeiras e Paisagens do Brasil [An Article by Goethe on the Palms and Landscapes of Brazil]." *Provincia de Sao Pedro*, 10 (1947), 89-92.
  Rpt. of No. 1945-11.
  In Portuguese.
  /BOTANY/PLACES: BRAZIL

1947-35 **Wohlbold**, Hans. "Goethes Schau der Natur." In *Die Arche: Zeugnisse aus dem geistigen Europa*. Herford: Die Arche, 1947.
  Inserts: Goethe, "Die Natur" [aus dem Tiefurter Journal]; "Der Versuch als Vermittler von Objekt und Subjekt"; "Metamorphose der Pflanzen" [Prosaauffsatz]. 32 pp.
  /EDITION: SELECTIONS

1948-1 ***Barthel**, E[rnst]. *Goethes Farben- und Wissenschaftslehre*. Baden-Baden: Bühler, 1948. 288 pp.
  /CHROMATICS/EPISTEMOLOGY

1948-2 **Bergstraesser**, Arnold. "Die Epochen der Geistesgeschichte in Goethes Denken." *Monatshefte*, 40 (1948), 127-36.
  /RESEARCH: MORPHOLOGY/RESEARCH: HISTORIOGRAPHY

1948-3 **Bizzarrini**, G[?]. "W. Goethe nella storia delle scienze mediche e naturali [Goethe in the History of the Medical and Natural Sciences]." *Minerva medica*, 39, vol. 1, No. 15 (1948), 623-6.
  In Italian.

434

/GENERAL INTRODUCTION

1948-4 **Eckermann**, Johann Peter. *Gespräche mit Goethe in den letzten Jahren seines Lebens.* Ed. and intro. Ernst Beutler. Vol. 24 of *Gedenkausgabe.* Zürich: Artemis-Verlag, 1948. 925 pp.
Rpt. of No. 1836-5.
/EDITION

1948-5 **Fuchs**, Arthur. "Wie verhalten sich Atomphysik und Goetheanismus zu nicht-sinnlichen Wirklichkeitsgebieten?" *Das Goetheanum*, 27 (1948), 118-9.
/RESEARCH: PHYSICS

1948-6 **Goethe**, J. W. von. "An Essay on Granite." Trans. Norbert Guterman. In *The Permanent Goethe.* Ed., sel. and intro. by Thomas Mann. Permanent Library. New York: The Dial Press, 1948, pp. 589-92.
/TRANSLATION: ENGLISH

1948-7 **Goethe**, Johann Wolfgang von. "Die sinnlich-sittliche Wirkung der Farben." Leipzig: Berger & Wirth, 1948. 12 pp.
Herausgegeben zum 125. Jahrestag der eigenen Fertigung von Druckfarben." "Privatdruck."
/EDITION

1948-8 *****Grohmann**, Gerbert. *Lesebuch der Pflanzenkunde.* Freiburg i[n] Br[eisgau]: Novalis-Verlag, 1948.
Rpt. No. 1956-10.
Rev. Hermann Poppelbaum, *Das Goetheanum*, 27 (1948), 196-7.
/RESEARCH: BOTANY

1948-9 **Grohmann**, Gerbert. "Das Löffelkraut (Cochlearia officinalis)." *Das Goetheanum*, 27 (1948), 20-22.
/RESEARCH: BOTANY

1948-10 **Grohmann**, Gerbert. "Die Pflanze als Lichtsinnesorgan der Erde: Nach einem am Goetheanum gehaltenen Vortrag." *Das Goetheanum*, 27 (1948), 146-8; 154-5.
/RESEARCH: BOTANY

1948-11 **Grohmann**, Gerbert. *Die Pflanze: Ein Weg zum Verständnis ihres Wesens: Erster Band.* Freiburg i[n] Br[eisgau]: Novalis-Verlag, 1948. 207 pp.
Cf. vol. II, No. 1951-16.

Trans. into English, No. 1974-16.
"Herausgegeben von der Naturwissenschaftlichen Sektion der
Freien Hochschule für Geisteswissenschaft am Goetheanum."
Rev. H[ermann]. P[oppelbaum]., *Das Goetheanum*, 28 (1949),
54-5.
/RESEARCH: BOTANY

1948-12 **Hodel**, Sebastian. *Goethes Metamorphosengedanke in Miss-
geburtenlehre und Erkenntnistheorie.* Veröffentlichungen der
medizinischen Sektion am Goetheanum Dornach. Basel: Verlag R.
G. Zbinden & Co., 1948. viii, 57 pp.
Rpt. of No. 1947-18.
/PATHOLOGY/MORPHOLOGY/EPISTEMOLOGY
/SÖMMERING, S

1948-13 **Kiesselbach**, Anton. "Goethes Zwischenkieferstudien."
*Medizinische Monatsschrift: Zeitschrift für allgemeine Medizin und
Therapie*, 2 (1948), 427-30.
"Aus dem Anatomischen Institut der Außenstelle der Medizin-
ischen Fakultät der Universität München in Regensburg.
Leiter: Professor Dr. W. Pfuhl."
/OSTEOLOGY

1948-14 **Kipp**, Friedrich A. *Höherentwicklung und Menschwerdung.*
Stuttgart: Hippokrates-Verlag Marquardt & Cie., 1948. 60 pp.
Rev. G[erbert]. Grohmann, *Das Goetheanum*, 27 (1948), 197-8.
/RESEARCH: BIOLOGY/BIOLOGY: EVOLUTION

1948-15 **Kipp**, Friedrich A. "Zum Problem der 'spezifischen Sinnes-
energien.' Ein Beitrag zur Goetheschen Farbenlehre." *Die Drei*, 18
(1948), 271-85.
/RESEARCH: CHROMATICS/CHROMATICS/MÜLLER,
J/RUNGE, P

1948-16 *****Klein**, E[dmond J.]. "Die Urpflanze." *Die Kommenden*, 2
(1948), 10-13.
/BOTANY

1948-17 **Loesche**, Martin. *Goethes geistige Welt.* Welt und Genius.
Stuttgart: S. Hirzel Verlag, 1948. 380 pp.
/GENERAL INTRODUCTION/NATURPHILO-
SOPHIE/PHILOSOPHY

1948-18 **Matthaei**, Rupprecht. "Grundlagen der farbigen Gestaltung:

VI." *Farben, Lacke, Anstrichstoffe [Stuttgart]*, 2 (1948), 5-8; 21-4.
Continuation of No. 1947-26.
Cf. continuation, No. 1948-19.
/RESEARCH: CHROMATICS/CHROMATICS

1948-19 **Matthaei**, Rupprecht. "Grundlagen der farbigen Gestaltung:
VII. Die zweite Wandlung." *Farben, Lacke, Anstrichstoffe
[Stuttgart]*, 2 (1948), 72-4; 88-91.
Continuation of No. 1948-18.
Cf. continuation, No. 1949-116.
/RESEARCH: CHROMATICS/CHROMATICS

1948-20 **May**, Eduard. "Zum Goethejahr 1949: Erkenntnistheoretische
und methodologische Betrachtungen zur Naturforschung Goethes."
Zeitschrift für philosophische Forschung, 3 (1948), 501-11.
/EPISTEMOLOGY/METHOD

1948-21 **Müller**, Armin. "Objektive Schönheit der lebendigen Natur."
n.p.: n.p., December 1948.
In Mappe III E 21/C91: "Goethe und die Farbenlehre 1913-.
Sammelmappe Zeitungsausschnitte" at the Frankfurter Goethe-
Museum.
/CHROMATICS

1948-22 **Müller**, Günther. *Gestaltung-Umgestaltung in Wilhelm Meisters
Lehrjahren*. Halle (Saale): Max Niemeyer Verlag, 1948. 100 pp.
Rpt. No. 1968-24.
/RESEARCH: LITERARY CRITICISM/WORKS: WILHELM
MEISTERS LEHRJAHRE/RESEARCH: MORPHOLOGY

1948-23 **Naegler**, W[?]. "Goethe als Meteorologe." *Meteorologische
Rundschau*, 1 (1948), 311.
/METEOROLOGY

1948-24 **Popplebaum**, Hermann. "Aus der sinnlich-übersinnlichen
Sprache der Naturreiche." *Das Goetheanum*, 27 (1948), 301-3.
Cf. continuation, No. 1948-25.
"Erster Teil eines Vortrags bei der öffentlichen Sommertagung
am Goetheanum."
/EPISTEMOLOGY

1948-25 **Poppelbaum**, Hermann. "Rituale und Tänze der Vögel." *Das
Goetheanum*, 27 (1948), 306-8.
Continuation of No. 1948-24.

/RESEARCH: ETHOLOGY

1948-26 *__Portmann__, Adolf. "Von der Idee des Humanen in der gegen-wärtigen Biologie." *Basler Universitätsreden*, 22 (1948).
Rpt. Nos. 1950-65 and 1956-35.
Trans. into Dutch, No. 1961-36.
/RESEARCH: ANTHROPOLOGY

1948-27 *__Purkyne__, Jan. "Beiträge zur Kenntnis des Sehens in subjektiver Hinsicht." In *Johannis Evangelistae Purkyne opera selecta*. Opera Facultatis Medicae Universitatis Carolinae Pragensis, 1. Pragae: Spolek ceskych lékaru, 1948.
Rpt. of No. 1819-12.
/RESEARCH: SENSORY PHYSIOLOGY/RESEARCH: CHROMATICS

1948-28 __Reimprecht__, Richard. "Die Metamorphose des Weinstocks: Anekdote." n.p.: n.p., 6 November 1948.
In Mappe III E 21/C91: "Goethe und die Farbenlehre 1913-. Sammelmappe Zeitungsausschnitte" at the Frankfurter Goethe-Museum.
/VINOCULTURE

1948-29 __Rille__, J[?]. H. "Aus der Geschichte der Pellagra im Südtirol und in der Lombardei: zugleich ein Beitrag zu Goethes Italienischer Reise." *Gesnerus: Vierteljahrsschrift für Geschichte der Medizin und der Naturwissenschaften*, 5 (1948), 109-24.
"Nach einem Vortrag im österreichischen Institut für Kultur und Wissenschaft in Innsbruck am 28. Mai 1946."
/MEDICINE/PLACES: TIROL/PLACES: LOMBARDY

1948-30 *__Roth__, Karl. "Meine Protanopie." Med. Diss. Erlangen 1948. 67 pp.
/RESEARCH: CHROMATICS/RESEARCH: MEDICINE

1948-31 *__Schmidt__, Herbert. "Untersuchungen über einen gleichstufigen Farbenkreis." Diss. Erlangen 1948. 33 pp.
/RESEARCH: CHROMATICS

1948-32 __Seidel__, Fritz. *Goethe gegen Kant: Goethes wissenschaftliche Leistung als Naturforscher und Philosoph*. Philosophische Reihe. Berlin: Altberliner Verlag Lucie Groszer[, 1948]. 118 pp.
/GENERAL INTRODUCTION/KANT, I/EPISTEMOLOGY

1948-33 *Stehli, Georg J. "Aus Goethes mikroskopischen Studien."
Mikrokosmos, 38 (1948/1949), 241-4.
/MICROSCOPY

1948-34 Steiner, Rudolf. "Das Gewahrwerden der Idee in der Wirklich-
keit." *Das Goetheanum*, 27 (1948), 273-4.
"Aus den Einleitungen zu Goethes naturwissenschaftlichen
Schriften" [1882ff.].
/EPISTEMOLOGY/METHOD

1948-35 Steiner, Rudolf. "Goetheanismus als Erwartungsstimmung
künftigen Christentums." *Das Goetheanum*, 27 (1948), 377-8; 385-6.
"Aus einem Vortrag vom 12. Januar 1919 ("Der Goetheanismus,
ein Menschen-Umwandlungsimpuls und Auferstehungsgedanke)."
/RESEARCH: THEOLOGY

1948-36 *Steiner, Rudolf. "Goethe's beschouwing van de wereld der
kleuren." Trans. F. C. J. Los. s'Gravenhaage, 1948.
Dutch trans. of ?
/CHROMATICS

1948-37 Steiner, Rudolf. "Der Goethesche Typusgedanken." *Das
Goetheanum*, 27 (1948), 265-6.
"Aus den Einleitungen zu Goethes naturwissenschaftlichen
Schriften" [1882ff.].
/MORPHOLOGY/EPISTEMOLOGY

1948-38 Steiner, Rudolf. "Goethes Grundbegriff über die Menschen-
gestalt." *Das Goetheanum*, 27 (1948), 241-2.
"Aus den Einleitungen zu Goethes naturwissenschaftlichen
Schriften" [1882ff.].
/ANATOMY/ANTHROPOLOGY

1948-39 Steiner, Rudolf. "Goethes Methode, um in die organische Welt
einzudringen." *Das Goetheanum*, 27 (1948), 249-50.
"Aus den Einleitungen zu Goethes naturwissenschaftlichen
Schriften" [1882ff.].
/BIOLOGY/EPISTEMOLOGY

1948-40 Steiner, Rudolf. "Goethes zentrale Entdeckung." *Das
Goetheanum*, 27 (1948), 233-4.
"Aus den Einleitungen zu Goethes Naturwissenschaftlichen
Schriften" [1882ff.].

439

/METHOD

1948-41 **Steiner**, Rudolf. "Goethe und die Mathematik." *Das Goetheanum*, 27 (1948), 177.
Rpt. of No. 1921-28.
"Aus einem Vortragszyklus "Grenzen der Naturerkenntnis", Dornach, 29. September 1920.
/MATHEMATICS

1948-42 **Steiner**, Rudolf. "Das System der Farbenlehre." *Das Goetheanum*, 27 (1948), 289-90.
"Aus den Einleitungen zu Goethes naturwissenschaftlichen Schriften" [1882ff.].
/CHROMATICS

1948-43 **Steiner**, Rudolf. "Über die philosophische Grundlage für ein wissenschaftliches System der Organismen." *Das Goetheanum*, 27 (1948), 257-8.
"Aus den Einleitungen zu Goethes naturwissenschaftlichen Schriften" [1882ff.].
/BIOLOGY/EPISTEMOLOGY

1948-44 **Troll**, Wilhelm. "Urbild und Ursache in der Biologie." *Sitzungsberichte der Heidelberger Akademie der Wissenschaften*, 6 (1948), 121-44.
/BIOLOGY/EPISTEMOLOGY

1948-45 ***Villalobos**, Dominguez. "Goethe y la teoria de los colores [Goethe and the Theory of Colors]." *La Nación*, Buenos Aires, margo 28, 1948.
In Spanish.
/CHROMATICS

1948-46 **Vortriede**, Werner. "Zu Goethes Morphologie: Betrachtung eines Gedichts." *Trivium: Schweiz. Vierteljahresschrift für Literaturwissenschaft*, 6 (1948), 218-23.
/WORKS: FAUST/MORPHOLOGY

1948-47 **Wohlbold**, Hans. "Goethe und die Naturwissenschaft." In *Goethe-Almanach*. Wien: Bellaria-Verlag, 1948, pp. 204-14.
/GENERAL INTRODUCTION

1948-48 **Wohlbold**, Hans. "Das heilige Licht." *Die Kommenden*, 2, No. 16 (1948), 4.

/CHROMATICS/NEWTON, I

1949-1 **Adams**, George. "Goethe's Concept of 'Light and Darkness' and the Science of the Future." *The Golden Blade*, 1949, pp. 64-76. Rpt. No. 1977-1.
/CHROMATICS/METHOD/RESEARCH: CHROMATICS

1949-2 **Adams**, George and Olive **Whicher**. *The Living Plant and the Science of Physical and Ethereal Spaces; a Study of the Metamorphosis of Plants in the light of modern geometry and morphology.* Clent, Worcestershire: Goethean Science Foundation, 1949. 77 pp. Library of Congress QK 46.A3
/RESEARCH: BOTANY/RESEARCH: MORPHOLOGY/MATHEMATICS

1949-3 **Albrecht**, Erich A. "Geoffroy Saint-Hilaire a Translator of Goethe?" *Modern Language Notes*, 64 (1949), 47-9.
/SAINT-HILAIRE, G/BOHTLINGK, N/STEINER, R

1949-4 **Alverdes**, Friedrich. "Goethes Morphologie." *Forschungen und Fortschritte*, 25 (1949), 258-62.
/MORPHOLOGY

1949-5 **Andrade**, E. N. da C. "Goethe as Natural Philosopher." *Nature*, 164 (1949), 338-40.
Cf. the reply by R. Weale, No. 1949-190.
/GENERAL INTRODUCTION

1949-6 **André**, Hans. "Goethes Naturanschauung in ihrer Bedeutung für die Gegenwart." *Die Neue Ordnung: Zeitschrift für Religion, Kultur, Gesellschaft*, 3 (1949), 441-54.
/GENERAL INTRODUCTION

1949-7 **Ankert**, Bruno. "Goethe als Botaniker." *Der Palmen-Garten: Frankfurt am Main*, 2, No. 8 (1949), 4.
In Mappe III E 61/C20: "Goethe und die Naturwissenschaften. Zeitungsausschnitte 1913 -" at the Frankfurter Goethe-Museum.
/BOTANY

1949-8 **Baehni**, Charles. "M. de Goethe, botaniste." *Gesnerus: Vierteljahrsschrift für Geschichte der Medizin und der Naturwissenschaften*, 6 (1949), 110-28.
"Conférence faite à Lausanne le 4 septembre 1949, devant la

S.H.S.N., et sous les auspices de la Societé suisse d'histoire de la médicine et des sciences naturelles."
/BOTANY

1949-9 **Baier**, Ernst. "Mineralogie und Geologie in Goethes Leben und Werk." *Experientia*, 5 (1949), 495-8.
/GEOLOGY/MINERALOGY

1949-10 **Balzer**, Georg. *Goethes Bryophyllum: Ein Beitrag zu seiner Pflanzenmorphologie*. Berlin-Kleinmachnow: Gartenverlag, 1949. 88 pp.
/BOTANY/MORPHOLOGY

1949-11 **Baravalle**, Hermann von. "Goethes Methodik und die moderne Physik." *Die Drei*, 19 (1949), 329-37.
/METHOD/PHYSICS/RESEARCH: PHYSICS

1949-12 **Bargmann**, Wolfgang. "Goethes Morphologie." Freiburg: Verlag Karl Alber, 1949. 26 pp.
Rpt. (extract) No. 1952-2.
/MORPHOLOGY

1949-13 **Bartlett**, Harley H. "Goethe as a Biologist." *Michigan Alumnus Quarterly Review*, 55, No. 24 (1949), 300-312.
/BOTANY

1949-14 **Benn**, Gottfried. *Goethe und die Naturwissenschaften*. Die kleinen Bücher der Arche, 208. Zürich: Verlag der Arche, 1949. 62 pp.
Rpt. of No. 1932-24.
Rev. R[ené]. Michéa [No. 1950-52].
/GENERAL INTRODUCTION

1949-15 **Benn**, Gottfried. *Goethe und die Naturwissenschaften*. Zürich: Verlag der Arche, 1949. 62 pp.
Rpt. of No. 1932-24.
/GENERAL INTRODUCTION

1949-16 ***Bernays**, A[?]. "Goethes Farbenlehre." *Dialectica*. 1949.
/CHROMATICS

1949-17 **Bertalanffy**, Ludwig von. "Goethes Naturauffassung." *Atlantis: Länder/Völker/Reisen*, 21 (1949), 357-63.
Trans. into English, No. 1951-4.

/GENERAL INTRODUCTION

1949-18 **Bindel**, Ernst. "Goethes Aufsatz 'Anschauende Urteilskraft'."
Das Goetheanum, 28 (1949), 356-7; 362-4.
/METHOD

1949-19 ***Bluntschli**, Hans. "Goethe als Naturforscher und Biologe.
Ansprache gehalten bei der Goethefeier der Universität Bern." Bern,
1949. 32 pp.
/GENERAL INTRODUCTION/BIOLOGY

1949-20 **Bochalli**, R[?]. "Goethes Beziehungen zur Medizin und Natur-
wissenschaft, zeitlich geordnet, mit besonderer Berücksichtigung von
'Dichtung und Wahrheit' und Eckermanns 'Gespräche mit Goethe'."
Hippokrates, 20 (1949), 436-43.
/MEDICINE/GENERAL INTRODUCTION/WORKS:
DICHTUNG UND WAHRHEIT/WORKS: CONVERSA-
TIONS

1949-21 **Boerger**, Alberto. "La universalidad de Goethe en relación con
América Latina [Goethe's Universality in Relation to Latin
America]." In his *Filosofía -- Biología -- Agronomia: Selección de
Conferencias*. Montevideo: Barreiro y Ramos, 1949, pp. 337-47.
In Spanish.
"Con motivo del bicentenario de su nacimento (28 de agosto de
1749), en la Asociación Cultural Uruguayo-Germana.
Montevideo, 1949"
/RECEPTION/HUMBOLDT, A VON

1949-22 **Brednow**, W[alter]. "Goethe und die naturwissenschaftlichen
Gesellschaften." *Zeitschrift für die gesamte innere Medizin und ihre
Grenzgebiete*, 4 (1949), 449-54.
/INSTITUTIONS: SCIENTIFIC SOCIETIES

1949-23 **Carus**, Carl Gustav. *Goethe. Zu dessen näherem Verständnis*.
Ed. and postscript Hans Krey. Dresden: W. Jess, 1949. 245 pp.
Rpt. of No. 1843-5.
Rpt. 4th edn. 1955.
/GENERAL INTRODUCTION

1949-24 **Casparé**, H[?]. E. "Goethe's Metamorphose der Planten." In
A. G. Degenaar, et al., eds. *Met Goethe door de 20e eeuw*. [Den
Haag:] Proteus-uitgave, 1949, pp. 15-20.
In Dutch.

/BOTANY

1949-25 **Christian**, Paul. "Die Wirklichkeit des Sehens und Goethes Farbenlehre." *Studium generale*, 2 (1949), 428-32.
/EPISTEMOLOGY/CHROMATICS

1949-26 **Cloß**, Alois. "Goethe als Naturforscher." In *Jahr der Ehrfurcht: Vier Reden zum Goethe-Jahr*. Graz: Leykam Verlag, 1949, pp. 71-104.
/GENERAL INTRODUCTION

1949-27 **Corrington**, J[?]. D. "Goethe, Rosenkavalier of Science." *Nature*, 142 (1949), 102-3.
/GENERAL INTRODUCTION

1949-28 **Degenaar**, A[?]. G. "Geneeskunde en de idee der metamorphose [Medicine and the Idea of Metamorphosis]." In A. G. Degenaar, et al., eds. *Met Goethe door de 20e eeuw*. [Den Haag:] Proteusuitgave, 1949, pp. 50-58.
In Dutch.
/MEDICINE/MORPHOLOGY

1949-29 **Degenaar**, A[?]. G. "Metamorphose als bevrijdingsproces [Metamorphosis as a Process of Liberation]." In A. G. Degenaar, et al., eds. *Met Goethe door de 20e eeuw*. [Den Haag:] Proteusuitgave, 1949, pp. 73-8.
In Dutch.
/BIOLOGY

1949-30 **Degenaar**, A[?]. G. et al., eds. *Met Goethe door de 20e eeuw [With Goethe through the 20th Century]*. [Den Haag:] Proteusuitgave, 1949. 160 pp.
Cf. Nos. 1949-24, -28, -29, -85, -86, -87 and -141.
In Dutch.
/GENERAL INTRODUCTION

1949-31 **Derbolav**, Josef. "Gestalt und Wirklichkeit: Goethes morphologische Methode und das Problem der Grenze zwischen Philosophie und Kunst." *Wissenschaft und Weltbild*, 2 (1949), 184-94.
/METHOD/MORPHOLOGY/AESTHETICS

1949-32 **Dissinger**, Arthur. "Goethe als Förderer von Döbereiner und dessen Platinerforschung." *Geistige Welt: Vierteljahresschrift für*

Kultur- und Geisteswissenschaften, 4, No. 1 (1949/1951), 1-13.
/DÖBEREINER, J/CHEMISTRY

1949-33 **Dorfles**, Gillo. "Goethe e la teoria dei colori [Goethe and the Theory of Color]." *La Rassegna d'Italia*, 4 (1949), 1231-4.
In Italian.
/CHROMATICS

1949-34 **Ebbecke**, U[?]. "Zur Goetheschen Farbenlehre." *Experientia*, 5 (1949), 498-501.
/CHROMATICS

1949-35 **Emmerich**, Liberata. "Goethe and the Earth Sciences." *Mineral Industries* [State College, Pennsylvania], 19, No. 2 (1949), 1-4.
/GEOLOGY/WORKS: WILHELM MEISTERS WANDER-JAHRE/WORKS: FAUST

1949-36 **Encke**[, ?]. "Goethea." *Der Palmen-Garten: Frankfurt am Main*, 2, No. 8 (1949), 3.
In Mappe III E 61/C20: "Goethe und die Naturwissenschaften. Zeitungsausschnitte 1913 -" at the Frankfurter Goethe-Museum.
/BOTANY

1949-37 **Engard**, Charles Joseph. "Poetic Scientist." *Science Monthly*, 68 (1949), 305-9.
/GENERAL INTRODUCTION

1949-38 **Erhard**, Hubert. "Goethe als Naturforscher. Zu Goethes 200. Geburtstag am 28. August 1949." *Naturwissenschaftliche Rundschau*, 2 (1949), 337-42.
/GENERAL INTRODUCTION

1949-39 **Faiss**, Fritz. "Napoleon aus blauem Glase oder Goethes Farben-lehre." *Deutsche Rundschau*, 75 (1949), 429-35.
/CHROMATICS

1949-40 **Fischer**, F[?]. P. "Zu Goethes Gedichten zur Farbenlehre." *Gesnerus: Vierteljahrsschrift für Geschichte der Medizin und der Naturwissenschaften*, 6 (1949), 72-110.
/WORKS: LYRICS/CHROMATIC

1949-41 **Fischer**, Hans. "Goethe und die wissenschaftliche Medizin seiner Zeit." *Gesnerus: Vierteljahrsschrift für Geschichte der Medizin*

und der Naturwissenschaften, 6 (1949), 158-78.
Rpt. No. 1962-4.
"Vortrag, gehalten anläßlich der von der Schweizerischen
Gesellschaft für Geschichte der Medizin und der Naturwis-
senschaften veranstalteten GOETHE-Feier der SNG in
Lausanne, 4. September 1949."
/MEDICINE

1949-42 *Fischer, W[alther]. "Goethe als Botaniker." *Kosmos*, 47
(1949), 313-16.
/BOTANY

1949-43 Franz, Leonhard. "Goethe und die Küstenveränderungen bei
Neapel." *Geographica Helvetica*, 4 (1949), 206-13.
/GEOGRAPHY/GEOLOGY

1949-44 *Friedman, H[?]. "Goethe's Morphology." University College,
London: British Goethe Festival Society, 1949.
/MORPHOLOGY

1949-45 Friedrich, Heinz. "Goethe -- anthropologisch beleuchtet." *Berliner Hefte für geistiges Leben*, 4, "2. Halbjahr" (1949), 186-8.
/CARUS, C/RECEPTION

1949-46 *Gittner, Hermann. "Goethes pharmazeutische Berater."
Pharmazeutische Zentralhalle, 88 (1949), 231-5.
/PHARMACOLOGY/INFLUENCES

1949-47 Goethe, J. W. von. "Ausflug nach Zinnwalde und Altenberg.
Ein Beitrag zum Goethejahr 1949." Ed. Bernhard Jasmund. Dres-
den: Sachsen-Verlag, 1949. 16 pp.
/PLACES: ZINNWALDE/PLACES: ALTENBERG

1949-48 [Goethe, J. W. von.] "Daß Sie mich bei so einer herrlich aus-
gezeichneten Pflanze zum Gevattersmann berufen. . ." *Der Palmen-
Garten: Frankfurt am Main*, 2, No. 8 (1949), 2-3.
Goethe's letter to Nees von Esenbeck of 24 April 1823.
In Mappe III E 61/C20: "Goethe und die Naturwissenschaften.
Zeitungsausschnitte 1913 -" at the Frankfurter Goethe-
Museum.
/EDITION/BOTANY

1949-49 Goethe, J. W. *Gedanken zur Naturforschung*. Sel., with a
postscript by Paul Niggli. Zürich: Fretz & Wasmuth Verlag, 1949.

48 pp.
Cf. No. 1949-135.
/EDITION: SELECTIONS

1949-50 [Goethe, J. W. von.] *Gesetz im Grenzenlosen: Goethes natur-wissenschaftliche Schriften.* Sel. and arr. Peter R. Hofstätter. Graz/Wien: Leykam-Verlag, 1949. 291 pp.
Cf. No. 1949-77.
/EDITION

1949-51 *Goethe, J. W. von. "Granit üzerine [Über den Granit]." Trans. Hayrullah Öhrs. Tercüme 1949, H. 49/51, Goethe özel sayisi, pp. 120-3.
/TRANSLATION: TURKISH

1949-52 Goethe, Jan [Johann] Wolfgang [von]. "Kosc sródszczekowa zarówno zwierzetom jak i czlowiekowi przypisac nalezy. [Os inter-maxillare ist ebenso dem Menschen, wie den Tieren zuzuschreiben]." *Problemy*, 5 (1949), No. 11, 746-51.
/TRANSLATION: POLISH

1949-53 [Goethe, J. W. von.] "Metamorfosi degli animali [Metamor-phose der Tiere]." Trans. R. Küfferle. *Antroposofia*, 4, No. 4 (1949), 109-11.
/TRANSLATION: ITALIAN

1949-54 Goethe, J. W. von. *Naturwissenschaftliche Schriften: Erster Teil.* Ed. Andreas Speiser. Vol. 16 of *Gedenkausgabe der Werke, Briefe und Gespräche, 28. August 1949.* Zürich: Artemis-Verlag, 1949. 997 pp.
Rpt. Nos. 1963-11, 1977-217 and 1979-29.
Cf. No. 1949-169.
/EDITION: SELECTIONS

1949-55 *Goethe, J. W. von. *Renkler teorisinin felsefe ile münasebeti [On Color Theory, Philosophy and Mathematics].* Trans. Nusret Hizir. Tercüme, 1949, H. 49/51, Goethe özel sayisi, pp. 124-6.
/TRANSLATION: TURKISH

1949-56 [Goethe, J. W. von.] "Saggio sulla metamorfosi delle piante [Account of the Metamorphosis of Plants]." Trans. Giorgio Negodi. Modena: Società Tip. Modenese, 1949. 76 pp.
/TRANSLATION: ITALIAN

1949-57 **Goethe**, Johann Wolfgang von. *Schriften zur Geologie und Mineralogie 1812-1832.* Vol. I.2 of *Leopoldina-Ausgabe.* Ed. Günther Schmid. Weimar: Hermann Böhlaus Nachfolger, 1949. 438 pp., 34 plates.
    Rev. J. Fränkel, *Erasmus*, 5 (1952), 98-104.
    /EDITION: SELECTIONS

1949-58 [**Goethe**, J. W. von.] [*Werke und Weltanschauung Goethes.*] Ed. Minshushugi Kagakusha Kyokai. Tokyo: Kan Verlag, 1949. 273 pp.
    /TRANSLATION: JAPANESE

1949-59 **Goethe**, J. W. von. *Wisdom and Experience.* Sel. Ludwig Curtius. Trans., ed. and intro. Hermann J. Weigand. New York: Pantheon, 1949. 299 pp.
    Publ. simul. by Routledge & Paul, London.
    Rpt. 1964.
    Cf. esp. sections "Nature" (pp. 85-112) and "Science and Philosophy" (pp. 113-48)."
    Rev. J. F. G. Rawlins, *Nature*, 14 April 1951.
    /TRANSLATION: ENGLISH

1949-60 **Goethe** *in unserer Zeit. Rudolf Steiners Goetheanismus als Forschungsmethode.* Ed. Guenther Wachsmuth. Dornach-Basel: Hybernia-Verlag, 1949. 243 pp.
    Partial trans. into English, No. 1971-6.
    Publ. by the Naturwissenschaftliche Sektion am Goetheanum Dornach.
    Rev. Rudolf Grosse, *Das Goetheanum*, 28 (1949), 204-5.
    /RESEARCH: VARIOUS

1949-61 *****Gothein**, Wolfgang. *Goethes Naturforschung.* Bekenntnisse zu Goethe, 6. Mainz: Internationaler Universum-Verlag, 1949.
    /GENERAL INTRODUCTION

1949-62 **Grohmann**, Gerbert. "Erkenntnistheoretisches zur Goetheschen Entwicklungslehre." *Die Drei*, 19 (1949), 72-5.
    /EPISTEMOLOGY/BIOLOGY: EVOLUTION

1949-63 **Grünthal**, Ernst. "Goethes 'Maximen und Reflexionen' zur Wissenschaft." In Grünthal, Ernst and Fritz Strauss. *Abhandlungen zu Goethes Naturwissenschaft.* Berner Beiträge zur Geschichte der Medizin und der Naturwissenschaften, 10. Bern: Verlag Paul Haupt, 1949, pp. 19-42.

/METHOD/EPISTEMOLOGY/WORKS: MAXIMEN UND
REFLEXIONEN

1949-64 **Grünthal**, Ernst. "Goethes Studien zur Hirnanatomie." In
Grünthal, Ernst and Fritz Strauss. *Abhandlungen zu Goethes Natur-
wissenschaft*. Berner Beiträge zur Geschichte der Medizin und der
Naturwissenschaften, 10. Bern: Verlag Paul Haupt, 1949, pp. 43-60.
Cf. No. 1943-13.
/ANATOMY/NEUROLOGY

1949-65 **Grünthal**, Ernst. "Ueber den Anlaß zur Entstehung von Goethes
Gedicht: 'Dauer im Wechsel'." In Grünthal, Ernst and Fritz Strauss.
Abhandlungen zu Goethes Naturwissenschaft. Berner Beiträge zur
Geschichte der Medizin und der Naturwissenschaften, 10. Bern: Ver-
lag Paul Haupt, 1949, pp. 61-4.
/WORKS: LYRICS

1949-66 **Grünthal**, Ernst. "Ueber die historischen Wurzeln von Goethes
naturwissenschaftlicher Denkweise." In Grünthal, Ernst and Fritz
Strauss. *Abhandlungen zu Goethes Naturwissenschaft*. Berner
Beiträge zur Geschichte der Medizin und der Naturwissenschaften,
10. Bern: Verlag Paul Haupt, 1949, pp. 5-18.
/INFLUENCES

1949-67 **Grünthal**, Ernst and Fritz **Strauss**. *Abhandlungen zu Goethes
Naturwissenschaft*. Berner Beiträge zur Geschichte der Medizin und
der Naturwissenschaften, 10. Bern: Paul Haupt, 1949. 115 pp.
Cf. Nos. 1949-63, -64, -65, -66 and -176.
Rev. H. Fischer, *Gesnerus*, 7 (1950), 93-4.
/COLLECTION

1949-68 **Hänsel**, Ludwig. "Newton -- Goethe -- Pascal: Die Farbenlehre
und das Problem der Mitte." In *Festschrift zum 200. Geburtstag
Goethes*. Ed. Eduard Castle. Wien: Österreichische Bundesverlag
für Unterricht, Wissenschaft und Kunst, 1949, pp. 113-46.
= *Chronik des Wiener Goethe-Vereins*, 52/53 (1949).
/CHROMATICS/NEWTON, I/PASCAL, B

1949-69 **Halbertsma**, K[laas]. T[jalling]. A[gnus]. "The 18th Century;
Beginning of the 19th Century; Goethe, Schopenhauer." In his *A His-
tory of the Theory of Colour*. Amsterdam: Swets & Zeitlinger, 1949,
pp. 53-80.
See esp. pp. 60-72 on Goethe.
/CHROMATICS/NEWTON, I

1949-70 **Harich**, Wolfgang. "Bemerkungen zu Goethes Naturanschauung." *Neue Welt: Halbmonatsschrift*, 4, No. 16 (1949), 87-132.
/GENERAL INTRODUCTION

1949-71 ***Harich**, Wolfgang. "Goethes Beitrag zum Materialismus. Zum
165. Jahrestag der Entdeckung des Zwischenkieferknochens."
Tägliche Rundschau [Berliner Ausgabe], 27 March 1949, Nr. 73.
/OSTEOLOGY

1949-72 **Henel**, Heinrich. "Goethe und die Naturwissenschaft." *Journal
of English and Germanic Philology*, 48 (1949), 507-32.
        Rpt. No. 1980-25.
        Rev. R[ené]. Michéa [No. 1950-52].
        /GENERAL INTRODUCTION

1949-73 **Hennig**, John. "Goethe's Interest in British Botany." *Proceedings of the Linnaean Society of London*, 161 (1949), 199-207.
        /BOTANY/INFLUENCES/HILL, J/NEES VON ESENBECK,
        C/BROWN, J

1949-74 **Hennig**, John. "Goethe's Interest in British Meteorology."
Modern Language Quarterly, 10 (1949), 321-37.
        "Goethe Issue. Essays in Honor of the Bicentenary of Goethe's
        Birth."
        /METEOROLOGY/INFLUENCES/HOWARD, L

1949-75 **Herberts**, Kurt. "Goethes Lebenswerk als Weg zu einer geistes-
gemäßen Naturwissenschaft. Festvortrag aus Anlaß d. 200. Geburtst.
v. Goethe." Düsseldorf, 1949. 8 pp.
        Rpt. No. 1950-29.
        Offprint from *Chemische Industrie*, NF 1, No. 4 (1949).
        /GENERAL INTRODUCTION/METHOD

1949-76 ***Hoepke**, H[?]. "Goethes Bedeutung für die Naturwissenschaften." *Kosmos*, 47 (1949), 289-92.
        /GENERAL INTRODUCTION

1949-77 **Hofstätter**, Peter R. "Nachwort des Herausgebers." In [Goethe,
J. W. von.] *Gesetz im Grenzenlosen: Goethes naturwissenschaftliche
Schriften*. Sel. and arr. Peter R. Hofstätter. Graz/Wien: Leykam-
Verlag, 1949, pp. 277-85.
        /GENERAL INTRODUCTION

1949-78 *__Hollitscher__, Walter. "Was ist das eigentlich mit Goethes Far-benlehre?" *Neues Deutschland*, 17. Aug. 1949.
/CHROMATICS

1949-79 *__Hübner__, Kurt. "Der Geist des Widerspruchs. Goethes Bedeutung für die Entwicklung der Naturwissenschaft." *Berliner Zeitung*, No. 193, 19 Aug. 1949.
/GENERAL INTRODUCTION

1949-80 __Hundt__, Rudolf. "Beilage. Geraer Goethe-Erinnerungen." [Gera:] Kulturamt der Stadt Gera, 1949. 8 pp.
  Library of Congress Pt 2208.G6H8 Suppl.
/PLACES: GERA/GEOLOGY

1949-81 __Hundt__, Rudolf. *Goethe und die Geologie Ostthüringens*. [Gera:] Kulturamt der Stadt Gera, 1949. 52 pp.
  Cf. No. 1949-101.
/GEOLOGY/PLACES: THÜRINGEN

1949-82 __Husemann__, Gisbert. "Kommende Natur-Erkenntnis im Geiste Goethes." *Die Drei*, 19 (1949), 383-8.
/RESEARCH: VARIOUS/RECEPTION

1949-83 __Ipsen__, Gunther. "Einleitung." In Goethe, [J. W. von]. *Schriften über die Natur*. Kröners Taschenausgabe, 62. Ed. and sel. Gunther Ipsen. Stuttgart: Alfred Kröner Verlag, 1949, pp. 1-11.
/GENERAL INTRODUCTION

1949-84 __Irmen__, Friedrich. "Der mögliche Sinn der Wissenschaft Goethes in unserer Zeit." In *Universidad Nacional de Cuyo: Facultad de Filosofia y Letras: Goethe: 1749 -- 28 de agosto -- 1949*. Mendoza: Universidad Nacional de Cuyo, 1949, pp. 157-99.
/GENERAL INTRODUCTION

1949-85 __Julius__, Frits H[endrik]. "Goethe's kleurenleer als een weg tot het diepere wezen van de natuur [Goethe's Chromatics as a Path into the Deeper Being of Nature]." In A. G. Degenaar, et al., eds. *Met Goethe door de 20e eeuw*. [Den Haag:] Proteus-uitgave, 1949, pp. 60-71.
  In Dutch.
/CHROMATICS

1949-86 __Julius__, F[rits]. H[endrik]. "Naar aanleiding van Goethes gedicht 'Die Metamorphose der Pflanzen' [An Introduction to Goethe's Poem

"The Metamorphosis of Plants"]." In A. G. Degenaar, et al., eds. *Met Goethe door de 20e eeuw*. [Den Haag:] Proteus-uitgave, 1949, pp. 23-30.
 In Dutch.
 /BOTANY/WORKS: LYRICS

1949-87 **Julius**, F[rits]. H[endrik]. "Naar aanleiding van het gedicht 'Die Metamorphose der Tiere' [An Introduction to the Poem "The Metamorphosis of Animals"]." In A. G. Degenaar, et al., eds. *Met Goethe door de 20e eeuw*. [Den Haag:] Proteus-uitgave, 1949, pp. 31-41.
 In Dutch.
 /ZOOLOGY/WORKS: LYRICS

1949-88 **Kaulhausen**, Marie-Hed. "Formen der Mitteilung und Goethes Morphologie." *Muttersprache*, 3 (1949), 221-30.
 /LANGUAGE/MORPHOLOGY

1949-89 **Kiesselbach**, Anton. "Goethe als Osteologe." *Naturwissenschaftliche Rundschau [Stuttgart]*, 2 (1949), 342-5.
 /OSTEOLOGY

1949-90 **Kiesselbach**, Anton. "Goethe und die Wirbeltheorie des Schädels." *Medizinische Monatsschrift: Zeitschrift für allgemeine Medizin und Therapie*, 3 (1949), 621-3.
 /OSTEOLOGY

1949-91 *****Kipp**, Friedrich A. "Arterhaltung und Individualisierung in der Tierreihe." *Verhandlungen der deutschen Zoologen in Mainz 1949*. Leipzig: 1949, pp. 24-7.
 Rpt. No. 1983-51.
 /RESEARCH: ZOOLOGY

1949-92 **Kipp**, Friedrich A. "Über den Vogelzug." *Sternkalender*, 21 (1949), 58-62.
 Rpt. No. 1983-55.
 /RESEARCH: ORNITHOLOGY

1949-93 **Kirnbauer**, Franz. "Goethe, Naturwissenschaften und Technik." *Blätter für Technikgeschichte*, 11 (1949), 1-35.
 /GENERAL INTRODUCTION/TECHNOLOGY

1949-94 **Klages**, Ludwig. *Goethe als Seelenforscher*. 3rd edn. Zürich: S. Hirzel Verlag, 1949. 92 pp.

Rpt. of No. 1932-180.
/PSYCHOLOGY/RESEARCH: PSYCHOLOGY

1949-95   **Klickstein**, Herbert. S.   "Johann Wolfgang Goethe and Chemistry." *The Library Chronicle of the Friends of the University of Pennsylvania Library*, 16 (1949/1950), 18-27.
/CHEMISTRY

1949-96   **Klie**, Walter.   "Einzelzüge aus Goethes Bemühungen um biologische Kenntnisse." *Niedersächsische Heimatkalender*, 3 (1949), 71-6.
/BIOLOGY

1949-97 **Knauer**, Helmut. "Die Bedeutung von Goethes geologischen und mineralogischen Forschungen. I." *Das Goetheanum*, 28 (1949), 164-6.
/GEOLOGY/MINERALOGY

1949-98 **Knauer**, Helmut. "Die Bedeutung von Goethes geologischen und mineralogischen Forschungen. II." *Das Goetheanum*, 28 (1949), 171-3.
/GEOLOGY

1949-99 ***Knisch**, Rudolf. "Goethes Verhältnis zur Mathematik, Physik und Astronomie." *Linzer Sternenbote*, 3, No. 8/9 (1949), 1-7.
/MATHEMATICS/PHYSICS/ASTRONOMY

1949-100 **Kober**, Leopold. "Goethes Roman über das Weltall und die moderne Geologie." In *Festschrift zum 200. Geburtstag Goethes*. Ed. Eduard Castle. Wien: Österreichische Bundesverlag für Unterricht, Wissenschaft und Kunst, 1949, pp. 81-5.
= *Chronik des Wiener Goethe-Vereins*, 52/53 (1949).
/WORKS: WILHELM MEISTERS WANDERJAHRE /GEOLOGY

1949-101 ***Kretschmer**, Ernst Paul. "Geraer Goethe-Erinnerungen." Supplement to Rudolf Hundt. *Goethe und die Geologie Ostthüringens*. [Gera:] Kulturamt der Stadt Gera, 1949.
Cf. No. 1949-81.
/PLACES: GERA/GEOLOGY

1949-102 **Kuchenbuch**, Heribert. "Taten und Leiden des Lichtes: Zu Vorträgen über Goethe als Wissenschaftler." *Die Neue Zeitung [München]*, 7 April 1949.

In Mappe III E 61/C20: "Goethe und die Naturwissenschaften. Zeitungsausschnitte 1913 -" at the Frankfurter Goethe-Museum.
/CHROMATICS

1949-103 **Kuhn**, Hermann. *Geprägte Form: Goethes Morphologie und die Münzkunst.* Weimar: Hermann Böhlaus Nachfolger, 1949. 62 pp. + 24 plates.
/RESEARCH: NUMISMATICS/RESEARCH: MORPHOLOGY

1949-104 **Lange**, Victor. "Goethe: Science and Poetry." *Yale Review*, NS 38 (1949), 623-39.
/GENERAL INTRODUCTION

1949-105 **Lindemann**, Hans A. "Goethe como investigador y filosofo [Goethe as Scientist and Philosopher]." *Anales de la Sociedad Cientifica Argentina*, 148 (1949), 292-309.
In Spanish.
"Homenaje de la Sociedad Cientifica Argentina a Johann Wolfgang von Goethe en el segundo centenario de su nacimento. Conferencia pronunciada el 26 de agosto de 1949."
/GENERAL INTRODUCTION

1949-106 **Locher-Ernst**, L[ouis]. "Zwei Briefe über Goethes Naturwissenschaft." *Das Goetheanum*, 28 (1949), 316-19.
/GENERAL INTRODUCTION

1949-107 **Loesche**, Martin. "Gedanken Goethes in der neuzeitlichen Biologie." Bremen: Johs. Storm Verlag, 1949. 26 pp.
"Vortrag, gehalten als Auftakt des Goethejahres am 2. Januar 1949 für die Goethegesellschaft, Ortsvereinigung Bremen und den Naturwissenschaftlichen Verein Bremen im Festsaale des Rathauses."
/BIOLOGY/RESEARCH: BIOLOGY/RECEPTION

1949-108 **Lombardo-Radice**, Lucio. "Le metamorfosi delle specie nel pensiero di Wolfango Goethe [The Metamorphoses of Species in Goethe's Thought]." *Società*, 5, No. 4 (1949), 646-61.
Rpt. No. 1958-21.
In Italian.
/MORPHOLOGY/BIOLOGY: EVOLUTION

1949-109 **Ludwig**, V[inzenz]. O[skar]. "Goethe und die Tierwelt." In

his *Blicke in Goethes Welt*. Wien: Verlag Julius Lichtner, 1949, pp. 38-43.
/ZOOLOGY

1949-110 **Ludwig**, V[inzenz]. O[skar]. "Altmeister Goethe als Wegführer Theodor Billroths." In his *Blicke in Goethes Welt*. Wien: Verlag Julius Lichtner, 1949, pp. 30-37.
/BILLROTH, T

1949-111 **Magnus**, Rudolf. *Goethe as a Scientist*. Trans. Heinz Norden. New York: Henry Schuman, 1949. 253 pp.
Rpt. No. 1961-28.
English trans. of No. 1906-19.
Rev. George Urdang, *Isis*, 42 (1951), 160.
/GENERAL INTRODUCTION

1949-112 **Martin**, Gottfried. "Goethes Theorie der Naturwissenschaften." *Philosophische Studien*, 1 (1949), 419-29.
/METHOD/EPISTEMOLOGY

1949-113 *****Matthaei**, Rupprecht. "Am farbigen Abglanz haben wir das Leben. Zur Wiedereröffnung der Ausstellung zur Farbenlehre im Goethe-National-Museum Weimar." *Schöpferische Gegenwart*, 2, No. 8/9 (1949), 596-7.
/CHROMATICS/EXHIBITION

1949-114 **Matthaei**[, Rupprecht]. "Geistige Entwicklung Goethes in der Farbenlehre." *Thüringsches Tageblatt*, 18 August 1949.
In Mappe III E 21/C91: "Goethe und die Farbenlehre 1913-. Sammelmappe Zeitungsausschnitte" at the Frankfurter Goethe-Museum.
/CHROMATICS

1949-115 **Matthaei**, Rupprecht. "Goethes naturwissenschaftliche Begründung einer Harmonielehre." *Kosmos: Handweiser für Naturfreunde*, 45 (1949), 298-304.
"Über den gleichen Gegenstand sprach der Verfasser am 5. März 1949 in der Senckenbergischen Naturforschenden Gesellschaft in Frankfurt a. M."
/CHROMATICS

1949-116 **Matthaei**, Rupprecht. "Grundlagen der farbigen Gestaltung: VIII. Zusammenfassende Betrachtung. *Farben, Lacke, Anstrichstoffe [Stuttgart]*, 3 (1949), 146-51.

Continuation of No. 1948-19.
Cf. continuation, No. 1949-117.
/RESEARCH: CHROMATICS/CHROMATICS

1949-117 **Matthaei**, Rupprecht. "Grundlagen der farbigen Gestaltung: IX. *Farben, Lacke, Anstrichstoffe [Stuttgart]*, 3 (1949), 420-25. Continuation of No. 1949-116.
Cf. continuation, No. 1950-49.
/RESEARCH: CHROMATICS/CHROMATICS

1949-118 **Matthaei**, Rupprecht. "Mein Weg zu einer Beurteilung der Farbenlehre Goethes." *Hamburger Akademische Rundschau*, 3 (1949), 665-84.
/CHROMATICS/MATTHAEI, R

1949-119 **Matthaei**, Rupprecht. "Über die Anfänge von Goethes Farbenlehre." *Goethe*, NF 11 (1949), 249-62.
/CHROMATICS

1949-120 **Matthaei**, Rupprecht. "Ein Versuch Goethe's zur Farbenlehre und seine Wandlung." *Natur und Volk*, 79 (1949), 165-74.
/RESEARCH: CHROMATICS/CHROMATICS

1949-121 **Matthaei**, Rupprecht. "Wie Goethe Farbenblinde untersuchte." *Monatsblätter für Augenheilkunde*, 115 (1949), 97-108.
/CHROMATICS/COLORBLINDNESS

1949-122 **May**, Eduard. "Zum Goethejahr 1949. Erkenntnistheoretische und methodologische Betrachtungen zur Naturforschung Goethes." *Zeitschrift für philosophische Forschung*, 3 (1949), 501-11.
/METHOD/EPISTEMOLOGY

1949-123 **Messedaglia**, Luigi. "Granoturco e pellagra. Scipione Maffei e Wolfango Goethe in guerra contro il granoturco [Maize and Pellagra. Scipione Maffei and Goethe at War against Maize]." *Annali dell'Accademia di Agricoltura di Torino*, 92 (1949-1950), 27-43.
In Italian.
/AGRONOMY/MAFFFEI, S

1949-124 **Meyer**, Heinrich. "Goethe as a Scientist: A Problem in Historical Method." *Monatshefte*, 41 (1949), 415-23.
Rev. R[ené]. Michéa [No. 1950-52].
/GENERAL INTRODUCTION/RECEPTION

1949-125 **Meyer-Abich**, Adolf. "Goethes Kompensationsprinzip, das erste holistische Grundgesetz der modernen Biologie." In *Biologie der Goethezeit: Klassische Abhandlungen über die Grundlagen und Hauptprobleme der Biologie von Goethe und den grossen Naturforschern seiner Zeit.* Ed. Adolf Meyer-Abich. Stuttgart: Hippokrates-Verlag Marquandt, 1949, pp. 282-302.
/BIOLOGY

1949-126 **Meyer-Abich**, Adolf. "Goethes Naturforschung in ihrer geistesgeschichtlichen Gestalt." In *Biologie der Goethezeit: Klassische Abhandlungen über die Grundlagen und Hauptprobleme der Biologie von Goethe und den grossen Naturforschern seiner Zeit.* Ed. Adolf Meyer-Abich. Stuttgart: Hippokrates-Verlag Marquandt, 1949, pp. 9-36.
/GENERAL INTRODUCTION

1949-127 ***Meyer-Abich**, Adolf. "Werden und Vergehen, die neuen Probleme der Biologie. Mit Wiedergabe einer Zeichnung Goethes zum Os intermaxillare." *Welt am Sonntag [Hamburg]*, No. 8, 20 February 1949.
/BIOLOGY/OSTEOLOGY

1949-128 **Michéa**, R[ené]. "Goethe, savant méconnu." *Études Germaniques*, 4 (1949), 162-73.
/GENERAL INTRODUCTION

1949-129 ***Möhrke**, Edwin. "Goethe als Mitte morphologischer Betrachtung. Frankfurter Gelehrten-Kongreß wird zu intellektuellem Zeitspiegel." *Die Neue Zeitung*, 27 August 1949.
/MORPHOLOGY/RESEARCH: MORPHOLOGY

1949-130 **Moller**, Ingeborg. "Goethes verdensanskuelse [Goethe's View of Development]." In her *Goethe: et omriss av hans liv og vark.* Oslo: Gyldendal Norsk Forlag, 1949, pp. 127-32.
In Norwegian.
/MORPHOLOGY/PHILOSOPHY

1949-131 ***Muckenhuber**, Leopoldine. "Ein Goethe-Dokument des Naturhistorischen Museums." *Annalen des Naturhistorischen Museums in Wien*, 57 (1949/1950), pp. 141-7.
/EDITION/SCHREIBER, C VON

1949-132 **Müller**, Annemarie. "Goethe als Lehrmeister der Naturbetrachtung." *Die neue Schau: Monatsschrift für das kulturelle Leben*

im deutschen Haus, 10 (1949), 158-9.
/GENERAL INTRODUCTION

1949-133 **Neuschlosz**, S. Marcelo. "Goethe y las ciencias fisico-naturales [Goethe and the Natural Sciences]." *Anales de la Universidad de Chile*, 107 (1949), 147-72.
In Spanish.
/GENERAL INTRODUCTION

1949-134 **Niggli**, Paul. "Goethe als Naturforscher." *Neue Schweizer Rundschau*, NS 17 (1949), 229-40.
/GENERAL INTRODUCTION

1949-135 **Niggli**, Paul. "Nachwort." In Goethe, J. W. *Gedanken zur Naturforschung*. Sel., with an postscript by Paul Niggli. Zürich: Fretz & Wasmuth Verlag, 1949, pp. 45-8.
/GENERAL INTRODUCTION

1949-136 **Noggler**, Josef. "Goethe und die Alchimie." *Das Antiquariat*, 5 (1949), 112-15.
/ALCHEMY

1949-137 *****Opfermann**, H[?]. C. "'Mit kleingemalten Bildern glückte es nicht jedermann.' Goethe tat etwas für den Farbfilm. Menschliches Auge und physikalische Scheinfarben." *Neue Zeitung [Berliner Ausgabe]*, 29. August 1949, No. 195.
/CHROMATICS/RESEARCH: PHOTOGRAPHY

1949-138 *****Paukner-Swoboda**, Gertrud. "Goethe und die Naturwissenschaft." *Jahrbuch der Gesellschaft für Natur und Technik [Wien]*, 1949, 34-40.
/GENERAL INTRODUCTION

1949-139 **Pellis**, Arturo. "W. Goethe, lo scienziato, il filosofo, l'uomo [Goethe the Scienist, the Philosopher, the Man]." *Stoa*, 5, No. 3 (1949), 67-78.
In Italian.
/GENERAL INTRODUCTION

1949-140 **Pfannenstiel**, Max. "Die Entdeckung des menschlichen Zwischenkiefers durch Goethe und Oken: Auf Grund neuer Dokumente dargestellt." *Die Naturwissenschaften: Wochenschrift für die Fortschritte der reinen und der angewandten Naturwissenschaften*, 36 (1949), 193-8.

Cf. No. 1949-148.
/OSTEOLOGY

1949-141 **Pfeiffer**, E[hrenfried]. "Goethes Biological Mission." In A. G. Degenaar, et al., eds. *Met Goethe door de 20e eeuw.* [Den Haag:] Proteus-uitgave, 1949, pp. 42-9.
/BIOLOGY

1949-142 **Pinto**, Roquette. "Goethe als Naturforscher." *Deutsche Nachrichten Sao Paulo*, 11 January 1949.
In Mappe III E 61/C20: "Goethe und die Naturwissenschaften. Zeitungsausschnitte 1913 -" at the Frankfurter Goethe-Museum.
/GENERAL INTRODUCTION

1949-143 *****Podestà**, Hans. "Goethes Lehre von den pathologischen Farben." *Kosmos*, 45 (1949), 310-12.
/CHROMATICS

1949-144 **Podestà**, Hans. "Goethes 'Umgewendeter Regenbogenstreif' und das umgekehrte Spektrum." *Die Naturwissenschaften: Wochenschrift für die Fortschritte der reinen und der angewandten Naturwissenschaften*, 36 (1949), 339-40.
/CHROMATICS

1949-145 **Poppelbaum**, Hermann. "Die Entwicklungsidee und ihr Schatten." *Das Goetheanum*, 28 (1949), 3-5.
/BIOLOGY: EVOLUTION

1949-146 **Poppelbaum**, Hermann. "Goethean Biology: An Unpaid Debt." *The Golden Blade*, 1949, pp. 51-63.
Trans. into German, No. 1949-147.
/BIOLOGY

1949-147 **Poppelbaum**, Hermann. "Goethe und die Biologie: Eine unbezahlte Schuld." Trans. K. Sandkühler. *Die Drei*, 19 (1949), 94-106.
German trans. of No. 1949-146.
/BIOLOGY

1949-148 **Poppelbaum**, Hermann. "Nachklang zum Goethejahr." *Das Goetheanum*, 28 (1949), 413-4.
Discusses No. 1949-140.
/OSTEOLOGY

1949-149 **Poppelbaum**, Hermann. "Wo Ursachen- und Zweckdeutung unzulänglich werden. I." *Das Goetheanum*, 28 (1949), 276-7.
> Cf. continuation, No. 1949-150.
> "Nach einem Vortrag am Goetheanum, 6. Juli 1949."
> /METHOD

1949-150 **Poppelbaum**, Hermann. "Wo Ursachen- und Zweckdeutung unzulänglich werden. II." *Das Goetheanum*, 28 (1949), 282-4.
> Continuation of No. 1949-149.
> "Nach einem Vortrag am Goetheanum, 6. Juli 1949."
> /METHOD

1949-151 ***Portmann**, Adolf. "Biologisches zur ästhetischen Erziehung." In his *Leben und Umwelt*. Verlag Sauerländer, 1949.
> Rpt. No. 1956-25.
> /RESEARCH: BIOLOGY/AESTHETICS/EDUCATION

1949-152 **Proskauer**, Heinrich Oskar. *Goethes Farbenlehre heute: im Goethejahr 1949*. Basel: R. G. Zbinden, 1949. 36 pp.
> /CHROMATICS

1949-153 ***Reißmann**, Willi. "Goethes Farbenlehre, ein Beispiel organischer Denkweise." *Schöpferische Gegenwart*, 2, No. 8/9 (1949), 594-6.
> /CHROMATICS/EPISTEMOLOGY

1949-154 **Renner**, Otto. "Goethes Verhältnis zur Pflanzenwelt, von Jena gesehen." In *Dem Tüchtigen ist diese Welt nicht stumm: Beiträge zum Goethe-Bild*. Jena: Wilhelm Gronau Verlag, 1949, pp. 100-120.
> /BOTANY

1949-155 **Riese**, Walther. "Goethe's Conception of Evolution and its Survival in Medical Thought: A Tribute on the Occasion of the Bicentenary of Goethe's Birth." *Bulletin of the History of Medicine*, 23 (1949), 546-53.
> /BIOLOGY: EVOLUTION/RESEARCH: MEDICINE

1949-156 **Rille**, J[?]. H. "Goethe entdeckt in Südtirol eine neue Krankheit." *Innsbrucker Universitäts-Almanach auf das Goethe-Jahr 1949*, 1949, pp. 191-228.
> Expanded version of No. 1947-29.
> Rpt. No. 1950-67.
> "Vortrag im Österreichischen Institut für Kultur und Wissen-

schaft, Innsbruck, 28. Mai 1946."
/MEDICINE/PLACES: TIROL

1949-157   *Rohmeder, Guillermo.   "Goethe, el naturalista [Goethe the Naturalist]." *Cultura, Supplemento de Trópico (número dedicado a Goethe).* Tumcán, agosto 28, 1949.
In Spanish.
/GENERAL INTRODUCTION

1949-158   R[onchi]., V[asco].   "Teoria dei colori (Della)." *Dizionario Letterario Bompiani: Opere.* Milano: Velantino Bompiani Editore, 1949, pp. 376-7.
In Italian.
/CHROMATICS

1949-159   *Sayili, Aydin.   "Goethe'nin ilim cephesi [Goethe as a Man of Science]." *Dergisi Ankara Üniversitesi dil ve tarih-cografya fakültesi (Goethe Sayisi),* 7, No. 3 (1949), 55-67.
In Turkish.
/GENERAL INTRODUCTION

1949-160   Schaefer, Karl Ernst.   "Goethe's Scientific Method." Unpublished typescript. 1949. 14 pp.
/GENERAL INTRODUCTION/METHOD/WEIZSÄCKER, V VON

1949-161   *Schierbeek, A[braham].   "Goethe als Natuuronderzoeker. Vordracht, gehouden ter herdenkung van het tweede eeuwfeest van Goethe's geboorte voor de Klasse der Wetenschappen van de Kon- Vlaamse Akademie van Wetenschappen, Letteren en Schone Kunsten, op 10 September 1949 en voor de Rijksuniversiteit te Groningen op 5 October 1949 [Goethe as a Natural Scientist. . .]." Groningen: Wolters, 1949. 30 pp.
In Dutch.
/GENERAL INTRODUCTION

1949-162   Schierbeek, A[braham].   "Goethe en de natuurwetenschappen [Goethe and the Sciences]." *De Gids,* 112 (1949), 128-44.
In Dutch.
/GENERAL INTRODUCTION

1949-163   Schirber, Catalina.   "Goethe, sabio naturalista [Goethe as a Scientist]." *Estudios germanicos: Número especial dedicado a Johann Wolfgang Goethe [Universidad de Buenos Aires],* 9 (1949),

191-204.
In Spanish.
/GENERAL INTRODUCTION

1949-164 **Schöndorfer**, Ulrich. "Die Natur in Goethes Weltbild." *Wissenschaft und Weltbild*, 2 (1949), 171-4.
/GENERAL INTRODUCTION

1949-165 **Schüepp**, Otto. "Goethe als Botaniker." *Gesnerus: Vierteljahrsschrift für Geschichte der Medizin und der Naturwissenschaften*, 6 (1949), 144-58.
"Referat, hegalten an der Frühjahrsversammlung der schweizerischen botanischen Gesellschaft in Lugano, 14. März 1949."
/BOTANY

1949-166 **Sherrington**, Sir Charles. *Goethe on Nature & on Science*. 2nd rev. and enl. edn. Cambridge: Cambridge University Press, 1949. 54 pp.
Exp. rpt. of No. 1942-25.
"This Second Edition has been reset, having been revised throughout and considerably extended and annotated by the author."
Rev. R[ené]. Michéa [No. 1950-52].
Rev. L. A. Willoughby, *Euphorion*, 51 (1957), 63-4.
/GENERAL INTRODUCTION

1949-167 **Sieglbauer**, Felix. "Goethes Begriff der Morphologie." *Innsbrucker Universitäts-Almanach auf das Goethe-Jahr 1949*, 1949, pp. 165-90.
Rpt. of No. 1933-42.
"Nach einem am 6. Dezember 1932 im Naturwissenschaftlich-medizinischen Verein in Innsbruck mit erläuternden Demonstrationen gehaltenen Vortrag. . ."
/MORPHOLOGY

1949-168 *****Soeder**, Michael. "Hippokrates und Goethe. Eine Studie." *Hippokrates*, 20 (1949), 681-2.
/HIPPOCRATES

1949-169 **Speiser**, Andreas. "Goethes Farbenlehre." *Gesnerus: Vierteljahrsschrift für Geschichte der Medizin und der Naturwissenschaften*, 6 (1949), 65-71.
Rpt. No. 1951-46.

Cf. No. 1949-54.
"Aus der Einleitung zur Farbenlehre in der GOETHE-Ausgabe des Artemis-Verlags. Vortrag, gehalten anläßlich der von der Schweizerischen Gesellschaft für Geschichte der Medizin und der Naturwissenschaften veranstalteten GOETHE-Feier der SNG in Lausanne, 4. September 1949."
/CHROMATICS

1949-170 **Stäglich**, Hans. "Goethe und Schopenhauer: Eine chronologische Bibliographie." *Schopenhauer-Jahrbuch*, 33 (1949/ 1950), 114-23.
    Rpt. of No. 1932-300.
    Exp. edn. No. 1960-44.
    /BIBLIOGRAPHY/SCHOPENHAUER, A/CHROMATICS

1949-171 **Steiner**, Hans. "Goethe und die vergleichende Anatomie." *Gesnerus: Vierteljahrsschrift für Geschichte der Medizin und der Naturwissenschaften*, 6 (1949), 129-44.
    "Vortrag, gehalten anläßlich der von der Schweizerischen Gesellschaft für Geschichte der Medizin und der Naturwissenschaften veranstalteten GOETHE-Feier der SNG in Lausanne, 4. September 1949."
    /COMPARATIVE ANATOMY

1949-172 **Steiner**, Rudolf. *Goethes naturwissenschaftliche Schriften. Sämtliche Einleitungen zu Goethes Naturwissenschaftlichen Schriften in 'Kürschners Deutsche National-Literatur.* Freiburg i. Br.: Novalis-Verlag, 1949. 339 pp.
    Rpt. (excerpts) from Nos. 1882-10, 1884-5 and 1884-6.
    /GENERAL INTRODUCTION

1949-173 **Steiner**, Rudolf. *Grundlinien einer Erkenntnistheorie der Goetheschen Weltanschauung, mit besonderer Rücksicht auf Schiller.* Freiburg in Breisgau: Novalis-Verlag, 1949. 171 pp.
    Rpt. of No. 1886-9.
    /EPISTEMOLOGY

1949-174 **Steiner**, Rudolf. "Unsere Zeit und Goethe." *Das Goetheanum*, 28 (1949), 25-6.
    /GENERAL INTRODUCTION

1949-175 **Steudel**, Johannes. "Die 'hippokratische Verfahrensart' in Goethes Denken." *Ärztliche Forschung*, 3 (1949), 429-35.
    /MEDICINE/HIPPOCRATES

1949-176 **Strauss**, Fritz. "Goethes Forschungen zur Morphologie." In Grünthal, Ernst and Fritz Strauss. *Abhandlungen zu Goethes Naturwissenschaft*. Berner Beiträge zur Geschichte der Medizin und der Naturwissenschaften, 10. Bern: Verlag Paul Haupt, 1949, pp. 65-113.
/MORPHOLOGY

1949-177 **Stummer**, Albert. "Goethes Wissen vom Bau und Leben des Weinstockes." In *Festschrift zum 200. Geburtstag Goethes*. Ed. Eduard Castle. Wien: Österreichische Bundesverlag für Unterricht, Wissenschaft und Kunst, 1949, pp. 146-63.
= *Chronik des Wiener Goethe-Vereins*, 52/53 (1949).
/VINOCULTURE

1949-178 **Thetter**, Reinmar. "Metamorphose der Substanz: *Eine Skizze*." *Das Goetheanum*, 28 (1949), 286-7; 290-2; 299-300.
/MORPHOLOGY

1949-179 ***Tischner**, Rudolf. "Goethe und die Zwecke in der Natur." *Hippokrates*, 20 (1949), 501-4.
/EPISTEMOLOGY/BIOLOGY

1949-180 **Trapp**, Marianne. *Goethes naturphilosophische Denkweise*. Kleine philosophische Reihe, 2. Stuttgart: F. Fromann, 1949. 93 pp.
Rev. R[ené]. Michéa [No. 1950-52].
/EPISTEMOLOGY/NATURPHILOSOPHIE/METHOD

1949-181 **Trevelyan**, Humphrey. "Goethe as Thinker." In William Rose, ed. *Essays on Goethe*. London: Cassell & Co., 1949, pp. 121-40.
/GENERAL INTRODUCTION

1949-182 **Trevelyan**, Humphrey. "The Significance of Goethe's Science." In *1749-1949. Das Goethe-Jahr. The Goethe-Year*. Ed. Wilhelm Unger. Parts 5-12. London, 1949, pp. 26-32.
/GENERAL INTRODUCTION

1949-183 **Troll**, Wilhelm. "Goethe und die Grundlagen des Naturverständnisses. Ein Vortrag." Anhang zu: *Otto Schnell zum Gedächtnis. Ein Nachruf von A. Seybold*. Heidelberg: Quelle & Meyer, 1949, pp. 17-32.
Rpt. No. 1950-76.
/PHILOSOPHY/METHOD

1949-184 **Troll,** Wilhelm. "Die Urbildlichkeit der organischen Gestaltung und Goethes Prinzip der "Variablen Proportionen." *Experientia*, 5, No. 12 (1949), 491-5.
    Rpt. No. 1956-51.
    /MORPHOLOGY/BIOLOGY/RESEARCH: MORPHOL-OGY/RESEARCH: BIOLOGY

1949-185 **Urdang,** George. *Goethe and Pharmacy*. Madison, Wisconsin: American Institute of the History of Pharmacy, 1949. 76 pp., 22 illustr.
    /PHARMACOLOGY/CHEMISTRY/WIEGLEB, J /DÖBEREINER, J

1949-186 **Viëtor,** Karl. "Zweiter Teil: Der Naturforscher." In his *Goethe: Dichtung: Wissenschaft: Weltbild*. Bern: A. Francke AG Verlag, 1949, pp. 373-416.
    Trans. into English, No. 1950-77.
    /GENERAL INTRODUCTION

1949-187 **Vultée,** Joachim von. "Goethes geologische Studien." *Forum: Zeitschrift für das geistige Leben an den deutschen Hochschulen*, 3 (1949), 287-9.
    /GEOLOGY

1949-188 **Wachsmuth,** Andreas B[runo]. "'Sich verselbsten' und 'entselbstigen' -- Goethes Altersformel für die rechte Lebensführung." *Goethe*, NF 11 (1949), 263-92.
    Rpt. No. 1966-45.
    /METHOD

1949-189 ***Waldner,** Franz. "Goethe als Höhlenforscher." *Natur und Land*, 35 (1949), 158-60.
    /GEOLOGY

1949-190 **Weale,** R[?]. "Goethe and Colour." *Nature*, 164 (1949), 629.
    Reply to Andrade, No. 1949-5.
    /CHROMATICS

1949-191 **Weinhandl,** Ferdinand. "Goethes Morphologie." In *Festschrift zum 200. Geburtstag Goethes*. Ed. Eduard Castle. Wien: Österreichische Bundesverlag für Unterricht, Wissenschaft und Kunst, 1949, pp. 85-113.
    = *Chronik des Wiener Goethe-Vereins*, 52/53 (1949).

/MORPHOLOGY

1949-192 **Weizsäcker**, Viktor von. "Zur Farbenlehre: Aus der Jahres-
feier der Heidelberger Akademie der Wissenschaften am 22. Mai
1949." In *Goethe und Heidelberg*. Heidelberg: F. H. Kerle Verlag,
1949, pp. 351-60.
"Herausgegeben von der Direktion des Kürpfälzischen
Museums."
/CHROMATICS

1949-193 **Whyte**, L[ancelot]. L[aw]. "Goethe and the Formative
Process." *Horizon*, 19 (1949), 240.
/MORPHOLOGY

1949-194 **Whyte**, L[ancelot]. L[aw]. "Goethe's Single View of Nature
and Man." *German Life and Letters*, NS 2 (1949), 287-97.
Originally a British Goethe Festival Society Lecture delivered at
University College, London, on 5 May 1949.
/GENERAL INTRODUCTION/METHOD

1949-195 **Wilkinson**, Elizabeth M. "'Tasso -- ein gesteigerter Werther'
in the Light of Goethe's Principle of 'Steigerung'." *Modern Lan-
guage Review*, 44 (1949), 305-28.
Trans. into German, Nos. 1951-58 and 1974-46.
/WORKS: TORQUATO TASSO/WORKS: DIE LEIDEN DES
JUNGEN WERTHER

1949-196 **Wilson**, Michael. *What is Colour?: The Goethean Approach to
a Fundamental Problem*. Clent, Stourbridge, Worcestershire:
Goethean Science Foundation, 1949. 56 pp.
"Handbook for the Goethe Exhibition, 1949."
/CHROMATICS

1949-197 **Witzenmann**, Herbert. "Goethes Idee des Experiments und die
moderne Naturwissenschaft." *Die Drei*, 19 (1949), 59-72.
/METHOD

1949-198 **Wolf**, [Karl] Lothar. "Polarität und Steigerung in Goethes
Naturbetrachtung." *Kosmos: Handweiser für Naturfreunde*, 45
(1949), 296-7.
/MORPHOLOGY/METHOD